Readings in Biomedical Ethics

Readings in Biomedical Ethics

A Canadian Focus

Third Edition

Edited by

Eike-Henner W. Kluge
University of Victoria

PEARSON
Prentice
Hall

Toronto

National Library of Canada Cataloguing in Publication

Readings in biomedical ethics : a Canadian focus / edited by
Eike-Henner W. Kluge. — 3rd ed.

Includes bibliographical references.
ISBN 0-13-120066-6

1. Medical ethics—Canada. 2. Bioethics—Canada. I. Kluge, Eike-Henner W.

R724.R43 2005   174.2'0971   C2004-901064-6

ISBN 0-13-120066-6

Vice President, Editorial Director: Michael J. Young
Executive Acquisitions Editor: Christine Cozens
Marketing Manager: Ryan St. Peters
Supervising Developmental Editor: Suzanne Schaan
Production Editor: Jennifer Handel
Copy Editor: Gillian Scobie
Proofreader: Kathleen Richards
Production Coordinator: Peggy Brown
Permissions Research: Christina Beamish
Page Layout: Carolyn E. Sebestyen
Art Director: Julia Hall
Cover Design: Julia Hall
Cover Image: Eyewire

1 2 3 4 5   09 08 07 06 05

Printed and bound in Canada.

Contents

Preface

The reason for this new edition of *Readings in Biomedical Ethics* continues to be the same as for the original one: While the ethical principles that should govern the delivery of health care are the same across societies, the issues themselves are very much a function of the individual social and legal settings. The Canadian setting is profoundly different from that of the U.S. U.S. legal cases have no standing in Canadian courts, and U.S. social concerns about the delivery of health care are frequently misplaced in the Canadian context. If they apply at all, they have to be fundamentally reformulated. The issues of resource allocation and euthanasia are but two cases in point. In the U.S., where health care is treated as a commodity, the physician-patient relationship is strained by economic concerns and access to health care may become severely problematic. Likewise, severe illness may threaten economic ruin for U.S. patients and for their next-of-kin. Cost therefore assumes an important role in the debate about assisted suicide and euthanasia. This is not the case in Canada. Further examples include informed consent and abortion. In each case, the problematic is different because the setting is different — and to teach bioethics without acknowledging this difference is to ignore what is central to bioethics: the *application* of ethical reasoning to *actual* concerns.

However, the Canadian setting is changing. Canadians as a group are getting older, and older populations require more health care. This puts an increasing strain on available resources. Furthermore, as health care becomes more sophisticated, it becomes increasingly expensive. The *Canada Health Act* promised to provide Canadians with universal and equal access to health care, and Canadians have become more knowledgeable about the types of health services that are, in principle, available. Therefore, when some of these services are not being delivered, Canadians feel that their rights are being violated. The recent Royal Commission on the Future of Health Care[1] took a careful look at some of the issues that arise in this connection and made sweeping recommendations; the legal case of *Cameron v. Nova Scotia (Attorney General)*[2] indicates just how far Canadians are willing to go on an individual basis when they feel their right to appropriate health care is not being met.

Moreover, the ethical perspective of the Canadian public has increasingly shifted towards an emphasis on individual autonomy. This is reflected in changed expectations about such things as individual involvement in health care decision making, even for children. Access to medical records is also implicated, as are issues of professional accountability, and the like.

Then there are the burgeoning developments in the new reproductive technologies and in genetic engineering. As in many other countries, these issues have become a matter of hot public debate because they go to the very heart of what it is to be a human person. From a purely technical perspective, the tremendous promises of the technology are appreciated, but at the same time, from an ethical and social perspective, the dangers they pose are felt to be great. In 1993, the Royal Commission on New Reproductive Technologies made a series of recommendations to Parliament,[3] and Parliament has since attempted three times to pass appropriate legislation. Closely connected is the question of reproductive autonomy itself: Does it include only the right to refrain from having children — for instance through birth control or abortion — or does it also have a flip side? Namely, that it may be unethical to have children if the children will be born severely disabled, or if the number of children that are born will place an undue burden on the rest of society.

Finally, the last little while has seen a profound reassessment of the role of health care professionals, both as private individuals and as professionals. This is evidenced by changes in the nature of the professional/patient relationship as well as by a shift in the understanding of how health care professionals should behave towards third parties, towards society in general — and even towards each other. It is also evidenced by an increasing concern about the interactions between health care professionals and the health care industry as a whole.

These developments are part of a dynamic that is reshaping how Canadians view health care and the structure of the Canadian health care system. The overall situation can only be described as one of tremendous flux, and its outcome is unpredictable. The readings in this volume reflect some of these developments and the emerging opinions on how the issues should be seen. An attempt has been made to give a balanced presentation. This has not always been possible since, in many cases, the views that exist are legion. The *Further Readings* at the end of each chapter are intended to remedy this by indicating resources that might usefully be consulted when studying the relevant issues.

Benchmark legal cases have also been included, for, although ethics is not law, the delivery of health care is nevertheless embedded in a social context and therefore cannot be divorced from the law. And Canadian law is constantly changing.

The people whom I would like to thank include, of course, everyone at Pearson Education Canada, as well as the reviewers who made such valuable suggestions, including Jonathan Breslin (University of Toronto Joint Centre for Bioethics) and Ian Wilks (Acadia University). The students in my bioethics courses and seminars posed insightful questions, and frequently prompted me to reexamine ideas and search out writings with new perspectives. In putting together this volume, I have also benefited from the comments and suggestions of many ethicists and philosophers who provided insight about what is important in contemporary bioethics. I thank all of them.

Notes

1. See Chapter 3: Royal Commission on the Future of Health Care in Canada, *Building on Values: The Future of Health Care in Canada* (Ottawa: 2002). This is the so-called *Romanow Report*.

2. *Cameron v. Nova Scotia (Attorney General)* [1999] N.S.J. No. 297.

3. Royal Commission on New Reproductive Technologies, *Proceed with Care: Final Report of the Royal Commission on New Reproductive Technologies* (Ottawa: Minister of Supply and Services, 1993) 2 vols.

PART I: HEALTH CARE AND ETHICS

CHAPTER 1
ETHICAL THEORY

Some people think that there are no objective standards of right and wrong: that right and wrong depend on how they *feel* or that it is determined by the *views of the society* in which they are embedded. Others believe that there are absolute standards that are independent of what people think about them — or whether people are aware of them in the first place.

Whether they realize it or not, all these people are holding *meta-ethical* positions. They are saying something *about* ethics: that ethics is a matter of feelings (ethical non-cognitivism), that it is relative to a particular point of view (ethical relativism), or that it is objective in nature (ethical objectivism).

These differences in opinion have practical implications. If ethical objectivism is correct, then it makes sense to study ethics and to try to understand what makes an action ethically acceptable and what doesn't. If ethical non-cognitivism is correct, then studying ethics is a waste of time. Finally, if ethical relativism is correct, then ethical judgements are always relative to the speaker, and there is no one standard of ethical conduct that can legitimately be applied to all people.

Meta-Ethical Positions

Ethical Non-cognitivism

The basis of ethical non-cognitivism is that ethical disagreement can be a highly emotional affair where no amount of reasoning is likely to convince the other party. Even when our logic is shown to be faulty, we tend to insist on our respective position because it just "feels" right. Statements like, "I just know I'm right," or "I can't argue with you — you just don't understand!" reflect this position.

However, while we may be expressing our feelings when we make moral claims, we are doing more than that: we are also making cognitively significant claims about the world. Furthermore, our feelings or emotions may be fundamentally at variance with what we take to be ethically correct. For instance, it is quite possible for a physician to reject abortions on an emotional level and yet agree that, ethically speaking, women have a right to abortions. This stance would be impossible if ethical assertions were merely expressions of the emotions we felt.[1]

Ethical Relativism

Ethical relativism avoids these problems. It says that while ethical statements *are* cognitively meaningful, they do not hold in any objective sense because they depend on our point of view.[2]

Ethical relativism allows us to account for the fact that different people hold different ethical positions. This is very attractive in a multicultural country like Canada because it allows us to accord equal respect to distinct values.

However, such respect is bought at a price. If we accept ethical relativism, then ethical disagreement among people who do not share the same perspective becomes impossible. Since all our ethical judgements would be relative, the fact that we had different perspectives would mean that we were not really disagreeing at all. On this approach, all ethical claims would carry the implicit rider "from my (our) point of view." What at first glance looked like a disagreement would become crossed monologues. Therefore we could not really say that people who advocate sex-selection or who practise gender-based discrimination are morally wrong — or, for that matter, that laws allowing such actions should be changed because they are immoral. They would only be wrong (or immoral) from our point of view, and we would have to reject as moral imperialism any attempt at changing the relevant laws. This approach is troublesome.

Further, as Socrates already pointed out over two thousand years ago, ethical relativism confuses what is believed, legislated, or otherwise promulgated by a group of individuals with the question whether the people who accept this are *correct*. Believing that one is right does not necessarily make one right — in ethics any more than in mathematics or in embryology.

In addition, ethical relativism assumes that if people agree on something, then it must be true. A moment's reflection shows that this consensus approach is rather silly. Historically, all sorts of propositions were universally accepted: for instance, that witches could change into cats, that combustion is due to phlogiston, that the earth is flat and is the centre of the universe, and that melancholy is due to an imbalance of the four humours. However, the fact that people agreed on these propositions did not make them true.

Moreover, as a matter of logic, the lack of universal agreement on matters of ethics does not mean that there are no universally valid ethical propositions. That would be like saying that because there is no agreement on how prions produce mad cow disease, prions are not involved in the transmission of the disease. There may be all sorts of reasons why people don't agree on these things — including the possibility that people are not sufficiently sophisticated to understand the nature of the relevant biochemical processes.

The same holds true with ethical statements. People may just not be sufficiently sophisticated to have found the correct answer. As Kohlberg[3] and Piaget[4] have shown, our level of moral understanding depends on our level of intellectual sophistication, which changes over time and with training.

On the other hand, even if there were general agreement on a particular ethical issue, this would not establish the validity of the relevant ethical claim. For instance, there used to be general agreement that people of different races do not merit the same treatment because they are different. However, racial discrimination cannot be ethically justified in this fashion. Nor can we claim that we ought to kill socially useless people, or that one sex is superior to the other. In all of these cases we can say that while we understand how people could have come to hold such views historically, they were morally wrong, the fact of their agreement notwithstanding.

Finally, ethical relativism is also suspect for a more *pragmatic reason*: it is fundamentally at variance with our social practice. For instance, the people who prosecuted Nazi or Bosnian war criminals did not justify their actions by saying, "We understand that your actions were ethically above reproach from your point of view. However, we are the stronger party; therefore we will judge you according to our own ethical standards." Instead, they prosecuted the alleged war criminals for crimes against humanity because no matter what was accepted or legitimate according to the standards of the accused, what the accused did was ethically wrong in some absolute sense that transcends individual ethical frameworks. The accused knew — or should have known — that what they were doing was morally wrong. The fact that the accuseds' societies accepted and possibly even encouraged their behaviour did not excuse them.

One can generalize the preceding. We frequently make ethical claims about practices in other societies and about the principles that supposedly motivate them. We condemn judicial torture and repression through the work of the United Nations (U.N.) and Amnesty International; we object to the deliberate killing or genital mutilation of female infants in certain countries through the work of the U.N. and of International Planned Parenthood; and we maintain that drug trafficking is ethically reprehensible no matter what. Our critique is not blunted by the realization that these practices may well be defensible within the framework of the other society or from the perspective of the other point of view. On the contrary: We decry the very fact of such ethical divergence as fundamentally misguided.

Ethical Objectivism

By contrast, ethical objectivism holds that right and wrong are objective phenomena. On this view, if we say that euthanasia is morally wrong or that it is ethically appropriate to allow people to make their own health care decisions, we are making claims about the moral nature of the world. In other words, if we are moral objectivists, then we hold to the view that people's actions and dispositions have certain moral properties or qualities, and that this is not a matter of point of view or a matter of how we feel — although these, too, may of course be involved — but a matter of how the world really is. The problem that ethical objectivists face is identifying some sure way of recognizing these moral properties, and of specifying what these properties are. As we shall see in a moment, there is no shortage of objectivist ethical theories, and it is disagreement on this issue that grounds some of the deepest controversies in health care ethics.

Discussion

The differences between these meta-ethical theories have more than merely theoretical significance. If ethical objectivism is wrong, there is little point to reasoned discussion about the ethics of health care. The solution to disagreements about issues such as resource allocation, the right to health care, or the ethical duties of nurses or physicians, lies not in discussion and understanding, but in political manoeuvring — or even in the use of power. This approach would be extremely troublesome in the Canadian context, with its deliberate and conscious acceptance of cultural diversity.

What, then, is ethics?

As a discipline, it is a branch of philosophy. It deals with questions of right and wrong conduct, and with what we ought to do and what we ought to refrain from doing. It considers issues of rights and obligations and how these are related to the social setting.

Ethics is not the only discipline that deals with such issues. Law, psychology, sociology and theology deal with them as well. However, unlike psychology and sociology, ethics is not centrally concerned with describing and analyzing how people feel or why they have the attitudes they do. Instead, it is normative or *prescriptive* in nature.

Law is also prescriptive because it tells people how they ought to behave. However, law is based on the rules that societies have promulgated to regulate the behaviour of their members. In that sense, law is arbitrary and depends on the will of the lawmakers. Moreover, laws may be unethical — like the laws that gave second-rank status to native Americans, that declared women nonpersons, or that allowed the nonconsensual sterilization of the mentally severely handicapped. And finally, laws hold only in the jurisdictions in which they have been passed. Ethics, on the other hand, deals with persons insofar as they are persons. It is therefore jurisdiction-invariant, and its injunctions are binding even if no law recognizes them.

There are two fundamental questions that ethical objectivism has to answer: What are these so-called moral facts? And why do people differ in their moral positions? These are very difficult questions. They are the subject of the study of theoretical ethics.

The authors of the articles in this anthology share the assumption that ethical objectivism is correct. It is on this basis that they examine the issues that arise in the delivery of health care. This does not mean that they all share the same ethical viewpoint. Just as there are different meta-ethical positions, so there are different ethical theories. The readings in this volume exemplify how a difference in ethical theory can lead to a difference in conclusion on a particular issue. To appreciate this fully, it may be useful to give a brief sketch of some of the ethical theories on which the articles are based.

Ethical Theories

There are several kinds of objectivist ethical theories. The most common ones are *teleological* or consequentialistic ethics, *deontological* or rights and duties-oriented ethics, *virtue* ethics, *religious* ethics and *feminist* ethics.

Teleological or Consequentialistic Theories

The most common teleological or consequentialistic ethics in our society is utilitarianism.[5] Historically, its best-known proponent is perhaps John Stuart Mill. It is frequently used by health care administrators. For instance, it underlies the cost/benefit and cost/effectiveness considerations used in deciding whether to expand the emergency department of a hospital or to add a new psychiatric wing; it plays a major role in decisions about whether to use a medical as opposed to a surgical approach for cardiac problems.

Utilitarianism takes as its basic principle the so-called *principle of utility*. It goes something like this:

> One should always act in such a way as to bring about the greatest good and the least harm for the greatest number of people.

Or, alternatively,

> One should always act in such a way as to maximize the balance of good over harm for the greatest number of people.

The principle of utility leaves undefined the nature of the good that one is supposed to aim at and the nature of the harm that is to be avoided. This opens the door to different versions of utilitarianism. One such version defines the good in terms of material well-being or pleasure. It is called *hedonistic utilitarianism*.[6] Another identifies it as happiness, and is called *eudaemonistic utilitarianism*.[7] A third says that the good consists in the attainment of certain ideals. This is *ideal utilitarianism*.[8] A fourth variation claims that the good is really a combination of several of these goods. Not surprisingly, it is called *mixed utilitarianism*.[9] There is no agreement on which notion of the good is really correct.

Just as there are differences within utilitarianism about what the good is, so there are differences about how we are supposed to identify this good. Some claim that a special sort of insight or *intuition* is involved,[10] which allows us to identify what has *intrinsic value*. Other utilitarians focus on the *nature of human beings* and maintain that the good can be derived from human nature itself.[11] Still others say that good can only be identified by looking at what society prefers. While the first two approaches would yield an absolute answer as to the nature of the good, a preference-based approach insists that what counts as the good may change over time, as social attitudes and preferences change.

Finally, utilitarian theories may differ on how the test of utility is to be *applied. Act utilitarianism* proceeds on a case-by-case basis. It evaluates each situation on its own terms, without reference to universal rules or guidelines.[12] Health care professionals who adopt this approach would not follow general rules or guidelines of ethical decision making. Instead, they would calculate the utility of each situation separately and on its own.

Rule utilitarianism, on the other hand, maintains that utility is not something that can be calculated for individual acts but only for general rules of conduct. The basic position of this approach could be expressed as follows:

> Those rules of conduct are morally obligatory that produce, or are likely to produce, the greatest amount of good and the least amount of harm for the greatest number of people.[13]

Therefore, when it comes to dealing with actual situations, the decision making would identify the rule that should be applied in a particular case or on a particular occasion.

At first glance it might seem that, practically speaking, the differences among the various types of teleological theories are really unimportant. However, this is not true. Consider the following case:

> A small-town hospital is deciding whether to perform induced abortions. Some physicians who have privileges at the hospital say they are personally opposed to abortions and will not perform them. On the other hand, two of the local physicians are willing to do them. The hospital board has to decide whether to brave the storm of protest that it thinks will come from the more outspoken and religious members of the community if abortions are permitted, or simply continue with its previous policy of not doing abortions.

For the sake of discussion, let us ignore the impact that criminal legislation and the Code of Ethics of the medical profession would have on this case and consider only what would happen under the various utilitarian approaches.

If we assume that the hospital board follows a *rule utilitarian* approach, then if the board was moved by *hedonistic* considerations it would try to balance the problems the community would face if the hospital did abortions against the problems that the community would face if it continued not to do them. Here it would take into account such factors as the social resources that would be necessary to raise unwanted children, the cost of taking care of failed abortion attempts by women who tried to induce their own abortions or have had them induced by nonmedical persons, the cost of the abortions themselves, and the impact that they might have on health care within the community. On balance, the hospital would probably decide that the greatest amount of pleasure and/or material good for society would be achieved if it performed induced abortions. The storm of protest that might result would be more than outweighed by the long-term savings in health costs alone.

On the other hand, if the board decided to adopt an *ideal utilitarian* perspective it might well reason differently. It would consider that ideal values like compassion and respect for life are fundamental in our society. It would balance these values against the strong emphasis that our society places on autonomy and self-determination and try to arrive at a solution. On this basis, it might well decide to perform abortions, but only under certain conditions such as in cases of rape or incest, or when there are medical indications — and even then, only as long as the pregnancy was not so far advanced that the foetus could survive if removed from the mother's body.

If the board adopted a *mixed utilitarian* perspective, it would try to balance ideal and hedonistic considerations against each other. It would be impossible to say beforehand what the board might decide because its decision would depend on the relative weight that was attached to the various parameters.

Alternatively, if the board adopted a *eudaemonistic utilitarian* outlook, it would proceed still differently. It would look for statistical data about the psychological sequelae of abortions and compare these with the effect on the happiness of mother, child and other affected parties when abortions are denied. It would then compare these with data about society's mood when abortions are performed as opposed to when they are not. It would try to calculate the greatest amount of overall "good," and reach a decision on this basis. In the current social climate, this would probably mean that the board would opt for going ahead with allowing abortions.

Finally, if the board were to approach the issue from an *act utilitarian* perspective, all the preceding types of considerations that deal with the nature of the good would still apply. However, the board would not try to decide what sort of *policy* it should adopt. Instead, it would set up a committee to look at each case separately without reference to hard-and-fast guidelines. The only principle that would guide the committee's deliberations would be the principle of utility. However, it is probably fair to say that it is unlikely that any hospital board would operate for long in this fashion. The running of a health care institution requires policies: something that is ruled out by the very nature of act utilitarianism.

Deontological Ethics

Deontological theories are not concerned with outcomes but with duties and rights. There are two major types: *monistic* approaches, which say that there is only one basic principle from which all judgements and rules of right and wrong must ultimately be derived; and *pluralistic* approaches, which say that there are several basic principles.[14]

The position of Immanuel Kant is probably the best-known and most influential monistic deontological ethics. Kant called his basic principle the "categorical imperative." He gave several formulations of it.[15] However, he claimed that all of them were equivalent to one another.

Two of these formulations are of special interest in health care. The first he simply called "categorical imperative." It goes like this: "Act only according to that maxim by which you can at the same time will that it should become a universal law."[16] The second version, which he called the "practical imperative," he stated as follows: "Act so that you treat humanity, whether in your own person or in that of another, always as an end and never as a means only."[17]

Each of these formulations provides a test for ethical acceptability. An example might clarify how this is the case:

> A physician has a patient with metastasized cancer of the lungs. The cancer is inoperable; it is unresponsive to chemotherapy and radiation treatment, and most likely it will be fatal within a year. The physician knows that the patient is psychologically labile and that if she was told of her condition, she would react extremely emotionally and might even suffer psychological harm. The physician wants to spare her patient the psychological trauma that she is convinced will result if this information is disclosed to the patient before the disease has progressed to the point of seriously incapacitating her. The physician, therefore, lies about the diagnosis and prognosis so as to give the patient a little time before she has to face the truth.

While lying to the patient might be defensible from a humanitarian perspective, Kant would argue that it is unethical because it fails the first test. The *maxim* or general rule guiding the physician would be to "lie when motivated by humanitarian considerations." However, Kant would say that if this maxim were to become a universal law, it would mean that anyone, on any occasion involving humanitarian motives, should lie.

However, what counts as a humanitarian motive depends on the perspective and values of the individual whose motive it is. Consequently no one could ever be sure that he or she was not being lied to by other people. Not only would that completely erode our confidence in other people, but it would also mean that for all practical purposes the distinction between lying and telling the truth would disappear.[18] The maxim would thus fail the *universalizability test*.

Kant would argue further that the actions of the physician would fail the *end-in-itself test*. To lie to the patient is to withhold the information the patient needs in order to make reasonable, rational, and appropriate decisions about how to conduct the rest of her life. Therefore, to lie is to treat her not as an autonomous rational being who is an end-in-herself, but as an object, something to be manipulated. It does not matter that she is being manipulated with the best of intentions and "for her own good"; she is being manipulated nonetheless.

Unlike the Kantian monistic approach, *pluralistic deontological* ethics maintains that there are several basic or fundamental principles that are irreducible to each other and that have to be balanced against each other in a given situation. Among pluralistic deontologists, the following principles have found general acceptance:[19]

1. *Principle of Autonomy and Respect for Persons:*
   Everyone has a fundamental right to self-determination. This right is limited only by unjust infringement on the rights of others. ("Your right to swing your fist stops where my face begins.")

2. *Principle of Impossibility:*
   A right that cannot be fulfilled is ineffective as a right, and an obligation that cannot be met under the circumstances ceases to be effective as an obligation (e.g., one cannot have a right to health care resources that are

not available; and one cannot have a duty to save the life of an incurably dying patient).

3. *Principle of Fidelity or Best Action:*
    Whoever has an obligation also has the duty to discharge that obligation in the best manner possible (e.g., if there is a duty to perform an operation, then the duty is to use the greatest skill and care possible).

4. *Principle of Equality and Justice:*
    A right is effective to the degree that it preserves or promotes justice (e.g., the duty to provide preferential health-resource allocation for persons with disabilities is based on this).

5. *Principle of Beneficence:*
    Everyone has a duty to maximize the good.

6. *Principle of Non-Malfeasance:*
    Everyone has a duty to minimize harm.[20]

The last two principles aim at the production of a particular kind of outcome. Hence they are really teleological in nature. However, there is a way of interpreting these principles so that they lose this teleological veneer. If we interpret the Principle of Beneficence as follows:

> Everyone has a duty to maximize the good of others where the nature of this good is defined by the other persons themselves.[21,22]

and if we interpret the Principle of Non-Malfeasance like this:

> Everyone has a duty to minimize harm to others where the nature of this harm is defined by the other persons themselves.

then the two principles are acceptable within a deontological framework. They are unacceptable when interpreted in any other way. It is precisely the failure to interpret the principles in this derivative sense that gives rise to professional *paternalism*.

The multiplicity of principles raises the question of what happens when the different principles conflict. For instance, what happens when the Principle of Equality and Justice conflicts with that of Beneficence, or the Principle of Autonomy with that of Best Fidelity or of Non-Malfeasance?

To deal with this problem, some deontologists have suggested that ethical principles should be understood as holding only *prima facie*.[23] That is to say, they should be understood merely as approximations that serve as guides. When deciding which principle takes priority in a given case, one should consider not only the nature of the act in question but also the personal, social and material aspects of the situation in which the relevant individuals are embedded.[24] This approach has become widely accepted.

Feminist Ethics

An ethical approach that has acquired some prominence of late is *feminist ethics*. It has been described as the "ethics of caring and response."[25] Historically, its focus was the moral experience of women in what it describes as a male-dominated and male-oriented world. It argued that the moral and social experiences of women differ from those of men, and that these differences must be taken into account when ethically evaluating a particular situation. Ethical issues and dilemmas should not be resolved by blindly balancing competing rights and duties, or by automatically turning to virtues or applying principles such as autonomy, equality, and impartiality. Instead, they should be resolved by looking at the particulars of each situation and by determining how the responsibilities of the various actors arise from the relationships in which they are embedded.[26] Disagreements and problems should be solved, not in the spirit of exclusionary decision making but in the spirit of cooperative resolution.

Further, feminist ethics seeks to ground the difference between itself and more traditional ethical orientations by looking at the difference in social experience between men and women. The writings of Nel Noddings[27] and Carol Gilligan[28] are particularly noteworthy in this regard. The point they make is that directly or indirectly, the overt social structure of most societies has been male dominated, and the female experience in most of these societies has traditionally involved a greater or lesser degree of discrimination, which has left women disproportionately powerless.[29] The philosopher Annette Baier has given more systematic expression to the feminist theoretical. She argues that traditional ethical theories are not so much wrong but that they capture only certain aspects of moral reality.[30]

In the health care sector, feminists can point to medical experimentation as an illustrative example of such discrimination. As has recently been argued very persuasively,[31] medical experimenters have not directed their attention to the health care needs of women in an appropriate fashion because traditional rules have excluded women from being experimental subjects. Traditionally the excuse has been that participating in such experiments might pose a special risk to women's ability to bear (healthy) children. By contrast, no such considerations have been raised against the inclusion of fertile men in medical experimentation even though their ability to father (healthy) children might also be impaired. Not only does this reflect an inherent sexist bias at the very heart of traditional experimental protocols, it is also discriminatory in a much more profound fashion: Female health care needs have essentially remained under-serviced.

A feminist ethical approach, when applied to biomedical issues, would therefore argue that questions about issues such as informed consent to research or abortion should not be decided by appealing to a set of virtues, by applying a set of principles, or even by attempting to balance conflicting duties and rights. Instead, one should arrive at a conclusion based on the social situation of the women and the reality of their bodily and social experiences in a male-dominated and male-oriented society. And more generally, divorced from a purely female-oriented concern, such an approach should acknowledge the functional embedding of all persons in their social contexts and should attempt to reach a resolution on the basis of consensus and cooperation.

Nevertheless, most feminist writings focus on the experiences of women. It is therefore not surprising that a great deal of feminist biomedical ethics has been concerned with matters that centre on the reproductive capacities of women. Issues such as abortion, contraception, the right to have (or refrain from having) children, maternal–foetal conflict and assisted reproduction constitute noteworthy examples. The readings included below reflect this concern.

Virtue Ethics

Virtue ethics, as its name indicates, is based on the concept of virtue. As one of the most noted modern proponents of the theory has put it, a morally upright person is one who performs the right kinds of acts because he or she has a certain kind of character: namely, a virtuous character. This virtuous character is one that allows the individual to realize those characteristics and qualities that are definitive of human beings.[32]

Virtue ethics shares several important traits with other ethical approaches. Like feminist ethics, it rejects the position that ethics is fundamentally concerned with duties and rights.[33] Instead, it argues that the fundamental concern of ethics is the development of a virtuous character.[34] It is similar to deontological ethics in that it rejects the thesis that the greatest good for the greatest number is the ultimate aim of ethical action. At the same time, it has a certain similarity to teleological ethics in its central insistence that we should foster the attainment of a virtuous character or disposition.[35]

So far as virtue ethics is concerned, the virtues that find their most obvious expression in health care are those of compassion and care. This is not surprising, since these *other-directed* virtues have been synonymous with health care since its very beginning. This is also what makes virtue ethics so attractive to hands-on care-givers like physicians and nurses. However, virtue ethics also maintains that health care provides the opportunity for *self-directed* virtues, such as courage and forbearance. Consequently, it also has something to recommend it from the patient's perspective. *Social* virtues, such as justice and beneficence, have also emerged as important in recent discussions. These are virtues that find ready acceptance from the perspective of society as a whole.[36]

Still, it is probably fair to say that the application of virtue ethics to health is not yet completely worked out. One of the problems of virtue ethics as it is currently structured is that it provides no readily apparent conflict resolution mechanism. However, health care professionals are increasingly faced with limited resources, which means that they are faced with conflicting demands for materials, personnel, and time. Conflict resolution mechanisms are particularly important for dealing with such situations in order to decide who shall have when not all can have, or who shall have when not all can have whatever is available. Further, since health care measures frequently have a threshold level of effectiveness, a shared or cooperative approach will not be effective for any of the parties concerned and, in fact, may harm all of them to some degree. In cases like these, it is unclear which virtue would provide an answer

— or should prevail. Finally, in a multicultural society like Canada, it is difficult to see what set of virtues all parties to the social contract would agree on. To fall back on the claim that these virtues can be identified by looking at what is good for human nature is to assume that all parties would agree on what human nature really is. So far, there has been no agreement on that score.

Religiously Oriented Ethics

Religiously oriented ethics evaluate ethical situations by reference to the set of religiously grounded guidelines or principles that are characteristic of the religion in question.[37] These principles or guidelines differ from religion to religion, although there is considerable overlap among religions that belong to the same grouping, for instance Islam, Christianity and Judaism.[38]

Probably the best-known example of how a religiously based ethics can affect the delivery of health care comes from acute care. Jehovah's Witnesses will refrain from accepting transfusions and blood products as a matter of religiously based ethical principle. Hence Jehovah's Witnesses view the non-consensual provision of blood and blood products to their children as a fundamental violation of the role of parents as substitute decision makers for their children. Another example comes from members of the Church of Christ, Scientist. Adherents of this religion reject all scientifically based health care interventions because, according to their belief, ill health is a consequence of inadequate belief in the workings of the divine being. Ill health should therefore be cured by appropriate counselling and religious observances, not by active medical care.

However, the impact of religiously based ethics on the delivery on health care is much more profound than these two examples would suggest. The controversy over the moral status of abortion has historically been defined by the conflicting positions of opposing sides, one of which has a religious basis. Likewise, the controversies surrounding issues such as assisted reproduction, euthanasia, and withholding or withdrawal of treatment are heavily coloured by ethical positions that are based on religious precepts.

Nevertheless, the influence of religiously based ethics on biomedical controversies notwithstanding, in Canada there is a definite limit to the applicability of religious ethics in the arena of health care: a limit which, unlike the case of any other ethical perspective, is set by Canadian law. The Canadian Charter of Rights and Freedoms guarantees freedom of religion.[39] This guarantee entails that any institution receiving public funds for its operations and any health care provider under public jurisdiction may not establish or follow policies that have a sectarian and religious basis. Consequently, the impact of religious ethics on the delivery of health care is limited to private decisions made by individual health care consumers and to personal decisions made by health care professionals.

This does not mean that religiously based ethics has no impact on the delivery of health care in general. As was already indicated, the ongoing debate over such things as abortion, euthanasia and assisted suicide, as well as over the development and use of the new reproductive technologies is very much coloured by religiously based positions. It is merely to say that while public policy decisions may *agree* with a particular religion on a specific issue, such policy may never be *based* on a religious precept or be defensible solely in terms of a religious belief.

Agapistic Ethics or the Ethics of Respect for Life

Agapistic ethics is an ethics of love and respect for all living things. It evaluates ethical situations by asking what love and respect for life would dictate. The spectrum of approaches that fall under this heading is very wide. Some extreme agapistic ethics argue that all life — and in particular all animal life — has equal moral standing;[40] others maintain that only animal life capable of sensation and experiencing pain has moral worth.

Agapistic ethics does not deny the need for research and experimentation. What it objects to is the treatment of nonhuman animals as though they had no moral standing. Such a position, so it contends, amounts to "speciesism," which is to say, the adoption of a racist attitude at the level of species.[41]

As with all other ethical approaches, there are variations on this position. Some agapists recognize differences among types of living things, and also among types of animals. They accept that living things like bacteria, worms, and similar entities don't have the same moral status as animals with nervous systems that allow them to sense the world and experience pain.[42] Nevertheless, even these agapists demand that no matter what their status, animals be used only when absolutely necessary, and only when it can be shown that animal experimentation is essential for developing a particular health care modality, and only if the cost in animal terms is proportional to the advancement in health care that would result from such an undertaking.[43]

Agapistic ethical approaches are most commonly encountered in the context of animal experimentation. They contend that animals should not be used to develop and test such things as surgical procedures, pharmacological products or medical devices. Computer simulations should be used whenever possible, the use of human cell lines should be extended, and other alternatives to animal experimentation should be sought.[44]

Interestingly enough, agapists usually focus solely on the rights of nonhuman animals. The treatment that human beings visit on each other tends to escape their concern. Thus, few agapists have objected to certain violent methods of abortion even though they would condemn these methods as cruel and immoral if used to kill nonhuman animals. Likewise, most agapists have not objected to destructive experimentation on human foetuses for the purpose of developing reproductive techniques, even when the foetuses are at a stage of development that would trigger animal rights concerns. The reason for this probably lies in the assumption that there are mechanisms to safeguard the rights of human animals; whereas nonhuman animals cannot speak for themselves, and therefore require special attention.

Clearly, it is impossible for health care professionals to use an extreme agapistic approach in their professional lives. If one cannot draw an ethically valid distinction among different types of living things — for instance, if one cannot say that one type of living thing (say a human being) is ethically more important than another (say, a bacterium, an insect or a rat) — then one cannot use antibiotics, institute public health measures to control disease vectors, or take appropriate steps to save the lives of human beings suffering from parasitic worms. However, that would leave precious little room for health care as the notion is ordinarily understood. Only dietary and lifestyle measures would be ethically allowed, and only therapeutic practices such as bonesetting, midwifery or psychiatry would be permissible.

Of course, if agapism is interpreted in its more moderate form, the consequences would not be quite so severe. However, by allowing a distinction among different kinds of living things, this form of agapism prompts the question: On what basis is this distinction being drawn?[45] It also prompts a further question: Why should the line be drawn on the basis of one particular set of criteria rather than another? For instance, why should one accept that birds occupy a more privileged ethical niche than filarial worms or trypanosomes? Why should one be more concerned about groundhogs than, say, microphages or viruses?

The usual reply here is that these animals have nervous systems that allow them to sense the world and to experience pain. However, this invites the question of why the ability to sense and to experience pain should be considered special. Is it a matter of *definition* that beings that sense and experience pain have a special moral status, or is there a more fundamental reason?

Furthermore, in some cases even this modified version of agapism presents its proponents with a dilemma. For example, allowing abortions for reasons of personal choice involves accepting the thesis that some animals may be killed for private value reasons. After all, human foetuses are also a form of animal life. On the other hand, consistent application of the same modified agapistic approach would require rejecting all abortions once the nervous system of the human foetus has started to develop. The modified version would also present its proponents with the dilemma of what to do when trying to control rodent-borne disease vectors such as the plague.

This is not to say that the agapistic approach has no relevance to the Canadian health care scene. Canadian society accepts the principle of respect for life as an important value. It even enshrines it in certain laws and regulations. However, Canadian society does not commit the logical mistake of confusing love and respect with obligation. Life — all life — merits special consideration and must be treated with respect. It might even be an appropriate object of love. But the fact that we respect or love something does not mean that we have an obligation towards it. Of course, we may voluntarily accord certain rights to something because we love or respect it. But that is an entirely different matter.

Therefore, agapistic perspectives do have something valuable to say for biomedical ethics. However, what they have to say can be accommodated by accepting the premise that consistent ethical behaviour is governed not only by respect for ethical rights and obligations, but also by respect for personal and subjective values; and that these values may — and appropriately should — include the value of respect for life.

The Use of Ethical Theories

People in real life rarely follow one ethical theory. They usually combine several of them. This is not surprising. Most people are not trained in ethics and therefore have little practice in keeping their ethical reasoning theoretically consistent.

At the same time, this mixing of ethical approaches can lead to severe problems in planning and delivery. For example, the administrator of a hospital may use cost/benefit considerations when deciding how many dialysis machines to purchase, but turn to deontological considerations when evaluating the professional actions of the staff who take cost/benefit considerations into account when deciding which patient should be dialyzed. Or, at a more general level, proponents of emergency health care sometimes advance deontological arguments that focus on the needs of particular individuals, whereas proponents of preventive health care measures, who tend to use a utilitarian perspective, usually try to maximize the common good. The conflict that is built into the very nature of the problematic is irresolvable unless the difference in ethical perspectives is identified and settled.

Bioemedical Ethics and Bioethicists

Biomedical Ethics as a Discipline

Biomedical ethics — or bioethics, as it is also called — is a sub-species of ethics. It consists in the application of ethical reasoning to issues that arise in the delivery of health care. It had its Western beginnings with Hippocrates (fifth century BC), who is credited with formulating the first code of ethics for health care professionals. This was the famous *Hippocratic Oath*.[46] In rough strokes, the *Oath* outlined how physicians should conduct themselves in their professional practice. It became the basis of later Islamic, Jewish and Christian codes of medical practice. To this day, many consider it foundational for all health care ethics.

From its very beginning, biomedical ethics had a close connection with formal and analytical philosophy — in particular with the philosophy of Aristotle; however, it always retained its Hippocratic emphasis on practical concerns. Its basic precepts, which centred around such principles as "Protect the patient's secrets" and "Above all, do no harm" were periodically updated and revised by such people as Galen (131–200 AD), Razes (864–930 AD), Avicenna (980–1037 AD) and Maimonides (1135–1204 AD) who were both physicians and philosophers. The first codes of medical ethics for the English-speaking world were written by John Gregory (1724–1773) and Thomas Percival (1740–1840). The first code of nursing ethics was written by Florence Nightingale (1820–1910) in 1860.

Religious elements tended to play an important role in these early codes, and it was only in the twentieth century that philosophical ethics came to predominate. This resulted in what was called philosophical bioethics, and provided it with a worked-out theoretical basis. The research and teaching of bioethics became institutionalized in North America with the establishment in 1969 of The Institute of Society, Ethics and the Life Sciences in Hastings-on-Hudson (later known as the Hastings Center), the Kennedy Institute of Ethics at Georgetown University in 1971, and the Centre for Bioethics of the Clinical Research Institute in Montreal in 1976. Nowadays, bioethics is a specialized field of study leading either to a certificate or to a graduate degree.

Modern bioethics has a close association with medicine, nursing and the other health sciences such as pharmacology, epidemiology and health care economics. After all, its very purpose is to deal with ethical issues that arise in the delivery of health care, whether that be in the research sector, at the health planning stage or in the hands-on health care setting. However, modern bioethics also has a close association with the law. There are two reasons for this. *First*, the law — both case law and legislation — identifies the social boundaries and conditions for health care delivery. These boundaries and conditions may create ethical dilemmas or problems, for instance in matters such as abortion, human experimentation or standards of professional practice. *Second*, ethical analysis and theory may function as a resource for the development of case law — the case of *Morgentaler* is here a good example[47]— and for the formulation of medical statutes, as for instance in the case of provincial legislation dealing with the providing of health care [48] or the proposed new federal law dealing with the new reproductive technologies.[49]

What, then, is modern biomedical ethics? In a nutshell, it is the discipline that deals with the ethics of health care in the broadest possible sense of that term. It has a theoretical and a practical side. *Theoretical biomedical ethics* applies formal ethical theory to the notion of health itself and to the types of issues that arise in the delivery of health care. In other words, it tries to work out a general ethical framework within which the notions of health and of health care delivery can be situated. The results are generally policy-oriented and include speculations about the right to health care, the nature of personhood and the ethics of deliberate death, experimentation, informed consent, the moral status of the new reproductive technologies, etc. *Applied* biomedical ethics is case-oriented. It applies ethical theories and concepts to specific problems as these occur in the arena of everyday practice.

Theoretical biomedical ethics tends to be university-based, and purely academic in nature. Applied bioethics is practised by consultants who are called in on specific cases, or by bioethicists who are on staff in health care institutions. However, the distinction between theoretical and applied biomedical ethics is not hard and fast. Theoretical bioethicists may also work as consultants, have cross-appointments with health care institutions or even function as expert witnesses in courts of law. Likewise, applied bioethicists may also do research in bioethical theory and publish in learned journals. Moreover, the methodology that is used by either type of bioethicist may vary. For instance, it may be theory-driven, principle-based or casuistic in nature. Finally, the people who engage in biomedical ethics may have diverse backgrounds. They may be philosophers with specialized degrees in biomedical ethics, lawyers with a specialization in health law, health care professionals with training in biomedical ethics or even theologians who have been trained in the application of religiously-based ethical concepts to issues in health care. The single common denominator that unites them all is their use of ethics, and of ethical concepts and methodologies: If it cannot be justified in ethical terms it is not biomedical ethics, no matter what the species of ethics.

Notes

1. Someone might attempt to explain such a stance in terms of self-deception. However, it is not at all clear that this would be successful. It would have to deny the reality of the overt emotional stance. For an interesting recent discussion of emotion, see Robert M. Gordon, *The Structure of Emotions: Investigations in Cognitive Philosophy* (New York: Cambridge University Press, 1987).

2. For a sympathetic approach to ethical relativism, see R.B. Perry, *Realms of Value* (Cambridge, Mass.: Harvard University Press, 1954), and E. Westermarck, *The Evolution and Development of the Moral Ideal* (New York: Macmillan, 1906), and E. Westermarck, *Ethical Relativity* (New York: Harcourt Brace, 1932). For a critique see G.E. Moore, *Ethics* (London: Cambridge University Press, 1912), and Brandt, *Ethical Theory* (ref. note 9). For a good presentation of different cultural values and their impact on the ethics of health care decision making, see the proceedings of the *Conference on Transcultural Dimensions* (Washington: Fidia Research Group, 1990). See also E. Pellegrino, P. Mazzarella and P. Corsi, eds., *Transcultural Dimensions in Medical Ethics* (Frederick, Maryland: University Publishing Group, 1992).

3. Lawrence Kohlberg, *The Philosophy of Moral Development* (Chicago: Harper and Row, 1971).

4. See Piaget, *Judgment and Reasoning in the Child* (London: Routledge and Kegan Paul, 1928).

5. Aside, that is, from religiously oriented ethical approaches. Some of these also contain consequentialistic reasoning.

6. Cf. Brandt, *op. cit.,* for a discussion of this notion. Traditionally, the concept of pleasure as the ultimate good is associated with Epicurus and his school in ancient Greece. For a modern variant, distinguishing between various types of pleasures, see Jeremy Bentham, *An Introduction to the Principles of Morals and Legislation*, chapters iv ff.

7. Cf. Lennart Nordenfelt, *On the Nature of Health* (Dordrecht and Boston: D. Reidel Publishing Co., 1987), chapter 3.

8. See G.E. Moore, *Principia Ethica* (Cambridge: Cambridge University Press, 1903).

9. For some interesting discussion on this issue, see Henry Sidgewick, *The Methods of Ethics* II:3; J. Bentham, *The Principles of Morals and Legislation* 1–4; J.S. Mill, *Utilitarianism* 2, 4, etc. See also Brandt, *Ethical Theory,* and G.E. Moore, *Principia Ethica*.

10. See Moore, *op. cit.*

11. W.R. Ross, *The Right and the Good* (Oxford: Clarendon Press, 1938).

12. See Brandt, *Ethical Theory*, 380–391.

13. Strictly speaking, this is an oversimplification. A complete formulation would require qualifiers that allow for the resolution of conflict among rules, where that set of rules is correct which, when followed conscientiously by all members of society, would maximize the welfare or good for all. See Brandt, *Ethical Theory*, 253 ff.

14. See W.K. Frankena, "Morality and Moral Philosophy," in *Ethics* (Englewood Cliffs, N.J.: Prentice-Hall, 1973), and R.B. Brandt, *Ethical Theory* (Englewood Cliffs, N.J.: Prentice-Hall, 1959), for analogous discussions.

15. Cf. A.J. Paton, *The Categorical Imperative* (London: Hutcheson, 1947).

16. Immanuel Kant, *Foundations of the Metaphysics of Morals*, 422 [Prussian Academy page numbering].

17. Kant, *Foundations*, 429.

18. For a similar point see S. Bok, *Lying* (New York: Random House, 1978), chapter 4.

19. What follows is based in part on J.E. Magnet and E.W. Kluge, *Withholding Treatment from Defective Newborn Children* (Cowansville, Que.: Brown Legal Publ., 1985).

20. Perhaps a more familiar way of expressing this principle in the health care setting is *primum non nocere:* above all, do not harm. It is also sometimes expressed as "Do not intentionally or knowingly injure the patient" or as "Do not intentionally or knowingly expose the patient to unjustified risk." *Cf.* Tom L. Beauchamp and James F. Childress, *Principles of Biomedical Ethics,* 2nd edition (New York and Oxford: Oxford University Press, 1983), 106–147, especially at 108 ff. Also T.M. Garrett, H.W. Baillie and R.H. Garrett, *Health Care Ethics: Principles and Problems* (Englewood Cliffs, N.J.: Prentice-Hall, 1989), 51–55.

21. Another formulation of this principle is that we have a "duty to help others further their important and legitimate interest" when we can do so with minimal risks to ourselves.

22. Tom L. Beauchamp and James F. Childress, *Principles of Biomedical Ethics* (New York and Oxford: Oxford University Press, 1979), 136.

23. W.R. Ross, *The Right and the Good* (Oxford: Clarendon Press, 1938).

24. Ibid., chapter 2.

25. Nel Noddings, "Feminist Fears in Ethics," *Journal of Social Philosophy* (Fall/Winter 1990), reprinted in D.T. Goldberg, *Ethical Theory and Social Issues,* 2nd ed. (Orlando, FLA: Holt, Rinehart and Winston, Inc., 1990), 215–225, at 223.

26. C.J. Gilligan, *In a Different Voice* (Cambridge: Harvard University Press, 1982); J. Grimshaw, *Philosophy and Feminist Thinking* (Minneapolis: University of Minnesota Press, 1989); N. Noddings, *Caring: A Feminist Approach to Ethics and Moral Education* (Berkeley: University of California Press, 1984); S. Sherwin, *No*

Longer Patient: Feminist Ethics and Health Care* (Philadelphia: Temple University Press, 1992); R. Tong, *Feminine and Feminist Ethics* (Belmont, CA: Wadsworth, 1993).

27. N. Noddings, *Caring: A Feminist Approach to Ethics and Moral Education* (Berkeley: University of California Press, 1984).

28. C.J. Gilligan, *In a Different Voice* (Cambridge: Harvard University Press, 1982).

29. See Sherwin, *op. cit.* at 13.

30. Annette Baier, "What Do Women Want in a Moral Theory?" *Nous* 19 (March 1985): 53–56.

31. V. Merton, "The Exclusion of Pregnant, Pregnable, and Once-Pregnable People (A.K.A. Women) from Biomedical Research," *Am J Law Med* XIX:4 (1993): 369–451.

32. Alasdair MacIntyre, *After Virtue: A Study in Moral Theory* (London: Duckworth, 1981).

33. G.E.M. Anscombe, "Modern Moral Philosophy," *Philos* 33 (1958): 1–19.

34. MacIntyre, *After Virtue: A Study in Moral Theory*. For a classic statement, see Aristotle, *Nicomachean Ethics*. For an attempt to apply it in the health care setting, see R.J. Christie and C.B. Hoffmaster, *Ethical Issues in Family Medicine* (New York and London: Oxford University Press, 1986).

35. Alasdair MacIntyre, *After Virtue: A Study in Moral Theory*, 150 ff.

36. See Christie and Hoffmaster, *Ethical Issues in Family Medicine*.

37. R. McCormick, "Theology and Bioethics," *Hastings Center Rep* 19:2 (1989): 5–10. For specific examples, see E.D. Pellegrino, J.P. Langan, and J.C. Harvey, eds., *Catholic Perspectives on Medical Morals* (Dordrecht: Kluwer Academic, 1989).

38. For an overview of some of the possible differences, see E.D. Pellegrino, P. Mazzarella and P. Corsi, eds., *Transcultural Dimensions in Medical Ethics* (Frederick, MA: University Publishing Group, 1992).

39. *Constitution Act*, 1982, R.S.C. 1985, Appendix II, No. 44, Schedule B, Part I, Canadian Charter of Rights and Freedoms s. 2(a).

40. Albert Schweitzer, *Civilization and Ethics*, 3rd ed. (London: Black, 1949). For a more recent position, see Tom Regan, *The Case for Animal Rights* (Berkeley: University of California Press, 1983), and Peter Singer, *Animal Liberation* (New York: Avon Books, 1975); P. Rodd, *Biology, Ethics and Animals* (Oxford: Clarendon Press, 1990).

41. Singer, *op. cit.*

42. B.E. Rollin, *The Unheard Cry: Animal Consciousness, Animal Pain and Science* (Oxford: Oxford University Press, 1990).

43. R.M. Baird and S.E. Rosenbaum, eds., *Animal Experimentation: Moral and Ethical Aspects* (Buffalo, N.Y.: Prometheus, 1991).

44. See Regan, *op. cit.*

45. Tom L. Beauchamp, "Problems in Justifying Research on Animals," in *National Symposium on Imperatives in Research Animal Use: Scientific Needs and Animal Welfare* (Washington, D.C.: NIH, Publication No. 85-2746, 1985), 80 ff. *et passim*.

46. L. Edelstein, *Ancient Medicine* (Baltimore: Johns Hopkins Univ. Press, 1967).

47. *See R. v. Morgentaler* [1988] 1 S.C.R. 30, included in this volume, where the court took judicial notice of the gradualistic notion of personhood advanced by W. Sumner.

48. The Canadian constitution makes health care a matter of provincial jurisdiction; that is why legislation that deals specifically with health care is provincial in nature. The federal government can deal with health care only by attaching conditions to its transfer of federal funds to the provinces or by regulating a specific kind of action through the *Criminal Code*.

49. At the time of publication, the proposed legislation — the new *Assisted Human Reproduction Act* — had been passed by the Commons and awaited final passage in Senate, and Royal Proclamation. It would control certain practices — for example, genetic engineering, surrogacy and human stem cell research — and prohibit others, such as cloning for reproductive purposes, creating stem cell lines specifically for research purposes or doing anything that would ensure or increase the probability that an embryo will be of a particular sex. The law will be part of the *Criminal Code*. The reason for placing it into the *Criminal Code* is that in Canada, health care is a matter of provincial jurisdiction. Therefore, the only way the federal government can ensure that the reproductive technologies will be controlled in a consistent and uniform fashion is to use its legislative powers in the area of criminal law. For relevant excerpts of the proposed law, see Chapter 16, pp. 423–426, "Bill C-13: An Act Respecting Assisted Human Reproduction."

Further Readings

Deontological and Utilitarian Ethics:

Beauchamp, Tom L., and James F. Childress. *Principles of Biomedical Ethics*, 5th ed. New York and Oxford: Oxford Univ. Press, 2001.

> This is a classic text in biomedical ethics written by a deontologist and a utilitarian for the U.S. setting. Its usefulness is somewhat marred by the internal conflict between competing ethical approaches, and the U.S. focus, in its social and legal considerations, limits its applicability to the Canadian setting.

Bowie, Norman E., ed. *Ethical Theory in the Last Quarter of the Twentieth Century*. Indianapolis: Hackett Publishing, 1983.

> This is a collection of essays by Stevenson, Frankena, Brandt, and Melden on value judgements, moral-point-of-view theories, utilitarianism and the rights-based approach. It can serve as a way to focus some of the perspectives in the other readings mentioned.

Donagan, A. *The Theory of Morality*. Chicago: Chicago Univ. Press, 1977.

> A somewhat technical statement of a modern Kant-derived deontological theory.

Engelhardt, Jr., H.T. *The Foundations of Bioethics*. New York and London: Oxford Univ. Press, 1986.

> A classic application of deontological ethics to health care. The focus tends to be on the U.S. setting, which limits its usefulness for the Canadian context.

Frankena, William K. "Deontological Theories," in *Ethics*. Englewood Cliffs, N.J.: Prentice Hall, 1963.

> This selection from Frankena's classic introductory text on ethical theory discusses various types of deontological theories and attempts to relate them to one another.

Haering, Bernard. "Ethos, Ethical Code and the Morality of the Physician." In *Medical Ethics*, chapter 4. Notre Dame, Ind.: Fides, 1973.

Bernard Haering is a Catholic theologian who writes on medical ethics. This excerpt is from his text, which for years has served as a standard and middle-of-the-road guide to Catholic physicians.

Pellegrino, E.D., J.P. Langan and J.C. Harvey, eds. *Catholic Perspectives on Medical Morals*. Dordrecht: Kluwer Academic, 1989.

A good collection of essays on the relationship between Catholicism and ethics in the context of health care. It addresses foundational issues within the pluralistic perspective that characterizes contemporary Catholic thought. The points raised in these discussions can be applied to other religious perspectives.

Rawls, John. *A Theory of Justice*. Cambridge: Harvard Univ. Press, 1971; revised edition 1999.

A modern classic deontological ethical approach. Difficult reading.

Taylor, Paul. "Utilitarianism." In *Principles of Ethics: An Introduction*. Belmont, Calif.: Wadsworth, 1975.

A classic exposition of utilitarian theory for those who do not want to go to the full-length work of Richard Brandt and others.

Feminist Ethics:

Baier, Annette. *Postures of the Mind*. Minneapolis, MN: Univ. of Minnesota Press, 1985.

A philosophical presentation of the ethics of love and trust. Baier recommends that traditional ethics must make room for love, trust, human bonding and friendship.

Chinn, P.L., and C.E. Wheeler. "Feminism and Nursing." *Nurs Outlook* 33(2) (March–April 1985): 74–78.

This is a good introductory paper applying, as the title suggests, feminist ethical theory to nursing issues.

Crowley, M.A. "Feminist pedagogy: nurturing the ethical ideal." *ANS* 11(3) (April 1989): 53–61.

Donchin A. "Understanding Autonomy Relationally: Toward a Reconfiguration of Bioethical Principles," *The Journal of Medicine and Philosophy* 2001;26(4): 365–386.

Gilligan, C. *In a Different Voice*. Cambridge, MA: Harvard Univ. Press, 1982.

This is the classical work in feminist ethical theory. It is more reflective and not quite as extreme as later feminist writings. In it, Gilligan lays the foundation for an ethics of caring by trying to tie it to the different experiences that women have in (Western) society.

Noddings, N. *Caring: A Feminist Approach to Ethics and Moral Education*. Berkeley: Univ. of California Press, 1986.

This is a companion work to Gilligan's seminal study. Noddings adopts a more "philosophical" approach and erects a theoretical framework on Gilligan's work. In some ways, it can be described as a feminist version of Kohlberg's work.

Manning, R.C. "A Care Approach," in *A Companion to Bioethics*. Ed. Helga Kuhse and Peter Singer. Malden, MA: Blackwell, 1998.

An informative article in a very useful volume devoted to different topics in the field of biomedical ethics.

Nussbaum, Martha. *Love's Knowledge*. Oxford: Oxford Univ. Press, 1990.

As the title indicates, a philosophical presentation of the ethics of love. Nussbaum is one of the premier philosophers of the present time.

Rawlinson, M.C. "The Concept of a Feminist Bioethics," *J Med Philos* 2001;26(4): 405–416.

Raymond, J.G. "Medicine as patriarchal religion." *J Med Philos* 7(2) (May 1982): 197–216.

Sherwin, S. "Concluding remarks: a feminist perspective." *Health Care Women Int* 8(4) (1987): 293–304.
> A classic but short statement by a Canadian feminist philosopher.

Sherwin, S. *No Longer Patient: Feminist Ethic and Health Care*. Philadelphia: Temple Univ. Press, 1992.
> This is an extensive and in-depth development of the implications of feminist theory on the delivery of health care by a well-known Canadian feminist philosopher.

Tong, Rosemary. *Feminist Approaches to Bioethics: Theoretical Reflections and Practical Applications*. Boulder, CO: Westview Press, 1997.

Virtue Ethics:

Aristotle. *Nicomachean Ethics* (any edition).
> The original classical statement of virtue ethics by one of the founders of ethics as a field of study.

Foot, P. *Virtues and Vices*. Oxford: Basil Blackwell, 1978.
> A relatively recent statement of virtue ethics by one of Britain's best-known ethicists.

Geach, P. *The Virtues*. Cambridge: Cambridge Univ. Press, 1977.

Kruschwitz, R.B., and R.C. Roberts, eds. *The Virtues: Contemporary Essays on Moral Character*. Belmont, Calif.: Wadsworth, 1987.
> A collection of essays on virtue theory, which spans the whole spectrum of possible positions in virtue theory. Somewhat dated, but still very good.

MacIntyre, A. *After Virtue: A Study in Moral Theory*. London: Duckworth, 1985.
> Somewhat dated, but still the best-known exposition of virtue ethics in the last 20 years.

Useful Web Sites

http://www.bioethics.ca/links.html   This is the home site of the Canadian Bioethics Society. It features both English and French. It is the best site for Canadian links and for news about what's currently going on in bioethics in Canada.

http://www.ethics.ubc.ca/   The UBC Centre for Applied Ethics maintains this site. It has links to both national and international sites.

http://www.fes.umontreal.ca/bioethique/   A French-Canadian Web site with research links.

http://www.georgetown.edu/research/kie/   The Web site for Georgetown University's Kennedy Center for Bioethics.

http://www.ncbcenter.org/home.html   This is the Web site for the National Catholic Bioethics Center in the U.S. It is an invaluable resource for research in Catholic bioethics.

http://www.princeton.edu/~bioethic/   An excellent resource for international links.

http://www.thehastingscenter.org/   The Hastings Center is one of the oldest bioethics centres in the world. This Web site is a very useful research tool.

http://www.utoronto.ca/jcb/   The University of Toronto has one of the largest bioethics centres in Canada. This is its Web site. It has many useful links.

CHAPTER 2
HEALTH AS AN ETHICAL ISSUE

Introduction

"What is truth?" The question has occupied philosophers, lawyers and theologians since ancient times. *"What is health?"* must surely rank a close second in terms of difficulty. Time and again, physicians and philosophers have tried to define the notion, only to find that as their knowledge advanced, the definitions they have settled on seem inadequate. And yet it is clear that if health care is to be assigned its proper place in the sphere of social endeavours and if the health care professions are to have a clearly defined role and mandate, the notion has to have an appropriate and acceptable definition.

The issue has become particularly pressing in recent times as modern societies are increasingly realizing that they have an obligation to provide at least some level of health care for their members. If the nature of health cannot be satisfactorily defined, then the limits of this social obligation cannot be drawn properly, either. That, in turn, will have important implications for social policy formulation.

Furthermore, when people say that societies have an obligation to provide at least some level of health care for their members, they are not only talking about health care on an individual basis. They also have in mind the sorts of services that are usually referred to as public health measures. These are services that are designed to maintain, raise and promote the health, collectively, of all of society. Here, too, the notion of health plays a central role. Therefore, without some common understanding of what exactly health is, these services can be identified only in a very haphazard fashion.

There are still other reasons for seeking a definition. For instance, it is a crime in most countries — Canada included —to cut people open, to give them noxious chemicals, to incarcerate them or to subject them to invasive physical procedures. *Prima facie*, surgical interventions, the administration of pharmaceuticals, psychiatric commitment, dental work, and even the most basic of nursing functions all would seem to be implicated. The only thing that sets them apart as non-criminal is that they are recognized as *health care*. However, we need a proper definition of "health" in order to define and delimit this category properly.

For these and similar reasons, people some time ago started to look for a definition of "health." The WHO took the lead in 1958 when it promulgated its by now famous definition. It is included below. However, in some quarters the reaction to the WHO definition was less than enthusiastic. As a whole series of authors soon pointed out, the definition is extremely vague. For instance, what does "well-being" mean, or "infirmity"? It is also circular: it defines "health" in terms of its correlative, "disease," where the notion of disease could itself only be defined in terms of health. Furthermore, the definition is far too inclusive. It would have us classify social and moral problems as health problems. The selection from Daniel Callahan captures the thrust of most of this criticism very well.

Other definitions attempted to overcome these problems. For instance, health was variously defined as "a state of physiological normalcy" or a "proper working order of the human body";[1] as "the general condition of the body with respect to efficient or inefficient discharge of functions"; as "spiritual, moral or mental soundness or well-being";[2] the ability to function "in a given physical and social environment";[3] the "well-working of the organism as a whole"; "an activity of the living body in accordance with its specific excellence";[4] or simply as "a state of physical well-being."[5]

To date, none of these definitions has proved wholly satisfactory. In fact, the very attempt to define the term "health" has itself been criticized. On a general level, this criticism maintains that an overall definition is impossible because concepts like those of health and disease are inherently value-laden. They include not only descriptive components but also normative ones. According to some of these critics,[6] this means that it is impossible in *principle* to give a general definition of "health," because to say that something is a disease commits us to saying something about human nature and about the nature of human well-being. However, this involves theories about the human good — which, in turn, involves considerations of what counts as the proper human state. That, however, is not something that can be identified in the abstract; it is a function of one's philosophical views and of socially conditioned perceptions.

The selection by W. Miller Brown gives a brief analytical overview of some of the better-known attempts to define "health" and "disease." Brown comes to the conclusion that these notions can only be given proper definitions if there is a theory of medicine — and to his mind, there is none. Medicine, so he believes, is a set of practices. As he puts it, "As a practical discipline, medicine and its concepts of 'disease' and 'health' are bound up with medical practice and the interests of doctors and patients as well as with the advances of science." If he is correct, this has tremendous implications for the formulation of health care policies. Among other things, it means that health policy formulation – such as the development of the *Canada Health Act* and the like – will necessarily be a time-bound affair that is incapable of attaining some absolute and fixed goal and is subject to changes in social and scientific practice.

Who is right? The issue is important because if we cannot give a value-free definition of health, then we will always have to ask ourselves whether the health services that are provided by our society are so coloured by our values that they in fact amount to a cultural agenda. This would have to be of particular concern to Canadians because Canada, by choice and by Charter, is a multicultural society.

Notes

1. Joel Feinberg, "Disease and Values," in *Doing and Deserving: Essays in the Theory of Responsibility,* Joel Feinberg (Princeton: Princeton University Press, 1974), 253–255.
2. *Oxford English Dictionary.*
3. René Dubos, "Health as Ability to Function," in T.L. Beauchamp and L. Walters, eds., *Contemporary Issues in Bioethics* (Belmont: Dickenson Publ. Co., 1978), 99.
4. Leon Kass, "Regarding the End of Medicine and the Pursuit of Health," in *Contemporary Issues in Bioethics*, ref. note 3, 108.
5. Daniel Callahan, "The WHO Definition of Health," included below. A somewhat more theoretical and developed analysis is offered by Ellen Idler, "Definition of Mental Health and Illness and Medical Sociology," *Society, Science and Medicine* 3A, 723–731. She claims that these and other definitions are based on a Parsonian model of illness and disease: one that defines it as "an abstract, biomedical conception of pathological abnormality in people's bodies, where this is indicated by certain abnormal signs and symptoms which can be measured, recorded, classified and analyzed." To be quite correct, so she argues, the concept should be modified so that "subjective reality plays a role in determining whether an individual becomes ill in the first place." For other attempts to define "health," see President's Commission for the Study of Ethical Problems in Medicine and Biomedical and Behavioral Research, *Securing Access to Health Care: A Report on the Ethical Implications of Differences in the Availability of Health Services* (Washington D.C.: U.S. Government Printing Office, 1983), 3 vols., vols. two and three.
6. Tristram Englehardt, Jr., "Human Well-Being and Medicine: Some Basic Value-Judgments in the Biomedical Science," in *Science, Ethics and Medicine,* H.T. Engelhardt and D. Callahan, eds. (Institute of Society, Ethics and the Life Sciences, 1976).

Preamble: Constitution of the World Health Organization

World Health Organization

The States Parties to this Constitution declare, in conformity with the Charter of the United Nations, that the following principles are basic to the happiness, harmonious relations and security of all peoples:

Reproduced by permission of WHO from *Basic Documents. Thirty-Ninth Edition* (Geneva: World Health Organization, 1992), pp. 1–2.

Health is a state of complete physical, mental and social well-being and not merely the absence of disease or infirmity.

The enjoyment of the highest attainable standard of health is one of the fundamental rights of every human being without distinction of race, religion, political belief, economic or social condition.

The health of all peoples is fundamental to the attainment of peace and security and is dependent upon the fullest co-operation of individuals and States.

The achievement of any State in the promotion and protection of health is of value to all.

Unequal development in different countries in the promotion of health and control of disease, especially communicable disease, is a common danger.

Healthy development of the child is of basic importance; the ability to live harmoniously in a changing total environment is essential to such development.

The extension to all peoples of the benefits of medical, psychological and related knowledge is essential to the fullest attainment of health.

Informed opinion and active co-operation on the part of the public are of the utmost importance in the improvement of the health of the people.

Governments have a responsibility for the health of their peoples which can be fulfilled only by the provision of adequate health and social measures.

Accepting these principles, and for the purpose of co-operation among themselves and with others to promote and protect the health of all peoples, the Contracting Parties agree to the present Constitution and hereby establish the World Health Organization as a specialized agency within the terms of Article 57 of the Charter of the United Nations.

The WHO Definition of Health

Daniel Callahan

There is not much that can be called fun and games in medicine, perhaps because unlike other sports it is the only one in which everyone, participant and spectator, eventually gets killed playing. In the meantime, one of the grandest games is that version of king-of-the-hill where the aim of all players is to upset the World Health Organization (WHO) definition of "health." That definition, in case anyone could possibly forget it, is, "Health is a state of complete physical, mental, and social well-being and not merely the absence of disease or infirmity." Fair game, indeed. Yet somehow, defying all comers, the WHO definition endures, though literally every other aspirant to the crown has managed to knock it off the hill at least once. One possible reason for its presence is that it provides such an irresistible straw man; few there are who can resist attacking it in the opening paragraphs of papers designed to move on to more profound reflections.

But there is another possible reason which deserves some exploration, however unsettling the implications. It may just be that the WHO definition has more than a grain of truth in it, of a kind which is as profoundly frustrating as it

Daniel Callahan, "The WHO Definition of Health," *Hastings Center Report,* 1:3 (1973). Reproduced by permission. © The Hastings Center.

is enticingly attractive. At the very least it is a definition which implies that there is some intrinsic relationship between the good of the body and the good of the self. The attractiveness of this relationship is obvious: it thwarts any movement toward a dualism of self and body, a dualism which in any event immediately breaks down when one drops a brick on one's toe; and it impels the analyst to work toward a conception of health which in the end is resistant to clear and distinct categories, closer to the felt experience. All that, naturally, is very frustrating. It seems simply impossible to devise a concept of health which is rich enough to be nutritious and yet not so rich as to be indigestible.

One common objection to the WHO definition is, in effect, an assault upon any and all attempts to specify the meaning of very general concepts. Who can possibly define words as vague as "health," a venture as foolish as trying to define "peace," "justice," "happiness," and other systematically ambiguous notions? To this objection the "pragmatic" clinicians (as they often call themselves) add that, anyway, it is utterly unnecessary to know what "health" means in order to treat a patient running a high temperature. Not only that, it is also a harmful distraction to clutter medical judgment with philosophical puzzles.

Unfortunately for this line of argument, it is impossible to talk or think at all without employing general concepts; without them, cognition and language are impossible. More damagingly, it is rarely difficult to discover, with a bit of probing, that even the most "pragmatic" judgment (whatever *that* is) presupposes some general values and orientations, all of which can be translated into definitions of terms as general as "health" and "happiness." A failure to discern the operative underlying values, the conceptions of reality upon which they are based, and the definitions they entail, sets the stage for unexamined conduct and, beyond

that, positive harm both to patients and to medicine in general.

But if these objections to any and all attempts to specify the meaning of "health" are common enough, the most specific complaint about the WHO definition is that its very generality, and particularly its association of health and general well-being as a positive ideal, has given rise to a variety of evils. Among them are the cultural tendency to define all social problems, from war to crime in the streets, as "health" problems; the blurring of lines of responsibility between and among the professions, and between the medical profession and the political order; the implicit denial of human freedom which results when failures to achieve social well-being are defined as forms of "sickness," somehow to be treated by medical means; and the general debasement of language which ensues upon the casual habit of labeling everyone from Adolf Hitler to student radicals to the brat next door as "sick." In short, the problem with the WHO definition is not that it represents an attempt to propose a general definition, but it is simply a bad one.

That is a valid line of objection, provided one can spell out in some detail just how the definition can or does entail some harmful consequences. Two lines of attack are possible against putatively hazardous social definitions of significant general concepts. One is by pointing out that the definition does not encompass all that a concept has commonly been taken to mean, either historically or at present, that it is a partial definition only. The task then is to come up with a fuller definition, one less subject to misuse. But there is still another way of objecting to socially significant definitions, and that is by pointing out some baneful effects of definitions generally accepted as adequate. Many of the objections to the WHO definition fall in the latter category, building upon the important insight that definitions of crucially important terms with a wide public use have ethical, social, and political implications; defining general terms is not an abstract exercise but a way of shaping the world metaphysically and structuring the world politically.

Wittgenstein's aphorism, "Don't look for the meaning, look for the use," is pertinent here. The ethical problem in defining the concept of "health" is to determine what the implications are of the various uses to which a concept of "health" can be put. We might well agree that there are some uses of "health" which will produce socially harmful results. To carry Wittgenstein a step further, "Don't look for the uses, look for the abuses." We might, then, examine some of the real or possible abuses to which the WHO definition leads, recognizing all the while that what we may term an "abuse" will itself rest upon some perceived *positive* good or value.

Historical Origin and Context

Before that task is undertaken, however, it is helpful to understand the historical origin and social context of the WHO definition. If abuses of that definition have developed, their seeds may be looked for in its earliest manifestations.

The World Health Organization came into existence between 1946 and 1948 as one of the first major activities of the United Nations. As an outcome of earlier work, an Interim Commission to establish the WHO sponsored an International Health Conference in New York in June and July of 1946. At that Conference, representatives of 61 nations signed the Constitution of the WHO, the very first clause of which presented the now famous definition of "health." The animating spirit behind the formation of the WHO was the belief that the improvement of world health would make an important contribution to world

peace; health and peace were seen as inseparable. Just why this belief gained ground is not clear from the historical record of the WHO. While there have been many historical explanations of the origin of World War II, a lack of world health has not been prominent among them; nor, for that matter, did the early supporters of the WHO claim that the Second World War or any other war might have been averted had there been better health. More to the point, perhaps, was the conviction that health was intimately related to economic and cultural welfare; in turn, that welfare, so it was assumed, had a direct bearing on future peace. No less important was a fervent faith in the possibilities of medical science to achieve world health, enhanced by the development of powerful antibiotics and pesticides during the war.

A number of memorandums submitted to a spring 1946 Technical Preparatory Committee meeting of the WHO capture the flavor of the period. The Yugoslavian memorandum noted that "health is a prerequisite to freedom from want, to social security and happiness." France stated that "there cannot be any material security, social security, or well-being for individuals or nations without health ... the full responsibility of a free man can only be assumed by healthy individuals ... the spread of proper notions of hygiene among populations tends to improve the level of health and hence to increase their working power and raise their standard of living. ..." The United States contended that "international cooperation and joint action in the furtherance of all matters pertaining to health will raise the standards of living, will promote the freedom, the dignity, and the happiness of all peoples of the world."

In addition to those themes, perhaps the most significant initiative taken by the organizers of the WHO was to include mental health as part of its working definition. In its memorandum, Great

Britain stated that "it should be clear that health includes mental health," but it was Dr. Brock Chisholm, soon to become the first director of the WHO, who personified what Dr. Chisholm himself called the "visionary" view of health. During the meeting of the Technical Preparatory Committee he argued that: "The world is sick and the ills are due to the perversion of man; his inability to live with himself. The microbe is not the enemy; science is sufficiently advanced to cope with it were it not for the barriers of superstition, ignorance, religious intolerance, misery and poverty. ... These psychological evils must be understood in order that a remedy might be prescribed, and the scope of the task before the Committee therefore knows no bounds."

In Dr. Chisholm's statement, put very succinctly, are all of those elements of the WHO definition which led eventually to its criticism: defining all the problems of the world as "sickness," affirming that science would be sufficient to cope with the causes of physical disease, asserting that only anachronistic attitudes stood in the way of a cure of both physical and psychological ills, and declaring that the cause of health can tolerate no limitations. To say that Dr. Chisholm's "vision" was grandiose is to understate the matter. Even allowing for hyperbole, it is clear that the stage was being set for a conception of "health" which would encompass literally every element and item of human happiness. One can hardly be surprised, given such a vision, that our ways of talking about "health" have become all but meaningless. Even though I believe the definition is not without its important insights, it is well to observe why, in part, we are so muddled at present about "health."

Health and Happiness

Let us examine some of the principal objections to the WHO definition in more detail. One of them is that, by including the notion of "social well-being" under its rubric, it turns the enduring problem of human happiness into one more medical problem, to be dealt with by scientific means. That is surely an objectionable feature, if only because there exists no evidence whatever that medicine has anything more than a partial grasp of the sources of human misery. Despite Dr. Chisholm's optimism, medicine has not even found ways of dealing with more than a fraction of the whole range of physical diseases; campaigns, after all, are still being mounted against cancer and heart disease. Nor is there any special reason to think that future forays against those and other common diseases will bear rapid fruits. People will continue to die of disease for a long time to come, probably forever.

But perhaps, then, in the psychological and psychiatric sciences some progress has been made against what Dr. Chisholm called the "psychological ills," which lead to wars, hostility, and aggression? To be sure, there are many interesting psychological theories to be found about these "ills," and a few techniques which can, with some individuals, reduce or eliminate anti-social behavior. But so far as I can see, despite the mental health movement and the rise of the psychological sciences, war and human hostility are as much with us as ever. Quite apart from philosophical objections to the WHO definition, there was no empirical basis for the unbounded optimism which lay behind it at the time of its inception, and little has happened since to lend its limitless aspiration any firm support.

Common sense alone makes evident the fact that the absence of "disease or infirmity" by no means guarantees "social well-being." In one sense, those who drafted the WHO definition seem well aware of that. Isn't the whole point of their definition to show the inadequacy of negative definitions? But in another sense, it may be doubted that they really did grasp that point. For the third principle enunciated in the WHO Constitution says that "the health of all peoples is fundamental to the attainment of peace and security. ..." Why is it fundamental, at least to peace? The worst wars of the 20th century have been waged by countries with very high standards of health, by nations with superior life-expectancies for individuals and with comparatively low infant mortality rates. The greatest present threats to world peace come in great part (though not entirely) from developed countries, those which have combated disease and illness most effectively. There seems to be no historical correlation whatever between health and peace, and that is true even if one includes "mental health."

How are human beings to achieve happiness? That is the final and fundamental question. Obviously illness, whether mental or physical, makes happiness less possible in most cases. But that is only because they are only one symptom of a more basic restriction, that of human finitude, which sees infinite human desires constantly thwarted by the limitations of reality. "Complete" well-being might, conceivably, be attainable, but under one condition only: that people cease expecting much from life. That does not seem about to happen. On the contrary, medical and psychological progress have been more than outstripped by rising demands and expectations. What is so odd about that, if it is indeed true that human desires are infinite? Whatever the answer to the question of human happiness, there is no particular reason to believe that medicine can do anything more than make a modest, finite contribution.

Another objection to the WHO definition is that, by implication, it makes the medical profession the gatekeeper for happiness and social well-being. Or if not exactly the gatekeeper (since political and economic support will be needed from sources other than medical), then

the final magic-healer of human misery. Pushed far enough, the whole idea is absurd, and it is not necessary to believe that the organizers of the WHO would, if pressed, have been willing to go quite that far. But even if one pushes the pretension a little way, considerable fantasy results. The mental health movement is the best example, casting the psychological professional in the role of high priest.

At its humble best, that movement can do considerable good; people do suffer from psychological disabilities and there are some effective ways of helping them. But it would be sheer folly to believe that all, or even the most important, social evils stem from bad mental health: political injustice, economic scarcity, food shortages, unfavorable physical environments, have a far greater historical claim as sources of a failure to achieve "social well-being." To retort that all or most of these troubles can, nonetheless, be seen finally as symptoms of bad mental health is, at best, self-serving and, at worst, just plain foolish.

A significant part of the objection that the WHO definition places, at least by implication, too much power and authority in the hands of the medical profession need not be based on a fear of that power as such. There is no reason to think that the world would be any worse off if health professionals made all decisions than if any other group did; and no reason to think it would be any better off. That is not a very important point. More significant is that cultural development which, in its skepticism about "traditional" ways of solving social problems, would seek a technological and specifically a medical solution for human ills of all kinds. There is at least a hint in early WHO discussions that, since politicians and diplomats have failed in maintaining world peace, a more expert group should take over, armed with the scientific skills necessary to set things right; it is science which is best able to vanquish that old Enlightenment bogeyman, "superstition."

More concretely, such an ideology has the practical effect of blurring the lines of appropriate authority and responsibility. If all problems — political, economic and social — reduce to matters of "health," then there ceases to be any way to determine who should be responsible for what.

The Tyranny of Health

The problem of responsibility has at least two faces. One is that of a tendency to turn all problems of "social well-being" over to the medical professional, most pronounced in the instance of the incarceration of a large group of criminals in mental institutions rather than prisons. The abuses, both medical and legal, of that practice are, fortunately, now beginning to receive the attention they deserve, even if little corrective action has yet been taken. (Counterbalancing that development, however, are others, where some are seeking more "effective" ways of bringing science to bear on criminal behavior.)

The other face of the problem of responsibility is that of the way in which those who are sick, or purportedly sick, are to be evaluated in terms of their freedom and responsibility. Siegler and Osmond (*Hastings Center Studies*, Vol. 1, No. 3, 1973, pp. 41–58) discuss the "sick role," a leading feature of which is the ascription of blamelessness, of nonresponsibility, to those who contract illness. There is no reason to object to this kind of ascription in many instances — one can hardly blame someone for contracting kidney disease — but, obviously enough, matters get out of hand when all physical, mental, and communal disorders are put under the heading of "sickness," and all sufferers (all of us, in the end) placed in the blameless "sick role." Not only are the concepts of "sickness" and "illness" drained of all content, it also becomes impossible to ascribe any freedom or responsibility to those caught up

in the throes of sickness. The whole world is sick, and no one is responsible any longer for anything. That is determinism gone mad, a rather odd outcome of a development which began with attempts to bring unbenighted "reason" and free self-determination to bear for the release of the helpless captives of superstition and ignorance.

The final and most telling objection to the WHO definition has less to do with the definition itself than with one of its natural historical consequences. Thomas Szasz has been the most eloquent (and most single-minded) critic of that sleight-of-hand which has seen the concept of health moved from the medical to the moral arena. What can no longer be done in the name of "morality" can now be done in the name of "health": human beings labeled, incarcerated, and dismissed for their failure to toe the line of "normalcy" and "sanity."

At first glance, this analysis of the present situation might seem to be totally at odds with the tendency to put everyone in the blame-free "sick role." Actually, there is a fine, probably indistinguishable, line separating these two positions. For as soon as one treats all human disorders — war, crime, social unrest — as forms of illness, then one turns health into a normative concept, that which human beings must and ought to have if they are to live in peace with themselves and others. Health is no longer an optional matter, but the golden key to the relief of human misery. We *must* be well or we will all perish. "Health" can and must be imposed; there can be no room for the luxury of freedom when so much is at stake. Of course the matter is rarely put so bluntly, but it is to Szasz's great credit that he has discerned what actually happens when "health" is allowed to gain the cultural clout which morality once had. (That he carries the whole business too far in his embracing of the most extreme moral individualism is another story, which cannot be dealt with here.)

Something is seriously amiss when the "right" to have healthy children is turned into a further right for children not to be born defective, and from there into an obligation not to bring unhealthy children into the world as a way of respecting the right of those children to health! Nor is everything altogether lucid when abortion decisions are made a matter of "medical judgment" (see *Roe vs. Wade*); when decisions to provide psychoactive drugs for the relief of the ordinary stress of living are defined as no less "medical judgment"; when patients are not allowed to die with dignity because of medical indications that they can, come what may, be kept alive; when prisoners, without their consent, are subjected to aversive conditioning to improve their mental health.

Abuses of Language

In running through the litany of criticisms which have been directed at the WHO definition of "health," and what seem to have been some of its long-term implications and consequences, I might well be accused of beating a dead horse. My only defense is to assert, first, that the spirit of the WHO definition is by no means dead either in medicine or society. In fact, because of the usual cultural lag which requires many years for new ideas to gain wide social currency, it is only now coming into its own on a broad scale. (Everyone now talks about everybody and everything, from Watergate to Billy Graham to trash in the streets, as "sick.") Second, I believe that we are now in the midst of a nascent (if not actual) crisis about how "health" ought properly to be understood, with much dependent upon what conception of health emerges in the near future.

If the ideology which underlies the WHO definition has proved to contain many muddled and hazardous ingredients, it is not at all evident what should take its place. The virtue of the WHO definition is that it tried to place health in the broadest human context. Yet the assumption behind the main criticisms of the WHO definition seem perfectly valid. Those assumptions can be characterized as follows: (1) health is only a part of life, and the achievement of health only a part of the achievement of happiness; (2) medicine's role, however important, is limited; it can neither solve nor even cope with the great majority of social, political, and cultural problems; (3) human freedom and responsibility must be recognized, and any tendency to place all deviant, devilish, or displeasing human beings into the blameless sick-role must be resisted; (4) while it is good for human beings to be healthy, medicine is not morality; except in very limited contexts (plagues and epidemics) "medical judgment" should not be allowed to become moral judgment; to be healthy is not to be righteous; (5) it is important to keep clear and distinct the different roles of different professions, with a clearly circumscribed role for medicine, limited to those domains of life where the contribution of medicine is appropriate. Medicine can save some lives; it cannot save the life of society.

These assumptions, and the criticisms of the WHO definition which spring from them, have some important implications for the use of the words "health," "illness," "sick," and the like. It will be counted an abuse of language if the word "sick" is applied to all individual and communal problems, if all unacceptable conduct is spoken of in the language of medical pathologies, if moral issues and moral judgments are translated into the language of "health," if the lines of authority, responsibility, and expertise are so blurred that the health profession is allowed to pre-empt the rights and responsibilities of others by re-defining them in its own professional language.

Abuses of that kind have no possibility of being curbed in the absence of a definition of health which does not contain some intrinsic elements of limitation

— that is, unless there is a definition which, when abused, is self-evidently *seen* as abused by those who know what health means. Unfortunately, it is in the nature of general definitions that they do not circumscribe their own meaning (or even explain it) and contain no built-in safeguards against misuse, e.g., our "peace with honor" in Southeast Asia — "peace," "honor"? Moreover, for a certain class of concepts — peace, honor, happiness, for example — it is difficult to keep them free in ordinary usage from a normative content. In our own usage, it would make no sense to talk of them in a way which implied they are not desirable or are merely neutral: by well-ingrained social custom (resting no doubt on some basic features of human nature) health, peace, and happiness are both desired and desirable — good. For those and other reasons, it is perfectly plausible to say the cultural task of defining terms, and settling on appropriate and inappropriate usages, is far more than a matter of getting our dictionary entries right. It is nothing less than a way of deciding what should be valued, how life should be understood, and what principles should guide individual and social conduct.

Health is not just a term to be defined. Intuitively, if we have lived at all, it is something we seek and value. We may not set the highest value on health — other goods may be valued as well — but it would strike me as incomprehensible should someone say that health was a matter of utter indifference to him; we would well doubt either his sanity or his maturity. The cultural problem, then, may be put this way. The acceptable range of uses of the term "health" should, at the minimum, capture the normative element in the concept as traditionally understood while, at the maximum, incorporate the insight (stemming from criticisms of the WHO definition) that the term "health" is abused if it becomes synonymous with virtue, social tranquillity, and ultimate happiness. Since there

are no instruction manuals available on how one would go about reaching a goal of that sort, I will offer no advice on the subject. I have the horrible suspicion, as a matter of fact, that people either have a decent intuitive sense on such matters (reflected in the way they use language) or they do not; and if they do not, little can be done to instruct them. One is left with the pious hope that, somehow, over a long period of time, things will change.

In Defense of WHO

Now that simply might be the end of the story, assuming some agreement can be reached that the WHO definition of "health" is plainly bad, full of snares, delusions, and false norms. But I am left uncomfortable with such a flat, simple conclusion. The nagging point about the definition is that, in badly put ways, it was probably on to something. It certainly recognized, however inchoately, that it is difficult to talk meaningfully of health solely in terms of "the absence of disease or infirmity." As a purely logical point, one must ask about what positive state of affairs disease and infirmity are an absence of — absent from what? One is left with the tautological proposition that health is the absence of non-health, a less than illuminating revelation. Could it not be said, though, that at least intuitively everyone knows what health is by means of the experiential contrast posed by states of illness and disease; that is, even if I cannot define health in any positive sense, I can surely know when I am sick (pain, high fever, etc.) and compare that condition with my previous states which contained no such conditions? Thus one could, in some recognizable sense, speak of illness as a deviation from a norm, even if it is not possible to specify that norm with any clarity.

But there are some problems with this approach, for all of its commonsense appeal. Sociologically, it is well known that what may be accounted sickness in one culture may not be so interpreted in another; one culture's (person's) deviation from the norm may not necessarily be another culture's (person's) deviation. In this as in other matters, commonsense intuition may be nothing but a reflection of different cultural and personal evaluations. In addition, there can be and usually are serious disputes about how great a deviation from the (unspecified) norm is necessary before the terms "sickness" and "illness" become appropriate. Am I to be put in the sick role because of my nagging case of itching athlete's foot, or must my toes start dropping off before I can so qualify? All general concepts have their borderline cases, and normally they need pose no real problems for the applicability of the concepts for the run of instances. But where "health" and "illness" are concerned, the number of borderline cases can be enormous, affected by age, attitudinal and cultural factors. Worse still, the fact that people can be afflicted by disease (even fatally afflicted) well before the manifestation of any overt symptoms is enough to discredit the adequacy of intuitions based on how one happens to feel at any given moment.

A number of these problems might be resolved by distinguishing between health as a norm and as an ideal. As a norm, it could be possible to speak in terms of deviation from some statistical standards, particularly if these standards were couched not only in terms of organic function but also in terms of behavioral functioning. Thus someone would be called "healthy" if his heart, lungs, kidneys (etc.) functioned at a certain level of efficiency and efficacy, if he was not suffering physical pain, and if his body was free of those pathological conditions which even if undetected or undetectable could impair organic function and eventually cause pain. There could still be dispute about what should count as a "pathological" condition, but at least it would be possible to draw up a large

checklist of items subject to "scientific measurement"; then, having gone through that checklist in a physical exam, and passing all the tests, one could be pronounced "healthy." Neat, clean, simple.

All of this might be possible in a static culture, which ours is not. The problem is that any notion of a statistical norm will be superintended by some kind of ideal. Why, in the first place, should anyone care at all how his organs are functioning, much less how well they do so? There must be some reason for that, a reason which goes beyond theoretical interest in statistical distributions. Could it possibly be because certain departures from the norm carry with them unpleasant states, which few are likely to call "good": pain, discrimination, unhappiness? I would guess so. In the second place, why should society have any interest whatever in the way the organs of its citizens function? There must also be some reason for that, very possibly the insight that the organ functioning of individuals has some aggregate social implications. In our culture at least (and in every other culture I have ever heard of) it is simply impossible, finally, to draw any sharp distinction between conceptions of the human good and what are accounted significant and negatively evaluated deviations from statistical norms.

That is the whole point of saying, in defense of the WHO definition of health, that it discerned the intimate connection between the good of the body and the good of the self, not only the individual self but the social community of selves. No individual and no society would (save for speculative, scientific reasons only) have any interest whatever in the condition of human organs and bodies were it not for the obvious fact that those conditions can have an enormous impact on the whole of human life. People do, it has been noticed, die; and they die because something has gone wrong with their bodies. This can be annoying, especially if one would, at the moment of death, prefer to be busy doing other things. Consider two commonplace occurrences. The first I have alluded to already: dropping a heavy brick on one's foot. So far as I know, there is no culture where the pain which that event occasions is considered a good in itself. Why is that? Because (I presume) the pain which results can not only make it difficult or impossible to walk for a time but also because the pain, if intense enough, makes it impossible to think about anything else (or think at all) or to relate to anything or anyone other than the pain. For a time, I am "not myself" and that is simply because my body is making such excessive demands on my attention that nothing is possible to me except to howl. I cannot, in sum, dissociate my "body" from my "self" in that situation; my self is my body and my body is my pain.

The other occurrence is no less commonplace. It is the assertion the old often make to the young, however great the psychological, economic, or other miseries of the latter: "at least you've got your health." They are saying in so many words that, if one is healthy, then there is some room for hope, some possibility of human recovery; and even more they are saying that, without good health, nothing is possible, however favorable the other conditions of life may be. Again, it is impossible to dissociate good of body and good of self. Put more formally, if health is not a sufficient condition for happiness, it is a necessary condition. At that very fundamental level, then, any sharp distinction between the good of bodies and the good of persons dissolves.

Are we not forced, therefore, to say that, if the complete absence of health (i.e., death) means the complete absence of self, then any diminishment of health must represent, correspondingly, a diminishment of self? That does not follow, for unless a disease or infirmity is severe, it may represent only a minor annoyance, diminishing our selfhood not

a whit. And while it will not do to be overly sentimental about such things, it is probably the case that disease or infirmity can, in some cases, increase one's sense of selfhood (which is no reason to urge disease upon people for its possibly psychological benefits). The frequent reports of those who have recovered from a serious illness that it made them appreciate life in a far more intense way than they previously had are not to be dismissed (though one wishes an easier way could be found).

Modest Conclusions

Two conclusions may be drawn. The first is that some minimal level of health is necessary if there is to be any possibility of human happiness. Only in exceptional circumstances can the good of self be long maintained in the absence of the good of the body. The second conclusion, however, is that one can be healthy without being in a state of "complete physical, mental, and social well-being." That conclusion can be justified in two ways: (a) because some degree of disease and infirmity is perfectly compatible with mental and social well-being; and (b) because it is doubtful that there ever was, or ever could be, more than a transient state of "complete physical, mental and social well-being," for individuals or societies; that's just not the way life is or could be. Its attractiveness as an ideal is vitiated by its practical impossibility of realization. Worse than that, it positively misleads, for health becomes a goal of such all-consuming importance that it simply begs to be thwarted in its realization. The demands which the word "complete" entail set the stage for the worst false consciousness of all: the demand that life deliver perfection. Practically speaking, this demand has led, in the field of health, to a constant escalation of expectation and requirement, never ending, never satisfied.

What, then, would be a good defini-tion of "health"? I was afraid someone was going to ask me that question. I sug-gest we settle on the following: "Health is a state of physical well-being." That state need not be "complete," but it must be at least adequate, i.e., without significant impairment of function. It also need not encompass "mental" well-being; one can be healthy yet anxious, well yet depressed. And it surely ought not to encompass "social well-being," except insofar as that well-being will be impaired by the presence of large-scale,

serious physical infirmities. Of course my definition is vague, but it would take some very fancy semantic footwork for it to be socially misused; that brat next door could not be called "sick" except when he is running a fever. This defini-tion would not, though, preclude all social use of the language of "pathology" for other than physical disease. The image of a physically well body is a pow-erful one and, used carefully, it can be suggestive of the kind of wholeness and adequacy of function one might hope to see in other areas of life.

On Defining 'Disease'

W. Miller Brown

The task of understanding disease and health for most philosophers has been seen as a conceptual one, finding some characterization that fits what have come to be called our common 'intuitions' about health and disease and that is also consonant with current medical practice and scientific work in biology and relat-ed fields. Of the related concepts of dis-ease, illness, and health, the concept of disease has come to seem more tractable, perhaps because of the long history of medical practice which has made the control and treatment, of disease its pri-mary concern. Though there have been some efforts to understand health in a "positive" sense (Whitbeck, 1981), most recent writers on the subject have char-acterized health as the absence of sick-ness or illness, of debilitating and seri-ous disease (Boorse, 1981; Boorse, 1977; Burns, 1977). In this "negative" and more narrow sense, an understanding of the concept of health will depend on a

prior understanding of the concept of disease. In this paper I want to examine the two most prominent kinds of approach to analyzing the underlying concept of disease.

The first kind takes as its task to fit an account of disease into the objective and theoretical structure of modern bio-logical science, showing that a character-ization of disease can be given that makes no appeal to non-scientific stan-dards, norms, or values. Thus disease may be an impairment, i.e., deviation from the normal structural or functional integrity of the body, organ-system, or biosynthetic process; it may be a mal-adaptation or incapacity or disfunction-ing. It is the task of empirical science to devise theories that describe and explain both the normal bodily processes and states and also those deviations from them which, on this account, are the pri-mary features of disease. By far the most forceful and persuasive version of the

"On Defining Disease," by W. Miller Brown, *The Journal of Medicine and Philosophy*, vol. 10, no. 4 (1985), pp. 311–328. Copyright © The Journal of Medicine and Philosophy, Inc. Reprinted by permission.

objectivist viewpoint is one which relies on the notion of biological function.

The other approach sees the central fact of disease to be not only that it is a physical state or process of an organism, but one that is undesirable, disvalued, or bad. Accordingly, in addition to having a descriptive component, the concept of disease also has a normative one, appealing to what various people value, what contributes to their well-being, or what enables them to perform desirable activities. To characterize something as a disease is therefore to appeal to certain norms or values; it is to make a value judgment of some kind about a physical condition. In what follows, I will describe these approaches more fully and evaluate their success and limitations.

I

The objectivist approach has been skilfully and forcefully presented by Christopher Boorse in a number of recent papers. Boorse's aim is to show that "disease judgments are value-neutral" and to give a fully adequate analysis of the concept of disease as a "theoretical concept" as opposed to one used in practical judgments of treatment or in the assessment of "positive" health, a state transcending the absence of disease. This analysis must ignore ordinary usage and examine "what physicians call disease" (Boorse, 1977, pp. 550–553).

Boorse's analysis of disease relies on two subsidiary concepts: that of a function and that of statistical normality. According to Boorse, ... the ultimate function of an organic system or process will ... be determined by the "goals at the apex of the hierarchy", for example, individual survival and reproduction. (I will return to a consideration of what these might be.)

There are two roles in Boorse's analysis for the notion of statistical normality. The first is as an empirical measure of what particular functions are typical of a given type of organism. Char-

acterization of a type of organism, a species, is a result of abstraction and "averaging" over large populations to arrive at an ideal type, what Boorse calls "the species design", which has been stabilized by selection pressures of the organism's environment. Such averaging is difficult, however, when trait variations occur too frequently to be "averaged out". In this case they can be included disjunctively or relativized to sex and age. Thus the reference class for functional normality, i.e., statistical frequency, will be an ideal type of reference class, such as: human, male, neonate, etc.

The second use of statistical normality is to refer to the normal functioning of those traits that are normal to a given reference class. Thus a given trait in a member of the reference class must not only perform the typical function but must do so with "at least statistically typical efficiency, i.e., at efficiency levels within or above some chosen central region of their population distribution" (Boorse, 1977, p. 558) when the appropriate (statistically normal) kind of occasion arises. Such a state Boorse calls "functional readiness". With one qualification, Boorse's definition of 'disease' is at hand. This qualification is to account, if possible, for what are virtually universal diseases, for example, tooth decay, lung inflammation, and atherosclerosis. Some of these are in large part due to a hostile environment such as atmospheric pollution, so Boorse is ready to attribute some losses of functional ability to such factors and accept them as disease states (which is surely in accord with medical practice) in spite of their statistical normality.

On Boorse's account, then, a disease is "a type of internal state which is either an impairment of normal functional ability, i.e., a reduction of one or more functional abilities below typical efficiency, or a limitation on functional ability caused by environmental agents" (Boorse, 1977, p. 567).

Let us consider whether Boorse's account is adequate. Since it depends on the concept of function, our first task should be to examine the adequacy of Boorse's construal of this concept. "The basic notion of a function", he writes, "is of a contribution to a goal". And further, "the function of any part or process, for the biologist, is its ultimate contribution to certain goals at the apex of the hierarchy of means-end processes in an organism" (1977, p. 556). As a *general* analysis of functions, Boorse's view, which he develops elsewhere (Boorse, 1976), has been shown to be inadequate (Grim, 1977). The objections raised are to the adequacy of his notion of "goals" and "functions" when considered in various ordinary, usually individual and intentional, senses. However, Boorse's analysis is not actually of 'function', but rather of the complex notion 'performing the function Z in the G-ing of S at t,'[1] so he should not claim, as he does, that "the basic notion of a function is of a contribution to a goal". His claim is hardly an interesting one if what he discusses is a notion that includes mention of some particular goal. In any case, some functions seem not to be goal-directed at all: thus the atmosphere of Venus functions to limit human habitation, and krill function as the base of the ocean food chain. Boorse's original account fails, too, because he analyses "the function of X" in terms of "functions being performed". But many things have functions without ever performing them. The function of the incisors is to tear food even if someone never eats more than ground vegetables. A function of chicken epithelium is to induce the formation of teeth (Gould, 1980a). We come to know such things through complex chains of reasoning which involve among other things the kind of empirical studies into the normal activities of humans and other animals of the sort Boorse stipulates in his brief account of *biological* functions. Boorse may acknowledge, then, that his general account of function is inadequate on many grounds, but perhaps still adequate for biology (if we ignore the functions of non-expressed genes). His concept of functions will be a stipulative one and correspondingly his notion of disease need not accord with common or general usage, but only with that of biologists interested in physiology.

Recall, however, that the definition we are considering relies on the determination of a "reference class" in order to establish which functions are statistically normal. But choice of reference class will clearly determine what conditions are statistically normal and what ones are statistically abnormal. Which population shall be chosen? Boorse suggests that by abstracting from some "sufficiently large sample of a population", a "species design" will "emerge" as a standard reference. But what population do we consider initially? The species? But if that is to be identified by the species design, the process is clearly circular. This is one version of the "species problem" (Ruse, 1973) which continues to haunt biological taxonomy. Its central feature is the problem of showing that classification of organisms into species is "non-arbitrary" (Simpson, 1951, p. 129) or "objective" (Mayr, 1963).

Let us suppose, however, that further development of biology permits subsumption of correlations of phenotypic characters under laws of molecular biology, thus rendering such correlations less suspect or accidental or worse biased by the predilections and preoccupations of human classifiers (Hull, 1974). Even so, difficulties remain, since further subdivisions of reference classes are to be made to effect standardization, for example, by sex and age, and perhaps also by race (Boorse, 1977, p. 558). Indeed, further divisions by occupation, geography, religious, and ethnic background, and so forth may be needed. Boorse cites J. A. Ryle's example of the adaptability of the "poor ... physique" of "the small stocky Durham miner", but rejects Ryle's view that his condition may be normal (Boorse, 1977, pp. 548–549). Yet many diseases epidemiologically isolate subpopulations not previously deemed biologically significant: AIDS, Tay-Sachs disease, caisson disease, etc. It cannot be enough to argue here, too, that we find "natural kinds" by statistical correlations of normalizing traits, since so much depends on choice of populations which in turn seems to be guided by interests other than those of the theoretical biologist. In practice, of course, the choice of such populations may not be so difficult. But it is *theory*, not *practice*, which Boorse seeks to analyse.

Even if these objections could be met, one further hurdle which Boorse himself notes remains at the level of theory. How are we to determine those highest-level goals of organisms which lower-level processes function to achieve? "To some extent", Boorse admits, these "are indeterminate and must be determined by a biologist's interests" (Boorse, 1977, p. 556). It may be true that what interests the physiologist is what promotes individual survival and reproduction. But Boorse's account was designed to show that the concept of disease is non-normative. At best, what he has shown is that *given* such a choice of highest-level goals, "function statements will be value-free, since what makes a causal contribution to a biological goal is certainly an empirical matter" (1977, p. 556). But such "empirical matters" are significant only in terms of the goals chosen. What assurance do we have that these are the goals of the system whose "species design" we have determined? Deviations from the design can count as diseases only if they detract from achieving the system's goals; otherwise they could be improvements of design (Bunzl, 1980). So we must establish the non-normative character of such goals. We could, of course, appeal to the role played by individuals in some larger system. Survival and reproduction of individuals contribute to the highest-level goals of the species. Proper functioning of individuals then contributes to the proper functioning of

the species. But unless this latter goal can be specified non-normatively, efforts to understand individual functioning non-normatively will also fail.

Any efforts to clarify individual functioning and hence disease in terms of the proper functioning of the species also face the problem that long term individual survival after reproduction may not be evolutionarily relevant. Indeed, the individuals of many species die shortly after, or even during, reproductive activity, e.g., the salmon (Gould, 1980). Alternatively, what functions normally to assure individual survival and reproduction may not be conducive to survival of the species. An organism infectious to some other species may itself not survive the success of its mortal invasion of its host. A genetic disease in the parasite, i.e., a mutation, could abnormally result in inhibiting reproduction and hence virulence, thus enhancing survival of the parasite species as well as its host (Dubos, 1965).

It may be that such objections can be met, or, as is more likely, accepted. A functionalist of a non-dogmatic sort might well accept some degree of normativism in an analysis, perhaps arguing that biology itself must involve normative judgments of various kinds. Still, such a functionalist account would, if at all successful, define quite a narrow and technical conception linked to biological theory and the interests of theoretical biologists. To the extent that the analysis tries to do more, to account for more general conceptions of disease as applied to human beings, providing "an explanatory theory" of the concept "in the discursive context of medical textbooks and research papers" (Boorse, 1977, p. 551), it runs into serious difficulties.

Boorse relies on the American Medical Association's (AMA's) *Standard Nomenclature* and on various medical texts to determine what should be covered by the definition of 'disease'. Relying on these sources, however, leads him to include too much, which he admits, apparently thinking he is siding with standard medical usage. Thus he includes not only diseases, but injuries and impairments of various kinds: "not only infectious syndromes like malaria and syphilis, but also birth defects like spina bifida, growth disorders like cancer, functional impairments like limb paralysis and all kinds of injuries and causes of death" (1977, pp. 550–551). In addition, he thinks he is forced to include as diseases "obesity and inanition, seasickness, broken bones, gunshot wounds, foreign bodies in the stomach, supernumerary toes, animal bites, and drowning, electrocution, asphyxiation, incineration and 'general crushing'" (1977, pp. 550–551).[2]

However, as Caroline Whitbeck has shown (1978, pp. 216–217), the categories of such manuals are primarily for record keeping purposes to insure uniformity. Moreover, on more careful reading of the 1962 *Standard Nomenclature* of the AMA and the later 1965 World Health Organization's *International Classification of Disease*, it is clear that both do distinguish among "diseases, injuries, impairments and simple anomalies".

In addition, Boorse's definition includes such conditions as "fever, diarrhea, dyspnea, hypoglycemia, and so on", which are admittedly "not considered individual diseases by medical authorities", but are rather symptoms and signs of many disease entities. Most of this is the result of insisting on the *principle* that health is the absence of disease. As Boorse notes (ruefully, I think), if we distinguish disease from injury and accept the principle, one can be both healthy and dead (1977, pp. 551–552).

But if Boorse includes too much, he must also exclude, as he acknowledges, such "universal" diseases as "dental caries, lung irritation, atherosclerosis, and benign hypertrophy of the prostate in old men" (1977, p. 556). Some he picks up by including as diseases environmental injuries, but not the deformities and degenerative conditions associated with aging. As more and more conditions of the aged have become treatable, however, they are being considered as diseases of aging in spite of their near universality. Indeed some researchers are even suggesting that aging itself is a metabolic disease (Caplan, 1981).

II

There have been other efforts at "objective" definitions of 'disease' or 'health' relying, for example, on the notions of adaptation, homeostasis, and suffering or disability which Boorse effectively criticizes. In the meantime, any such definitions have been challenged as fundamentally missing the central fact about disease and health: that they are essentially connected with human interest, what we value and desire, and are therefore properly to be analyzed, at least in part, as normative concepts. Lester King made such a claim nearly thirty years ago: "Disease is the aggregate of those conditions which, judged by the prevailing culture, are deemed painful, or disabling, and which, at the same time, deviate from either the statistical norm or from some idealized status" (1954, p. 197). King goes little further than this in offering a close analysis, though he states that "the ideal itself is derived in part from the statistical norm, and in part from the abnormal which seems particularly desirable" (1954, p. 197). Each of King's two conditions can be emphasized. As we have seen, Boorse attempts to specify a definition based on the idea of a statistical norm while repudiating any inference to what is "desirable". Others have gone in the other direction. As H. T. Engelhardt, Jr. argues,

The concept of disease acts not only to describe and explain, but also to enjoin to action. ... It is a normative concept; it says what ought not to be. As such, the concept incorporates criteria of evaluation, designating certain states of affairs as desirable and others as not so. It delineates and establishes social roles such as being sick or being a physician. ... The concept is both aesthetic and ethical, suggesting what is beautiful and what is good (1975, p. 127).

Engelhardt ascribes far too much power to a concept to do things. Even the correct ascription of disease to someone may not "enjoin to action". The results of the disease may be deemed desirable (through conferral of immunity to more severe diseases, for example) and thus justify doing nothing. Where the disease's etiology is entirely unknown, it is not clear how acknowledging the disease's presence in any way explains it. Furthermore, though social roles may be constitutive of medical practice, and though the concepts of disease and health may reflect those roles and practices in some way, the concepts themselves surely do not "establish" them. Nor does it make much sense to say of a disease that it "ought not to be" when no responsibility can be ascribed (Goosens, 1980, p. 102). Since many undesirable physical conditions are not diseases and sometimes cases of diseases are desirable, the normative position must be carefully formulated to capture the basic claim while being faithful to medical practice and more common usage.

The basic claim of normative analyses, then, is that the concept of disease is bound up with correlative concepts of harm and benefit. William Goosens (1980, p. 107) has offered a necessary (though not sufficient) condition in the following "limited proposal". A disease, he argues, is a physical state or condition that constitutes "some threat" to the "well-being" of some persons. However, it is difficult to imagine *any* physical state or condition that would not constitute *some* threat to the well-being of *some* person, especially when 'well-being' is so broadly characterized as to vary with persons' "internal physical states, the environment, and their goals and aspira-

tions" (1980, p. 110). Goosens formulates his proposal this way so as to include as diseases those conditions which have instances or cases "with nothing disvaluable", such as a case of cowpox which immunizes someone against smallpox, or an imaginary disease which causes sterility and no other effects in persons who "value not reproducing themselves" (1980, p. 103).

A more sophisticated analysis, however, is Caroline Whitbeck's (1978). Her initial formulation has been criticized for failing to establish her claim that disease is a value-laden concept. Goosens has pointed out that by identifying a disease as what "people wish to be able to prevent", Whitbeck at best *mentions* values (i.e., wants or wishes), but does not use them in the analysis (Goosens, 1980, p. 101). Whitbeck has replied that "the term 'disease' is value-laden in a distinct and hitherto unrecognized sense" (1981, p. 624). A term is value-laden in this sense, "the capability sense if, and only if, the concept or the definition of the term warrants the conclusion that people have an interest in being able to influence things of that type" (1981, p. 614). Whatever we may think of Whitbeck's claim to have discovered a new sense of value-ladenness, it is possible to modify slightly her definition of 'disease' to make its normative character explicit and easily recognizable and thereby to meet Goosens' objection. Accordingly, Whitbeck may be construed as proposing the following definition.

A disease is any type of psycho-physiological process such that:

[1] People wish *to be able* to prevent or terminate the process because [it is *undesirable* in that] it interferes with the bearer's psycho-physiological capacity to do those things that people commonly wish and expect to be able to do;

[2] Either the process is statistically abnormal in those at risk or people have some other basis for a

reasonable hope of finding means to prevent or effectively to treat the process; and

[3] The process is not also *necessary* for doing anything that people commonly want and expect to be able to do (1978, p. 211; 1981, p. 615).

Whitbeck's formulation is designed to accomplish several improvements over accounts such as the one offered by Boorse. First, it is limited to human diseases, not all animal and plant diseases. Second, by distinguishing among diseases, injuries, and impairments, she avoids some of the absurdities of Boorse's all-inclusive scheme. Third, she stresses that a disease is a process, thus distinguishing it from its effects or its cause and from other physical states and conditions not considered to be diseases. Fourth, she insists that a disease is a *type* of process, not to be confused with its instances, i.e., particular cases of diseases, which she acknowledges may on some occasions, as Boorse and others have shown, be desirable. And fifth, she can maintain the analytic connection with "disvalue". Let us see what the effect of the three conditions is for her proposal.

The first condition relativizes the application of the concept to "societal context" or "group". "By 'people'", she writes, "I always mean the members of some human society" (1978, p. 211). It thus explains in what sense a disease may be undesirable. The second condition singles out as diseases either those processes which are statistically abnormal (the phrase "in those at risk" presumably does the work of Boorse's reference classes) or certain other undesirable conditions that are virtually universal, the "universal diseases" which were so troubling for Boorse. Thus a process is a disease (if it meets (1) and (3)) although (a) people in a given locale wish to prevent it, but (b) everyone there has it and so it is not recognized locally as a disease. This is so because in some wider context it still is

statistically abnormal. Alternatively, those nearly universal conditions of aging, etc., which have come to be preventable or treatable can also be recognized as diseases. Finally, the third condition is intended to avoid designating such things as pregnancy as a disease, it being necessary to what people commonly want and expect to be able to do, namely, have babies, even though it can be debilitating, etc. (1981, p. 625, n. 1).

Although Whitbeck makes several interesting and perceptive distinctions which most other writers have failed to make, her proposal has several odd consequences. The first is the result of relativization of the concept of disease to "societal group" and hence to time and place. Since she has proposed that the concept is essentially "relative to societal context", in some cases it will make no sense for us to note that what was once called a disease is now known not to be one. This familiar distinction between appearance and reality which is closely linked to our sense of the possibility of progress in medicine is now threatened. Suppose that (for whatever reason) the members of some human society at one time do, but at a later time do not, wish to be able to prevent or terminate some psycho-physiological process or other. Is it first a disease and then not one (or *vice versa*)? Or suppose some group of people do not commonly want and expect to have children. (They have decided to allow their members to die out or have mastered *in vitro* gestation techniques.) They want to be able to prevent pregnancy since it interferes (for those at risk — and perhaps others) with their activities and goals. They have a good basis for supposing they can prevent it. For them, on Whitbeck's analysis, pregnancy is a disease.

One problem here, of course, is that we do not know enough about Whitbeck's view of a "societal context". Nor are we told precisely what counts as a psycho-physiological *process* as opposed to a "change" — the basis for her parallel definition of an "injury" — and an "anomaly" — the basis for her definition of an "impairment" (1978, pp. 213–214). it is doubtful that there are *any* entirely "static conditions" (1977, p. 625) in human physiology or anatomy, so unless we know how to draw the lines, her account will founder on some of the same shoals that wrecked Boorse. How, for example, are we to classify genetic diseases? Although such conditions are usually manifested by pathological processes, they are themselves more like impairments. Yet Whitbeck insists that

> any attempt to blur the distinction between disease and impairment threatens to obscure the distinction between diseases and their manifestations ... a distinction which medicine has been careful to make at least since the time of Sydenham. (1978, p. 214)

Elsewhere, however, she insists that "there is no clear division between the clinical and pathological level" (1977, p. 626). Moreover, she explicitly rejects any effort to identify diseases with their causes, citing helminthic, genetic, and deficiency diseases as involving a "complex of processes" including the clinical and pathological manifestations, which are dependent on, but separable from, their causes (1978, Section 2).

Given this technical sense of 'process' and Whitbeck's definition of 'disease' that relativizes it to societal context, even genetically based racial characteristics might be considered manifestations of disease. Certainly such traits have been disvalued in many societies and interfered with what persecuted racial minorities have commonly wished to do. And although there has been no reason to hope to find means to prevent such traits, neither has there been for hemophilia or sickle-cell anemia.[3]

In answer to these problems, we might refer to medical *practice* and not to *theory* for a more fluid and evolving characterization of disease, but one still that does not yield to the extreme relativism of Whitbeck's proposal. A radical relativism in medicine is, I think, even more implausible than one in ethics because of the closer connection of medical practice and its concepts to the nearly invariant circumstances of human life as seen by biology. Neither relativism is decisively refutable, though both can be rendered relatively harmless. Even so, further difficulties await the proposal we are considering, for we can now ask how adequate it is to capture the sense of 'disease' current in *our* society.

There are, first of all, types (and many more imaginable) of diseases which in all respects may be considered desirable, or at least not undesirable. Typically these are ones which during their "entire course" are asymptomatic or which are so mildly symptomatic (i.e., "non-diagnostic") that they are deemed to be "sub-clinical". Yet such diseases may have beneficial consequences, for example, in conferring immunity to more violent yet similar diseases, as cowpox did before the development of smallpox vaccine. (Sickle-cell trait may be another example.) Second, there seem to be many instances of diseases which fail by Whitbeck's definition because they do not interfere, in the way she stipulates, with the bearer's psycho-physiological capacities. We could cite very mild diseases, including the common cold, various minor skin diseases such as acne, jock itch, diaper rash, warts, and such conditions as lung and throat irritations caused by smoking, and mild nutritional or vitamin deficiencies. Whitbeck seems to argue (1978, p. 216)[4] that we can consider these to be diseases because they bear "significant resemblances" to cases which do have dire symptoms; but clearly this is an *ad hoc* adjustment to her view and not a very persuasive one, given her account, though I think this is an illuminating way to deal with such cases. Similar cases arise when a disease affects some redundant system of the body and thus is not incapacitating (Goosens, 1980, p. 108, n. 4). And there are some processes which seem to meet her definition which are not diseases: starvation, for example, which she mentions (1978, p. 214), and perhaps heat stroke or heat exhaustion. Finally, the interesting case of genetic diseases. It is clear that Tay-Sachs disease and phenylketonuria are genetic diseases, but is our inability to synthesize ascorbic acid a disease, or the processes of aging? For Boorse the answer is "No": "What there cannot be ... is a universal genetic disease" (1977, p. 567). For Whitbeck, the answer would seem to be "Yes": Vitamin C deficiency, and the processes of aging have often prevented people from doing what they have commonly wished and even expected to be able to do, and some argue that we now have reasonable hope of finding means to prevent even some of the processes of aging.

It may, of course, be possible to tinker with these definitions so as to render them, extensionally at least, a bit more successful, though I am not optimistic that this can be done in ways that will satisfy deep predilections for neat, compact, simple formulations, ones that smack of a veridical glimpse of the true nature of disease. But why not? And why, in any case, do we find such variety among incompatible proposals for understanding the concepts of disease and health and related notions? The answers to these questions are to be found, I think, by considering whether the approach, of which these efforts at definition are typical, is a fruitful one.

III

In some ways, of course, the approach is a fruitful one. It sets philosophers (and physicians) to look at practices and concerns in medicine with eyes to system and generality, an activity contagious for philosophers. The difficulties with doing this are not due to serious problems with medicine; rather, they derive from the concepts themselves, their vagueness, complexity and richness of cultural and historical associations. Refinements of terminology in medicine do occur constantly as a result of many factors: developing research, the need for systematization, and often under pressure from courts, insurance companies, and others who seek to sharpen conceptual boundaries for their own purposes which may be in part at variance with those of medical practice. Such changes and refinements are complex, partly based on empirical findings, partly on decisions arising from broad social concerns. They are made by clarifying, making distinctions, and linking theoretical insight and research to the demands of practice and treatment. Philosophers on occasion have contributed to such efforts through the kind of conceptual analysis they offer. Recent examples are attempts to arrive at useful agreement about the concepts of 'death', 'consent', and 'competence' where traditional philosophical concerns overlap some of those of medical practice and the law (Culver and Gert, 1982).

It is not surprising, therefore, that, when reflecting on developments of modern biology and the corresponding sophistication of medicine, accompanied as such changes are with refinements of theory, the development of new and precisely defined technical terms and improved classification, philosophers should feel that they, too, can contribute to such progress. Boorse and Whitbeck seek to share in a long tradition beginning with Thomas Sydenham in the seventeenth century (if not earlier with Paracelsus), and leading to Rudolf Virchow's work in the mid-nineteenth century, to characterize the "disease entity" or clinical picture of a disease (Whitbeck, 1977, Section 1). This was done in terms of the growing knowledge of anatomy and physiology, refined techniques of diagnosis, and, above all, insights into the etiology of diseases which led to the mastery and in some cases the virtual elimination of infectious diseases in this century. Corresponding to these developments were powerful social forces working toward uniformity in medicine: standardization of medical education, state certification requirements for physicians, the guild organization of medical societies, and the expansion of private and state programs of medical insurance and systems of health care. Efforts to define key concepts of medicine reflect this tendency to uniformity while drawing our attention to the predominant concerns of current medical practice.

However understandable and even useful this philosophical search for fundamental similarities among diseases, it seems to assume that philosophical definition will make a contribution to medical theory. Boorse writes of 'health' and 'disease' as "theoretical" concepts. Whitbeck calls them basic concepts of "medical science". This is a mistake, I think, which lies in the assumption that there is a theory of medicine to which such analyses can contribute. What sort of theory could this be? There are two kinds that occur to me. One is a kind of *philosophical* theory *about* medicine. Indeed, Whitbeck refers to her own efforts to develop "a philosophical theory", by which she seems to mean coming to understand "how a given concept relates to a host of others" (1981, p. 611). Boorse in turn calls his analysis an "explanatory theory", one that seeks to explain the whole body of usage of the concept in medicine (1977, p. 551). It is difficult to see why such efforts might plausibly constitute theories, though they do have a kind of empirical aspect, seeking as they do empirical evidence of sorts in the form of pertinent examples and familiar usage of words. They are efforts at abstraction, aided to some

degree by empirical generalization. It is tempting, but probably misleading, to think of these as descendents of earlier philosophic efforts to find the essences of other concepts such as 'art', justice', or 'explanation'. (Both Boorse and Whitbeck think of the objects of their analyses [as] "universals" or "types".) But if they are theories in some limited sense, they are not solely empirical. As explications of widely used terms, they have the clear marks of recommendations. The variety of definitions results from differences in scope and emphasis in the corresponding analyses.

I believe this may well be inevitable because of the nature of medicine itself. A second view of a theory of medicine might hold that medicine is a part of biology, or some set of sub-disciplines like physiology or endocrinology. But this, too, I think, is a mistake. The concepts of 'disease' and 'health' are not biological concepts, or at least not ones of theoretical biology. At the same time, we may well agree that at some level disease processes or entities or disease pathology can be explained by biological or physiological laws, if there are any (Smart, 1963, Ch. 111; Simon, 1971, Ch. 1), as well as by appeal to other factors such as the environment. Developmental biology (ontogeny), for example, is a kind of historical science (like geology, and evolutionary biology or phylogeny) that has two components, one a history, a story or chronicle of individual or statistically normal development, the other a theory of those processes and changes which constitute the underlying mechanisms of developments. A disease *could* be considered a type of statistical variation in the history of the organism. But what kind of variation? Not every variation is a disease. And so we return to the need to specify which variations may be good or bad or dysfunctional (which, as we have seen, leads to trouble for the functionalist). But here the point is that the biologist as such really has no interest in such deviations except insofar as they lead to development in theory. By analogy we could ask what sense it could make to think of sunspots as a symptom of a solar disease. it would clearly only be in terms of our own mundane interests that such a question could arise. But to the astrophysicist, they are only indications of fundamental processes and the natural history of stellar evolution.

There can be, then, only in a very indirect and derivative sense a *theoretical* medicine, and accordingly it makes little sense to argue that 'disease' is a theoretical concept of medicine. Medicine is largely a practical activity since it is concerned with diagnosis and treatment of illness, usually as a matter of medical crisis; and, as such, it is more akin to a technology. Theory *in* medicine, as in electronics, is borrowed from fundamental sciences like biology, chemistry, and physics. Research in medicine, when it is not biology, chemistry, and physics, is a kind of technological enterprise allied to these sciences and only rarely leading directly to development in theory. This is not to say, of course, that there is not frequent hypothesis formation and testing as part of medical research into disease etiology, pathology, and treatment, and it may contribute to work in more fundamental disciplines. But they are developments in these latter areas, such as molecular biology or cell physiology, that are the theoretical basis for advances in medicine. (Most medical research, such as efforts to develop a new vaccine, to control immunological responses, or to find effective treatments, is a kind of applied science. However, the concerns of medicine frequently motivate more fundamental research in biology, and as a consequence in many cases the lines between medicine and other disciplines will surely be drawn as a matter of emphasis or research goals.) As a practical discipline, medicine and its concepts of 'disease' and

'health' are bound up with medical practice and the interests of doctors and patients as well as with the advances of science. And it is this fact which adds to the complexity and variety that confounds efforts to find simple definitions.

But if there is no theoretical medicine, how is it possible to understand the practical diagnosis and treatment of disease and the goals of any preventive or positive health program? If medicine begins, as I think it does, in crisis and treatment, then it begins with a variety of circumstances which may characterize illness and disease (which are, as it were, the criterion characteristics of 'disease'): the involuntary occurrence of pain, suffering and illness, gross physical dysfunction, disfigurement or progressive debility, statistically abnormal structures or processes, the discovery of causal agents of such conditions, the development of techniques for changing undesirable or unwanted conditions, or the disruption of social roles. The physician relies on biology and other fields to find the causal, not conceptual, factors which correlate and explain such circumstances and characteristics. At various times, by custom, decision, and practice, some characteristics have come to be more decisive than others, a fact reflected in the limited descriptive success of the definitions I have criticized. But even this limited success may be short-lived as the distinction between treatment of disease and other medical activities blurs. Nutritional counseling, stress control, a concern with degenerative conditions of aging, and the complex circumstances of the development of cancers have begun to realign medical practice as well as conceptual patterns. Philosophical definition can then be seen as reflecting or even clarifying these changes, but not as contributions to theory.

Notes

1. The full definition is: *X* is performing the function *Z* in the *G*-ing of *S* at *t*, *means*, At *t*, *X* is *Z*-ing and the *Z*-ing of *X* is making a causal contribution to the goal *G* of the goal-directed system *S*. A typical example is the heart's pumping to circulate blood in the circulatory system of animals (Boorse, 1976, p. 80).

2. In a short addendum to a reprint of his original article (1981, p. 560), Boorse suggests that he now prefers "as a terminological policy" to "avoid 'disease' as a generic term for all pathological conditions". The specific scope of 'disease', however, remains obscure.

3. Except recently, perhaps, by the prospect of genetic engineering. I owe this example, as well as several other suggestions, to a reviewer of an earlier draft of this paper. A similar case is that of Benjamin Rush who supposed that blacks suffered from congenital leprosy (Szasz, 1970, pp. 154–156).

4. The text is apparently garbled here.

References

Boorse, C.: 1976, 'Wright on functions', *Philosophical Review* 87, 70–86.

Boorse, C.: 1977, 'Health as a theoretical concept', *Philosophy of Science* 44, 542–573.

Boorse, C.: 1981, 'On the distinction between disease and illness', in A. L. Caplan, H. T. Engelhardt, Jr., and J. J. McCartney (eds.), *Concepts of Health and Disease: Interdisciplinary Perspectives*. Reading, Mass.: Addison-Wesley, pp. 545–560, Bunzl, M.: 1980, 'Comment on "health as a theoretical concept"', *Philosophy of Science* 47, 116–118.

Burns, C.: 1977, 'Diseases and healths: Some legacies in the philosophies of modern medical science', in H. T. Engelhardt, Jr., and S. F. Spicker (eds.), *Evaluation and Explanation in the Biological Sciences*. Dordrecht, Holland: D. Reidel, pp. 29–47.

Caplan, A. L.: 1981, 'The "unnaturalness" of aging — A sickness unto death?', in A. L. Caplan, H. T. Engelhardt, Jr., and J. J. McCartney (eds.), *Concepts of Health and Disease: Interdisciplinary Perspectives*. Reading, Mass.: Addison-Wesley, pp. 611–626.

Culver, C. M., and Gert, B.: 1982, *Philosophy in Medicine: Conceptual Issues in Medicine and Psychiatry*. New York: Oxford University Press.

Dubos, R.: 1965, *Man Adapting*. New Haven: Yale University Press.

Engelhardt, H. T., Jr.: 1975, 'The concepts of health and disease', in H. T. Engelhardt, Jr., and S. F. Spicker (eds.), *Evaluation and Explanation in the Biological Sciences*. Dordrecht, Holland: D. Reidel, pp. 125–141.

Goosens, W.: 1980, 'Values in health and medicine', *Philosophy of Science* 47, 100–115.

Gould, S. J.: 1980, *The Panda's Thumb: More Reflections in Natural History*, Essay 6, 'Death before birth, or a mite's *nunc dimittis*', pp. 69–75.

Gould, S. J.: 1980a, 'Hen's teeth and horse's toes', *Natural History* 89, 24–28.

Grim, P.: 1977, 'Further notes on functions', *Analysis* 37, 169–176.

Hull, D.: 1974, *Philosophy of Biological Science*. Englewood Cliffs, New Jersey: Prentice-Hall.

King, L.: 1954, 'What is disease?', *Philosophy of Science* 21, 193–203.

Mayr, E.: 1963, *Animal Species and Evolution*. Cambridge, Mass.: Belnap.

Ruse, M.: 1977, *The Philosophy of Biology*. London: Hutchinson University Library.

Simpson, G. G.: 1951, 'The species concept', *Evolution* 5, 285–298.

Simon, M. A.: 1971, *The Matter of Life: Philosophical Problems of Biology*. New Haven: Yale University Press.

Smart, J. J. C.: 1963, *Philosophy and Scientific Realism*. London: Routledge and Kegan Paul.

Szasz, T. S.: 1970, *The Manufacture of Madness*. New York: Dell.

Whitbeck, C.: 1977, 'Causation in medicine: The disease entity model', *Philosophy of Science* 44, 619–637.

Whitbeck, C.: 1978, 'Four basic concepts of medical science', in P. D. Asquith and I. Hocking (eds.), *Proceedings of the 1978 Biennial Meeting of the Philosophy of Science Association*, Philosophy of Science Association, East Lansing, Mich., Vol. 1, pp. 210–222.

Whitbeck, C.: 1981, 'A theory of health', in A. L. Caplan, H. T. Engelhardt, Jr., and J. J. McCartney (eds.), *Concepts of Health and Disease: Interdisciplinary Perspectives*. Reading, Mass.: Addison-Wesley, pp. 611–626.

Further Readings

Boorse, C. "On the Distinction Between Disease and Illness." *Concepts of Health and Disease: Interdisciplinary Perspectives*. Eds. A.L. Caplan, H.T. Engelhardt, Jr., and J.J. McCartney. Reading, MA: Addison-Wesley, 1981, pp. 545–560.

Boorse, C. "Health as a Theoretical Concept," *Philos of Science* 44 (1977), 542–573.

Bunzl, M. "Comment on 'Health as a Theoretical Concept,'" *Philos of Science* 47 (1980), 116–118.

Burns, C. "Diseases and Health: Some Legacies in the Philosophies of Modern Medical Science." *Evaluation and Explanation in the Biological Sciences*. Eds. H.T. Engelhardt, Jr., and S.F. Spicker. Dordrecht, Holland: D. Reidel, 1977, pp. 29–47.

Caplan, A.L. "The 'Unnaturalness' of Aging—A Sickness unto Death?" *Concepts of Health and Disease: Interdisciplinary Perspectives*. Eds. A.L. Caplan, H.T. Engelhardt, Jr., and J. J. McCartney. Reading, MA: Addison-Wesley, 1981, pp. 611–626.

Culver, C.M., and B. Gert. *Philosophy in Medicine: Conceptual Issues in Medicine and Psychiatry,* New York: Oxford Univ. Press, 1982.

DeVito, S. "On the Value-Neutrality of the Concepts of Health and Disease: Unto the Breach Again." *J Med Philos* 25:5 (Oct. 2000): 539–67.

Engelhardt, H.T., Jr. "The Concepts of Health and Disease." *Evaluation and Explanation in the Biological Sciences*. Eds. H.T. Engelhardt, Jr., and S.F. Spicker. Dordrecht, Holland: D. Reidel, 1975, pp. 125–141.

Fedoryka, K. "Health as a normative concept: towards a new conceptual framework." *J Med Philos* 22:2 (Apr. 1997):143–160.

Fulford, K.W. "What Is (mental) disease?": An Open Letter to Christopher Boorse." *J Med Ethics* 27:2 (Apr. 2001): 80–85.

Fulford, K.W. "Praxis Makes Perfect: Illness as a Bridge Between Biological Concepts of Disease and Social Conceptions of Health." *Theoret Med* 14:4 (Dec. 1993): 305–320.

Goosens, W. "Values in Health and Medicine." *Philos Science* 47 (1980), 100–115.

King, L. "What Is Disease?" *Philos Science* 21 (1954): 193–203.

Kottow, M.H. "The Rationale of Value-Laden Medicine." *J Eval Clin Pract* 8:1 (Feb. 2002): 77–84.

Kovacs, J. "The Concept of Health and Disease." *Med Health Care Philos* 1:1 (1998): 31–9.

Mayr, E. *Animal Species and Evolution.* Cambridge, MA: Belnap, 1963.

Nesse, R.M. "On the Difficulty of Defining Disease: A Darwinian Perspective." *Med Health Care Philos* 4:1 (2001): 37–46.

Nordenfelt, L. "On the Goals of Medicine, Health Enhancement and Social Welfare." *Health Care Anal* 9:1 (2001): 15–23.

Nordenfelt, L. "On the Place of Fuzzy Health in Medical Theory." *J Med Philos* 25:5 (Oct. 2000): 639–49.

Payne, J. "Two Alternative Notions of Health." *Med Law* 19:3 (2000): 373–379.

Raikka, J. "The Social Concept of Disease." *Theor Med* 17:4 (Dec. 1996): 353–361.

Richman, K.A., and A.E. Budson. "Health of Organisms and Health of Persons: An Embedded Instrumentalist Approach." *Theor Med Bioeth* 21:4 (2000): 339–354.

Ruse, M. *The Philosophy of Biology.* London: Hutchinson Univ. Library, 1977.

Schaffner, K.F. "Coming Home to Hume: A Sociobiological Foundation for a Concept of 'Health' and Morality." *J Med Philos* 24:4 (Aug. 1999): 365–375.

Stempsey, W.E. "A Pathological View of Disease." *Theor Med Bioeth* 21:4 (2000): 321–330.

Szasz, T.S. *The Manufacture of Madness.* New York: Dell, 1970.

Whitbeck, C. "Causation in Medicine: The Disease Entity Model" *Philos Science* 44 (1977): 619–637.

Whitbeck, C. "On the Aims of Medicine: Comments on 'Philosophy of Medicine as the Source for Medical Ethics." *Metamedicine* 2:1 (Feb. 1981): 35–41.

Whitbeck, C. "A Theory of Health," *Concepts of Health and Disease: Interdisciplinary Perspectives.* Eds. A.L. Caplan, H.T. Engelhardt, Jr., and J.J. McCartney. Reading, MA.: Addison-Wesley, 1981, pp. 611–626.

Widder, J., and M. Glawischnig-Goschnik. "The Concept of Disease in Palliative Medicine." *Med Health Care Philos* 5:2 (2002): 191–197.

CHAPTER 3
THE RIGHT TO HEALTH CARE

Introduction

As the recent Report of the Royal Commission on the Future of Health Care (*Building on Values: The Future of Health Care in Canada*, Final Report of the Royal Commission on the Future of Health Care) has confirmed, most Canadians believe that everyone has the right of timely access to medically necessary health care as part of their Canadian heritage. They believe that access to such care should not depend on social standing or the ability to pay but should be on an equitable basis. Furthermore, most Canadians also believe that everyone has the right to the same level of services, no matter what province they are in. Finally, most Canadians believe that even though insuring these services is a provincial matter, health care should be portable so that they do not lose their health care rights when they travel from their home province. In other words, most Canadians believe that health care should be a socially insured service in the spirit of the current *Canada Health Act*.

Canadians have not always felt this way. Until the 1930s, they agreed with the citizens of most other countries that health care is a commodity like all others, and that those who could not afford to pay for it did not have a right to it. However, the experiences of the depression of the 1930s fostered a gradual change in this perspective, and by the 1940s the outlook had changed fundamentally. First in Saskatchewan and then in other provinces, the now-prevailing attitude became politically dominant. It led to the establishment of universal health and hospital insurance, in Saskatchewan in 1945[1] and successively in the other provinces. It was reflected in the Hall Report of 1964 and in the Lalonde Report of 1974 and ultimately led to the *Canada Health Act* of 1984, which was proclaimed in 1985. Today, all Canadian provinces and territories have a universal health care system, where physicians and hospitals provide services according to province-wide schedules, and where only certain services have to be paid for by patients themselves.[2]

Not all countries share the current Canadian perspective, and not all countries that accept the general principle share the conviction to the same degree. For instance, although the U.K. accepts the general principle of social responsibility for health care, it also believes that society does not have an obligation to provide all medically possible or even all medically indicated services to its citizens. It therefore allows the growth of private clinics and private hospitals for those who are able to pay.

Closer to home, the U.S. has traditionally maintained that health care is a service like all other services, and therefore should be available only to those who can pay. While in recent years the U.S. has moved towards a more socially responsible perspective by establishing Medicare and Medicaid programs, the fact remains that there are over 45 million uninsured people in the U.S. who have either inadequate access to health care, or none at all.[3]

The readings in this chapter begin with an excerpt from the *Canada Health Act*. This excerpt presents the key values of *universality*, *comprehensiveness*, *portability*, *equality* and *public administration* — values that are definitive of the Canadian health care system as it is currently constituted. In 1990 John Iglehart, one of the most acute health care analysts, compared the Canadian health care system with those in the U.S. and the U.K. He argued that while Canada's commitment to universal health care is something of which Canada could be "justifiably proud," the system is threatened by rising costs.[4] He argued further that Canada could not continue to fund the system solely by tax dollars. Other sources of funding — and other methods of funding —would have to be explored. He also suggested that attempts to deal with this problem had been exacerbated by the fact that while health care is a provincial responsibility, a lot of the funding comes from the federal government which had reduced transfer payments to the provinces. Finally, he suggested that any attempt to retain the provincial health care plans, "which are admired throughout the world," might well be threatened unless a more meaningful dialogue was instituted between the federal and the provincial governments.

Iglehart's words are still relevant today — and turn out to have been prophetic. Many of the difficulties that he pointed out have in fact materialized, leading to what many see as a funding crisis in health care. In response to this, the federal government struck the Royal Commission on the Future of Health Care — the so-called Romanow Commission. The Royal Commission reported back to Parliament in 2002. In its Report, which, appropriately enough, is entitled *Building on Values: The Future of Health Care in Canada,* it recommended that the basic principles of the *Canada Health Act* should be retained but that the implementation of these principles should undergo some fundamental changes. The highlights of these recommendations are included below.

Benjamin Freedman and Françoise Baylis begin from the assumption that society does have a moral obligation to provide health care as a socially insured service. However, they go on to argue that to restrict public health care funding only to so-called medically necessary procedures — in other words, to adopt what they call a *purposive* rather than a *functional approach* — is shortsighted and ethically questionable. Not only will such an approach result in serious inequities and dislocated service delivery, but it also ignores other important values that are associated with the delivery of health care. It is an intriguing question how the perspective of Freedman and Baylis meshes with the recommendations of the Romanow Commission.

Notes

1. It was enacted in the *Saskatchewan Hospitalization Act*, 1946, which followed the *Health Services Act* of 1945. The program outlined in this legislation did not become fully operative until an agreement was reached with the College of Physicians and Surgeons of Saskatchewan, with the so-called Saskatoon Agreement of 1962. See also Mr. Justice Emmett Hall, *Report of the Royal Commission on Health Services* (Ottawa: Queen's Printer, 1964), for a discussion of the evolution of health services in Canada.

2. This threatens the principle of equitable access. The final Report of the Royal Commission on the Future of Health Care in part addresses this issue in its main recommendations, which are included below.

3. President's Commission for the Study of Ethical Problems in Medicine and Biomedical and Behavioral Research, *Securing Access to Health Care: A Report on the Ethical Implications of Differences in the Availability of Health Services* (Washington, D.C.: U.S. Government Printing Office, 1983), 3 vols.

4. John K. Iglehart, "Canada's Health Care System Faces Its Problems," *New England Journal of Medicine* 322. 8 (1990): 562–71.

Canada Health Act

Program Criteria

Program criteria   7. In order that a province may qualify for a full cash contribution referred to in section 5 for a fiscal year, the health care insurance plan of the province must, throughout the fiscal year, satisfy the criteria described in sections 8 to 12 respecting the following matters:

(a) public administration;

(b) comprehensiveness;

(c) universality;

(d) portability; and

(e) accessibility. 1984, c. 6, s. 7.

Public administration   8. (1) In order to satisfy the criterion respecting public administration,

(a) the health care insurance plan of a province must be administered and operated on a non-profit basis by a public authority appointed or designated by the government of the province;

(b) the public authority must be responsible to the provincial government for that administration and operation; and

(c) the public authority must be subject to audit of its accounts and financial transactions by such authority as is charged by law with the audit of the accounts of the province.

Designation of agency permitted   (2) The criterion respecting public administration is not contravened by reason only that the public authority referred to in subsection (1) has the power to designate any agency *(a)* to receive on its behalf any amounts payable under the provincial health care insurance plan; or

(b) to carry out on its behalf any responsibility in connection with the receipt or payment of accounts rendered for insured health services, if it is a condition of the designation that all those accounts are subject to assessment and approval by the public authority and that the public authority shall determine the amounts to be paid in respect thereof. 1984, c. 6, s. 8.

Comprehensiveness 9. In order to satisfy the criterion respecting comprehensiveness, the health care insurance plan of a province must insure all insured health services provided by hospitals, medical practitioners or dentists, and where the law of the province so permits, similar or additional services rendered by other health care practitioners. 1984, c. 6, s. 9.

Universality 10. In order to satisfy the criterion respecting universality, the health care insurance plan of a province must entitle one hundred per cent of the insured persons of the province to the insured health services provided for by the plan on uniform terms and conditions. 1984, c. 6, s. 10.

Portability 11. (1) In order to satisfy the criterion respecting portability, the health care insurance plan of a province

(a) must not impose any minimum period of residence in the province, or waiting period, in excess of three months before residents of the province are eligible for or entitled to insured health services;

(b) must provide for and be administered and operated so as to provide for the payment of amounts for the cost of insured health services provided to insured persons while temporarily absent from the province on the basis that

(i) where the insured health services are provided in Canada, payment for health services is at the rate that is approved by the health care insurance plan of the province in which the services are provided, unless the provinces concerned agree to apportion the cost between them in a different manner, or

(ii) where the insured health services are provided out of Canada, payment is made on the basis of the amount that would have been paid by the province for similar services rendered in the province, with due regard, in the case of hospital services, to the size of the hospital, standards of service and other relevant factors; and

(c) must provide for and be administered and operated so as to provide for the payment, during any minimum period of residence, or any waiting period, imposed by the health care insurance plan of another province, of

the cost of insured health services provided to persons who have ceased to be insured persons by reason of having become residents of that other province, on the same basis as though they had not ceased to be residents of the province.

Requirement for consent for elective insured health services permitted

(2) The criterion respecting portability is not contravened by a requirement of a provincial health care insurance plan that the prior consent of the public authority that administers and operates the plan must be obtained for elective insured health services provided to a resident of the province while temporarily absent from the province if the services in question were available on a substantially similar basis in the province.

Definition of "elective insured health services"

(3) For the purpose of subsection (2), "elective insured health services" means insured health services other than services that are provided in an emergency or in any other circumstance in which medical care is required without delay. 1984, c. 6, s. 11.

Accessibility

12. (1) In order to satisfy the criterion respecting accessibility, the health care insurance plan of a province

(a) must provide for insured health services on uniform terms and conditions and on a basis that does not impede or preclude, either directly or indirectly whether by charges made to insured persons or otherwise, reasonable access to those services by insured persons;

(b) must provide for payment for insured health services in accordance with a tariff or system of payment authorized by the law of the province;

(c) must provide for reasonable compensation for all insured health services rendered by medical practitioners or dentists; and

(d) must provide for the payment of amounts to hospitals, including hospitals owned or operated by Canada, in respect of the cost of insured health services.

Reasonable compensation

(2) In respect of any province in which extra-billing is not permitted, paragraph (1)(c) shall be deemed to be complied with if the province has chosen to enter into, and has entered into, an agreement with the medical practitioners and dentists of the province that provides

(a) for negotiations relating to compensation for insured health services between the province and provincial organizations that represent practising medical practitioners or dentists in the province;

(b) for the settlement of disputes relating to compensation through, at the option of the appropriate provincial organizations referred to in paragraph (a), conciliation or binding arbitration by a panel that is equally representative of the provincial organizations and the province and that has an independent chairman; and

(c) that a decision of a panel referred to in paragraph *(b)* may not be altered except by an Act of the legislature of the province. 1984, c. 6, s. 12.

Conditions for Cash Contributions or Payments

Conditions 13. In order that a province may qualify for a full cash contribution referred to in section 5 or payment of the full amount referred to in section 6 for a fiscal year, the government of the province

(a) shall, at the times and in the manner prescribed by the regulations, provide the Minister with such information, of a type prescribed by the regulations, as the Minister may reasonably require for the purposes of this Act; and

(b) shall give recognition to the contributions and payments by Canada under this Act in any public documents, or in any advertising or promotional material, relating to insured health services and extended health care services in the province. 1984, c. 6, s. 13.

Defaults

Referral to Governor in Council consultation process 14. (1) Subject to subsection (3), where the Minister, after consultation in accordance with subsection (2) with the minister responsible for health care in a province, is of the opinion that

(a) the health care insurance plan of the province does not or has ceased to satisfy any one of the cri-

teria described in sections 8 to 12, or

(b) the province has failed to comply with any condition set out in section 13,

and the province has not given an undertaking satisfactory to the Minister to remedy the default within a period that the Minister considers reasonable, the Minister shall refer the matter to the Governor in Council.

(2) Before referring a matter to the Governor in Council under subsection (1) in respect of a province, the Minister shall

(a) send by registered mail to the minister responsible for health care in the province a notice of concern with respect to any problem foreseen;

(b) seek any additional information available from the province with respect to the problem through bilateral discussions, and make a report to the province within ninety days after sending the notice of concern; and

(c) if requested by the province, meet within a reasonable period of time to discuss the report.

Where no consultation can be achieved (3) The Minister may act without consultation under subsection (1) if the Minister is of the opinion that a sufficient time has expired after reasonable efforts to achieve consultation and that consultation will not be achieved. 1984, c. 6, s. 14.

Order reducing or withholding contribution 15. (1) Where, on the referral of a matter under section 14, the Governor in Council is of the opinion that the health care insurance plan of a province does not or has ceased to satisfy any one of the criteria described in sections 8 to 12 or that a province has failed to comply with any condition set out in section 13, the Governor in Council may, by order,

(a) direct that any cash contribution or amount payable to that province for a fiscal year be reduced, in respect of each default, by an amount that the Governor in Council considers to be appropriate, having regard to the gravity of the default; or

(b) where the Governor in Council considers it appropriate, direct that the whole of any cash contribution or amount payable to that province for a fiscal year be withheld.

Amending orders

(2) The Governor in Council may, by order, repeal or amend any order made under subsection (1) where the Governor in Council is of the opinion that the repeal or amendment is warranted in the circumstances.

Notice of order

(3) A copy of each order made under this section together with a statement of any findings on which the order was based shall be sent forthwith by registered mail to the government of the province concerned and the Minister shall cause the order and statement to be laid before each House of Parliament on any of the first fifteen days on which that House is sitting after the order is made.

Commencement of order

(4) An order made under subsection (1) shall not come into force earlier than thirty days after a copy of the order has been sent to the government of the province concerned under subsection (3). 1984, c. 6, s. 15.

Reimposition of reductions or withholdings

16. In the case of a continuing failure to satisfy any of the criteria described in sections 8 to 12 or to comply with any condition set out in section 13, any reduction or withholding under section 15 of a cash contribution or an amount payable to a province for a fiscal year shall be reimposed for each succeeding fiscal year as long as the Minister is satisfied, after consultation with the minister responsible for health care in the province, that the default is continuing. 1984, c. 6, s. 16.

When reduction or withholding imposed

17. Any reduction or withholding under section 15 or 16 of a cash contribution or payment may be imposed in the fiscal year in which the default that gave rise to the reduction or withholding occurred or in the following fiscal year. 1984, c. 6, s. 17.

Extra-Billing and User Charges

Extra-billing

18. In order that a province may qualify for a full cash contribution referred to in section 5 for a fiscal year, no payments may be permitted by the province for that fiscal year under the health care insurance plan of the province in respect of insured health services that have been subject to extra-billing by medical practitioners or dentists. 1984, c. 6, s. 18.

User charges 19. (1) In order that a province may qualify for a full cash contribution referred to in section 5 for a fiscal year, user charges must not be permitted by the province for that fiscal year under the health care insurance plan of the province.

Limitation (2) Subsection (1) does not apply in respect of user charges for accommodation or meals provided to an in-patient who, in the opinion of the attending physician, requires chronic care and is more or less permanently resident in a hospital or other institution. 1984, c. 6, s. 19.

Deduction for extra-billing 20. (1) Where a province fails to comply with the condition set out in section 18, there shall be deducted from the cash contribution to the province for a fiscal year an amount that the Minister, on the basis of information provided in accordance with the regulations, determines to have been charged through extra-billing by medical practitioners or dentists in the province in that fiscal year or, where information is not provided in accordance with the regulations, an amount that the Minister estimates to have been so charged.

Deduction for user charges (2) Where a province fails to comply with the condition set out in section 19, there shall be deducted from the cash contribution to the province for a fiscal year an amount that the Minister, on the basis of information provided in accordance with the regulations, determines to have been charged in the province in respect of user charges to which section 19 applies in that fiscal year or, where information is not provided in accordance with the regulations, an amount that the Minister estimates to have been so charged.

Consultation with province (3) The Minister shall not estimate an amount under subsection (1) or (2) without first undertaking to consult the minister responsible for health care in the province concerned.

Separate accounting in Public Accounts (4) Any amount deducted under subsection (1) or (2) from a cash contribution in any of the three consecutive fiscal years the first of which commences on April 1, 1984, shall be accounted for separately in respect of each province in the Public Accounts for each of those fiscal years in and after which the amount is deducted.

Refund to province (5) Where, in any of the three fiscal years referred to in subsection (4), extra-billing or user charges have, in the opinion of the Minister, been eliminated in a province, the total amount deducted in respect of extra-billing or user charges, as the case may be, shall be paid to the province.

Saving (6) Nothing in this section restricts the power of the Governor in Council to make any order under section 15. 1984, c. 6, s. 20.

Report of the Royal Commission on the Future of Health Services in Canada

A System Based on Canadian Values

Early in my mandate, I challenged those advocating radical solutions for reforming health care — user fees, medical savings accounts, de-listing services, greater privatization, a parallel private system — to come forward with evidence that these approaches would improve and strengthen our health care system. *The evidence has not been forthcoming.* I have also carefully explored the experiences of other jurisdictions with co-payment models and with public-private partnerships, and have found these lacking. There is no evidence these solutions will deliver better or cheaper care, or improve access (except, perhaps, for those who can afford to pay for care out of their own pockets). More to the point, the principles on which these solutions rest cannot be reconciled with the values at the heart of medicare or with the tenets of the *Canada Health Act* that Canadians overwhelmingly support. It would be irresponsible of me to jeopardize what has been, and can remain, a world-class health care system and a proud national symbol by accepting anecdote as fact or on the dubious basis of making a "leap of faith."

Some have described it as a perversion of Canadian values that they cannot use their money to purchase faster treatment from a private provider for their loved ones. I believe it is a far greater perversion of Canadian values to accept a system where money, rather than need, determines who gets access to care.

It has been suggested to me by some that if there is a growing tension between the principles of our health care system and what is happening on the ground, the answer is obvious. Dilute or ditch the principles. Scrap any notion of national standards and values. Forget about equal access. Let people buy their way openly to the front of the line. Make health care a business. Stop treating it as a public service, available equally to all. But the consensus view of Canadians on this is clear. No! Not now, not ever. Canadians view medicare as a moral enterprise, not a business venture.

Tossing overboard the principles and values that govern our health care system would be betraying a public trust. Canadians will not accept this, and without their consent, these new solutions are doomed to fail. Canadians want their health care system renovated; they do not want it demolished.

But we must also recognize that since the earliest days of medicare, public and private sector care providers (including fee-for-service doctors) have been part of our health care system. Our system was never organized according to a strict protocol; it evolved in accordance with the existing capacity of public and private providers, changing notions of what constitute "core services," and the wishes of Canadians.

One of the most difficult issues with which I have had to struggle is how much private participation within our universal, single-payer, publicly admin-

Source: *Building on Values: The Future of Health Care in Canada*, Final Report of the Royal Commission on the Future of Health Services, pp. xx–xxi and xxiv–xxxiv, © 2002. Reproduced with the permission of the Minister of Public Works and Government Services, 2003, and Courtesy of the Privy Council Office.

istered system is warranted or defensible. On the one hand, I am confronted by the fact that the private sector is already an important part of our public system. The notion of rolling back its participation is fraught with difficulty. On the other hand, I am acutely aware of the potential risks to the integrity and viability of our health care system that might result from an expanded role for private providers.

At a minimum, I believe governments must draw a clear line between direct health services (such as hospital and medical care) and ancillary ones (such as food preparation or maintenance services). The former should be delivered primarily through our public, not-for-profit system, while the latter could be the domain of private providers. The rapid growth of private MRI (magnetic resonance imaging) clinics, which permit people to purchase faster service and then use test results to jump the queue back into the public system for treatment, is a troubling case-in-point. So too is the current practice of some workers' compensation agencies of contracting with private providers to deliver fast-track diagnostic services to potential claimants. I agree with those who view these situations as incompatible with the "equality of access" principle at the heart of medicare. Governments must invest sufficiently in the public system to make timely access to diagnostic services for all a reality and reduce the temptation to "game" the system. In order to clarify the situation in regard to diagnostic services, I am therefore recommending that diagnostic services be explicitly included under the definition of "insured health services" under a new *Canada Health Act*.

Recommendations

Establish a new Canadian Health Covenant as a tangible statement of Canadians' values and a guiding force for our publicly funded health care system. A proposed new Canadian Health Covenant would confirm our collective vision for the future of health care in Canada and clearly outline the responsibilities and entitlements of individual Canadians, health providers, and governments in regard to the system.

Create a Health Council of Canada to facilitate collaborative leadership in health. A new Health Council of Canada would help foster collaboration and co-operation among provinces, territories, and the federal government. The Council would play a key role in setting common indicators and benchmarks, in measuring and tracking the performance of the health system, and in reporting results regularly to Canadians. ...

Modernize the Canada Health Act *by expanding coverage and renewing its principles.* ... The five principles of the CHA should be reaffirmed, the principle of comprehensiveness updated and the principle of portability limited to guaranteeing portability of coverage within Canada. A new principle of accountability should be added to the CHA ... to [allow Canadians to] hold the appropriate people accountable for what happens in our health care system. The current scope of publicly insured services should also be expanded beyond hospital and physician care to include ... diagnostic services and priority home care services. ... Finally, the CHA should include an effective dispute resolution process.

Clarify coverage by distinguishing between direct and ancillary health services, and change practices contrary to the spirit of medicare. The growing reliance on private advanced diagnostic services is eroding the equal access principle at the heart of medicare. The CHA must include public coverage for medically necessary diagnostic services. ... [The] current practice by which some workers' compensation agencies contract with private providers to deliver fast-track diagnostic services to potential claimants [should also be reconsidered].

Provide stable, predictable and long-term funding through a new dedicated cash-only transfer for medicare. [The revision of the] ... *Canada Health Act* [should include] an increased share of federal funding and ... an escalator provision that is set in advance for five years to ensure future funding is stable, predictable and increases at a realistic rate, commensurate with our economic growth and capacity to pay.

Address immediate issues through targeted funding. Five new targeted funds should be established:

- A Rural and Remote Access Fund: to improve timely access to care in rural and remote areas.
- A Diagnostic Services Fund: to improve wait times for diagnostic services.
- A Primary Health Care Transfer: to support efforts to remove obstacles to renewing primary health care delivery.
- A Home Care Transfer: to provide a foundation for an eventual national home care strategy.
- A Catastrophic Drug Transfer: to allow provincial drug programs to expand and improve coverage for their residents ...

Enable the establishment of personal electronic health records for each Canadian building on the work currently underway in provinces and territories. ...

Take clear steps to protect the privacy of Canadians' personal health information, including an amendment to the Criminal Code of Canada. ...

Provide better health information to Canadians, health care providers, researchers and policymakers — information they can use to guide their decisions. ... In addition to electronic health records, [the new agency of] Canada Health Infoway should take the lead in establishing a comprehensive source of trusted health information. ...

Expand the scope, effectiveness and co-ordination of health technology assessment across Canada. ...[T]he current work of the Canadian Coordinating Office for Health Technology Assessment should become a vital part of the Health Council of Canada and provide a national focus for health technology assessment.

Create new research centres for health innovation. ... [F]our new Centres for Health Innovation should be established focusing on rural and remote health, health human resources, health promotion and pharmaceutical policy.

Forge stronger linkages with researchers in other parts of the world and with policymakers across the country. ...

Address the need to change the scopes and patterns of practice of health care providers to reflect changes in how health care services are delivered, particularly through new approaches to primary health care. ... [T]he growing emphasis on collaborative teams and networks of health providers ... means that traditional scopes of practice also need to change ... [with] new roles for nurses, family physicians, pharmacists, case managers ... [etc.]

Take steps to ensure that rural and remote communities have an appropriate mix of skilled health care providers to meet their health care needs. ...

Substantially improve the base of information about Canada's health workforce. ... [T]he Health Council of Canada [should] collect, analyze and provide regular reports on critical issues including the recruitment, distribution, and remuneration of health care providers.

Review current education and training programs for health care providers to focus more on integrated approaches for preparing health care teams. ...

Establish strategies for addressing the supply, distribution, education, training, and changing skills and patterns of practice for Canada's health workforce. ...

Finally make a major breakthrough in implementing primary health care and transforming Canada's health care system. ... Canadians should have access to an integrated continuum of care 24 hours a day, 7 days a week, no matter where they live.

Use the proposed new Primary Health Care Transfer as the impetus for fundamental change in how health care services are delivered across the country. ...

Build a common national platform for primary health care based on four essential building blocks. ...

Integrate prevention and promotion initiatives as a central focus of primary health care targeted initially at reducing tobacco use and obesity, and increasing physical activity in Canada. ...

Implement a new national immunization strategy. ... We ... need to take steps to ensure that Canada is well prepared to face new and emerging problems resulting from globalization and the evolution of infectious diseases.

Use the new Diagnostic Services Fund to shorten waiting times for diagnostic services. [There are] ... long waiting times for essential diagnostic tests. The new Diagnostic Services Fund should be used ... to purchase equipment ... [and] to train the necessary staff and technicians. ...

Implement better ways of managing wait lists. ... Steps must be taken to put centralized approaches in place within health regions, on a provincewide basis or even, in some cases, on a national basis. Patients also have a right to good information about how long they can reasonably expect to wait for treatment and what other options are available to them.

Take deliberate steps to measure the quality and performance of Canada's health care system and report regularly to Canadians. ...

Ensure that the health care system responds to the unique needs of official language minorities. ...

Address the diverse health care needs of Canadians. ...

Establish a new Rural and Remote Access Fund to support new approaches for delivering health care services and improve the health of people in rural and remote communities. ...

Use a portion of the Fund to address the demand for health care providers in these communities. ...

Expand telehealth to improve access to care. Telehealth uses information technologies to link ... [p]eople in rural and remote locations ... to family physicians, specialists and other health services. ...

Use the proposed new Home Care Transfer to establish a national platform for home care services. ...

Revise the Canada Health Act *to include coverage for home care services in priority areas. ...* [I]mmediate steps should be taken to bring [home mental health case management and intervention services, post-acute home care, and palliative home care] ... under the umbrella of the *Canada Health Act. ...*

Improve the quality of care and support available to people with mental illnesses by including home mental health case management and intervention services as part of the Canada Health Act. ...

Expand the Canada Health Act *to include coverage for post-acute home care including medication management and rehabilitation services. ...*

Provide Canada Health Act *coverage for palliative home care services to support people in their last six months of life. ...*

Introduce a new program to provide ongoing support for informal caregivers. [The role of significant others who] ... provide direct support in the home ... should be recognized by allowing informal caregivers to take time off work and to qualify for special benefits. ...

Take the first steps to better integrate prescription drugs into Canada's health care system. [We] ... need to begin the process of integrating coverage for prescription drugs within medicare as part of a longer term strategy to ensure all Canadians benefit from comprehensive prescription drug coverage.

Use the new Catastrophic Drug Transfer to offset the cost of provincial and territorial drug plans and reduce disparities in coverage across the country. There are serious disparities across Canada in terms of catastrophic coverage for prescription drugs. Under this proposed new program, provinces and territories would receive additional funds to help cover the costs of prescription drug plans and protect Canadians against the potentially "catastrophic" impact of high cost drugs. ...

Establish a new National Drug Agency to control costs, evaluate new and existing drugs, and ensure quality, safety, and cost-effectiveness of all prescription drugs. ...

Establish a national formulary of prescription drugs to provide consistency across the country, ensure objective assessments of drugs, and contain costs. ...

Develop a new medication management program for chronic and some lifethreatening illnesses as an integral part of primary health care. ...

Review aspects of Canadian patent law. ...The extensive 20-year guarantee of exclusive access to the Canadian market ... [is] ... consistent with international standards. ... However, certain aspects of Canada's patent laws should be reviewed to improve access to generic alternatives and to contain costs.

Consolidate Aboriginal health funding from all sources and use the funds to support the creation of Aboriginal Health Partnerships to manage and organize health services for Aboriginal peoples and promote Aboriginal health. Aboriginal health programs are funded from a vari-

ety of sources including the federal government, provincial and territorial governments, local Bands and, in some cases, municipal governments and regional health authorities. ... Under this new approach, funding from all sources would be consolidated and allocated to new Aboriginal Health Partnerships (AHP), created solely and specifically to organize health services and improve the health of the communities and people they serve.

Establish a clear structure and mandate for Aboriginal Health Partnerships to use the funding to address the specific health needs of their populations, improve access to all levels of health care services, recruit new Aboriginal health care providers, and increase training for non-Aboriginal health care providers. ...

Ensure ongoing input from Aboriginal peoples into the direction and design of health care services in their communities. ...

Take clear and immediate steps to protect Canada's health care system from possible challenges under international law and trade agreements and to build alliances within the international community. ...

Play a leadership role in international efforts to improve health and strengthen health care systems in developing countries. ...

Reduce our reliance on the recruitment of health care professionals from developing countries. ... Canada has made extensive use of foreign-trained medical graduates, particularly in communities that have had trouble attracting Canadian doctors. ... [However], we have an obligation to ... [stop] ... luring physicians away from developing countries where their services are desperately needed.

Purpose and Function in Government-Funded Health Coverage

Benjamin Freedman and Françoise Baylis

Abstract

Government-funded health insurance programs that claim to provide comprehensive funding of their clients' demands have commonly adopted a purposive (deductive) approach to the problem of health care funding. This involves determining the extent of covered benefits by seeking an "adequate" definition of health or health care. Payment is then limited to only those procedures medically required or indicated. In this paper we argue that the purposive approach is inadequate, and that attempted adherence to it results in a curious dislocation of service, serious inequities, and an unhealthy contemplation of the definition of health. These problems are the result of structural deficiencies in the approach, and so will not be rectified by tinkering with the definitions adopted. As an alternative, we present an outline of a functional (inductive) approach, which seeks to identify which of the expectations of its clients the government health insurance system may realistically satisfy.

Government-funded health insurance schemes are under increasing pressure to reconcile finite medical resources with seemingly infinite demands for medical services. Consequently, problems regarding the macroallocation of available resources must constantly be readdressed. The substantive macroallocational questions are familiar: What proportions of health care funding should be directed toward acute, chronic, or preventive care, or toward research in these respective areas? What, if any, provision should be made for the funding of novel therapies? When more than one approach to a disorder is available (e.g., medical or surgical treatment of angina pectoris), should the insurance program reward the use of the cheapest option (one assumption underlying the DRG system; see Wasserman 1983), the option which the physician believes is clinically preferable, or that which the patient prefers, perhaps on grounds of compatibility with lifestyle?

Questions such as these underline the need for a demarcation principle which government-funded health insurance programs could use to determine what should and should not be funded. The usefulness of such a principle is obvious, particularly from the government's perspective, when one considers how quickly new approaches to health care are adopted by health care providers (creating a demand for insurance reimbursement on their behalf). Current examples would include transportation, advanced diagnostic and imaging equipment, and expensive techniques for the treatment of infertility (most notoriously, *in vitro* fertilization).

Benjamin Freedman and Françoise Baylis, "Purpose and Function in Government-Funded Health Coverage," in *Journal of Health Politics, Policy and Law*, Volume 12, No 1 pp. 97–112.

A demarcation principle would serve to limit the constantly expanding claims for health insurance coverage which feed upon (and, when successful, fuel) the unrealistic expectation that the government-funded health care system can guarantee everyone a long, happy, and productive life.

At present, the approach to funding adopted by government health care programs is eclectic. Aside from strictly medical concerns, attention is given to factors deriving from economics, politics, and public policy. Even within the mélange of compromise that constitutes health insurance, however, we may discern a basic theme of demarcation: absent special considerations, a purposive (deductive) approach is commonly used in deciding whether a specific service should be a covered benefit. The results of this theme may be reconstructed in almost syllogistic terms: the insurance scheme should fund that which yields, or leads to, health (major premise); the proposed service does (or does not) yield or lead to health (minor premise); therefore the proposed service should (should not) be reimbursed. Presented in this way, the deductive approach is, of course, an artificial reconstruction of a more complicated reality. In the cases that we will be presenting, however, it plausibly captures an important theme in insurance decision making as that is publicly presented.

The Preamble to the Ontario Health Insurance Plan's *Schedule of Benefits* (1983), for example, states at the outset that "Insured medical services are limited to the services which are medically necessary..." (p. 1). This we understand to mean that only those services designed to restore health ("medically necessary") are to be funded. The purposive concept of medical necessity is therefore ostensibly an *exclusive* criterion of demarcation — that is, a necessary but not sufficient condition for coverage. However, medical necessity also serves as an *inclusive* criterion of demarcation. The fitting of contact lenses, for example, is not a covered benefit unless it is being done to correct aphakia, myopia greater than nine diopters, irregular astigmatism, or keratoconus (p. 20). Similarly, other services commonly sought for reasons of vanity or convenience are not covered benefits unless they are called for by some substantial degree of medical necessity. A case in point is cosmetic surgery, which is not an insured benefit "except where medically required" (p. 19).

The deductive model, idealized as it is, is a plausible — sometimes, the *only* plausible — reconstruction of a number of specific decisions on insurance coverage. Although it is initially appealing, we shall argue that this form of reasoning results in some obvious inequities and distortions in government coverage practice. An alternative approach, which may be termed functional or inductive, will be suggested. The functional approach would have us resolve the problem of demarcation by asking whether the specific service in question represents a demand which the health care system may efficiently satisfy. The question of whether the funded service supplies "health" or "health care" is thereby intentionally finessed.

The examples we shall be using are drawn largely from Canadian (and predominantly Ontarian) experiences. They are intended to serve for purposes of illustration alone. If successful, they point to problems and approaches generally prevalent among any government-funded insurance scheme which claims to comprehensively fund the health demands of the serviced population.

The Purposive Approach

In ordinary language, "purpose" broadly refers to the end one has in view in acting in a certain way (i.e., "purposively"). The use of the term implies the conscious choice of both a goal and an action designed to achieve the stated goal. By extension, we may think of objects as purposively designed. For example, a television receiver is built with the end of it serving as a decoder of electronic impulses. In designing it, a certain size and shape are chosen on the grounds of fitness toward that end (Turkel 1984); any components which prove unreliable in achieving that end are either discarded or redesigned. Social institutions, such as traffic regulation, can also be construed as purposive. A panoply of elements (road markings, rules, etc.) are chosen subordinate to the primary goal of the swift and accident-free motion of traffic.

Similarly, some view medical practice as a purposive enterprise. It is usual to distinguish medical from nonmedical interventions — to demarcate medical practice — by referring to current beliefs concerning what promotes or conserves health; in theory new forms of medical treatment are accepted into practice and old ones discarded primarily on the basis of their fitness to serve the purpose of health. It is on this basis alone that physicians, in the course of their daily practice, "may, unquestioned and with impunity, slice, puncture, bind, grind, inject, and extract various organic and inorganic substances into and from" their patients (Freedman 1984, 5).

As health is the organizing principle and rule of demarcation for medical practice, it is natural to assume that this concept should apply as well to that system which funds medical practice. That is, it seems natural to assume that problems of demarcation in health care funding cannot be decided unless prior agreement has been arrived at concerning the definition of health, so that the nature of "medically necessary" services may be ascertained. By extension, a government-funded health insurance program may be purposively understood as an institution designed to secure health, although it is constrained by economic and political factors.

If the purpose of the government-funded insurance system is to promote health, and if that purpose is to serve as its rule of demarcation, a definition of health must be presented. However, the definition of health and related concepts (such as illness and disease) has resisted numerous scholarly efforts. Those definitions which have gained favorable attention have succeeded by stipulating a definition which could then be explicated or operationalized (Boorse 1975). But this approach will not serve the purposes of a government-funded health insurance scheme, since these purposes require a definition or an understanding of health with a basis in social consensus and usage.

The most widely known and most frequently criticized definition of health is found in the Preamble to the Constitution of the World Health Organization: "Health is a state of complete physical, mental and social well-being and not merely the absence of disease or infirmity" (WHO 1976). Daniel Callahan, a relatively sympathetic commentator on the WHO definition, notes nonetheless that this definition fosters "the cultural tendency to define all social problems, from war to crime on the streets, as 'health' problems" (Callahan 1973, 78). It "makes the medical profession the gate-keeper for happiness and social well-being ... the final magic-healer of human misery" (p. 81).

These eloquent criticisms relate to the one point that makes the WHO definition of health inadequate for the purposes of our discussion: it provides a government-funded health insurance scheme with no rule of demarcation whatsoever. Because of the wide currency the WHO definition enjoys, this criticism has been voiced in the world of practice as well as in the dusty pages of journals. For example, in Canada abortions are not illegal, provided that (among other conditions) they have been approved by a committee of physicians that finds the abortion necessary to preserve the life or health of the applicant.[1] Some abortion committees have adopted the WHO understanding as their working definition of health. According to many critics, this indicates that the committees have abandoned the effort at demarcating therapeutic abortions from those sought for nontherapeutic reasons.

Mindful of the need for demarcation, Callahan offered the following definition of health as a counterproposal: "Health is a state of physical well-being," a state which need not be "complete" but must be "at least adequate, i.e., without significant impairment of function" (Callahan 1973, 87). With this narrow definition of health, mental illness would qualify as "ill health," if at all, only if it substantially interfered with functioning.

Would Callahan's definition, or one equally narrow, represent a satisfactory rule of demarcation for government-funded health insurance schemes? It is important to examine this question at some length, because the narrowness of the definition as well as its common-sense roots make it attractive to economically pressed governments. Therefore, even if Callahan would not use his definition of health as a rule of demarcation, governments faced with competing priorities might be tempted to do so.

In judging the adequacy of any proposed rule of demarcation, two different kinds of questions may be asked. First, *could* the rule serve (i.e., would it clearly distinguish between those services to be included and those to be excluded from the funding system)? Second, *should* the rule serve (i.e., if applied, would it yield satisfactory results)? The first question concerns the formal adequacy of the rule; the second, its substantive adequacy.

The notions of "well-being" and of "impairment of function" are two crucial elements of Callahan's definition which are unavoidably ambiguous; these ambiguities speak to the issue of formal adequacy. To revert to the example introduced earlier, consider a patient suffering from exercise-onset angina pectoris. Two types of treatment are available. One option is medical management, which requires of the patient a commitment to control of diet, a modification of activity, and the tolerance of some degree of continued pain. The alternative is surgical intervention, which avoids the above problems at the expense of discrete surgical risk and substantial surgical and hospitalization costs. An appeal to "well-being" and "functioning" fails to indicate which of these forms of treatment should appropriately be funded. The problem is further complicated when one considers that the judgments of the patient and of the physician may differ; and, whereas people tend to think of "health" or "therapy" as technical concepts whose application is in the hands of professionals, they tend to define other concepts like "well-being" and "functioning" for themselves. The formal adequacy of Callahan's definition is therefore in question.

What about the substantive adequacy of the definition as a demarcation rule? This may seem to beg the question. We need a demarcation rule because we don't know what should and what should not be funded; therefore, how can we question such a rule by saying that it includes or excludes the wrong items? But this point presumes a false dichotomy, as often occurs when applying deductive approaches to social questions. We may (we almost certainly do) have some idea of the results desired from a rule of demarcation. We likely wish to develop a demarcation rule to sharpen an initially hazy understanding, rather than to fill a total vacuum.

Substantively, a rule may be faulty because it is either overinclusive, underinclusive, or both. Callahan's definition of health, if used as a demarcation rule, would be both. It would be overinclusive because it fails to account for the quantity of resources expended in marginal improvements in well-being or functioning. It does not tell us when the game is no longer worth the candle; and, as was noted at the outset, it is because medicine continues to yield improvements in these parameters, albeit at ever-increasing expense, that the problem we are discussing arises.

Callahan's definition would be under-inclusive as well, because if it were applied rigorously benign and worthwhile services would be excluded from coverage. In his concern to combat the view that medicine should be held responsible to deliver perfect happiness, Callahan eliminates any role medicine might legitimately satisfy in this direction. Sometimes medical expertise is necessary to provide a modicum of happiness; if the costs thereby incurred are trivial enough, and the benefits (even in mere happiness) great enough, why should the required service not be funded?

Consider the following. The removal of tattoos is not usually necessary to restore function; nor, strictly speaking, is it a necessary component of well-being. Yet, the safe eradication of tattoos may require medical expertise. In Ontario, in most cases the provincial health insurance scheme does not cover the cost of tattoo removal. However, an exception is made for the eradication of prisoner-of-war or concentration camp tattoos. In some isolated instances well-being or functioning might require the removal of such tattoos, and to these cases Callahan's principle would extend. But in the usual case physical well-being and functioning are not impaired by these offensive tattoos. Is it wrong to fund this service simply out of consideration for the victims' feelings, in a situation where practical concern for these feelings requires medical expertise?

Evidently a definition of health from either end of the continuum — the relatively inclusive WHO definition, and the rather exclusive definition proposed by Callahan — will not serve as a satisfactory demarcation principle. However, quite apart from the specific problems arising from any particular definition of health, a further obstacle confronts the definitional approach to health care funding in that no definition of health has garnered general agreement. This lack of consensus is no mere accident. While on the surface the debate concerning the definition of health is technical in nature, it is clear in the writings of Szasz (1961), Kass (1975), and others that this debate serves an ideological role as well. Often the definitions advocated reflect broad views concerning such disparate issues as technocracy, nature versus nurture, and the allowable limits of eccentricity in liberal societies. Unhappily, therefore, it may be the case that consensus regarding the definition of health will have to wait for prior consensus on political and social ideology.

Also, the economic facts of health care may be another source of dissent regarding the definition of health and disease. Consider a study by Campbell, Scadding, and Roberts (1979), in which subjects were presented with a number of conditions and asked whether these represented "disease." The conditions ranged from malaria and tuberculosis to drowning and starvation. Physicians, and especially general practitioners, were more likely to characterize a condition as "disease" than were lay respondents. The authors suggest that the operational equivalents of "disease" are different in the two groups. For the layman, "disease" means "Do I need a doctor?" For the physician, it means "Is it useful for me to use this label?" An alternative suggestion compatible with the observed differences is that physicians, especially family practitioners, have a vested economic interest in broadening the scope of the term "disease."

We have been arguing that reliance upon the definition of health for the purposive elucidation of a government-funded insurance program is unlikely to result in a consensual, usable, and fair system. To this one might object that the preceding argument has erred in identifying the purpose of a government-funded health insurance system as the provision of "health." A health insurance system cannot provide *health*, but at best can only provide *health care*.

This amended purposive description is not, however, immune from the criticisms noted above. The objection purports to take a realistic look at what the government-funded insurance system actually does: it funds "health care." This is presumed to be a less ambiguous concept than "health." However, the definition of health care itself is crucially dependent upon prior agreement on the definition of health, so the objection only succeeds in pushing the problems we have noted one step back.

Others will object that the health care system provides neither "health" nor "health care" but "medical care" *tout court*. This, however, is no more serious an objection, for although the term "medical care" is perhaps even less ambiguous than the term "health care," the problem remains in that "medical care" is commonly understood to require that a physician's expertise be applied on behalf of restoring or preserving the health of patients. Furthermore, if we were to be fully realistic, we would have to admit that government-funded health insurance systems do not fund medical care or health care any more than they fund health. Rather, they fund health care providers, as public monies are made available precisely to pay for medical services rendered.

Structural Deficiencies of the Purposive Approach

As noted above, the two definitions of health drawn from either end of the continuum fail to adequately demarcate insurable services. It does not necessarily follow from this, however, that a definition in between these extremes would not serve.

Allowing for the remote possibility that a consensual definition of health were to be adopted, some important structural problems would remain to confront any purposive system of government-funded health insurance. These problems derive from the approach's top-down, deductive fashion of reasoning, and therefore would not be solved by any improvement in the formulation of the premises. In particular, they would persist despite changes in the definition of health or health care.

An inherent problem with the purposive-deductive approach is its rationalization of the issue of demarcation. In principle, once the premises have been adopted, all of the solutions are present; as logicians say, deductive reasoning produces no new knowledge not already embedded in the premises. Two difficulties follow from this. The purposive approach does not in principle allow for an incremental solution to the issues, within which some procedures might be funded on a trial basis while other relevantly similar procedures await the lessons of experience. Furthermore, this rationalized approach does not permit any wisdom of quantification, a problem noted earlier in reference to Callahan. It does not allow us by its premises to say that some procedure does not fall on the "fundable" side of the demarcation line, but that it is still worthy of funding (e.g., tattoo removal), or alternatively that some procedure might fall on the "fundable" side of the demarcation line, but that it is nonetheless too expensive a proposition to fund (e.g., heart transplants).

A further problem is who decides whether some service is fundable under the definition consensually adopted. He almost certainly will be some professional: possibly the individual health care provider, but more likely some government official. Thus, control of the health insurance system passes into the hands of the technocracy, and the patient is lost in the shuffle, as is indeed lay input in general (which currently may be provided through political representation and control). How is the technocracy to resolve these problems? In the deductive mode of reasoning, issues of application are reduced to a search for semantic clarity and consensus. Practical issues of whether it is useful, fair, or right to cover a given treatment for a given condition are converted into an obsessive contemplation of the definition of health.

Problems of the Purposive Approach in Practice

The purposive-deductive approach is necessarily obsessed with determining whether a condition is "really" an illness. Two representative cases illustrate this point, though many other examples could be cited if space permitted. Jane Smith (a real case, though not her real name) approached an endocrinologist with a presenting complaint of excessive growth of facial and body hair. After an extensive workup (covered, incidentally, by the provincial health plan) in which no endocrinological disorder was established, she was diagnosed as suffering from "essential hirsutism." Mrs. Smith then requested of the physician a referral to an electrolysist, in the belief that the health care plan would then cover the cost of treatment. This request was refused. She was told that if the condition was causing her acute discomfort or embarrassment, she could be referred to a psychiatrist, who could then make the referral for hair removal. The kinds of questions the psychiatrist would be likely to ask could equally well have been asked by the endocrinologist. However, he felt constrained by the purposive nature of the system to validate the electrolytic referral by means of special

expertise (into mental illness) which he did not feel he possessed. Thus, inappropriate gate-keeping mechanisms which are both costly and inefficient were introduced. This case illustrates one way in which the technocratic and logomachistic tendencies of the purposive approach reinforce one another.

To further illustrate this point, consider the treatment of infertility, which might include hormonal therapy or surgery as well as counseling. These therapies ordinarily are thought to fall within the boundaries of medical care. But the purposive approach must question whether infertility itself is really a "disease." If we look to an American example, Great Southern Life of Houston, a private insurance company, is reported as having denied coverage for *in vitro* fertilization on the grounds that it is "not a treatment of an illness" *(Surrogate Parenting News* 1983). Presumably a government-funded health care system similarly concerned with purposive considerations might apply the same reasoning.

Another distinction covertly used is that of the internal versus the external. There is a vague feeling that health care is a concept that relates to the individual rather than to the environment, and that fundable, fee-for-service health care interventions may be demarcated in part as those which represent internal adjustments to the human organism rather than modifications of the organism's environment. When a malnourished patient is nursed back to health through intravenous infusions, that is health care; when he or she is given money or remunerative employment supplying the wherewithal for self-nourishment, that is not health care.

The distinction makes less sense in other contexts. What of a patient suffering from a definable illness whose comprehensive treatment would include environmental modification? A major and growing current example are those patients suffering from pan-allergic syndromes. It is sometimes claimed that the alleviation of the symptoms from this disorder requires a total readjustment of the patient's living arrangements, such as moving into a cabin tiled with ceramics and discarding a wardrobe laced with allergens. Although this is asserted to be the treatment of choice, it is "external" and therefore not a covered benefit under the government health insurance scheme. Similarly, prosthetics that are implanted, like heart pacemakers, are covered benefits under Ontario's health insurance scheme, whereas externally attached prosthetics, like limbs, generally are not paid for by the Ontario Health Insurance Plan (OHIP).

The Functional Approach: An Alternative

Most social institutions are established with a purpose in view. When a government-funded health insurance program is initiated, the purpose is vaguely understood to contribute to the provision of health or health care. This original purpose is in fact critical to the establishment of a government health insurance program, which is often given higher priority than comparable welfare schemes dealing in less critical services and commodities. But once an insurance scheme is in place, it would be foolish to freeze the system in its embryonic state. With the continuing development of a health insurance plan, as it confronts issues of macroallocation and demarcation, there is no need to restrict it to the a priori wisdom that went into its establishment. On these grounds we advocate a functional approach to government health care funding.

In accordance with common usage, we define a "function" as any output of a system which is positively evaluated, whether that output was intentional or not.[2] Purposes are therefore a subset of

functions, the latter including happy surprises in addition to anticipated outcomes. To revert to our earlier example, the purpose of a television set is to decode electronic signals. In most homes, however, it will also service a variety of additional functions: conversation piece, plant stand, and so on.

What would be distinctive about a functional approach to a government-funded health insurance plan? Three main differences stand between a purposive and a functional approach. These differences have to do with the characterization of those conditions which the government health insurance program should ameliorate, the demarcation of reimbursable from nonreimbursable services, and the relationship between the health plan and other government services.

With the purposive approach to the question of health care funding, funding decisions turn on whether a condition represents ill health, a disease, an illness. With a functional approach, in contrast, questions outside the realm of health are also considered. For example, has the condition resulted in impaired occupational performance? (In the infamous words of an anonymous Polish public health official, "Tuberculosis slows production.") Does the person afflicted with the condition experience disturbed functioning in other areas as a result? Is he severely distressed or depressed as a result of the condition? Is he experiencing pain? These types of considerations do sometimes appear in the purposive conception, but in a distorted, Procrustean way, as questions concerning "mental health" or "adjustment."

To illustrate this point, consider how the different approaches would deal with a difficult case of demarcation like sex-reassignment surgery. The purposive approach would need to discover whether the surgery represented the treatment of a genuine disease. In this context, the neologism "gender dysphoria" has been introduced, and psychiatrists continue to battle over its propriety and etiology. With a functional approach the questions considered in reaching a funding decision on a macro level (by bureaucrats) and in implementing the decision at the micro level (by physicians) are more straight-forward. How seriously has the applicant's life been affected? How likely is it that he/she will improve with the treatment? Is the cost justified by these bene-fits? Admittedly, similar questions might be asked by psychiatrists in the gender dysphoria debate. We suggest, however, that such questions are both clearer and more realistic when not filtered through the prism of a definition of disease.

The second contrast between the purposive and the functional approach is evident when deciding about the funding of discrete services. Whereas with the purposive approach one asks whether some service represents health care, with the functional approach one would ask if the service or procedure is good, worth-while, and desired.

Consider fertility interventions. For the vast majority of women, tubal liga-tion per se has almost no discrete med-ical justification (although it certainly will "cure" the "disorder" of fecundity). On these grounds, Kass (1975) has suggested that tubal ligation or vasectomy not be included within the medical orbit. But clearly, tubal ligation is a much-desired intervention; it has recently become the most popular form of female contracep-tion in Canada. And clearly, medical expertise is necessary to provide liga-tions. Also, from the economic point of view of the insurance plan, sterilization is one of the most efficient interventions available, obviating both medical costs or parturition and costs of care of the (for-ever-to-remain) unborn. Whereas the purposive conception forces government health care officials to conceptualize health matters in futile and disingenu-ous ways, the functional conception allows one to examine the real underly-

ing concerns. Does a requested procedure — for example, tubal ligation — repre-sent a treatment whose cost is rationally proportionate to the need it serves?

When the issue is phrased in this way, we are required to confront ques-tions which are never raised by the pur-posive approach. For example: Does the procedure in question address a human want or need, or perhaps something people *ought* to want or need? As difficult as these questions are, they seem to us to be the right ones to address. Among their advantages is the fact that their solution demands of us that we understand and respect the patient's perceptions of health care.

A recent study (Freedman 1983) yielded some suggestive data on this very point. The study included inter-views of Canadian women applying for microsurgical attempts at reversing a prior ligation (tubal reanatomosis). During the interviews, the women were asked "Do you see the reversal of the sterilization as a health procedure (like an appendectomy) or as a social proce-dure requiring medical assistance (like cosmetic surgery)?" Most of these women, both in questionnaires and dur-ing the subsequent interviews, classified the procedure they requested as med-ical, but the interview responses of some of the women revealed ambivalence stemming from a variety of considera-tions. The following representative statements are worthy of careful consid-eration as they encapsulate a lay response to the issue of demarcation: "I think for my mental and emotional well-being it is necessary. It is not like cos-metic surgery, like something I could do. It is something that is inside of me. I never thought I'd feel as strongly about [it]." "No [it's not a social procedure] ... I don't feel that having a tubal done is the same thing as having a reversal done. I'm having it [the reversal] done so that we can have children. ... So I really don't see it as being something that you do just to fit in. It's hard to explain but that's the way I feel about it."

How did these laypeople go about resolving this critical question of demarcation? What themes emerge from their responses? Hints are found of a variety of approaches, including the "internal/external" approach. However, their major point of consensus was the belief that because the procedure was so important to them personally, and because a doctor was needed to perform it, the procedure *must* be medical.

The population from which these responses were drawn would be expected to provide tendentious replies. It is in these women's interest to argue that the procedure they are requesting is medical in nature, and hence reimbursable. However, this fact only sharpens the point, because we would expect that they would be choosing the most persuasive demarcation principle available to support their claim.

The third divergence between the two approaches concerns the relationship between the health care system (and its public funding agent) and other elements of society. The purposive approach makes of the health care system a hermetically sealed enterprise, self-directed in terms of its original purpose and resistant to other legitimate social concerns and institutionalized values. On the other hand, with the functional approach, other social interests and resources are taken into account in deciding whether to supply a particular benefit when its request is justified in terms of health.

A functionalist perspective also allows one to consider whether the health care system is the best institution to respond to demands for particular needs. Needs (or wants) and the associated goods and services that have traditionally been seen as medical in nature may be better served by some other social institution. Alcoholism, obesity, and other diseases of lifestyle are notoriously resistant to treatment by the medical model. For the purposive approach, however, provided that

these conditions are diseases and that a physician is prepared to "treat" them, such treatments would be insured. The fact that other social institutions could better deal with these conditions is irrelevant from a purposive perspective. With a functional approach one questions whether we might not be better served by "divestiture" of these conditions from medicine, at least at this point in time. Conversely, the health care system may be better suited to providing some needs which traditionally have been served outside the medical model. One such possibility might be the care of the families of dying patients by physicians, nurses, or medical social workers, a role traditionally relegated to pastors and family support systems. The funding of such a service should not wait upon the discovery of a new "disease" ("impending grief syndrome"), but should proceed immediately upon the recognition that these forms of care are valid, useful, and best accomplished within the institutions of the health care system.

Questions for the Functional Approach

It might seem that the functional approach is necessarily heir to all of the criticisms presented above concerning the WHO definition of health. Under a functional approach, as under the WHO definition, the full range of human suffering and discontent become potential targets of a government-supported health care system. In fact, some might even argue that the functional approach is even more latitudinous than WHO, although it is hard to imagine what has been left out once "a complete state of physical, mental and social well-being" has been included.

This criticism, however, dissolves in the face of a critical distinction. The problem with the WHO definition, which is that it fails to exclude anything from coverage, arises in the context of a purposive system. In contrast, with a functional approach to health care funding, demarcation does not *end* with the recognition of a need or demand for services, but rather only *begins* at this point. It must then be determined whether the health care system, with its particular expertise and modalities of intervention, may redress that need efficiently; whether another social program or practice would better serve; or whether the need is so difficult to satisfy or so at odds with other values that it should not be served at all.

The whole point of the functional approach is the recognition that decisions regarding coverage involve more than semantics. In a purposive approach, once we know that a procedure serves health, we have an argument (which, to be sure, might need to be tempered by political or economic realities) that it should be funded. In a functional approach, when we know that a procedure satisfies a demand, we simply know that it is *potentially* fundable — not that it should be funded, let alone that it should be funded by the health care system.

A further point worth noting is that since functionalism contains no single decision rule for demarcation, it must address new problems which do not trouble a purposive system. However, the fact that a theory raises new questions does not necessarily count as a strike against it, provided that the questions are ones which are worth confronting. In fact, a theory might be deficient precisely because it fails to raise questions which should be answered, as at times the purposive approach slurs over the complications faced by the functional approach. In general the new problems which the functional approach must address are actually complications which arise due to the fact that patient choice is allowed, and that services traditionally considered nonmedical may be included within the boundaries of health care; therefore, a greater range of alternatives must be considered. For example, a possible negative consequence of allowing patient choice is that the costs involved might be greater. This criticism, however, also applies to the purposive approach, as the following examples will serve to illustrate.

Under the Ontario Health Insurance Plan postmastectomy breast reconstruction surgery is a covered service. This type of procedure fits comfortably within the naïve notion of health services, since it involves a direct "internal" procedure on a patient's behalf. On the other hand, prosthetic devices, being "external," have not been a covered benefit for adults and have represented a repeated source of political contention. A system which proceeds under the strong purposive principle of demarcation does not recognize the need to fund environmental adjustments, since these would fall under the rubric of social welfare rather than health care. Ontario, therefore, has long refused to cover the costs of breast prostheses and surgical brassieres for victims of breast cancer, while still funding surgical breast reconstruction for those interested in pursuing that course.

A complicated situation arose in Ontario when a woman eligible for a breast reconstruction procedure offered to exchange this service for a Tucker valve set (a prosthetic device needed for "normal" speech after she had undergone a tracheotomy). The trade would have been cost-effective for the Ministry of Health, and might have saved $1000 or more. The insurance plan declined the offer as there was no apt bureaucratic means of accepting it, given that the health insurance plan funds "services" and not "goods" (*London Free Press* 1982).

Another Ontario woman suffering from a lung condition lived at home, using a mobile oxygen cart. Eventually her monthly oxygen bills — which the public health insurance program would not cover — rose to over $700. At this point, entering the hospital became, for her, the only practical economic move, because then the insurance plan would supply her with oxygen gratis. The average cost of inpatient hospital care was estimated at approximately ten times the cost of the oxygen alone (*London Free Press* 1984). This situation similarly indicates the unreasoning prejudice a purposive system may have against environmental adjustment.

A functional approach would deal with such situations differently since patient choice would be independently relevant (if not necessarily decisive) in determining fundability. The implications of this are obviously quite serious, particularly as patients persist in expressing individual preferences on this issue, a fact which must be taken seriously by a system concerned with lay input. Honoring the choice of patients will at times be far more expensive than acceding to the choice dictated by a purposive demarcation rule. Patient autonomy in relation to funding decisions has not been an issue; but, without presuming any particular resolution, we suggest that it should be.

A functional conception would need to reexamine funding of the diverse forms of health care practice. In Ontario's quasi-purposive system, all reimbursements flow directly to, or indirectly from, physicians. Doctors may perform a service directly, or engage another professional (e.g., psychologist, physiotherapist) on a salaried basis to work under their direction, with the physician billing the government insurance program. Since physicians are certified specialists in "health," this arrangement is acceptable (although certainly not inevitable) under a purposive system. Similarly, although a physician may bill for consultation with a patient, parent, or other physician, he or she may not bill for consultation with nonphysician providers of health care. If a child is experiencing behavioral problems in school which have concerned the school psychologist, the physician may charge the government insurance plan for consultation with the parents, who may serve as middlemen between the school psychologist and the physician; but if the physician wishes to discuss the matter with the psychologist directly, he must do so on his own account. A functional system would necessarily call such arrangements into question.

As a result, in implementing a functional approach, a comprehensive government health plan would face bureaucratic dislocation. How serious would this be? To this, three points can be made: some dislocation has already occurred; some dislocation is good; and remaining dislocations need not all be faced at once.

Some dislocation has already occurred In Ontario, a system of psychiatric hospitals is run by the Ministry of Health. A system of facilities for the developmentally disabled is run by the Ministry of Community and Social Services (COMSOC). This kind of division would be preserved if a consistently functional approach were adopted. The facilities for the developmentally handicapped require a high level of expertise in development and programming, but the specific forms required — training of various sorts, behavioral techniques, and custodial care — are not specifically medical or nursing in nature (although both of these disciplines perform an important ancillary function). Indeed, because developmental handicap constitutes an "illness" under almost any definition, the division that currently exists between psychiatric and COMSOC facilities is inexplicable under a purposive conception.

Some dislocation is good Many of the decisions noted above (e.g., concerning prostheses and oxygen) would be inappropriate given a functionalist perspective. Their reversal involves dislocation in itself; but in the cases noted, that seems to be all to the good. Also, some bureaucratic awkwardness, intrinsic to a purposive system, would be resolved under a functional approach. While a physician may recover from the Ontario Health Insurance Plan on behalf of the examination of a patient carried out for investigation, confirmation, or documentation of an alleged sexual assault, a portion of its outlays on this behalf are then recovered from the Ministries of the Attorney General and the Solicitor General. Similar cumbersome paper shuffling may be involved in other instances which require medical expertise, albeit outside of medical treatment (e.g., in assessments for insurance or for the purpose of establishing workmen's compensation). It would seem that the only reason the money needs to be shuffled at present is to keep the accounts clear on behalf of a system that is purposively designed to fund health care.

Not all dislocations need be funded at once The saving grace of the functional approach is that it may, consistent with its own logic, be activated in an incre- mentalist fashion. The facts of bureaucratic life are, as are the facts of economic, political and medical life, all to be included within the calculation that should precede a decision on inclusion of a service within coverage.

In general, then, new questions of the division between medical and social services and of the cost-effectiveness of different modes of health care would directly arise under a functional system. Quantitative concerns would also need to be directly confronted: How serious is the need or desire? What value should be assigned to the honoring of the preferences of the patient? These questions need not be raised at all in a purposive system, which deals instead with questions concerning the nuances of the definitions of "health" and "health care." We will leave to others the task of parsing the seriousness of these questions. In choosing between these two approaches, however, we ought to consider which kinds of questions we want to contemplate, as well as which results we wish to achieve.

Notes

1. *Criminal Code of Canada*, R.S.C. 1970, c. C-34, §251. [This section of the *Criminal Code* was struck down in 1988 by the Supreme Court in *Morgentaler.* See *supra*, chapter 13. Ed.]

2. "... functional analysis seeks to understand a behavior pattern or a sociocultural institution by determining the role it plays in keeping the given system in proper working order or maintaining it as a going concern" (Hempel 1985). For a general discussion of the functional approach see the chapter "The Logic of Functional Analysis," in *Aspects of Scientific Explanation* (New York: The Free Press, 1985), 297–330.

References

Boorse, C. 1975. "On the Distinction Between Disease and Illness." *Philosophy and Public Affairs* 5 (Fall): 49–68.

Callahan, D. 1973. "The WHO Definition of 'Health.'" *The Hastings Center Studies* 1: 77–87.

Campbell, E. J. M., J. G. Scadding, and R. S. Roberts. 1979. "The Concept of Disease." *British Medical Journal* 2 (September): 757–62.

Freedman, B. 1983–85. "Study of Ethical Issues in Infertility" (unpublished material).

1985. "Ethical Issues in Clinical Obstetrics and Gynecology." *Current Problems in Obstetrics, Gynecology and Fertility* 7 (March): 1–47.

Hempel, C. G. 1985. *Aspects of Scientific Explanation.* New York: The Free Press.

Kass, L. R. 1975. "Regarding the End of Medicine and the Pursuit of Health." *The Public Interest* 40 (Summer): 11–42.

London Free Press. 1982. "OHIP won't pay for vocal device it calls luxury." 5 June: 2.

1984. "Woman needing pure oxygen may be forced into hospital." 3 August: 12.

Ontario Health Insurance Plan. 1983. *Schedule of Benefits: Physician Services*. 1 January. Ministry of Health of the Province of Ontario.

Surrogate Parenting News. 1983. "Insurance Coverage of In Vitro." 1 (October/November): 71–72.

Szasz, T. 1961. *The Myth of Mental Illness*. New York: Dell Publishing Co.

Taylor, F. K. 1971. "A Logical Analysis of the Medico-Psychological Concepts of Disease." *Psychological Medicine* 1: 356–64.

Turkel, Sherry. 1984. *The Second Self.* New York: Simon and Schuster.

Wasserman, J. 1983. "How DRGs Work." *The Hastings Center Report* 13 (October): 24.

World Health Organization. 1976. "Constitution of the World Health Organization." In *World Health Organization: Basic Documents*, ed. 26. Geneva: WHO.

Further Readings

Bell, Nora K. "The Scarcity of Medical Resources: Are There Rights to Health Care?" *J Med Philos* 4:2 (1979): 158–169.

Brock, D.W. "Children's Rights to Health Care," *J Med Philos* 26:2 (2001): 163–177.

Canadian Medical Association, *A Prescription for Sustainability*, submission of the CMA to the Romanow Commission, June 6, 2002. **http://www.cma.ca/cma/staticContent/ HTML/N0/l2/advocacy/news/2002/prescription_for_sustainability_eng.PDF**

Daniels, Norman. *Just Health Care*. Cambridge and London: Cambridge Univ. Press, 1985.

Deber, R.B. "Canadian Medicare: Can It Work in the United States? Will It Survive in Canada?" *Am J Law & Med* 19 (1993): 75–93.

Engelhardt, H.T., Jr. *The Foundations of Bioethics*. Chapter 8, "Rights to Health Care." New York and Oxford: Oxford Univ. Press, 1985.

Haft, H. "Is Health Care a Right or a Privilege?" *Physician Exec* 29:1 (Jan.–Feb. 2003): 26–29.

Hall, Mr. Justice Emmett. *Report of the Royal Commission on Health Services*. Ottawa: Queen's Printer, 1964.

Iglehart, J.K. "The United States looks at Canadian Health Care." *N Engl J Med* 321 (1989): 1767–1772.

Ingelfinger, Franz. "Haves and Have-Nots in the World of Disease." *N Engl J Med* 287 (Dec. 7, 1972): 1198–1199.

International Planned Parenthood, *Right to Health Care Charter*. **http://mirror. ippf.org/charter/guidelines/health.htm**

Kluge, E.-H. "Health Care as a Right: A Brief Look at the Canadian Health Care System." *Changing Health Care Systems from Ethical, Economic and Cross-Cultural Perspectives*. Ed. E.H. Loewy. New York: Kluwer Academic, 2001.

McKeown, Thomas, and C.R. Lowe. *An Introduction to Social Medicine*. 2nd ed. Oxford: Blackwell, 1974.

Miller, W.L., Å.B. Grødeland, and T.Y. Koshechkina. "If You Pay, We'll Operate Immediately." *J Med Ethics* 26:5 (2000): 305–311.

Moore, D.B. "Health Care as a Right." *Adv Nurse Pract* 8:11 (Nov. 2000): 104.

Royal Commission on the Future of Health Care (Romanow Commission). *Building on Values: The Future of Health Care in Canada*. Ottawa: 2002.

Sommers, B. "Provision of Health Care: How Much, if Any, Are We Entitled To?" *Princet J Bioeth* 3:1 (Spring 2000): 59–69.

Veatch, Robert. "Just Social Institutions and the Right to Health Care." *J Med Philos* 4:2 (1979).

CHAPTER 4
ALLOCATION OF RESOURCES

Introduction (a)

Macro-allocation

No matter how technologically advanced a society may be, the resources that are at its disposal are finite. This means that sooner or later, every society is faced with the problem of how to divide its resources among the services that its citizens expect as a matter of social entitlement. Health care is only one of these services. Education, transportation and defence are others. All have to be funded from the same limited resource pool. Consequently, sooner or later hard decisions have to be made: What proportion of the available resources should be assigned to health care? To education? To transportation? Policy decision-makers have to wrestle with these questions on a constant basis. These are questions of *macro-allocation*.

However, the issue of macro-allocation has another dimension: Once a certain quantity of social resources has been assigned to health care, how should these resources be allocated within the health care sector itself? How much should be apportioned to acute care? To continuing care? To preventive medicine? These are also macro-allocation questions.

As though these questions were not difficult enough, there are still other complicating issues. For instance, the average age of our population is rising. However, elderly people tend to consume more health care resources than younger persons and have conditions that are only infrequently encountered in young people. How much of the resources should be set aside specifically for seniors and for age-related diseases? Then there is the cost factor associated with the increasing technological sophistication of medicine and of health care delivery. Medical diagnostic tools and procedures like computer assisted tomography (CAT-scans), magnetic resonance imaging (MRIs), positron emission tomography (PET-scans), amniocentesis, and even something as simple as phenylketonuria (PKU) testing have improved the ability of physicians to diagnose the health needs of their patients — but they also involve tremendous capital and operating costs. Furthermore, in many cases the hidden costs that are associated with these modalities — for example, the downstream costs of saving severely disabled and premature newborn children or of saving elderly people who, in previous decades and with less sophisticated interventions, would have died — are tremendous. In other words, saving people's lives is very expensive in terms of aggregate social and health care expenditures.

Health care policy-makers, administrators and health care planners deal with budgets. They continually face the fact that no matter how beneficial a particular health care service may be, it has to be paid for, and it has downstream costs associated with it. Most health care consumers do not think in these terms. They tend to look at health care only from the perspective of people who want to benefit from health care and who claim such care as a matter of right. This is especially true in Canada, given the *Canada Health Act*. But are these claims legitimate? Health care administrators cannot lose sight of these questions because their job is to optimize the use of the available resources. By definition, they have to take a global (and utilitarian) perspective.

There have been various attempts to deal with the problem. Some have suggested that cost/benefit analysis provides the answer;[1] others have focused on cost/effectiveness coefficients;[2] still others have claimed that the differentials in the quality-adjusted-life-years (QALYs) that are gained by different types of interventions provide a solution; and so on. However, all these approaches are economically driven. A few years ago, Oregon tried to depart from this approach. Acknowledging that it is society itself that ultimately pays for health services, it tried to provide a role for social values and preferences when formulating macro-allocation policies.

The readings in the first part of this chapter deal exclusively with macro-allocation issues. The article by Robert Nelson and Theresa Drought is a discussion of the so-called Oregon Experiment and its attempt to solve the problem of health care rationing. (As an aside, it should be noted that for political reasons that are deeply rooted in U.S. society, the Oregon project has essentially been abandoned.) At first glance, the Oregon Experiment does not seem to have much relevance for Canada since it was a U.S. initiative. However, the Experiment raises a very important question: What sort of role — if any — should social values play in making macro-allocation decisions? This question has relevance even in the Canadian setting. Thus, one might fruitfully ask whether the recent Romanow Report (excerpts from which are included in Chapter 3) provides any mechanism that is responsive to the social-values issue, and how Canadian governments will go about reflecting social values as they proceed to restructure Canadian health care.

The second article in this section picks up on an issue of increasing importance in contemporary society: health care resource consumption by the elderly. As the demographic balance shifts towards an older population, the elderly, if they are treated like any other age group, will consume a disproportionately large share of limited health care resources. Is this ethically appropriate? Williams discusses this question in the context of the British National Health Service (NHS), which functions much like the provincial ministries of health in Canada. Among other things, he proposes what has been called the "fair innings argument" — the argument that the elderly have already had the opportunity to benefit from health care, and that it would be unfair to provide them with what in the end would only be minimal benefits at the expense of younger people who have "not yet lived." The fair-innings argument has provoked a variety of responses. Is Williams correct? And if he is correct, does this mean that the young should have priority over the aged? What about extremely premature newborns? Neonatal Intensive Care Units (NICUs) save the lives of many of these babies. Often the babies whose lives are saved are severely disabled. This entails tremendous expenditures not only for their families but also for society, which has to provide specialized health care, specialized schooling and other additional services as these infants grow up and mature. Some have questioned whether, in light of an overall scarcity of health care resources, it is ethically appropriate to save the lives of these individuals whose existence not only constitutes a drain on scarce resources but whose quality of life is something that most of us find scarcely acceptable in human terms.[3] How does Williams' analysis fare in this regard? If not, what changes would have to be made?

Notes

1. David Feeny, Gordon Guyatt and Peter Tugwell, eds., *Health Care Technology: Effectiveness, Efficiency and Public Policy* (Montreal: Institute for Research on Public Policy, 1986).

2. Eike-Henner W. Kluge, "Competition and Function: The Canada/US Free Trade Agreement and the Philosophy of Health Care," *Business and Professional Ethics Journal* 10:3 (Fall 1991): 29–52.

3. Helga Kuhse and Peter Singer, *Should the Baby Live? The Problem of Handicapped Infants* (New York and Melbourne: Oxford University Press, 1985).

Justice and the Moral Acceptability of Rationing Medical Care: The Oregon Experiment

Robert M. Nelson and Theresa Drought

In examining the Oregon plan, we will not question the assumption that society has an obligation to provide a "basic level" (Todd, 1989) or "decent minimum" (Buchanan, 1984) of medical care benefits, for such an obligation has achieved a certain level of consensus within our public debate. Rather, the issue is to determine of what this decent minimum consists.

It is unlikely that an agreed specification of a basic level of medical care will result from any particular theory of justice (Buchanan, 1984). Furthermore, the prevalent theories of justice fail to provide a firm basis for a guaranteed right to a decent minimum of medical care regardless of whether we could agree on the content of that right (Buchanan, 1984; Daniels, 1985). Whether the provision of

"Justice and the moral acceptability of rationing medical care: the Oregon experiment," by Robert M. Nelson & Theresa Drought, *The Journal of Medicine and Philosophy*, vol. 17, no. 1 (1992), pp. 97–117. Copyright © The Journal of Medicine and Philosophy Inc. Reprinted by permission.

medical care is an entitlement based on a claim against communal property (Engelhardt, 1986, pp. 360–365) or an enforceable duty of charity (Buchanan, 1984, pp. 66–72) appears to be of little practical significance in establishing a "basic" or "decent" level of benefits.

The Oregon plan assumes that the right to basic medical care is not an entitlement to a certain fixed level of benefits regardless of cost, for the communal resources that are committed to providing medical care may indeed be limited. A person's inability to obtain medical care because of a limit on available communal resources may be unfortunate, but not unfair (Engelhardt, 1986). In addition to whether available resources have been fairly distributed, the moral acceptability of any rationing scheme depends upon whether the resource scarcity is justified, that is, has an appropriate amount of resources been committed? An unwillingness to increase our contribution to communal resources in order to provide a certain "basic" level of medical care to those less fortunate may reflect a failure to act on a duty of charity (Buchanan, 1984).

The Problem of Cost-Sharing and Limited Financial Resources

The driving force for the Oregon legislation is clearly economic. The Oregon plan is predicated on a negative assessment of the ability of the state government to pay for all of the welfare programs, both social and medical, currently under its jurisdiction. The state's ability to pay for the non-federal share of the escalating cost of medical care provided through Medicaid is increasingly limited given decreasing tax revenues and a reluctance to increase taxes in the face of budget deficits.[1] Without an increase in tax revenue or a decrease in other social welfare programs, the state simply cannot afford

to provide all necessary medical care[2] to residents who are otherwise uninsured through employment or other mandated state and federal programs.

Given this limit on available resources, the government is faced with one of four choices for balancing the health care budget: (1) maintain (or decrease) the current level of spending and refuse to provide any medical care for a percentage of residents living below the federal poverty level (FPL); (2) maintain (or decrease) the current level of spending and refuse to provide certain forms of medical care for all residents living below the FPL; (3) maintain (or decrease) the current level of spending and cut reimbursement rates to providers in order to extend access to necessary medical care for most, it not all, residents living below the FPL;[3] and (4) increase the current level of spending in order to provide most, if not all, necessary medical care for all residents living below the FPL.

In order to control spending prior to the 1989 Basic Health Services Act, the Oregon legislature decreased eligibility requirements (first option) and cut reimbursement rates (third option) — a standard method of cost control for public and private agencies nationally. Limiting access through decreased eligibility resulted in a subsequent increase in the number of uninsured individuals seeking medical care.[4] The increase in uncompensated care gave rise to mounting operating losses suffered by providers and promoted cost-shifting to the private sector. At the same time, private insurers were taking steps to protect themselves from cost-shifting and were attempting to maintain financial solvency through the increasing use of co-payments, deductibles and premium increases. In fact, the support that the business community has given the Oregon Basic Health Services Act is based on the conviction that private insurance premiums would level off due to the increased coverage ending cost-shifting (Lund, 1990). ...[5]

Senate Bill 27, which is the centerpiece of the 1989 Oregon legislation, extends state provision of medical assistance to all eligible individuals whose family income is below the federal poverty level.[6] Any eligibility exclusions would be designed simply to eliminate duplicate coverage. The companion bill, SB 935, and the recently passed SB 1076, establish an employer mandate to provide "substantially similar" coverage for currently uninsured part- and full-time employees through the use of an employer payroll tax and tax credits. These two bills require full participation in providing minimum employee coverage by 1994. Finally, Senate Bill 534 creates a "high-risk" pool for the provision of medical insurance to individuals who have either been turned down for private insurance or who have one of a number of specified medical conditions. Taken together, the Oregon Basic Health Services Act would provide universal access to a basic minimum of medical services for all Oregon residents. The state would accept responsibility for all residents with incomes below the FPL; the business community would accept responsibility for all residents with incomes above the FPL and thus, presumably, employed.

Expanding access and increasing reimbursement can only lead to escalating medical care costs in the absence of restrictions on services to be provided. Accordingly, the mechanism proposed by SB 27 for holding down government spending on health care is the explicit rationing of medical procedures through the development of a "priority list." Once the priority list is generated, the legislature may decide to increase available revenue through taxes or by shifting resources from other programs in order to fund a certain level of medical care deemed "basic" (fourth option). Alternatively, the legislature may decide

to decrease or maintain current levels of spending through restricting funded services according to the priority list (second option).[7]

The argument in support of this new approach is that instead of rationing health care based on people's ability to pay, the legislature will be rationing medical care based on the cost and effectiveness of the intervention. Supporters of the Oregon Basic Health Services Act believe that this rationing scheme is a fairer and more just approach to distributing medical care than the system currently employed (Kitzhaber, 1989).

The unusual feature of the Oregon legislation is the manner in which the basic level of medical care would vary according to the legislative commitment of the state's financial resources. Senate Bill 27 established the Health Services Commission and charged it with the task of developing a "list of health services ranked by priority, from the most important to the least important, representing the comparative benefits of each service to the entire population to be served" (SB 27, p. 2). Once this list is compiled, an independent actuary will determine the rates necessary to cover the costs of the services. The Oregon Legislature would then commit a certain level of funds, whereupon the Adult and Family Services Division would contract with health care providers to provide the covered services, reimbursing at cost to the provider.[8] As a result, the practical definition of "adequate care"[9] is simply what the legislature (and, by extension, the residents of Oregon) is willing to pay for in relation to other competing social welfare programs and the overall economic burden of taxation (Kitzhaber, 1989, p. 11). As a result, the basic level of medical care "floats" according to the available economic resources.[10]

The Oregon proposal explicitly endorses a three-tier approach to the delivery of medical care (Kitzhaber, 1989). The government would provide a basic minimum of medical care for those under the FPL; the business community would provide medical care for their employees at a level equal to or greater than the government sponsored tier, depending on such factors as collective bargaining and worker availability; finally, individuals would be free to use their available resources to purchase medical care on the open market (Thurow, 1985).

The extent to which controlling the escalating costs of medical care requires withholding necessary interventions from patients, that is, rationing, is a matter of much controversy. The dividing issue appears to be whether the current level of expenditure in the United States for medical care is excessive, or not; for without some mechanism for the control of spending, increasing access to medical care will simply increase costs as well. Suggested mechanisms of cost control range from increased consumer awareness and managed care plans (Enthoven and Kronick, 1989), through malpractice reform and streamlined administrative costs (American Medical Association, 1989), to a single payor plan and global budgeting (Himmelstein and Woolhandler *et al.*, 1989).

None of these proposals discuss whether access to necessary medical care will be restricted for certain populations. One proposal explicitly maintains that everyone will have access to all necessary medical care (Himmelstein and Woolhandler *et al.*, 1989).[11] The starting point for these proposals is that the proper criteria for the distribution of medical care is need (Todd, 1989, p. 46), as opposed to resource limitation or ability to pay. ...

Substantial differences arise, however, as to whether the level of medical care that all persons will have access to is necessarily uniform (Himmelstein and Woolhandler, 1989)[12] or non-uniform; and, if non-uniform, whether the basic level of medical care is set independent of economic constraints (American Medical

Association, 1990; Enthoven and Kronick, 1989; Todd, 1989), or "floats" according to the level of available resources (Kitzhaber, 1990). Any policy that advocates universal access to non-uniform levels of medical care (that is, a two or more tier system) involves rationing to the extent that the lowest level of available benefits excludes some medically necessary interventions, though this observation is often obscured by a veil of political rhetoric. Alternately, if all medically necessary interventions are included within the minimum level of "basic" benefits (Todd, 1989; Himmelstein and Woolhandler, 1989), it is doubtful that such a program could successfully control medical expenditures.

Justice and the Withholding of Necessary Medical Care

The fundamental issue is whether it is inequitable or unjust that certain individuals will be denied access to some medically necessary procedures.

A discussion of equity or fairness in the delivery of health care generally starts with the observation that "illness [that is, medical need] is the proper ground for the receipt of medical care" (Outka, 1974, p. 590). The appropriate level of care to be provided to each individual is thus based on medical necessity. Given the distinction between the provision and distribution of medical care, one can ask whether there can be an equitable or just distribution of care in the event that not all needs can be met. The formal principle of justice simply requires that the reasons for discrimination be relevant to the resource being distributed (Beauchamp and Childress, 1989, p. 259). Consequently, under conditions of scarcity, a policy that excluded certain medically necessary procedures "would not be unjust or unequal if done by definable sorts of cases," for example, according to the "category of illness" (Ramsey, 1978, pp. 262–63).

If, however, we allow some individuals to purchase the otherwise excluded medically necessary procedure, it would appear that we are restricting access based on ability to pay rather than on the category of illness. This line of reasoning brings us back to the position that we either restrict an individual's ability to purchase medical care on the open market (a generally unacceptable option) or extend the available "basic" minimum of medical care to include all medically necessary procedures (and thus fail to address the issue of resource scarcity entirely). The Oregon plan allows for the possibility that individuals who earn less than the FPL will be denied access to medically necessary procedures, while other more fortunate residents will either have broader coverage or be able to purchase the otherwise restricted care.

According to the above view of justice, this possibility is simply unjust.

Yet are we (society) obligated to provide all necessary medical care to those who are unable to afford it? Is it a necessary requirement of justice that the basic level of benefits available to members of society include all medically necessary procedures, that is, are all members of society entitled to this level of medical care?

The stipulation that the basic level of available benefits should include all medically necessary services is problematic. Clearly this should not imply that the services to be provided are those which physicians in fact choose to provide, as the wasteful spending habits of physicians are felt to be part of the cause (not the solution) of our current health care crisis. A system based on the "rationalization of care" according to "reasonable expectations of the benefits involved" (Todd, 1989) would not necessarily provide all that is currently understood as medically necessary. The setting of limits around the performance of technically feasible medical interventions based on assessments of burden and benefit involves judgments of both economic and moral value. Practice guidelines may well improve the quality of delivered medical care and may reduce costs through the elimination of unnecessary tests and procedures. Guidelines, however, may not decrease the overall costs of medical care and would fail to address entirely the issue of the value of a particular intervention relative to other medical and social goods.

Egalitarian arguments in favor of a uniform level of medical care for all citizens would appear to curtail "individual rights to free association and the use of private property" (Engelhardt, 1986). There is no compelling reason why an individual should not be allowed to use his own private resources to purchase medical care above and beyond the established basic level of benefits.

Finally, the level of communal resources which are available for public welfare programs are limited by justified claims of private ownership that necessarily restrict the ability of government to tax individuals and businesses, and thus move property from private to public ownership. From this perspective, an individual's right to publicly sponsored medical care (as well as other welfare programs such as education and housing) is restricted by opposing rights of private property. It may be uncharitable, but not unjust, to fail to provide sufficient medical care to those less fortunate (Engelhardt, 1986, pp. 340–341). However, there is no *a priori* definition of communal property apart from those resources which are voluntarily (and charitably) committed to "communal undertakings" (Engelhardt, 1986, p. 133). Consequently, both the concept of adequate medical care and the level of communal resources to be committed to providing that care are matters of public discussion and negotiation (Engelhardt,

1986, p. 362) — a process (discussed below) which Oregon has indeed begun. There would thus appear to be no practical difference as to whether an entitlement to basic medical care is understood as a claim against communal property (Engelhardt, 1986, p. 361) or as an enforceable duty of charity (Buchanan, 1984, pp. 66–72). ...

The Physician's Obligation to the Patient

Senate Bill 27 requires a physician to inform a "patient of any service, treatment or test that is medically necessary but not covered ... if an ordinarily careful practitioner in the same or similar community would do so under the same or similar circumstances" (SB 27, Section 6, paragraph 7). Whereas ordinarily a physician would be liable for failing to provide a medically necessary service to a patient under his or her care, the Act provides immunity from "criminal prosecution, civil liability or professional disciplinary action" if the physician refuses to provide an unfunded service (SB 27, Section 10).

The requirement to inform a patient of medically necessary care that cannot be provided due to lack of funding maintains the role of the physician as "patient advocate," for it allows the patient the option of seeking the care in whatever way possible. Yet this advocacy role is purely as an advisor, for the physician is unable to act in a way consistent with the patient's need for medical care. The role of the physician as patient advocate is maintained at the expense of the physician's clinical autonomy. Yet the physician will also be under pressure to withhold marginally beneficial care that indeed would be covered under the Act in the interest of saving money. In the event of a budget deficit, Section 8 of SB 27 stipulates that the Oregon legislature should reduce medical care for those res-

idents under the FPL by eliminating services according to the priority list. If physicians are not prudent in the use of the state's fiscal resources, otherwise covered services could be eliminated in order to balance the budget.

The granting of immunity from criminal and civil liability is appropriate as physicians in Oregon would have no control over the resources necessary to provide the otherwise indicated medical care. Furthermore, the requirement to provide information to the patient upholds an equal standard of care as far as a physician's professional advice and personal involvement is concerned (Morreim, 1989). Finally, the granting of institutional civil and criminal immunity limits the obligations of health care providers to those established by contract (Morreim, 1989). The contract is by definition the basic minimum standard of medical care, for there is no standard apart from that established by the contract.

Whatever moral obligation a physician may feel towards providing medically necessary care to all patients will prevent an easy accommodation to a "business as usual" approach to the care of patients covered under the Act. The Oregon legislation reveals that under conditions of economic scarcity it is false to assume that physicians can maintain a pure patient advocacy role within the framework of external societal restrictions on resource use (Veatch, 1986; Morreim, 1988).

Establishing the Basic Level of Medical Care

Once having agreed that we may design a delivery system that provides more than one tier of medical care, the important issue remains, that is, at what level is the basic minimum of medical care to be established? Should the basic level of care include all medically necessary procedures? If not, how are we to determine which medically necessary procedures are to be included? As discussed above, the specification of the content of a general right to a basic level of medical care will be the result, not of the popular acceptance of a general theory of justice, but of a process of "open discussion and fair negotiation" (Engelhardt, 1986, p. 362) based on our own individual and communal moral values. The amount of resources to be committed to providing a given level of medical benefits is a "matter of collective choice" (Buchanan, 1984, p. 78) reflecting the complexity of our individual and communal "moral vision" (Engelhardt, 1986, p. 362); that is, both the resources available and the benefits provided are matters for public discussion.

The Oregon legislature, in passing the Basic Health Services Act, recognized that: (1) all residents should have access to a basic level of medical care; (2) available funds for providing medical care are limited; and thus (3) some otherwise medically necessary care may not be provided as part of this basic package. The Oregon Health Services Commission (HSC) was given the task of establishing a priority list which could be used to provide efficacious and cost effective medical care in a manner consistent with the expressed values of Oregon residents.

Open forums for public discussion of societal values related to health care have been held in Oregon since the early 1980s. The Oregon Health Decisions (OHD) program was formed in 1982 to look at issues posed by the increasing numbers of medically indigent Oregon residents following the economic recession at the start of the decade. Their mission was to increase public awareness and build consensus on bioethical issues, particularly: (1) what value is to be placed on more expensive curative medical care relative to the preventive services which are being increasingly curtailed by budget cutbacks; and (2) can the implicit rationing of medical care

through restricted access and decreased funding be made explicit and congruent with community values (Crawshaw *et al.*, 1985).

The OHD program was the seed for the 1989 Oregon Basic Health Services Act. Thousands of Oregon residents were involved in these discussions, and three "Citizens Health Care Parliaments" were held between 1984 and 1988 to develop recommendations based on a consensus of values expressed by the participants[13] (Crawshaw, 1986; Garland and Kitzhaber, 1988; Crawshaw *et al.*, 1990). The 1989 Act is intended to embody the recommendations put forth by these community conferences.

The Health Services Commission sought to develop a means of ranking medical services using ostensibly objective and quantifiable measures of quality of well-being, quality adjusted life-years (QALYs), actuarial costs, outcomes with and without treatment, and community values. A previous attempt at developing a priority list (Golenski and Blum, 1989) was discarded as vague and ill-defined, with too many medical procedures being given a high priority. The HSC developed a formula that compared various disease categories with and without treatment according to the quality and quantity of expected outcome. In addition, the formula included an estimate of the cost of specific treatments (Oregon Health Services Commission, 1990).

This formula has proven difficult to apply for a number of reasons. First, the list of "condition-treatment pairs"[14] is enormous; second, the data for many of the variables is either unreliable or simply unavailable; third, many important services, such as disease prevention and screening, are excluded; fourth, comorbidity is not addressed; and, fifth, the formula relies on the controversial concept of Quality Adjusted Life-Years (QALYs). Though the formula has not been discarded and continues to be modified in hopes of producing a list based on objective data, the Commission developed an alternative method whereby broader categories were defined under which the "condition-treatment pairs" may be ranked according to the formula (Oregon Health Services Commission, 1991).[15]

The use of QALYs in establishing allocation schemes for medical care is appealing for it combines the elements of cost, quality and benefit in a single scale that then allows for comparison among otherwise incommensurable treatments and health states (Menzel, 1990, pp. 79–80). However, questions have been raised as to whether one can meaningfully measure quality-of-life, and whether accurate data is currently available for determining the burden and benefit of most medical interventions (LaPuma and Lawlor, 1990). The Oregon HSC used provider panels to generate prognostic data concerning condition-treatment pairs — a method that can be criticized as simply relying on collective anecdotes. Additional criticisms have included: (1) the moral validity of comparing the quality of life with the risk of death (Carr-Hill, 1989); (2) the change in an individual's evaluation of risk over time (Rawles, 1989); (3) the use of community values as an indication of individual preference (Carr-Hill, 1989; LaPuma and Lawlor, 1990); and (4) the concern that utility and efficiency will take precedence over patient autonomy and welfare (LaPuma and Lawlor, 1990).

The Prior Consent of the Rationed

Apart from the practical concern that there is currently insufficient data to allow for the rational use of a QALY-based formula, the ethical criticisms raised may be adequately addressed provided that those affected by the rationing scheme have given their "prior consent" (Menzel, 1990, pp. 79–96). The moral force of this or any other rationing scheme

would thus be based, not on "aggregate welfare," but on respecting the autonomy and personal values of those who have designed and are affected by the policy (Menzel, 1990, pp. 10–19, 22–34).

An appeal to the "prior consent of a rational poor person" (Menzel, 1990, pp. 126–127) as a justification for rationing medical care fails to specify the mechanisms by which such consent would be obtained. Is a simple majority on a health care referendum sufficient, or would a more extensive consensus be required? Can we rely on an elected representative government to speak for the people, or on the deliberations of an appointed commission? Can a voucher system be designed by which the poor select their own mix of medical benefits up to a certain predetermined cost? Given that the level of communal resources available for medical care is also a matter for public discussion, what role do those funding the program, that is, residents with incomes above the FPL, have in consenting to the rationing scheme? Regardless of the mechanism, it is clear that prior consent, whether actual or presumed, "carries the burden of accurately discerning what people would in fact have agreed to" (Menzel, 1990, p. 34).

The Oregon attempt to establish a policy that would ration acute medical care presently fails to satisfy this moral requirement of "prior consent." Participation in the Oregon Health Decisions health care parliaments did not include adequate representation of minorities, the poor, and the medically indigent (Hasnain and Garland, 1990; Oregon Health Services Commission, 1990). The Quality of Well Being scale was developed through a telephone survey of only one thousand randomly selected residents, with no attempt to select adequate samples of individuals with different diseases and disabilities (Oregon Health Services Commission, 1990; Menzel, 1990, p. 84). It is unclear whether individuals were questioned about specific trade-offs between the potential risk of death versus the quality of life given treatment for various conditions. Further, there was no explicit link between initial questions of the value of various medical interventions and health states, and the subsequent use of those values by the Health Services Commission in determining allocations. The point is simple. Prior consent requires that the individuals whose medical care is being rationed should make the decisions over how to allocate the scarce resources.[16]

Concluding Remarks: The Moral Acceptability of Rationing

The reality of the Oregon plan, and of any program that excludes necessary medical treatments from the basic level of care, is that some patients will die for lack of more extensive insurance coverage. Whether this outcome is morally acceptable or not will depend on a number of factors, the primary one being what the basic level of coverage *in fact* includes. The death of an elderly nursing home patient who is denied dialysis; the death of a child with leukemia who is unable to obtain a bone marrow transplant; the death of a young mother who is unable to obtain appropriate obstetrical services; the death of several children for lack of necessary immunizations — all would be judged differently depending on our own

understanding of what a decent minimum of medical care ought to include. As long as this minimum excludes what would otherwise be medically necessary care, we need to abandon as myth the goal of providing medical care solely according to need.

In sum, the moral acceptability of any rationing scheme depends upon two related questions: (1) Is the resource scarcity justified, that is, has an appropriate amount of resources been committed? and (2) Have these resources been fairly distributed, that is, what is the minimum share that each individual will receive? The Oregon Basic Health Services Act of 1989 fails to give us any indication of the overall amount of available resources or the level of medical benefits that will be provided to residents with incomes below the Federal Poverty Level. As such, no judgment of moral acceptability can be made until the Oregon Legislature has established the level of funding that will be provided.

This is not to say that the Health Services Commission and the legislature of Oregon will necessarily fail to design a just rationing program even if such a program does not provide all medically necessary care. There can indeed be a just distribution of medical care that excludes certain medically necessary procedures, whether based on QALYs or any other value-based determination. However, such a system has as its moral justification the "prior consent" of the residents of Oregon and, in particular, of those residents most affected by the excluded medical care.

Notes

Supported in part by a National Research Service Award in Bioethics (RMN), National Center for Nursing Research, National Institutes of Health.

1. Oregon residents share with the rest of the country an unwillingness to increase taxes to pay for social programs, in spite of the fact that many people support an increase in government spending for health care (Blendon, 1988; Navarro, 1987). In the fall of 1990, Oregon residents approved Measure 5, which restricts the state's ability to increase revenue through the raising of property taxes.

2. The description of medical interventions as either necessary or unnecessary is ambiguous. On the one hand, it may imply real urgency, for example, that someone will die or suffer serious harm without the intervention. On the other hand, physicians use the term "necessary" to indicate what's ordinary and routine, so that "necessary" comes to mean standard interventions regardless of the urgency of need. As argued below, without a specification of the relative necessity of various medical interventions, it is impossible to judge the merits or demerits of any rationing scheme. The Oregon plan to prioritize medical care can be described as a ranking of medical interventions according to relative necessity. We choose to leave our use of the term "medically necessary" ambiguous (as does the "rationing" literature), for to remove all ambiguity would require an established set of rankings.

3. Cutting reimbursement rates, however, tends to decrease the number of providers willing to care for this population. The result is that access is actually decreased while services are only apparently maintained.

4. As of June 1989, Medicaid eligibility included families under 58% of the Federal Poverty Level (FPL), pregnant women or women with young children up to 100% FPL, medically needy, and aged, blind or disabled. This left some 140,000 Oregon residents uninsured, or 47% of the population living below the FPL (Zermer, 1989).

5. To affirm the value of universal access to medical care does not necessarily imply that a certain level of medical care benefits is a basic human right. Universal access may be proposed as a solution to the problem of uncompensated care and cost-shifting (Kitzhaber, 1989), rather than on the basis of an entitlement (Todd, 1989). Universal coverage may also be viewed as the only way to decrease the burden of administrative expenses and allow for an effective mechanism of global budgeting (Himmelstein and Woolhandler, 1989).

6. Eligibility will be extended to all residents whose income is below 100% of the Federal Poverty Level, including single adults and childless couples (who are excluded under current rules). Pregnant women and children under the age of six years will be covered up to 135% of the FPL, consistent with changes in federal Medicaid legislation effective April 1, 1990.

7. The fact that SB 27 does not stipulate a "basic" level of medical care independent of available funding has led to the concern that the level of funding provided may be so low as to exclude many otherwise "basic" procedures. If we could agree on a specification of what a "basic" level of medical care included, the available funding could be adjusted accordingly. The Health Services Commission struggled with the task of defining a minimum benefit level independent of the funding provided. The desire to define the basic minimum of medical care to be made available may arise out of a discomfort with the level being set purely on economic grounds, as well as in response to special interests who press for a definition that would include medical care directed at their own needs. The Commission was caught between two opposing problems. On the one hand, it is clear that a definition of basic minimum benefits potentially would undercut the intent of SB 27, given that Oregon residents to date have been unwilling to increase tax revenues to pay for medical care. On the other hand, if the level of funded benefits is so low as to be unacceptable, the state may fail to obtain the necessary federal waivers in order to allow the program to proceed, and may also lose the support of local citizen, labor and business groups. The success of SB 27 may then lie in having demonstrated that the "basic" level of medical care that society deems acceptable comes at a price which necessi-

tates the raising of additional tax revenue or the severe curtailing of other social welfare programs.

8. The latest version of the priority list defined 709 line items containing at least one condition/treatment pair, grouped under 17 categories of care ranked in order of importance. The Health Services Commission recommended a Standard Benefits Package to the Legislature, indicating that the first nine categories should be considered "essential services," the next four categories "very important," and the last four categories "valuable to certain individuals" (Oregon Health Services Commission, 1991). The Oregon Legislature has referred to line 585 as a "critical level" of funding. This would cover nearly all of the items under "essential" services, the majority of items under "very important" services, and little of the services deemed only "valuable to certain individuals" (Thome, 1991).

9. Kitzhaber's use of the term "adequate" to describe the level of medical care that the state chooses to provide appears to exclude the possibility that the state may choose to provide inadequate medical care. The moral acceptability of Oregon's rationing scheme not only rests on the method of distributing funded benefits, but also on the total level of benefits provided. Kitzhaber appears to exclude the possibility that the State of Oregon may fairly distribute an unacceptably low level of medical benefits.

10. The moral acceptability of the level of medical care provided may hinge on the reasons why the state's financial resources are limited. It is one thing to claim that the money just doesn't exist (that is, that further taxes would hurt the economy or that further expenditures are prohibited by law, as in a constitutional requirement for a balanced budget); another thing, to claim that the money exists but that taxes cannot be raised (for example, that increased taxes would be unpopular even if it wouldn't hurt the economy or break the law); and still another thing, to say that we are unwilling to reallocate from other areas such as education in order to increase health care spending.

11. It seems unlikely that all medically necessary services could be provided on an equal basis to the entire population simply on the savings achieved by a central administrative and financial control. Inevitably, the central budgeting committee would either need to establish explicit criteria for the rationing of medical care (as Oregon is attempting to do) or ration through planned scarcity and subsequent "queuing" (as in Canada).

12. The proposal by the Physicians for a National Health Program calls for a single comprehensive program that would provide equal access to all medically necessary services, that is, universal access to equal medical care. The authors appear a bit too sanguine about the possibility of a medical board capping expenditures through the determination of necessary versus unnecessary medical interventions. At the point that a necessary medical intervention must be eliminated in favor of balancing the budget, the restriction on the use of private financial resources and insurance in obtaining the benefit loses credibility. The point here is that their arguments in favor of universal access to equal medical care under a single national program are largely pragmatic, involving administrative savings, ease of application of benefits and the use of global budgeting. To the extent that an individual's liberty to purchase necessary though unfunded medical care through the use of personal resources is curtailed in the interest of an egalitarian system, such a program can be characterized as unjust (Engelhardt, 1986, p. 360).

13. While many residents were involved in these conferences, they were not truly representative of the overall population. In general, middle class, well-educated whites as well as health care professionals were over-represented, while minorities, the poor, and those with little education were under-represented. In particular, Medicaid recipients and the uninsured who will bear the burden of current rationing procedures were notable in their absence (Hasnain and Garland, 1990).

14. The formula is based on pairing ICD-9 diagnostic codes and the corresponding CPT procedural codes.

15. The line items based on condition-treatment pairs were ranked within the 17 categories according to the formula based on cost and QALYs. The categories were developed and ranked by the Health Services Commission taking into account the values and priorities expressed in the state-wide community meetings (Hasnain and Garland, 1990). The HSC then adjusted individual items in the overall priority list to more accurately reflect their collective judgments of the importance of the item in the overall ranking scheme (Thorne, 1991).

16. The Health Services Commission struggled with the definition of a basic level of medical care below which no resident of Oregon should fall. This task is outside of their mandate from the legislature and places the overall rationing scheme in jeopardy if the eventual level of resources committed to medical care falls below that necessary to fund the stipulated minimum level (see notes 7 and 8). Perhaps the Commission's desire to set a basic level of medical care is out of a recognition that they themselves should be willing to live under such a standard. If so, setting a decent minimum would serve as an affirmation of the moral principle of "prior consent." In addition, the desire to set a basic minimum level of medical care may acknowledge that the moral acceptability of any rationing scheme (and of the Commission's work) depends upon the balance between resources used and benefits provided.

References

American Medical Association: 1990, *Health Access America: The AMA Proposal to Improve Access to Affordable, Quality Health Care.* Chicago, Illinois.

Baker, T.: 1990, "Medicaid," personal communication, 18 September, Portland, OR.

Beauchamp, T. and Childress, J.: 2001, *Principles of Biomedical Ethics,* Fifth Edition, New York: Oxford University Press.

Blendon, R.J.: 1988, "What should be done about the uninsured poor?" *Journal of the American Medical Association* 260, 3176–3177.

Buchanan, A.: 1984, "The right to a decent minimum of health care," *Philosophy & Public Affairs* 13, 55–78.

Carr-Hill, R.: 1989, "Background material for the workshop on QALYS: Assumptions of the QALY procedure," *Social Science & Medicine* 29, 469–477.

Crawshaw, R., Carland, M., Hines, B., and Anderson, B.: 1990, "Developing principles for prudent health care allocation: The continuing Oregon experiment," *The Western Journal of Medicine* 152, 441–446.

Daniels, N.: 1985, "Fair equality of opportunity and decent minimums: A reply to Buchanan," *Philosophy & Public Affairs* 14, 106–110.

Daniels, N.: 1988, *Am I My Parents' Keeper?* New York: Oxford University Press.

Engelhardt, H.T., Jr.: 1986, *The Foundations of Bioethics,* New York: Oxford University Press.

Enthoven, A., and Kronick, R.: 1989, "A consumer-choice health plan for the 1990s: Universal health insurance in a system designed to promote quality and economy" (two parts), *The New England Journal of Medicine* 320, 29–37, 94–101.

Garland, M., and Kitzhaber, J.: 1988, *Principles for Health Care Resource Allocation*, Adopted by the 1988 Citizens Health Care Parliament. Portland, OR.

Hasnain, R., and Garland, M.: 1990, *Health Care in Common: Report of the Oregon Health Decisions Community Meetings Process*. Salem, OR: Oregon Health Decisions.

Himmelstein, D., Woolhandler, S., *et al.*: 1989, "A national health program for the United States: A physicians' proposal," *The New England Journal of Medicine* 320, 102–108.

LaPuma, J. and Lawlor, E.: 1990, "Quality-adjusted life-years: Ethical implications for physicians and policymakers," *Journal of the American Medical Association* 263, 2917–2921.

Menzel, P.: 1990, *Strong Medicine: The Ethical Rationing of Health Care*. New York: Oxford University Press.

Morreim, E.: 1989, "Stratified scarcity: Redefining the standard of care," *Law, Medicine & Health Care* 17, 356–367.

Outka, G.: 1974, "Social justice and equal access to health care," *The Journal of Religious Ethics* 2, 11–32, as reprinted in S.J. Reiser, A.J. Dyck, and W.J. Curran (eds.), *Ethics in Medicine*. Cambridge, MA: The MIT Press. pp. 584–593.

Ramsey, P.: 1978, *Ethics at the Edges of Life,* Yale University Press, New Haven.

Rawles, J.: 1989, "Castigating QALYs," *Journal of Medical Ethics* 15, 143–147.

Thurow, L.: 1985, "Medicine versus economics," *The New England Journal of Medicine* 313, 611–614.

Veatch, R.: 1986, "DRGs and the ethical allocation of resources," *Hastings Center Report* 16, 32–40.

Welch, H. and Larson, E.: 1988, "Dealing with limited resources: The Oregon decision to curtail funding for organ transplantation," *The New England Journal of Medicine* 319, 171–173.

Rationing Health Care by Age

Alan Williams

Introduction

As we grow older our recuperative powers diminish. Thus we accumulate a distressing collection of chronic incurable conditions. Some of these are no more than a minor nuisance, and we adapt as best we can; and when adaptation is not possible we learn to tolerate them. Some are more serious, involving severe disability and persistent pain, and may eventually become life threatening.

Alan Williams, "Rationing Health Care by Age," *British Medical Journal* 314 (Mar. 15, 1997) 820. Reprinted by permission of BMJ Publishing Group.

We are also at risk of various acute conditions (like influenza or pneumonia) which are more serious threats to the health of elderly people than to younger people. We also have more difficulty recovering from what younger people would regard as minor injuries (such as falls). When you add to all this the increased likelihood that illness (and other disruptions of our normal lifestyle) will leave us rather confused and in need of more rehabilitative and social support than a young person it is hardly surprising that NHS expenditure per person rises sharply after about age 65.

The Vain Pursuit of Immortality

People are also living longer, and people aged over 65 now form a much bigger proportion of the population than they used to. From the viewpoint of NHS expenditure this would not matter if the extra years of life were predominantly healthy years but it would if the extra years were ones of disability, pain, and increasing dependence on others.

The evidence on this is ambiguous. Many people remain fit and independent well into their 80s. Others enter their 60s already afflicted with the aftermath of stroke, heart disease, arthritis, or bronchitis. It is not clear whether things are getting worse at each year of age, or whether expectations are rising and people are now more likely to report disabilities once shrugged off as the inevitable consequence of getting old. That many of these conditions are incurable does not mean they are untreatable. Much can be done to reduce their adverse consequences, including many remedial activities which lie outside the NHS (such as home adaptations, domestic support, and special accommodation).

It is important to get away from the notion of "cure" as the criterion of benefit and adopt instead measures of effectiveness that turn on the impact of treatments on people's health related quality of life. Such an approach concentrates on the features that people themselves value, such as mobility, self care, being able to pursue usual activities (whatever they are), and being free of pain and discomfort and anxiety and depression.

Improving the quality of life of elderly people in these ways may not be very costly, but these unglamorous down to earth activities tend to lose out to high tech interventions which gain their emotional hold by claiming that life threatening conditions should always take priority. This vain pursuit of immortality is dangerous for elderly people: taken to its logical conclusion it implies that no one should be allowed to die until everything possible has been done. That means not simply that we shall all die in hospital but that we shall die in intensive care.

Reasonable Limits

This attempt to wring the last drop of medical benefit out of the system, no matter what the human and material costs, is not the hallmark of a humane society. In each of our lives there has to come a time when we accept the inevitability of death, and when we also accept that a reasonable limit has to be set on the demands we can properly make on our fellow citizens in order to keep us going a bit longer.

It would be better for that limit to be set, with fairly general consent, before we as individuals get into that potentially harrowing situation. When the time comes we shall probably each want an exception made in our case, because few of us are strong willed enough to act cheerfully in the general public interest when our own welfare is at stake. But if a limit is to be set, on what principles should it be determined? And what is their justification? And what role does age have?

In arguing for this article's proposition I have sought to make two contextual points clear: firstly, that ability to benefit should be measured in rather broader terms than cure or survival, and, secondly, that although chronological age is the best single predictor of increasing health problems, it is only a predictor, not a mechanistic determinant.

But age as an indicator of declining recuperative powers, of future health problems, of increasing need for health care, and of declining capacity to benefit from health care (because of shorter life expectancy) is only half the story. It addresses the issue of whether age is a good indicator of the extent to which people could benefit from health care but not in itself of whether they should be offered it. This more crucial step depends on what the objectives of the NHS are to be.

The NHS's Objectives

If we start with the proposition that the objective should be to improve as much as possible the health of the nation as a whole then the people who should get priority are those who will benefit most from the resources available. In some cases the old will benefit most, in others the young. But for treatments which yield benefits that last for the rest of a person's life (or for a long time) the young will generally benefit more, because the rest of a young person's life is usually longer than the rest of an old person's life. And even among old people themselves the life expectancy of a 70 year old is usually greater than that of an 80 year old. Where a treatment offers only modest benefits a person may have to live a long time to make treatment worthwhile — that is, to make the benefit to that person larger than the sacrifices of rival candidates who failed to get treated. So improving the health of the nation as a whole is likely, in some circumstances, to discriminate indirectly against older people.

Is this morally defensible? Well, if we behaved otherwise we would by implication be asserting that in order to provide small benefits for the elderly, young people should sacrifice large benefits. What makes old people more deserving of

health benefits than young people? One argument might be that all their lives they have been paying their taxes to finance the health care system (among other things), and just when they need health care most the government lets them down. But the government — that is, their fellow citizens — did not promise to do everything possible no matter what the costs.

The NHS is part of a social insurance system, not a savings club for each individual's health care expenditures. It is the lucky ones who do not get their money's worth out of the system, and the unlucky ones who need heavy NHS expenditures all their lives. The NHS is there to meet certain contingencies but not others. And many of the treatments which the NHS now offers to old people in certain contingencies were not even invented when they started contributing 40 or 50 years ago. So to argue, from a historical viewpoint, about an entitlement to get your money's worth seems inappropriate to any insurance scheme, and in particular to a social insurance scheme such as the NHS.

A different line of argument might be that as the number of years left becomes smaller and smaller, each is more precious. The implication of this argument is that elderly people value their small improvements more highly than young people do their much larger improvements. This raises a fundamental problem about whose values should count in a social insurance setting. Suppose that it were true that older people would spend relatively more on health care to get health improvements rather than other things, whereas younger people would spend relatively more on (say) education for their children and rather less on health benefits for themselves. Rational self interest drives individual citizens operating in private markets precisely in that direction.

But did we not take the NHS out of that context precisely because as citizens (rather than as consumers of health care) we were pursuing a rather different ideal

— namely, that health care should be provided according to people's needs, not according to what they were each willing and able to pay. A person's needs (constituting claims on social resources) have to be arbitrated by a third party, whose unenviable task it is to weigh different needs (and different people's needs) one against another. This is precisely what priority setting in health care is all about. So the values of the citizenry as a whole must override the values of a particular interest group within it.

A Fair Innings

So I can find no compelling argument to justify the view that the young should sacrifice large benefits so that the old can enjoy small ones. But I can find an argument which goes in the opposite direction. It is that one of the objectives of the health care system should be to reduce inequalities in people's lifetime experience of health. The popular folklore is rich in phrases indicating that we all have some vague notion of a "fair innings" in health terms. Put at its crudest, it reflects the biblical idea that the years of our life are three score and ten. Anyone who achieves or exceeds this is reckoned to have had a fair innings, whereas anyone who dies at an earlier age "was cut off in their prime" or "died tragically young." As has been observed, while it is always a misfortune to die if you wish to go on living, it is both a misfortune and a tragedy to die young. Why?

From my perspective (approaching the age of 70) I see clearly why it is a tragedy, because someone who dies young has been denied the opportunities that we older people have already had. If reducing inequalities in lifetime health is a worthy social objective, it will lead us to be willing to do more to enable young people to survive than we are willing to do to enable old people to survive.

But I do not think that the notion of a "fair innings" should be restricted to matters of survival and life expectancy.

Quality of life considerations concerning health may be just as important. Someone who has suffered a lifetime of pain and disability cannot be said to have had a fair innings even if she did live to be 80, and I would therefore extend the concept to embrace something more than just years of life. My preferred concept would be the number of quality adjusted life years a person had enjoyed. On the whole people's earlier years are healthy years, and their later years less healthy years, so this does not affect the general tenor of my argument. What it implies is that we need to consider, alongside age itself, the quality of a person's lifetime experience of health. The worse it has been, the more consideration they deserve, age for age.

Age Matters

So my overall conclusion is that age matters in two respects. Firstly, it affects people's capacity to benefit, and therefore places them at a general disadvantage if the objective is to maximise the benefits of health care. Secondly, the older you are the more likely you will have achieved what your fellow citizens would judge to have been a fair innings, and this will place old people at a disadvantage if the objective is to minimise the differences in lifetime experience of health. I would be the first to admit that I personally have had a fair innings and that it would not be equitable to deny a younger person large benefits in order to provide small ones for me. Indeed, I would go further: it would be equitable to provide small benefits for a young person even if by so doing I were denied large benefits, provided that the young person in question had a low probability of ever achieving a fair innings. Note that this argument does not mean that benefits to young people take absolute priority over benefits to old people. It simply means that we give rather more weight to them than to us.

Surveys of public opinion commonly find that most people, if pushed into a tight situation, would give priority to the young over the old when distributing a given amount of health care benefit. There is also little doubt that health care professionals share this general attitude. It does not, of course, stop them from being kind, considerate, and caring when old people need health care, but it manifests itself at the level of clinical policy-making, when different needs have to be prioritised. For the professionals what may be in their minds may be mostly old people's impaired capacity to benefit from health care. But I strongly suspect that some variant of the fair innings argument also underlies such views, and this is especially likely to be the case among the general public. When the views of older respondents in such surveys have been reported separately, they too give priority to the young over themselves.

So I am encouraged to hope that, in the interests of fairness between the generations, the members of my generation will exercise restraint in the demands we make on the health care system. We should not object to age being one of the criteria (though not the sole criterion) used in the prioritisation of health care, even though it will disadvantage us. The alternative is too outrageous to contemplate — namely, that we expect the young to make large sacrifices so that we can enjoy small benefits. That would not be fair.

Introduction (b)

Micro-allocation

The allocation of resources presents difficult problems when dealing with global budgets and groups of populations. The problems acquire a whole new dimension when one is face to face with individual persons and directly confronted with the consequences of one's decisions. The "phenomenon of the identified victim" — the reluctance to deny resources to persons with whom one is in direct contact — tends to assert itself.

An example may bring the issue into focus. Consider the following case: Monica Urgele is an elderly person occupying an acute-care hospital bed. Her condition does not warrant her being there. However, she has been there for some time, and she does not want to move to the extended-care facility that would be more appropriate for her needs. It has been known for some time that in many cases, to move patients like Monica against their will is to run the risk of shortening their life span considerably. Still, to leave her in an acute-care bed is to deprive a whole series of acute patients who could rotate in and out of the acute-care facility of appropriate care because they cannot be admitted: No bed is available. Does Monica Urgele take priority over these others? Should her physician discharge her to a more suitable facility and help the many at the (possible) cost of Monica Urgele's life expectancy? If we were Monica's physician, we would be less likely to relocate her than if we were an administrator who had to devise a policy about what to do with so-called bed-blockers.

Such individual allocation decisions have to be made all the time. They have to be made by the acute-care nurse who must decide how much time to spend with one patient at the expense of all the others who also need care; by the transplant committee that has to decide who shall have the only heart that is available for transplantation; the triage nurse in the emergency room who must decide who is to be taken care of first; or the long-term care nurse in the rural setting who has to make a service plan for seeing patients, where each patient lives some distance away; and so on. All of them have to make *micro-allocation* decisions: decisions that deal with selective allocation at the individual level. These decisions are some of the most difficult ones that health care professionals have to make. They are decisions that cannot be avoided because the available resources simply cannot be shared. The article by Martin McKneally *et al.* considers the various ethical, legal and medical parameters that go into making such decisions. As McKneally *et al.* point out, in many cases there are standardized protocols that tell us how these decisions should be made.[1] Usually, they focus on the needs of the patients, the potential outcome of the interventions, and so on. However, in recent times another aspect of allocation has attracted much attention: an aspect that had previously been neglected and that is not incorporated into most current protocols. It centres on the issue of lifestyle and responsibility. When one of the patients has led an immoderate lifestyle — has drunk too much, smoked, was quite sedentary, followed an imprudent diet, etc. — whereas another patient has been the model of a responsible person, should both have equal access to the scarce resources?

Some commentators maintain that neither desert nor fault should enter into considerations of allocation because neither desert nor fault lies wholly within the control of the individual. Furthermore, society does not apply the criteria of desert and fault in other areas; therefore, with what justification would it apply them here?[2] By contrast, Alvin Moss and Mark Siegler argue that patients who develop a medical condition through no fault of their own should have higher priority for scarce health care than patients whose conditions are brought about by irresponsible behaviour. It would be interesting to consider how either stance accords with the underlying philosophy of the *Canada Health Act*.

Finally, given modern techniques and technologies, we can often resuscitate and keep alive patients who previously would have died. Sometimes these interventions prolong the life of the patients for only a short time and at a severely reduced quality of life — or more correctly, at a severely reduced quality of dying. Should intervention be attempted under such circumstances, especially since resources are scarce and medically the attempt will be futile? Or should we adopt the position that intervention is synonymous with care, and that not to intervene is to give up caring? This raises the questions: What exactly is meant by futility? Should it be defined in medical terms alone? Should personal, social or other considerations enter the equation? Robert Truog, Allan Brett and Joel Frader address these issues in their article on futility. The issue is important because in the context of limited resources, what is given to the one is taken away from the other.

Notes

1. See also P. Singer, "A Review of Public Policies to Produce and Distribute Kidneys for Transplantation," *Archives of Internal Medicine* 150:3 (March 1990): 523–527.
2. Atterbury, "The Alcoholic in the Lifeboat: Should Drinkers Be Candidates for Liver Transplantation?" *Journal of Clinical Gastroenterology* 8 (1986): 1–4.

Should Alcoholics Compete Equally for Liver Transplantation?

Alvin H. Moss and Mark Siegler

The circumstances of liver transplantation are unique among organ transplantation because of the dire, absolute scarcity of donor livers and the predominance of one disease — alcohol-related end-stage liver disease — as the principal cause of liver failure. We propose that patients who develop end-stage liver disease through no fault of their own should have higher priority for receiving a liver transplant than those whose end-stage liver disease results from failure to obtain treatment for alcoholism. We base our proposal on considerations of fairness and on whether public support for liver transplantation can be maintained if, as a result of a first-come, first-served approach, patients with alcohol-related end-stage liver disease receive more than half the available donor livers. We conclude that since not all can live, priorities must be established for the use of scarce health care resources.

Until recently, liver transplantation for patients with alcohol-related end-stage liver disease (ARESLD) was not considered a treatment option. Most physicians in the transplant community did not recommend it because of initial poor results in this population[1] and because of a predicted high recidivism rate that would preclude long-term survival.[2] In 1988, however, Starzl and colleagues[3] reported 1-year survival rates for patients with ARESLD comparable to results in patients with other causes of end-stage liver disease (ESLD). Although the patients in the Pittsburgh series may represent a carefully selected population[3,4] the question is no longer, Can we perform transplants in patients with alcoholic liver disease and obtain acceptable results? but Should we? This question is particularly timely since the Health Care Financing Administration (HCFA) has recommended that Medicare coverage for liver transplantation be offered to patients with alcoholic cirrhosis who are abstinent. The HCFA proposes that the same eligibility criteria be used for patients with ARESLD as are used for patients with other causes of ESLD, such as primary biliary cirrhosis and sclerosing cholangitis.[5]

Should Patients with ARESLD Receive Transplants?

At first glance, this question seems simple to answer. Generally, in medicine, a therapy is used if it works and saves lives. But the circumstances of liver transplantation differ from those of most other lifesaving therapies, including long-term mechanical ventilation and dialysis, in three important respects:

Alvin H. Moss and Mark Siegler, "Should Alcoholics Compete Equally for Liver Transplantation?" *Journal of the American Medical Association* (1991) 265; 1295–98.

Nonrenewable Resource

First, although most lifesaving therapies are expensive, liver transplantation uses a nonrenewable, absolutely scarce resource — a donor liver. In contrast to patients with end-stage renal disease, who may receive either a transplant or dialysis therapy, every patient with ESLD who does not receive a liver transplant will die. This dire, absolute scarcity of donor livers would be greatly exacerbated by including patients with ARESLD as potential candidates for liver transplantation. In 1985, 63 737 deaths due to hepatic disease occurred in the United States, at least 36 000 of which were related to alcoholism, but fewer than 1000 liver transplants were performed.[6] Although patients with ARESLD represent more than 50% of the patients with ESLD, patients with ARESLD account for less than 10% of those receiving transplants (*New York Times*. April 3, 1990: B6 [col 1]). If patients with ARESLD were accepted for liver transplantation on an equal basis, as suggested by the HCFA, there would potentially be more than 30 000 additional candidates each year. (No data exist to indicate how many patients in the late stages of ARESLD would meet transplantation eligibility criteria.) In 1987, only 1182 liver transplants were performed; in 1989, fewer than 2000 were done.[6] Even if all donor livers available were given to patients with ARESLD, it would not be feasible to provide transplants for even a small fraction of them. Thus, the dire, absolute nature of donor liver scarcity mandates that distribution be based on unusually rigorous standards — standards not required for the allocation of most other resources such as dialysis machines and ventilators, both of which are only *relatively* scarce.

Comparison with Cardiac Transplantation

Second, although a similar dire, absolute scarcity of donor hearts exists for cardiac transplantation, the allocational decisions for cardiac transplantation differ from those for liver transplantation. In liver transplantation, ARESLD causes more than 50% of the cases of ESLD; in cardiac transplantation, however, no one predominant disease or contributory factor is responsible. Even for patients with end-stage ischemic heart disease who smoked or who failed to adhere to dietary regimens, it is rarely clear that one particular behavior caused the disease. Also, unlike our proposed consideration for liver transplantation, a history of alcohol abuse is considered a contraindication and is a common reason for a patient with heart disease to be denied cardiac transplantation.[7,8] Thus, the allocational decisions for heart transplantation differ from those for liver transplantation in two ways: determining a cause for end-stage heart disease is less certain, and patients with a history of alcoholism are usually rejected from heart transplant programs.

Expensive Technology

Third, a unique aspect of liver transplantation is that it is an expensive technology that has become a target of cost containment in health care.[9] It is, therefore, essential to maintain the approbation and support of the public so that organs continue to be donated under appropriate clinical circumstances — even in spite of the high cost of transplantation.

General Guideline Proposed

In view of the distinctive circumstances surrounding liver transplantation, we propose as a general guideline that patients with ARESLD should not compete equally with other candidates for liver transplantation. We are *not* suggesting that patients with ARESLD should *never* receive liver transplants. Rather, we propose that a priority ranking be established for the use of this dire, absolutely scarce societal resource and that patients with ARESLD be lower on the list than others with ESLD.

Objections to Proposal

We realize that our proposal may meet with two immediate objections: (1) Some may argue that since alcoholism is a disease, patients with ARESLD should be considered equally for liver transplantation.[10] (2) Some will question why patients with ARESLD should be singled out for discrimination, when the medical profession treats many patients who engage in behavior that causes their diseases.[11] We will discuss these objections in turn.

Alcoholism: How Is It Similar to and Different from Other Diseases?

We do not dispute the reclassification of alcoholism as a disease.[12] Both hereditary and environmental factors contribute to alcoholism, and physiological, biochemical, and genetic markers have been associated with increased susceptibility.[13] Identifying alcoholism as a disease enables physicians to approach it as they do other medical problems and to differentiate it from bad habits, crimes, or moral weaknesses. More important, identifying alcoholism as a disease also legitimizes medical interventions to treat it.[14]

Alcoholism is a chronic disease[12,15] for which treatment is available and effective. More than 1.43 million patients were treated in 5586 alcohol treatment units in the 12-month period ending October 30, 1987.[16] One comprehensive review concluded that more than two thirds of patients who accept therapy improve.[17] Another cited four studies in which at least 54% of patients were abstinent a minimum of 1 year after treatment.[18] A recent study of alcohol-impaired physicians reported a 100% abstinence rate an average of 33.4 months after therapy was initiated. In this study, physician-patients rated Alcoholics Anonymous, the largest organization of recovering alcoholics in the world, as the most important component of their therapy.[19]

Like other chronic diseases — such as type I diabetes mellitus, which requires the patient to administer insulin over a lifetime — alcoholism requires the patient to assume responsibility for participating in continuous treatment. Two key elements are required to successfully treat alcoholism: the patient must accept his or her diagnosis and must assume responsibility for treatment.[20,21] The high success rates of some alcoholism treatment programs indicate that many patients can accept responsibility for their treatment. ARESLD, one of the sequelae of alcoholism, results from 10 to 20 years of heavy alcohol consumption. The risk of ARESLD increases with the amount of alcohol consumed and with the duration of heavy consumption.[22] In view of the quantity of alcohol consumed, the years, even decades, required to develop ARESLD, and the availability of effective alcohol treatment, attributing personal responsibility for ARESLD to the patient seems all the more justified. We believe, therefore, that even though alcoholism is a chronic disease, alcoholics should be held responsible for seeking and obtaining treatment that could prevent the development of late-stage complications such as ARESLD. Our view is consistent with that of Alcoholics Anonymous: alcoholics are responsible for undertaking a program for recovery that will keep their disease of alcoholism in remission.[23]

Are We Discriminating Against Alcoholics?

Why should patients with ARESLD be singled out when a large number of patients have health problems that can be attributed to so-called voluntary health-risk behavior? Such patients include smokers with chronic lung disease; obese people who develop type II diabetes; some individuals who test positive for the human immunodeficiency virus; individuals with multiple behavioral risk factors (inattention to blood pressure, cholesterol, diet, and exercise) who develop coronary artery disease; and people such as skiers, motorcyclists, and football players who sustain activity-related injuries. We believe that the health care system should respond based on the actual medical needs of patients rather than on the factors (e.g., genetic, infectious, or behavioral) that cause the problem. We also believe that individuals should bear some responsibility — such as increased insurance premiums — for medical problems associated with voluntary choices. The critical distinguishing factor for treatment of ARESLD is the scarcity of the resource needed to treat it. The resources needed to treat most of these other conditions are only moderately or relatively scarce, and patients with these diseases or injuries can receive a share of the resources (i.e., money, personnel, and medication) roughly equivalent to their need. In contrast, there are insufficient donor livers to sustain the lives of all with ESLD who are in need.[24] This difference permits us to make some discriminating choices — or to establish priorities — in selecting candidates for liver transplantation based on notions of fairness. In addition, this reasoning enables us to offer patients with alcohol-related medical and surgical problems their fair share of relatively scarce resources, such as blood products, surgical care, and intensive care beds, while still maintaining that their claim on donor livers is less compelling than the claims of others.

Reasons Patients with ARESLD Should Have a Lower Priority on Transplant Waiting Lists

Two arguments support our proposal. The first argument is a moral one based on considerations of fairness. The second one is based on policy considerations and examines whether public support of liver transplantation can be maintained if, as a result of a first-come, first-served approach, patients with ARESLD receive more than half the available donor livers. Finally, we will consider further research necessary to determine which patients with ARESLD should be candidates for transplantation, albeit with a lower priority.

Fairness

Given a tragic shortage of donor livers, what is the fair or just way to allocate them? We suggest that patients who develop ESLD through no fault of their own (e.g., those with congenital biliary atresia or primary biliary cirrhosis) should have a higher priority in receiving a liver transplant than those whose liver disease results from failure to obtain treatment for alcoholism. In view of the dire, absolute scarcity of donor livers, we believe it is fair to hold people responsible for their choices, including decisions to refuse alcoholism treatment, and to allocate organs on this basis.

It is unfortunate but not unfair to make this distinction.[25] When not enough donor livers are available for all who need one, choices have to be made, and they should be founded on one or more proposed principles of fairness for distributing scarce resources.[26,27] We shall consider four that are particularly relevant:

- To each, an equal share of treatment.
- To each, similar treatment for similar cases.
- To each, treatment according to personal effort.
- To each, treatment according to ability to pay.

It is not possible to give each patient with ESLD an *equal share*, or, in this case, a functioning liver. The problem created by the absolute scarcity of donor livers is that of inequality; some receive livers while others do not. But what is fair, need not be equal. Although a first-come, first-served approach has been suggested to provide each patient with an equal chance, we believe it is fairer to give a child dying of biliary atresia an opportunity for a *first* normal liver than it is to give a patient with ARESLD who was born with a normal liver a *second* one.

Because the goal of providing each person with an equal share of health care sometimes collides with the realities of finite medical resources, the principle of *similar treatment for similar cases* has been found to be helpful. Outka[26] stated it this way: "If we accept the case for equal access, but if we simply cannot, physically cannot, treat all who are in need, it seems more just to discriminate by virtue of categories of illness, rather than between rich ill and poor ill." This principle is derived from the principle of formal justice, which, roughly stated, says that people who are equal in relevant respects should be treated equally and that people who are unequal in relevant respects should be treated differently.[27] We believe that patients with ARESLD are unequal in a relevant respect to others with ESLD, since their liver failure was preventable; therefore, it is acceptable to treat them differently.

Our view also relies on the principle of *To each, treatment according to personal effort*. Although alcoholics cannot be held responsible for their disease, once their condition has been diagnosed they can be held responsible for seeking treatment and for preventing the complication of ARESLD. The standard of personal effort and responsibility we propose for alcoholics is the same as that held by Alcoholics Anonymous. We are not suggesting that some lives and behaviors have greater value than others — an approach used and appropriately repudiated when dialysis machines were in short supply.[26–30] But we are holding people responsible for their personal effort.

Health policymakers have predicted that this principle will assume greater importance in the future. In the context of scarce health care resources, Blank[31] foresees a reevaluation of our health care priorities, with a shift toward individual responsibility and a renewed emphasis on the individual's obligation to society to maximize one's health. Similarly, more than a decade ago, Knowles[32] observed that prevention of disease requires effort. He envisioned that the next major advances in the health of the American people would be determined by what individuals are willing to do for themselves.

To each, treatment according to ability to pay has also been used as a principle of distributive justice. Since alcoholism is prevalent in all socioeconomic strata, it is not discrimination against the poor to deny liver transplantation to patients with alcoholic liver disease.[33] In fact, we believe that poor patients with ARESLD have a stronger claim for a donor liver than rich patients, precisely because many alcohol treatment programs are not available to patients lacking in substantial private resources or health insurance. Ironically, it is precisely this group of poor and uninsured patients who are most likely not to be eligible to receive a liver transplant because of their inability to pay. We agree with Outka's view of fairness that would discriminate according to categories of illness rather than according to wealth.

Policy Considerations Regarding Public Support for Liver Transplantation

Today, the main health policy concerns involve issues of financing, distributive justice, and rationing medical care.[34–37] Because of the many deficiencies in the U.S. health care system — in maternal and child health, in the unmet needs of the elderly, and in the millions of Americans without health insurance — an increasing number of commentators are drawing attention to the trade-offs between basic health care for the many and expensive, albeit lifesaving, care for the few.[9,25,38,39]

Because of its high unit cost, liver transplantation is often at the center of these discussions, as it has been in Oregon, where the legislature voted to eliminate Medicaid reimbursement for all transplants except kidneys and corneas.[9] In this era of health care cost containment, a sense of limits is emerging and allocational choices are being made. Oregon has already shown that elected officials and the public are prepared to face these issues.

In our democracy, it is appropriate that community mores and values be regarded seriously when deciding the most appropriate use of a scarce and non-renewable organ symbolized as a "Gift of Life." As if to underscore this point, the report of the Task Force on Organ Transplantation recommended that each donated organ be considered a national resource for the public good and that the public must participate in decisions on how to use this resource to best serve the public's interests.[40]

Much of the initial success in securing public and political approval for liver transplantation was achieved by focusing media and political attention not on adults but on children dying of ESLD. The public may not support transplantation for patients with ARESLD in the same way that they have endorsed this procedure for babies born with biliary atresia. This assertion is bolstered not only by the events in Oregon but also by the results of a Louis Harris and Associates[41] national survey, which showed that lifesaving therapy for premature infants or for patients with cancer was given the highest health care priority by the public and that lifesaving therapy for patients with alcoholic liver disease was given the lowest. In this poll, the public's view of health care priorities was shared by leadership groups also polled: physicians, nurses, employers, and politicians.

Just because a majority of the public holds these views does not mean that they are right, but the moral intuition of the public, which is also shared by its leaders, reflects community values that must be seriously considered. Also indicative of community values are organizations such as Mothers Against Drunk Driving, Students Against Drunk Driving, corporate employee assistance programs, and school student assistance programs. Their existence signals that many believe that a person's behavior can be modified so that the consequences of behavior such as alcoholism can be prevented.[42] Thus, giving donor livers to patients with ARESLD on an equal basis with other patients who have ESLD might lead to a decline in public support for liver transplantation.

Should Any Alcoholics Be Considered for Transplantation? Need for Further Research

Our proposal for giving lower priority for liver transplantation to patients with ARESLD does not completely rule out transplantation for this group. Patients with ARESLD who had not previously been offered therapy and who are now abstinent could be acceptable candidates. In addition, patients lower on the waiting list, such as patients with ARESLD who have been treated and are now abstinent, might be eligible for a donor liver in some regions because of the increased availability of donor organs there. Even if only because of these possible conditions for transplantation, further research is needed to determine which patients with ARESLD would have the best outcomes after liver transplantation.

Transplant programs have been reluctant to provide transplants to alcoholics because of concern about one unfavorable outcome: a high recidivism rate.

Although the overall recidivism rate for the Pittsburgh patients was only 11.5%, in the patients who had been abstinent less than 6 months it was 43%.[2] Also, compared with the entire group in which 1-year survival was 74%, the survival rate in this subgroup was lower, at 64%.[2]

In the recently proposed Medicare criteria for coverage of liver transplantation, the HCFA acknowledged that the decision to insure patients with alcoholic cirrhosis "may be considered controversial by some."[5] As if to counter possible objections, the HCFA listed requirements for patients with alcoholic cirrhosis: patients must meet the transplant center's requirement for abstinence prior to liver transplantation and have documented evidence of sufficient social support to ensure both recovery from alcoholism and compliance with the regimen of immunosuppressive medication.

Further research should answer lingering questions about liver transplantation for ARESLD patients: Which characteristics of a patient with ARESLD can predict a successful outcome? How long is abstinence necessary to qualify for transplantation? What type of a social support system must a patient have to ensure good results? These questions are being addressed.[43] Until the answers are known, we propose that further transplantation for patients with ARESLD be limited to abstinent patients who had not previously been offered alcoholism treatment and to abstinent treated patients in regions of increased donor liver availability and that it be carried out as part of prospective research protocols at a few centers skilled in transplantation and alcohol research.

Comment

Should patients with ARESLD compete equally for liver transplants? In a setting in which there is a dire, absolute scarcity of donor livers, we believe the answer is no. Considerations of fairness suggest that a first-come, first-served approach for liver transplantation is not the most just approach. Although this decision is difficult, it is only fair that patients who have not assumed equal responsibility for maintaining their health or for accepting treatment for a chronic disease should be treated differently. Considerations of public values and mores suggest that the public may not support liver transplantation if patients with ARESLD routinely receive more than half of the available donor livers. We conclude that since not all can live, priorities must be established and that patients with ARESLD should be given a lower priority for liver transplantation than others with ESLD.

Notes

The Center for Clinical Medical Ethics and Alvin H. Moss, MD, are supported by grants from the Henry J. Kaiser Family Foundation and the Pew Charitable Trusts. The opinions expressed are those of the authors and should not be taken to represent those of the foundation or trust.

The authors thank Abe Kaplan for assistance in literature review; Rolly Sullivan, MD, for information on alcoholism treatment programs; and Michael D. Swenson, MD, PhD, for review of an earlier draft of the manuscript.

1. Scharschmidt, B.F. "Human liver transplantation: analysis of data on 540 patients from four centers." *Hepatology.* 1984;4:95S–101S.

2. Kumar, S., Stauber, R.E., Gavaler, J.S., et al. "Orthotopic liver transplantation for alcoholic liver disease." *Hepatology.* 1990;11:159–164.

3. Starzl, T.E., Van Thiel, D., Tzakis, A.G., et al. "Orthotopic liver transplantation for alcoholic cirrhosis." *JAMA.* 1988;260:2542–2544.

4. Olbrisch, M.E., Levenson, J.L. "Liver transplantation for alcoholic cirrhosis." *JAMA.* 1989;261:2958.

5. Health Care Financing Administration. "Medicare program: criteria for Medicare coverage of adult liver transplants." *Federal Register.* 1990;55:3545–3553.

6. Office of Health Technology Assessment, Agency for Health Care Policy Research. *Assessment of Liver Transplantation.* Rockville, Md.: U.S. Dept. of Health and Human Services; 1990:3,25.

7. Schroeder, J.S., Hunt, S. "Cardiac transplantation update 1987." *JAMA.* 1987;258:3142–3145.

8. Surman, O.S. "Psychiatric aspects of organ transplantation." *Am J Psychiatry.* 1989;146:972–982.

9. Welch, H.G., Larson, E.B. "Dealing with limited resources: the Oregon decision to curtail funding for organ transplantation." *N Engl J Med.* 1988;319:171–173.

10. Flavin, D.K., Niven, R.G., Kelsey, J.E. "Alcoholism and orthotopic liver transplantation." *JAMA.* 1988;259:1546–1547.

11. Atterbury, C.E. "The alcoholic in the lifeboat: should drinkers be candidates for liver transplantation?" *J Clin Gastroenterol.* 1986;8:1–4.

12. Mendelson, J.H., Mello, N.K. *The Diagnosis and Treatment of Alcoholism.* 2nd ed. New York, NY: McGraw-Hill International Book Co.; 1985:1–20.

13. Blum, K., Noble, E.P., Sheridan, P.J., et al. "Allelic association of human dopamine D_2 receptor gene in alcoholism." *JAMA.* 1990;263:2055–2060.

14. Aronson, M.D. "Definition of alcoholism." In: Barnes, H.N., Aronson, M.D., Delbanco, T.L., eds. *Alcoholism: A Guide for the Primary Care Physician.* New York, NY: Springer-Verlag NY Inc.; 1987:9–15.

15. Klerman, G.L. "Treatment of alcoholism." *N Engl J Med.* 1989;320:394–395.

16. *Seventh Special Report to the U.S. Congress on Alcohol and Health.* Washington, DC: U.S. Dept. of Health and Human Services; 1990. Publication 90-1656.

17. Saxe, L. *The Effectiveness and Costs of Alcoholism Treatment: Health Technology Case Study No. 22.* Washington, DC: Congress of the United States, Office of Technology Assessment;1983:3–6.

18. Nace, E.P. *The Treatment of Alcoholism.* New York, NY: Brunner/Mazel Publishers; 1987:43–46.

19. Galanter, M., Talbott, D., Gallegos, K., Rubenstone, E. "Combined Alcoholics Anonymous and professional care for addicted physicians." *Am J Psychiatry.* 1990;147:64–68.

20. Johnson, B., Clark, W. "Alcoholism: a challenging physician-patient encounter." *J Gen Intern Med.* 1989;4:445–452.

21. Bigby, J.A. "Negotiating treatment and monitoring recovery." In: Barnes, H.N., Aronson, M.D., Delbanco, T.L., eds. *Alcoholism: A Guide for the Primary Care Physician.* New York, NY: Springer-Verlag NY Inc.; 1987:66–72.

22. Grant, B.F., Dufour, M.C., Harford, T.C. "Epidemiology of alcoholic liver disease." *Sem Liver Dis.* 1988;8:12–25.

23. Thoreson, R.W., Budd, F.C. "Self-help groups and other group procedures for treating alcohol problems." In: Cox, W.M., ed. *Treatment and Prevention of Alcohol Problems: A Resource Manual.* Orlando, Fla.: Academic Press Inc.; 1987:157–181.

24. Winslow, G.R. *Triage and Justice.* Berkeley: University of California Press; 1982:39–44, 133–150.

25. Engelhardt, H.T., Jr. "Shattuck Lecture: allocating scarce medical resources and the availability of organ transplantation." *N Engl J Med.* 1984;311:66–71.

26. Outka, G. "Social justice and equal access to health care." *J Religious Ethics.* 1974;2:11–32.

27. Beauchamp, T.L., Childress, J.F. *Principles of Biomedical Ethics.* 3rd ed. New York, NY: Oxford University Press; 1989:256–306.

28. Ramsey, P. *The Patient as Person.* New Haven, Conn.: Yale University Press; 1970:242–252.

29. Fox, R.C., Swazey, J.P. *The Courage to Fail.* 2nd ed. Chicago, Ill.: University of Chicago Press; 1978:226–265.

30. Annas, G.J. "The prostitute, the playboy, and the poet: rationing schemes for organ transplantation." *Am J Public Health.* 1985;75:187–189.

31. Blank, R.H. *Rationing Medicine.* New York, NY: Columbia University Press; 1988:1–37, 189–252.

32. Knowles, J.H. "Responsibility for health." *Science.* 1977;198:1103.

33. Moore, R.D., Bone, L.R., Geller, G., Marmon, J.A., Stokes, E.J., Levine, D.M. "Prevalence, detection, and treatment of alcoholism in hospitalized patients." *JAMA.* 1989;261:403–407.

34. Fuchs, V.R. "The 'rationing' of medical care." *N Engl J Med.* 1984;311:1572–1573.

35. Daniels, N. "Why saying no to patients in the United States is so hard: cost containment, justice, and provider autonomy." *N Engl J Med.* 1986;314:1380–1383.

36. Callahan, D. "Allocating health resources." *Hastings Cent Rep.* 1988;18:14–20.

37. Evans, R.W. "Health care technology and the inevitability of resource allocation and rationing decisions." *JAMA.* 1983;249:2047–2053, 2208–2219.

38. Thurow, L.C. "Learning to say no." *N Engl J Med.* 1984;311:1569–1572.

39. Caper, P. "Solving the medical care dilemma." *N Engl J Med.* 1988;318:1535–1536.

40. Task Force on Organ Transplantation. *Organ Transplantation: Issues and Recommendations.* Washington, DC: U.S. Dept. of Health and Human Services; 1986:9.

41. Louis Harris and Associates. *Making Difficult Health Care Decisions.* Boston, Mass.: The Loran Commission; 1987:73–89.

42. Fishman, R. *Alcohol and Alcoholism.* New York, NY: Chelsea House Publishers; 1986:27–34.

43. Beresford, T.P., Turcotte, J.G., Merion, R., et al. "A rational approach to liver transplantation for the alcoholic patient." *Psychosomatics.* 1990;31:241–254.

Resource Allocation

Martin F. McKneally, Bernard M. Dickens, Eric M. Meslin, Peter A. Singer

Mr. C is a 21-year-old computer programmer with cystic fibrosis. Chronic rejection and poorly controlled fungal infections are destroying the lungs he received 15 months ago. He has intermittently required positive-pressure ventilation to maintain adequate oxygenation during flareups of infection or rejection. C has been listed as a candidate for a second transplantation. However, given the presence of infection and the risks associated with repeat transplantation, his predicted chance of survival is 65% at 1 month and 38% at 24 months.[1]

Mrs. D is a 42-year-old schoolteacher. She has been listed as a candidate for double lung transplantation because of rapidly progressing pulmonary hypertension associated with hemoptysis and hypoxemia. She is unable to manage at home because of decompensated right heart failure unresponsive to maximal therapy. As a first-time lung transplant candidate who is free of infection, D has a predicted chance of survival of 82% at 1 month and 62% at 2 years.[1]

The surgeon has 1 matching donor organ available for these 2 patients. He knows that the best outcome can be achieved by transplanting both lungs of the donor into the same patient.[2]

When 63-year-old Mr. E is brought to the emergency department with severe but potentially reversible brain injury after a motor vehicle accident, the attending physician considers going through the charts of each patient in the intensive care unit (ICU) in the hope of finding someone whose need for intensive care is less than that of Mr. E. She also considers sending Mr. E to the floor, but knows that this will overtax the capabilities of the floor staff, who are not prepared to manage the patient's elevated intracranial pressure and seizures. Because of recent hospital closures in the region, no other facility is available to share responsibility for the care of patients with neurosurgical problems of this magnitude.

What Is Resource Allocation?

Resource allocation is the distribution of goods and services to programs and people. In the context of health care, macro-allocations of resources are made by governments at the national, provincial and municipal level. Meso-allocations are made at the level of institutions; for example, hospitals allocate their resources to programs such as cancer treatment, cardiology and dialysis. Micro-allocations are made at the level of the individual patient. Although these 3 levels are interrelated, in this article we focus on resource allocation from the perspective of the practising physician.

Commodity scarcity, illustrated by the lung-transplant case, is a shortage of a finite resource (such as an organ) because of natural limits to the availability of that resource. Fiscal scarcity, illustrated by the intensive care case, is a shortage of funds.[3]

Why Is Resource Allocation Important?

Rising public and professional expectations, an expanding pool of treatable patients and costly new technology must be balanced against tightly monitored health care budgets, competing government priorities and provincial deficits. Ethics, law, policy and empirical studies provide insights that can help clinicians as they try to distribute health care resources fairly.

Ethics

The ethics of resource allocation may be considered in relation to the concept of justice and the physician's fiduciary duty toward the patient. According to Aristotle's principle of distributive justice, equals should be treated equally and those who are unequal should be treated unequally. Unequal treatment is justified when resources are allocated in light of morally relevant differences, such as those pertaining to need or likely benefit.[4] Characteristics such as sex, sexual orientation, religion, level of education or age alone are morally irrelevant criteria for resource allocation. Because there is no overarching theory of justice to balance competing claims between morally relevant criteria such as need and benefit, fair, open and publicly defensible resource allocation procedures are critical.

The lack of a comprehensive theory of justice gives rise to unresolved issues in rationing; these have been categorized by Daniels as follows:[5]

1. *The fair chances versus best outcomes problem.* To what degree should producing the best outcome be favoured over giving every patient an opportunity to compete for limited resources?

2. *The priorities problem.* How much priority should we give to treating the sickest or most disabled patients?

3. *The aggregation problem.* When should we allow an aggregation of modest benefits to larger numbers of people to outweigh more significant benefits to fewer people?

4. *The democracy problem.* When must we rely on a fair democratic process as the only way to determine what constitutes a fair rationing outcome?

These questions help to frame discussions of resource allocation issues and the development of policies and practices that balance the obligations of physicians as citizens in a just society with their obligations to individual patients. The power imbalance that exists between physician and patient creates a fiduciary duty on the physician's part to promote the patient's best interest. The extent of this ethical duty, which is fundamental to the physician's role in resource allocation, is a matter of controversy. For instance, Levinsky has argued that "physicians are required to do everything that they believe may benefit each patient without regard to costs or other societal considerations."[6] By contrast, Morreim has argued that "the physician's obligations to the patient can no longer be a single minded, unequivocal commitment but rather must reflect a balancing. Patients' interests must be weighed against the legitimate competing claims of other patients of payers, of society as a whole, and sometimes even of the physician himself."[7]

Law

The Canadian Charter of Rights and Freedoms prohibits discrimination on various grounds, including physical or mental disability, but it applies only to governmental agencies, not to physicians or hospitals[8] unless they are under the day-to-day control of ministries of health or other branches of government.[9]

Human rights codes in several provinces prohibit discrimination on the basis of race, ethnicity, place of origin, religion, age, sex, sexual orientation and physical or mental disability. Evidence that resources were allocated purely on such grounds could lead to an inquiry and legal proceedings by a provincial human rights commission. However, if such factors were relevant to a medical prognosis, it is not clear how a human rights commission could challenge a physician's clinical assessment of a patient's eligibility for a particular treatment. Evidence might be needed of a systematic policy of discrimination or bias against a particular group on the part of the practitioner or institution.[10]

Because courts have been extremely reluctant to become involved in how physicians, hospitals and health authorities use their resources, the legal review of individual decisions involving resource allocation is improbable.[11] As a British judge has observed, "Difficult and agonizing judgments have to be made as to how a limited budget is best allocated to the maximum advantage of the maximum number of patients. That is not a judgment which the court can make."[12]

Nevertheless, the trial judge in a case heard in British Columbia criticized physicians for offering the explanation that they felt too constrained by the provincial medical insurance plan and their provincial medical association's standards to order a diagnostic CT scan. Although a finding of negligence was made on other grounds, the judge noted that while physicians may consider the financial impact of their decisions, financial considerations cannot be decisive. The physician's first duty is to the patient.[13]

It is understood in law that although there is no liability for making a decision that proves to be wrong,[14] there may be liability for making a decision *wrongly*. A decision is made wrongly if demands for economy distort the physician's judgement with respect to the care that is owed to the patient. An error in clinical judgement is not actionable, because the risk of being wrong is inherent in every exercise of judgement. However, to take decisive account of secondary concerns and subordinate the primary concern of care — the patient's well-being — to a budgetary issue is the wrong way for a physician to make a treatment decision.

Policy

Clear, fair and widely accepted institutional or professional policies can provide guidance for physicians who are faced with difficult resource allocation decisions. Policies developed for the allocation of organs have reduced conflict between teams and helped prioritize recipients within organ transplantation programs, using generally accepted and publicly reviewed principles and guidelines.[15]

In Oregon, a priority list of treatments is being developed by citizens' committees with input from physicians. This evolving experiment in public policy ranks health care services on the basis of effectiveness and perceived value to the community. Public funds are assigned by the government to make services "above the funding line" available to citizens "below the poverty line."[16] Public funds assigned by the government to pay for health care are spent on treatments according to their priority on the list. Through multiple iterations and public debate, this experiment is producing a useful model for engaging stakeholders from government, the medical profession, and the public in the process of health policy development.[17,18]

In Canada, the CMA has provided a framework for decision making on core and comprehensive health care services that incorporates 3 major dimensions: quality, economics and ethics.[19] As well, Deber and colleagues have proposed a "four-screen" model based on effectiveness, appropriateness, informed choice and public provision.[20] Finally, the CMA's Code of Ethics states that physicians should recognize [their] responsibility "to promote fair access to health care resources" and should "use health care resources prudently."[21]

Empirical studies

Given the importance of resource allocation decisions in health care today, there is a surprising lack of empirical studies on this topic. In contrast to the hundreds of published studies on advance directives,[22] for example, fewer than 2 dozen empirical studies on resource allocation (excluding cost-effectiveness analyses of various diagnostic tests and treatments) came to light in our literature search. In this section we review some of these studies with reference to the primary questions they address.

Is resource allocation occurring now? In a study of dialysis referrals, Mendelssohn and associates found that 67% of Ontario physicians believed rationing of dialysis was occurring at the time of the survey, and 91% believed that such rationing would occur in the future.[23]

How do health care providers make resource allocation decisions? This question has been addressed by survey methods in the context of dialysis,[23] transplantation,[24–26] rural medicine,[27] and critical care.[28] For instance, a survey by the Society of Critical Care Medicine found that critical-care physicians considered quality of life as viewed by the patient, probability of survival, the reversibility of the acute disorder and the nature of any chronic disorder as important factors

in deciding which patients to admit to the intensive care unit.[28]

Do people consider age a relevant variable in health care resource allocation? In a survey of public opinion in the United States, Zweibel and colleagues[29] found that most people accept the withholding of life-prolonging medical care from some critically ill older patients, but few would categorically withhold such care on the basis of age alone.

How do decision-makers balance concerns of efficiency and equity? Ubel and collaborators[30] surveyed prospective jurors, medical ethicists and experts in medical decision making to explore the trade-off between cost-effectiveness and equity in the setting of budget constraints. Many respondents said they would choose a less cost-effective test for the entire population over a more cost-effective test for half the population. Similarly, in a survey of public opinion in Australia, Nord and associates[31] found that a policy of maximizing cost-effectiveness received very limited support when the consequence was a loss of equity and access to services for elderly people and for people with limited potential for improving their health. In other words, equity was valued above cost-effectiveness in both of these surveys.

How Should I Approach Resource Allocation in Practice?

The clinician's goal is to provide optimal care within the limits imposed by the allocation of resources to health care generally and to the institution, program, and specific situation in which an individual patient is treated. The following guidelines may prove helpful in practice:

- Choose interventions known to be beneficial on the basis of evidence of effectiveness.

- Minimize the use of marginally beneficial tests or marginally beneficial interventions.

- Seek the tests or treatments that will accomplish the diagnostic or therapeutic goal for the least cost.

- Advocate for one's own patients but avoid manipulating the system to gain unfair advantage to them.

- Resolve conflicting claims for scarce resources justly, on the basis of morally relevant criteria such as need (e.g., the patient's risk of death or serious harm could be reduced by the treatment) and benefit (e.g., published evidence of effectiveness), using fair and publicly defensible procedures (ideally, incorporating public input).

- Inform patients of the impact of cost constraints on care, but do so in a sensitive way. Blaming administrative or governmental systems during discussions with the patient at the point of treatment should be avoided; it undermines care by reducing confidence and increasing anxiety at a time when the patient is most vulnerable.

- Seek resolution of unacceptable shortages at the level of hospital management (meso-allocation) or government (macro-allocation).

The Cases

Mrs. D should receive the double lung. Although her need is approximately equal to that of Mr. C, her ability to benefit is substantially greater. The surgeon knows from sound empirical evidence that repeat lung transplantation has a poor prognosis, particularly when chronic infection exists.[1] He can minimize recriminations related to the team members' feelings of loyalty toward Mr. C if the transplantation program policy clearly spells out specific and fair procedures to follow when difficult allocation decisions must be made involving similarly deserving patients.

The attending physician should provide appropriate care for Mr. E in the emergency department, as this is the only facility available. She should involve the administrator on call to bring in additional skilled personnel to provide interim care in the emergency department and to help her arrange for the patient's transfer to a facility prepared to care for him. In this way, she clarifies the responsibility of the hospital to resolve the meso-allocation problem at an administrative level. The hospital may in turn address the macro-allocation of resources at the provincial or regional level through its representatives to the government. The physician should not attempt to resolve problems of this magnitude on her own and should not compromise the care of Mr. E. She may choose to contribute to the resolution of similar problems in the longer term by making suggestions about system reform to the health ministry or by helping with appeals for public support of additional facilities.

Notes

1. Novick R.J., Kaye M.P., Patterson G.A., Andreassian B., Klepetko W., Menkis A.H., et al. Redo lung transplantation: a North American-European experience. *J Heart Lung Transplant* 1993;12:5–16.

2. DeHoyos A.L., Patterson G.A., Maurer J.R., Ramirez J.C., Miller J.D., Winton T.L. Pulmonary transplantation: early and late results of the Toronto Lung Transplant Group. *J Thorac Cardiovasc Surg* 1992;103:295–306.

3. Morreim E.H. *Balancing act: the new medical ethics of medicine's new economics.* Washington: Georgetown University Press; 1995:47–51.

4. Doyal L. Needs, rights, and the moral duties of clinicians. In Gillon R., Lloyd A., editors. *Principles of health care ethics.* Chichester: John Wiley; 1994:217–30.

5. Daniels N. Four unsolved rationing problems: a challenge. *Hastings Cent Rep* 1994;24:27–9.

6. Levinsky N.G. The doctor's master. *N Engl J Med* 1984;311:1573–5.

7. Morreim E.H. *Balancing act: 2.*

8. *Stoffman v. Vancouver General Hospital* (1990), 76 DLR (4th) 700 (SCC).

9. *Fleming v. Reid* (1991), 82 DLR (4th) 298 (Ont CA) 8.

10. *Korn v. Potter* (1996), 134 DLR (4th) 43 7 (BCSC).

11. *Ethridge v. British Columbia Attorney-General* (1995), 125 DLR (4th) 323 (BCCA).

12. *R. v. Cambridge Health Authority* ex parte B (1995) 2 All ER 129 (CA) at 137, Sir Thomas Bingham, M.R.

13. *Law Estate v. Simice* (1994), 21 CCLT (2d) 228 (BCSC).

14. *Whitebone v. Jordan* (1981), 1 All ER 2 67 (HL).

15. Hauptman P.J., O'Connor K.J. Medical progress procurement and allocation of solid organs for transplantation. *N Eng J Med* 1997;3 36:422–31.

16. Hadorn D.C. Setting health care priorities in Oregon: cost-effectiveness meets the rule of rescue. *JAMA* 1991;265:2218–25.

17. Garland M.J. Oregon's contribution to defining adequate health care. In Chapman A.R., editor. *Health care reform: a human rights approach.* Washington: Georgetown University Press; 1994:211–32.

18. Kitzhaber J., Kemmy A.M. On the Oregon trail [review]. *Br Med Bull* 1995; 51:808–18.

19. Canadian Medical Association. *Core and comprehensive health care services — a framework for decision-making.* Ottawa: The Association, 1994.

20. Deber R., Lutchmie N., Baranek P., Hilfer N., Duvalko K.M., Zlotnik-Shaul R., et al. *The public/private mix in health care* [commissioned by the National Forum on Health]. In press;1429–37.

21. Canadian Medical Association. Code of ethics. *Can Med Assoc 1* 1996;155: 1176A–B.

22. Tengs T.O., Adams M.E., Pliskin J.S., Safran D.G., Siegel J.E., Weinstein M.C., et al. Five hundred life-saving interventions and their cost-effectiveness. *Risk Anal* 1995;15:369–90.

23. Mendelssohn D.C., Kua B.T., Singer P.A. Referral for dialysis in Ontario. *Arch Intern Med* 1995;1 55:2473–8.

24. Olbrisch M.E., Levenson J.L. Psychosocial evaluation of heart transplant candidates: an international survey of process, criteria and outcomes. *J Heart Lung Transplant* 1991;10:948–55.

25. Levenson J.L., Olbrisch M.E. Psychosocial evaluation of organ transplant candidates: a comparative survey of process, criteria, and outcome in heart, liver and kidney transplantation. *Psychosomatics* 1993;34:314–23.

26. Mullen M.A., Kohut N., Sam M., Blendis L., Singer P.A. Access to adult liver transplantation in Canada: a survey and ethical analysis. *Can Med Assoc J* 1996;154:337–42.

27. Jecker N.S., Berg A.O. Allocating medical resources in rural America: alternative perceptions of justice. *Soc Sci Med* 1992;34:467–74.

28. The Society of Critical Care Medicine Ethics Committee. Attitudes of critical care medicine professionals concerning distribution of intensive care resources. *Crit Care Med* 1994;22:358–62.

29. Zweibel N.R., Cassel C.K., Karrison T. Public attitudes about the use of chronological age as a criterion for allocating health care resources. *Gerontologist* 1993;33:74–80.

30. Ubel P.A., DeKay M.L.,Baron J., Asch D.A. Cost-effectiveness analysis in a setting of budget constraints: is it equitable? *N Engl J Med* 1996;334:1174–7.

31. Nord E., Richardson J., Kuhse H., Singer P. Maximizing health benefits vs. egalitarianism: an Australian survey of health issues. *Soc Sci Med* 1995;41:1429–37.

The Problem with Futility

Robert D. Truog, Allan S. Brett, and Joel Frader

"Futility" is one of the newest additions to the lexicon of bioethics. Physicians, ethicists, and members of the media are increasingly concerned about patients and families who insist on receiving life-sustaining treatment that others judge to be futile. A clear understanding of futility has proved to be elusive, however. Many clinicians view futility the way one judge viewed pornography: they may not be able to define it, but they know it when they see it.[1]

The notion of futile medical treatment may go back to the time of Hippocrates, who allegedly advised physicians "to refuse to treat those who are overmastered by their diseases, realizing that in such cases medicine is powerless."[2] More recently, the concept has appeared frequently in court decisions and policy statements.[3–6] The so-called Baby Doe law exempts physicians from providing treatment that would be virtu-ally futile.[7] The Council on Ethical and Judicial Affairs of the American Medical Association (AMA) recently concluded that physicians have no obligation to obtain consent for a do-not-resuscitate (DNR) order when cardiopulmonary resuscitation (CPR) is deemed futile.[8] The fact that this concept has appeared in law and policy may seem to indicate that it is clearly understood and widely accepted. In reality, however, the notion of futility hides many deep and serious ambiguities that threaten its legitimacy as a rationale for limiting treatment.

Paradigms of Futility

Contemporary discussions of futility have centered primarily on cases involving patients in a persistent vegetative state and those involving the use of CPR. A third type of case, involving organ-replacement technology, has received little attention but is helpful to our understanding of futility.

Futility and the Persistent Vegetative State

The first type of scenario involving the question of futility is represented by the recent Minnesota case of Helga Wanglie.[9] Mrs. Wanglie was an 86-year-old woman who had been dependent on mechanical ventilation and in a persistent vegetative state for more than a year. Her husband insisted that she believed in maintaining life at all cost, and that when she was ready to go ... the good Lord would call her."[10] Her physicians, on the other hand, believed that the continued use of mechanical ventilation and intensive care was futile. When attempts to transfer her elsewhere failed, they sought to have a court appoint an independent conservator with responsibility for making medical decisions on her behalf. The judge denied this petition and reaffirmed the authority of her husband as legal surrogate. Three days later, Mrs. Wanglie died.

Cases like that of Mrs. Wanglie seldom reach the courts, but they are probably not rare. A similar call involving a child with severe brain damage was concluded with a settlement favorable to the family before a judicial decision.[11]

Futility in Cases Involving CPR

The second prototypical scenario involves the use of DNR orders. Although the techniques of CPR were originally intended only for use after acute, reversible cardiac arrests, the current practice is to use CPR in all situations unless there is a direct order to the contrary. Since cardiac arrest is the final event in all terminal illness, everyone is eventually a candidate for this medical procedure. DNR orders were developed to spare patients from aggressive attempts at revival when imminent death is anticipated and inevitable. Nevertheless, patients or families sometimes request CPR even when care givers believe such attempts would be futile. Some have argued that in these circumstances a physician should be able to enact a DNR order without the consent of the patient or family.[12-14]

Futility and Organ-Replacement Technology

Although the bioethical debate over the question of futility has been most concerned with cases involving CPR and the treatment of patients in a persistent vegetative state, a third type of futility-related judgment has gone essentially unchallenged. It involves the increasingly large number of interventions that could possibly prolong the life of virtually any dying patient. For example, extracorporeal membrane oxygenation can replace heart and lung function for up to several weeks. Physicians now use this intervention when they expect organ systems eventually to recover or while they await organs for transplantation. However, it could prolong the life of almost anyone with cardiorespiratory failure, reversible or not. Patients thus kept alive may remain conscious and capable of communicating. Care givers do not now offer this therapy to terminally ill patients, presumably because it would be futile. This judgment has gone largely unchallenged, yet it is not obvious why a clinician's unilateral decision not to use "futile" extracorporeal membrane oxygenation is inherently different from a decision not to use "futile" CPR or "futile" intensive care. If all three treatments can be characterized as objectively futile, then unilateral decisions not to offer them should be equally justified.

As it is used in these three cases, the concept of futility obscures many ambiguities and assumptions. These can be usefully grouped into two categories: problems of value and problems of probability.

Futility and Values

It is meaningless simply to say that an intervention is futile; one must always ask, "Futile in relation to what?" The medical literature provides many examples in which the importance of identifying the goals of treatment has not been fully appreciated. The effectiveness of CPR, for example, is often discussed in terms of whether patients who require the procedure can survive long enough to be discharged from the hospital.[15] This definition of success usually implies that short-term survival is a goal not worth pursuing. Patients or family members may value the additional hours of life differently, however. Indeed, physicians and other care givers have repeatedly been shown to be poor judges of patients' preferences with regard to intensive care.[16–18]

Schneiderman and colleagues have argued that treatments that merely preserve permanent unconsciousness or that cannot end dependence on intensive medical care should be considered futile.[19] Although society may eventually endorse decisions to override the previously expressed wishes of patients or the desires of surrogates who demand such treatments, it does not follow that the treatments are futile. Mr. Wanglie would have rejected this conclusion, and there is no reason to dismiss his view out of hand. The decision that certain goals are not worth pursuing is best seen as involving a conflict of values rather than a question of futility.

Certainly in this context, the plurality of values in our society makes agreement on the concept of futility difficult, if not impossible. Several groups have therefore attempted to arrive at a value-free understanding of the concept.[20,21] The most promising candidate thus far is the notion of "physiologic futility." As the guidelines on the termination of life-sustaining treatment prepared by the Hastings Center state, if a treatment is "clearly futile in achieving its physiological objective and so offer[s] no physiological benefit to the patient, the professional has no obligation to provide it."[20] For example, the physiologic objective of mechanical ventilation is to maintain adequate ventilation and oxygenation in the presence of respiratory failure, and the physiologic objective of CPR is to maintain adequate cardiac output and respiration in the presence of cardiorespiratory failure. The New York State Task Force on Life and the Law mistakenly concludes that CPR is physiologically futile when it will "be unsuccessful in restoring cardiac and respiratory function or [when] the patient will experience repeated arrest in a short time period before death occurs."[21] CPR is physiologically futile only when it is impossible to perform effective cardiac massage and ventilation (such as in the presence of cardiac rupture or severe outflow obstruction). Saying that CPR is physiologically futile when it will be unsuccessful in restoring cardiac function is like saying that mechanical ventilation is physiologically futile if it cannot restore respiratory function. The immediate physiologic effect of the intervention differs from the broader and more uncertain question of prognosis.

Physiologic futility, understood in narrow terms, comes close to providing a value-free understanding of futility. Unfortunately, it applies to a very small number of real cases involving CPR. Similarly, since in the case of Mrs. Wanglie mechanical ventilation could maintain adequate oxygenation and ventilation, her treatment could not be considered futile in the physiologic sense. Even the use of extracorporeal membrane oxygenation in terminally ill patients cannot be considered physiologically futile, since it can maintain circulation and ventilation. The concept of physiologic futility, therefore, falls short of providing guidance in most cases resembling those described above.

Futility and Statistical Uncertainty

In most medical situations, there is no such thing as never. Futility is almost always a matter of probability. But what statistical cutoff point should be chosen as the threshold for determining futility? The statement from the Council on Ethical and Judicial Affairs of the AMA concludes that physicians have no obligation to provide futile CPR, but it fails to specify any level of statistical certainty at which the judgment is warranted.[8] The AMA statement fails to acknowledge that this is even an issue. Should each physician decide independently what probability of success should be considered to indicate futility?

Even if we could agree on a statistical cutoff point for determining futility, physicians are often highly unreliable in estimating the likelihood of success of a therapeutic intervention. Psychological research [22,23] has shown that estimates of probability are susceptible to "severe and systematic errors."[22] Empirical studies have corroborated the limitations of clinical assessment in estimating both prognosis[24] and diagnosis.[25] Even in theory, statistical inferences about what might happen to groups of patients do not permit accurate predictions of what will happen to the next such patient. In addition, the tendency to remember cases that are unusual or bizarre predisposes physicians to make decisions on the basis of their experiences with "miraculous" cures or unexpected tragedies.

Schneiderman and colleagues recently argued that a treatment should be considered futile when 100 consecutive patients do not respond to it.[19] But how similar must the patients be? In assessing the efficacy of mechanical ventilation to treat pneumonia, for example, is it sufficient simply to recall the 100 most recent patients who received artificial ventilation for pneumonia? Or must this group be stratified according to age, etiologic organism, or coexisting illness? Clearly, many of these factors will make an important difference.

Futility and Resource Allocation

Although medical practice has increasingly emphasized patients' autonomy, there is growing pressure on physicians to slow the increase in health care costs by foreclosing some options. Thus, we have a tension between the value of autonomy, exercised in the form of consent to use or omit various interventions, and the desirability of a more Spartan approach to the consumption of medical resources. We promote patients' freedom to request whatever the medical menu has to offer, but we also require that interventions be guided by considerations of cost and the likelihood of benefit.[26] Unfortunately, there is no consensus about what constitutes a just method of balancing the preferences of individual patients against the diverse needs of society.

To some, the concept of futility provides at least a partial solution to this dilemma: it offers a reason to limit therapy without the need to define a fair procedure for allocating resources. This approach allows treatments to be denied on the grounds that they are simply not indicated, apart from the matter of cost. Despite its attractions, there are good reasons why we should not use this concept to solve problems of allocation.

First, arguments based on the futility concept conceal many statistical and value-laden assumptions, whereas strategies based on resource allocation force these assumptions to be stated explicitly. Societies may choose to limit the use of therapies that may be of value and have a reasonable likelihood of success in some cases. For example, the much discussed Oregon plan for allocating Medicaid funds[27] seeks to reflect community values in ranking various health care goals (placing preventive care ahead of cosmetic surgery, for example). Since rationing policies make explicit the values and probabilities that futility-based arguments leave implicit, it is clearly preferable to develop and adopt them rather than use futility arguments as a cover for limiting the availability of scarce and expensive resources.

Another problem with invoking the idea of futility in the debate over allocation is that we have no reason to believe that it is applicable in enough cases to make a difference in the scarcity of medical resources. Although it may be true that beds in the intensive care unit (especially those used for extracorporeal membrane oxygenation) are relatively scarce, it seems unlikely that patients similar to Helga Wanglie occupy an important fraction of those beds, let alone account for a major proportion of the cost of medical care in the United States. From a macroeconomic perspective at least, we must remain skeptical that an appeal to the idea of futility will get us very far.

Moving Beyond Futility

Our rejection of futility as a useful concept does not imply that we endorse patients' unrestricted demands for interventions such as those described in our prototypical scenarios. On the contrary, when providers oppose such demands they are usually acting from a profound sense that further treatment would be fundamentally wrong. Our task is to take account of that sense of wrongness without resorting to unilateral, provider-initiated declarations of futility.

In many of the situations in which questions of futility arise, providers believe that the treatment in question would not be in the patient's interests, even from the patient's perspective, and that any insistence by the patient (or surrogate) on further interventions is based on faulty reasoning, unrealistic expectations, or psychological factors, such as denial or guilt. In these circumstances, providers are obligated to make every effort to clarify precisely what the patient intends to achieve with continued treatment. If the patient's goals appear to reflect unrealistic expectations about the probable course of the underlying illness or the probable effect of medical interventions, providers should attempt to correct those impressions. Because inadequate or insensitive communication by providers probably accounts for a substantial proportion of unrealistic requests, such discussions will successfully resolve many conflicts.[14,28] Empirical studies of ethics consultations have demonstrated precisely this point.[29,30]

Although this appeal to the patient's interests may seem to contain some of the same ambiguities as arguments using the concept of futility, there is a subtle but important distinction between the two. Judgments about what is in the patient's interest are properly grounded in the patient's perspective, whereas judgments cast in the language of futility falsely assume that there is an objective and dispassionate standard for determining benefits and burdens. Nevertheless, even after providers make sustained attempts to clarify patients' preferences, some patients or surrogates will continue to demand life-sustaining interventions when the care givers feel deeply troubled about providing them. In many such cases, unrestrained deference to the wishes of the patient or surrogate conflicts with two other values that do not require a unilateral judgment of the futility of treatment: professional ideals and social consensus.

The ideals of medical professionals include respect for patients' wishes, to be sure, but they also include other values, such as compassionate action and the minimization of suffering. Consider, for example, a bedridden victim of multiple strokes who has contractures and bedsores and who "communicates" only by moaning or grimacing when she is touched. Physicians asked to perform chest compressions, institute mechanical ventilation, or use other life-sustaining interventions in such a patient may regard these actions as cruel and inhumane.[31] Moreover, physicians and other care givers have a legitimate interest in seeing that their knowledge and skills are used wisely and effectively. For example, if surgeons were repeatedly pressured to perform operations that they believed to be inappropriate, they would certainly suffer a loss of dignity and sense of purpose. Although appealing to professional ideals can serve as a convenient means of protecting the interests of physicians at the expense of patients' values, these ideals are legitimate factors to weigh against other values. To dismiss this perspective as irrelevant in decision making is to deny an essential part of what it means to practice medicine.

Although we believe that health care professionals should not be required to take part in care that violates their own morals, the law in this area remains uncertain. On the one hand, courts have upheld a state interest in protecting the ethical integrity of the medical profession. This may provide some basis for protecting doctors who wish to refrain from cruel or inhumane treatment, despite the wishes of the patient or surrogate.[32] On the other hand, in the two cases that have led to court decisions (those of Helga Wanglie[3] and of Jane Doe in Atlanta[33]), the judges upheld the surrogates' decision-making authority. Clearly, this area of the law remains to be defined.

Finally, social consensus is yet another expression of the values at stake in some medical decisions. In a pluralistic society, differences in personal values and interests occasionally run so deep that they cannot be resolved by the introduction of additional facts or by further private debate. At certain critical junctures, the resolution of these conflicts may require an explicit public process of social decision making.[34] Social consensus has been sought, for example, to address the issue of fair allocation of resources.[27] The involvement of society is also essential when the most highly charged questions of morality are at stake, as in the increasingly heated debate over euthanasia.[35]

In the prototypical scenarios described at the outset of this article, an ongoing attempt to achieve social consensus is perhaps most conspicuous with regard to the prolongation of life for patients in a persistent vegetative state. From a legal perspective, the relevant decisions began with the case of Karen Quinlan[36] and have extended through that of Nancy Cruzan.[37] These cases have increased awareness of the ethical issues raised by the situation of patients in a persistent vegetative state and have helped to consolidate the view that it is acceptable to withdraw life-sustaining treatment from patients in such a state. Controversy does remain about who has the ultimate authority to make these decisions. Some hold that the choice must remain with the patient or surrogate, whereas others believe that under some circumstances this prerogative may be overridden. For example, the Hastings Center[38] and the Society of Critical Care Medicine[39] have concluded that providing intensive care to patients in a persistent vegetative state is generally a misuse of resources, and the President's Commission stated that such patients should be removed from life support if such action is necessary to benefit another patient who is not in a persistent vegetative state.[40] It is unclear how this debate will conclude, but the confluence of medical, legal, and ethical thinking about the persistent vegetative state is an example of how social consensus may evolve.

In summary, the Wanglie case demonstrates how the resolution of these conflicts must proceed on many levels. Most such cases will benefit from sustained attempts to clarify the patient's values and the likelihood of the various relevant outcomes, and to improve communication with patients or their surrogates. When this approach fails, physicians and other care givers should ask themselves whether the care requested is consistent with their professional ethics and ideals. When these ideals appear to be violated, either alternative venues for such care should be found or the conflict should be addressed in a public forum. This broader review could be provided through institutional mechanisms, such as the hospital's ethics committee, or by the courts. The public scrutiny that attends such cases will further the debate over the appropriate use of medical resources and foster the development of consensus through legislation and public policy.

Conclusion

In outlining the perspectives of the principal stakeholders — patients and their surrogates, physicians, and society — we have avoided the construction of a rigid formula for resolving conflicts over interventions frequently regarded as futile. Because of clinical heterogeneity, pluralistic values, and the evolutionary nature of social consensus, most clinical decision making on behalf of critically ill patients defies reduction to universally applicable principles.

The notion of futility generally fails to provide an ethically coherent ground for limiting life-sustaining treatment, except in circumstances in which narrowly defined physiologic futility can be plausibly invoked. Futility has been conceptualized as an objective entity independent of the patient's or surrogate's perspective, but differences in values and the variable probabilities of clinical outcomes undermine its basis. Furthermore, assertions of futility may camouflage judgments of comparative worth that are implicit in debates about the allocation of resources. In short, the problem with futility is that its promise of objectivity can rarely be fulfilled. The rapid advance of the language of futility into the jargon of bioethics should be followed by an equally rapid retreat.

Notes

1. *Jacobellis v. State of Ohio*, 84 S Ct 1676 (1964).

2. Hippocrates. The art. In Reiser S.J., Dyck A.J., Curran W.J., eds. *Ethics in medicine: historical perspectives and contemporary concerns.* Cambridge, Mass.: MIT Press, 1977:6–7.

3. Capron A.M. In re Help Wanglie. *Hastings Cent Rep* 1991;21(5):26–8.

4. Lantos J.D., Singer P.A., Walker R.M., et al. The illusion of futility in clinical practice. *Am J Med* 1989;87:81–4.

5. Standards for cardiopulmonary resuscitation (CPR) and emergency cardiac care (ECC). V. Medicolegal considerations and recommendations. *JAMA* 1974;227: Suppl:864–6.

6. Appendix A: the proposed legislation. In *Do not resuscitate orders: the proposed legislation and report of the New York State Task Force on Life and the Law*. 2nd ed. New York: The Task Force, 1986:83.

7. 1994 Amendments to the Child Abuse Prevention and Treatment Act. *Pub Law* 98–457, 1984.

8. Council on Ethical and Judicial Affairs, American Medical Association. Guidelines for the appropriate use of do-not-resuscitate orders. *JAMA* 1991;265:1868–71.

9. Miles S.H. Informed demand for "non-beneficial" medical treatment. *N Engl J Med* 1991;325:512–5.

10. Brain-damaged woman at center of lawsuit over life-support dies. *New York Times*. July 5, 1991:A8.

11. Paris J.J., Crone R.K., Reardon F. Physicians' refusal of requested treatment: the case of Baby L. *N Engl J Med* 1990;322:1012–5.

12. Blackball U. Must we always use CPR? *N Engl J Med* 1987;317:1281–5.

13. Hackler J.C., Hiller F.C. Family consent to orders not to resuscitate: reconsidering hospital policy. *JAMA* 1990;264:1281–3.

14. Murphy D.J. Do-not-resuscitate orders: time for reappraisal in long-term care institutions. *JAMA* 1988;260:2098–101.

15. Bedell S.E., Detbanco T.L., Cook E.F., Epstein F.H. Survival after cardiopulmonary resuscitation in the hospital. *N Engl J Med* 1983;309:569–76.

16. Danis M., Gerrity M.S., Southerland L.I., Patrick D.L. A comparison of patient, family, and physician assessments of the value of medical intensive care. *Crit Care Med* 1988;16:594–600.

17. Danis M., Jarr S.L., Southerland L.I., Nocella R.S., Patrick D.L. A comparison of patient, family, and nurse evaluations of the usefulness of intensive care. *Crit Care Med* 1987;15:138–43.

18. Danis M., Patrick D.L., Southerland L.I., Green M.L. Patients' and families' preferences for medical intensive care. *JAMA* 1988;260:797–802.

19. Schneiderman L.J., Jecker N.S., Jonsen A.R. Medical futility: its meaning and ethical implications. *Ann Intern Med* 1990;112:949–54.

20. The Hastings Center. *Guidelines on the termination of life-sustaining treatment and the care of the dying*. Bloomington: Indiana University Press, 1987:32.

21. Appendix C: New York Public Health Law Article 29-B — orders not to resuscitate. In *Do not resuscitate orders: the proposed legislation and report of the New York State Task Force on Life and the Law*. 2nd ed. New York: The Task Force, 1986:96.

22. Tversky A., Kahneman D. Judgment under uncertainty: heuristics and biases. *Science* 1974;185:1124–31.

23. Elstein A.S. Clinical judgment: psychological research and medical practice. *Science* 1976;194:696–700.

24. Poses R.M., Bekes C., Copare F.J., Scott W.E. The answer to "What are my chances, doctor?" depends on whom is asked: prognostic disagreement and inaccuracy for critically ill patients. *Crit Care Med* 1989;17:827–33.

25. Poses R.M., Cebul R.D., Collins M., Fager S.S. The accuracy of experienced physicians' probability estimates for patients with sore throats: implications for decision making. *JAMA* 1985;254:925–9.

26. Aaron H., Schwartz W.B. Rationing health care: the choice before us. *Science* 1990;247:419–22.

27. Eddy D.M. What's going on in Oregon? *JAMA* 1991;266:417–20.

28. Younger S.J. Who defines futility? *JAMA* 1988;260:2094–5.

29. Brennan T.A. Ethics committees and decisions to limit care: the experience at the Massachusetts General Hospital. *JAMA* 1988;260:803–7.

30. La Puma J. Consultations in clinical ethics — issues and questions in 27 cases. *West J Med* 1987;146:633–7.

31. Braithwaite S., Thomasma D.C. New guidelines on foregoing life-sustaining treatment in incompetent patients: an anti-cruelty policy. *Ann Intem Med* 1986;104:711–5.

32. Meisel A. *The right to die*. New York: John Wiley & Sons, 1989:104.

33. *In re: Doe,* Civil Action No. D93064 (Fulton County, GA, October 17, 1991).

34. Callahan D. Medical futility, medical necessity: the-problem-without-a-name. *Hastings Cent Rep* 1991;21(4):30–5.

35. Misbin P.I. Physicians' aid in dying. *N Engl J Med* 1991;325:1307–11.

36. *In the Matter of Karen Ann Quinlan, an alleged incompetent.* 355 A.2d 647; or 70 NJ 10. March 31, 1976.

37. Annas G.J. Nancy Cruzan and the right to die. *N Engl J Med* 1990;323:670–3.

38. The Hastings Center. *Guidelines on the termination of life-sustaining treatment and the care of the dying.* Bloomington: Indiana University Press, 1987:112.

39. Task Force on Ethics of the Society of Critical Care Medicine. Consensus report on the ethics of foregoing life-sustaining treatments in the critically ill. *Crit Care Med* 1990;18:1435–9.

40. President's Commission for the Study of Ethical Problems in Medicine and Biomedical and Behavioral Research. *Deciding to forego life-sustaining ethical, medical, and legal issues in treatment decisions.* Washington, D.C.: Government Printing Office, 1983:188–9.

Further Readings

Atterbury, C.E. "The Alcoholic in the Lifeboat: Should Drinkers Be Candidates for Liver Transplantation?" *J Clin Gastroenterol* 8 (1986):1–4.

Brody, B.A., and A. Halevy. "Is Futility a Futile Concept?" *J Med Philos* 20:2 (Apr. 1995): 123–144.

Callahan, D. "Rationing, Equity, and Affordable Care." *Health Prog* 81:4 (July–Aug. 2000): 38–41.

Cassel, Christine, et al., eds. *Geriatric Medicine*. New York: Springer Verlag, 1990.

Cookson R, Dolan P. "Principles of justice in health care rationing." *J Med Ethics*. 26:5 (Oct. 2000):323–329.

Gross, M. "The Ethical Allocation of Scarce Resources in Surgery: Implants and Cost," *Can J of Surgery* 40:6 (1997): 421–423.

Kluge, E.-H.W. "Designated Organ Donation: Private Choice in Social Context." *Hastings Center Rep* (Sept.–Oct. 1989): 10–15.

Liu, Y., W. C. Hsiao, and K. Eggleston. "Equity in Health and Health Care: The Chinese Experience." *Soc Sci Med* 49:10 (Nov. 1999): 1349–1356.

Luce, J.M. "Physicians Do Not Have a Responsibility to Provide Futile or Unreasonable Care if a Patient or Family Insists." *Crit Care Med* 23:4 (Apr. 1995): 760–766.

A Prescription for Sustainability, submission of the CMA to the Romanow Commission, June 6, 2002. **http://www.cma.ca/cma/staticContent/HTML/N0/l2/advocacy/news/2002/prescription_for_sustainability_eng.PDF**

Rachels, James F. "Who Shall Live When Not All Can Live?" *Soundings: An Interdis J* 53 (Winter 1970): 339–355.

Report of the Council on Ethical and Judicial Affairs of the American Medical Association.

Ethical Implications of Age-Based Rationing of Health Care. Chicago, Ill.: American Medical Assoc, 1988. 1–88.

Rescher, Nicholas. "The Allocation of Exotic Medical Lifesaving Therapy." *Ethics* 79 (1969): 173–180.

Rivlin, M.M. "Why the Fair Innings Argument Is Not Persuasive." *BMC Med Ethics* 1:1 (2000): 1.

Thomasma, D.C. "The Ethical Challenge of Providing Healthcare for the Elderly." *Camb Q Healthcare Ethics* 4 (1995): 148–62.

Tsuchiya, A. "QALYs and Ageism: Philosophical Theories and Age Weighting." *Health Econ* 9:1 (Jan. 2000): 57–68.

Veatch, R.M. "Voluntary Risk to Health: The Ethical Issues." *JAMA* 243 (Jan. 4, 1980): 50–55.

Weber, L.J, and M.L. Campbell. "Medical Futility and Life-Sustaining Treatment Decisions." *J Neurosci Nurs* 28:1 (Feb. 1996): 56–60.

Williams, A. "Intergenerational Equity: An Exploration of the 'Fair Innings' Argument." *Health Econ* 6 (1997): 117–32.

CHAPTER 5
THE HEALTH CARE PROFESSIONAL–PATIENT RELATIONSHIP

Introduction

In human terms, the most important thing in the delivery of health care is the relationship between the health care professional and the patient. This is not to say that no other factors have to be taken into account, or that no other relationships are important. For instance, the availability of health care resources plays a crucial role because it defines the limits within which the delivery of care can take place. Likewise the relationship between the professional and the patient's next-of-kin, or with other health care professionals and society are also important, because they define the extended setting in which the delivery of care actually takes place.

However, the relationship between the professional and the patient is central because it is the basis of the health care professional's interaction with all the other parties. It is also the *raison d'être* of health care itself. Therefore it is logically primary. How this relationship is structured sets the tone for everything else.

It could be argued that the relationship between a public health professional and society as a whole is different. But even here similar ethical problems arise and similar ethical considerations apply. Issues such as those of authority, compliance, informed consent and, above all, trust are also implicated. The only difference is that in the case of public health, society itself has taken the place of the individual patient.

Of course the fact that society is composed of many individuals does introduce issues that do not exist in the usual health care professional–

patient relationship. The question of aggregate as opposed to individual rights constitutes a particular thorny — and distinctive — issue. However, even here the relationship between the health care professional and the individual patient remains important; because in the end, activities that are directed towards the public good must be translated into actions that affect individual patients. With this, the professional–patient relationship once again comes to the fore.

The traditional view held by physicians themselves was that the physician is the captain of the ship, and that the patient has to follow orders. We find this view expressed in the writings of Hippocrates — himself a physician — and those of later medical writers like Galen, Razes, Maimonides and so on. For the English-speaking world, this view found its classic statement in Thomas Percival's *Medical Ethics.* (Incidentally, Percival also had a similar view of nurses and other health care workers.)

While for centuries this was the outlook of physicians themselves, for a long time society did not entirely share this perspective. Until well into the nineteenth century, the physician was seen as a figure of last resort — and even then, as someone who gave advice, but whose advice could be ignored by the patient. It was not until the nineteenth century, and even more in the twentieth when medicine became a legally recognized service-provider monopoly, that the physician came to be seen as the primary decision-maker: as the person who knew best, and who therefore had not only the right but also the duty to make the decisions.

Nowadays, such a physician-centred perspective is no longer in vogue. In fact, this sort of approach to physician authority would be characterized as being extremely paternalistic in nature. The selections that follow present an examination of how the relationship between the health care professional and the patient should be structured from a contemporary perspective.

Years ago, Robert Veatch identified four models of the physician–patient relationship. He distinguished between what he called the engineering model, the priestly model, the collegial and the contractual model.[1]

According to the engineering model, the physician is nothing more than an "applied scientist," who simply presents the patient with diagnosis, prognosis and treatment options, but leaves the decision making completely up to the patient. Questions of ethics and values do not enter into the relationship so far as the physician is concerned. "The physician becomes a plumber without any moral integrity." What Veatch called the priestly model is what is also often called the paternalistic model. This model is exactly the reverse of the engineering model. The physician here acts on the basis of the principle "Benefit and do not harm the patient," but it is the physician who decides what constitutes benefit and harm. "The moral authority [of the physician] so dominates … that the patient's freedom and dignity are extinguished."

According to the collegial model, both physician and patient are connected by common bonds of mutual loyalty, common interests and goals. It is also characterized by the assumption that physician and patient come together as independent equals.

The contractual model questions this assumption of equality. It recognizes the differences in knowledge and power between physician and patient, and tries to compensate for this in terms of an assumed — and sometimes even explicit — contractual perspective that leaves both parties their own dignity and moral authority.

There have been various reactions to and modifications of Veatch's analysis. The article by James Childress and Mark Siegler, included below, is one of the more noteworthy. Contrary to Veatch, Childress and Siegler argue that the nature of the physician–patient relationship is more properly defined by the concept of autonomous negotiation that balances competing claims. Further, they argue that societal constraints also enter the picture.

However, patients interact not only with physicians but also with nurses. In fact, in many instances, more care is provided by nurses than by physicians — certainly on a continuing basis. It is not at all clear that an analysis that focuses on the physician–patient interaction captures the complexity of the nurse-patient relationship. In an article written especially for this volume, Janet Storch presents the perspective of the nurse.

Finally, a point about the health care professions and their social embedding. Health care professionals have a unique status in our society: They have intimate access to our person and to information about us. As well, many health care professions are service-provider monopolies.[2] That is to say, only duly qualified and licensed health care professionals may engage in the relevant actions. Moreover, many health care professions are self-governing — which means that they themselves set the standards against which the conduct of their members is measured.[3,4] Therefore it is important that the codes that govern the conduct of these professions be ethically appropriate and in keeping with the ethics that governs society as a whole. That is why these codes are published by the professions, so that society may verify that its trust in the professions is not misplaced, and that it has some basis for evaluating the ethical conduct of the individual professionals. The Code of Ethics of the Canadian Medical Association, along with the codes of medical associations from many other countries, can be accessed on the Web at **http://www.wma.net/e/ethicsunit/organizations.htm**. The Code of Ethics for Registered Nurses of Canada can be found at **http://www.cna-nurses.ca/pages/ethics/Code%20of%20Ethics%202002.pdf**, and the Code of Ethics of the International Council of Nurses, of which the Canadian Nurses Association is a member, can be found at **http://www.icn.ch/ethics.htm**.

Notes

1. Robert M. Veatch, "Models for Ethical Medicine in a Revolutionary Age," *Hastings Center Rep* 2 (June 1972): 7.

2. Kluge E.-H. W., "Physicians' Practice Profiles and the Patient's Right to Know," *J Clin Eval* 6:3 (2000): 235–239.

3. E. Freidson, *Professional Powers: A Study of the Institutionalization of Formal Knowledge*. Chicago: Chicago Univ. Press, 1986.

4. T. Parsons, *Essays in Sociological Theory*. Glencoe, Ill.: The Free Press, 1954.

Metaphors and Models of Doctor–Patient Relationships: Their Implications for Autonomy

James F. Childress and Mark Siegler

Introduction

Many metaphors and models have been applied to relationships between patients and physicians. One example is an interpretation of physician–patient relationships as paternalistic. In this case, the physician is regarded as a parent and the patient is regarded as a child. Opponents of such a paternalistic view of medicine rarely reject the use of metaphors to interpret medical relationships; rather, they simply offer alternative metaphors, for example, the physician as partner or the patient as rational contractor. Metaphors may operate even when patients and physicians are unaware of them. Physician–patient conflicts may arise if each party brings to their encounter a different image of medicine, as, for example, when the physician regards a paternalistic model of medicine as appropriate, but the patient prefers a contractual model.

As these examples suggest, metaphors involve seeing something as something else, for example, seeing a lover as a red rose, human beings as wolves, or medical therapy as warfare.

Metaphors highlight some features and hide other features of their principal subject.[1] Thus, thinking about a physician as a parent highlights the physician's care for dependent others and his or her control over them, but it conceals the patient's payment of fees to the physician. Metaphors and models may be used to describe relationships as they exist, or to indicate what those relationships ought to be. In either the descriptive or the prescriptive use of metaphors, this highlighting and hiding occurs, and it must be considered in determining the adequacy of various metaphors. When metaphors are used to describe roles, they can be criticized if they distort more features than they illuminate. And when they are used to direct roles, they can be criticized if they highlight one moral consideration, such as care, while neglecting others, such as autonomy.

Since there is no single physician–patient relationship, it is probable that no single metaphor can adequately describe or direct the whole range of relationships in health care, such as open heart surgery, clinical research, and psychoanalysis. Some of the most important

Kluwer Academic Publishers. *Theoretical Medicine and Bioethics* 5, 1984, 17–30, Childress & Siegler. With kind permission from Kluwer Publishers.

metaphors that have shaped health care in recent years include: parent–child, partners, rational contractors, friends, and technician–client. We want to determine the adequacy of these metaphors to describe and to direct doctor–patient relationships in the real world. In particular, we will assess them in relation to patient and physician autonomy.

Metaphors and Models of Relationships in Health Care

(1) The first metaphor is *paternal or parental*, and the model is paternalism. For this model, the locus of decision making is the health care professional, particularly the physician, who has "moral authority" within an asymmetrical and hierarchical relationship. (A variation on these themes appears in a model that was especially significant earlier — the priest–penitent relationship.) Following Thomas Szasz and Marc Hollender, we can distinguish two different versions of paternalism, based on two different prototypes.[2] If we take the *parent–infant relationship* as the prototype, the physician's role is active, while the patient's role is passive. The patient, like the infant, is primarily a dependent recipient of care. This model is applied easily to such clinical situations as anesthesia and to the care of patients with acute trauma, coma, or delirium. A second version takes the *parent–adolescent child relationship* as the prototype. Within this version, the physician guides the patient by telling him or her what to expect and what to do, and the patient co-operates to the extent of obeying. This model applies to such clinical situations as the outpatient treatment of acute infectious diseases. The physician instructs the patient on a course of treatment (such as antibiotics and rest), but the patient can either obey or refuse to comply.

The paternalist model assigns moral authority and discretion to the physician because good health is assumed to be a value shared by the patient and the physician and because the physician's competence, skills, and ability place him or her in a position to help the patient regain good health. Even if it was once the dominant model in health care and even if many patients and physicians still prefer it, the paternalist model is no longer adequate to describe or to direct all relationships in health care. Too many changes have occurred. In a pluralistic society such as ours, the assumption that the physician and patient have common values about health may be mistaken. They may disagree about the meaning of health and disease (for example, when the physician insists that cigarette smoking is a disease, but the patient claims that it is merely a nasty habit) or about the value of health relative to other values (for example, when the physician wants to administer a blood transfusion to save the life of a Jehovah's Witness, but the patient rejects the blood in order to have a chance of heavenly salvation).

As a normative model, paternalism tends to concentrate on care rather than respect, patients' needs rather than their rights, and physicians' discretion rather than patients' autonomy or self-determination. Even though paternalistic actions can sometimes be justified, for example, when a patient is not competent to make a decision and is at risk of harm, not all paternalistic actions can be justified.[3]

(2) A second model is one of *partnership*, which can be seen in Eric Cassell's statement: "Autonomy for the sick patient cannot exist outside of a good and properly functioning doctor–patient relation. And the relation between them is inherently a partnership."[4] The language of collegiality, collaboration, association, co-adventureship, and covenant is also used. This model stresses that health care professionals and their patients are partners or colleagues in the pursuit of

the shared value of health. It is similar to the paternalist model in that it emphasizes the shared general values of the enterprise in which the participants are involved. But what makes this model distinctive and significant is its emphasis on the equality of the participants' interpretations of shared values such as health, along with respect for the personal autonomy of all the participants.[5] The theme of equality does not, however, cancel a division of competence and responsibility along functional lines within the relationship.

Szasz and Hollender suggest that the prototype of the model of "mutual participation" or partnership is the adult–adult relationship. Within this model the physician helps the patient to help himself, while the patient uses expert help to realize his (and the physician's) ends. Some clinical applications of this model appear in the care of chronic diseases and psychoanalysis. It presupposes that "the participants (1) have approximately equal power, (2) be mutually interdependent (i.e., need each other), and (3) engage in activity that will be in some ways satisfying to both." Furthermore, "the physician does not know what is best for the patient. The search for this becomes the essence of the therapeutic interaction. The patient's own experiences furnish indispensable information for eventual agreement, under otherwise favorable circumstances, as to what 'health' might be for him."[6]

Although this model describes a few practices, it is most often offered as a normative model, indicating the morally desirable and even obligatory direction of practice and research.[7] As a normative model, it stresses the equality of value contributions and the autonomy of both professionals and other participants, whether sick persons or volunteers for research.

(3) A third model is that of *rational contractors*. Health care professionals and their patients are related or should

be related to each other by a series of specific contracts. The prototype of this model is the specific contract by which individuals agree to exchange goods and services, and the enforcement of such contracts by governmental sanctions. According to Robert Veatch, one of the strongest proponents of the contractual model in health care, this model is the best compromise between the *ideal of partnership*, with its emphasis on both equality and autonomy, and the *reality* of medical care, where mutual trust cannot be presupposed. If we could realize mutual trust, we could develop partnerships. In the light of a realistic assessment of our situation, however, we can only hope for contracts. The model of rational contracts, according to Veatch, is the only realistic way to share responsibility, to preserve both equality and autonomy under less than ideal circumstances, and to protect the integrity of various parties in health care (e.g., physicians are free not to enter contracts that would violate their consciences and to withdraw from them when they give proper notice).[8]

Such a model is valuable but problematic both descriptively and normatively. It neglects the fact that sick persons do not view health care needs as comparable to other wants and desires, that they do not have sufficient information to make rational contracts with the best providers of health services, and that the current structure of medicine obstructs the free operation of the marketplace and of contracts.[9] This model may also neglect the virtues of benevolence, care, and compassion that are stressed in other models such as paternalism and friendship.

(4) A fourth attempt to understand and direct the relationships between health care professionals and patients stresses *friendship*. According to P. Lain Entraglo,

> Insofar as man is a part of nature,
> and health an aspect of this nature
> and therefore a natural and objec-

tive good, the *medical relation* develops into comradeship, or association for the purpose of securing this good by technical means. Insofar as man is an individual and his illness a state affecting his personality, the medical relation ought to be more than mere comradeship — in fact it should be a friendship. All dogma apart, a good doctor has always been a friend to his patient, to all his patients.[10]

For this version of "medical philia," the patient expresses trust and confidence in the physician while the doctor's "friendship for the patient should consist above all in a desire to give effective technical help — benevolence conceived and realised in technical terms."[11] Technical help and generalized benevolence are made "friendly" by explicit reference to the patient's personality.

Charles Fried's version of "medical philia" holds that physicians are *limited, special-purpose friends* in relation to their patients. In medicine, as in other professional activities such as law, the client may have a relationship with the professional that is analogous to friendship. In friendship and in these relationships, one person assumes the interests of another. Claims in both sets of relationships are intense and demanding, but medical friendship is more limited in scope.[12]

Of course, this friendship analogy is somewhat strained, as Fried recognizes, because needs (real and felt) give rise to medical relationships, even if professionals are free not to meet them unless they are emergencies, because patients pay professionals for their "personal care," and because patients do not have reciprocal loyalties. Nevertheless, Fried's analysis of the medical relationship highlights the equality, the autonomy, and the rights of both parties — the "friend" and the "befriended." Because friendship, as

Kant suggested, is "the union of two persons through equal and mutual love and respect," the model of friendship has some ingredients of both paternalism (love or care) and anti-paternalism (equality and respect).[13] It applies especially well to the same medical relationships that fit partnership; indeed, medical friendship is very close to medical partnership, except that the former stresses the intensity of the relationship, while the latter stresses the emotional reserve as well as the limited scope of the relationship.

(5) A fifth and final model views the health care professional as a *technician*. Some commentators have referred to this model as plumber, others as engineer; for example, it has been suggested that with the rise of scientific medicine, the physician was viewed as "the expert engineer of the body as a machine."[14] Within this model, the physician "provides" or "delivers" technical service to patients who are "consumers." Exchange relations provide images for this interpretation of medical relations.

This model does not appear to be possible or even desirable. It is difficult to imagine that the health care professional as technician can simply present the "facts" unadorned by values, in part because major terms such as health and disease are not value-free and objective. Whether the "technician" is in an organization or in direct relation to clients, he or she serves some values. Thus, this model may collapse into the contractual model or a bureaucratic model (which will not be discussed in this essay). The professional may be thought to have only technical authority, not moral authority. But he or she remains a moral agent and thus should choose to participate or not in terms of his or her own commitments, loyalties, and integrity. One shortcoming of the paternalist and priestly models, as Robert Veatch notes, is the patient's "moral abdication," while one shortcoming of the technician model is the physician's "moral abdication."[15] The technician model offers autonomy to the patient, whose values dominate (at least in some settings) at the expense of the professional's moral agency and integrity. In other models such as contract, partnership, and friendship, moral responsibility is shared by all the parties in part because they are recognized, in some sense, as equals.

Relations Between Intimates and Between Strangers

The above models of relationships between physicians and patients move between two poles: intimates and strangers.[16] In relations of intimacy, all the parties know each other very well and often share values, or at least know which values they do not share. In such relations, formal rules and procedures, backed by sanctions, may not be necessary; they may even be detrimental to the relationships. In relations of intimacy, trust rather than control is dominant. Examples include relationships between parents and children and between friends. Partnerships also share some features of such relationships, but their intimacy and shared values may be limited to a specific set of activities.

By contrast, in relations among strangers, rules and procedures become very important, and control rather than trust is dominant.[17] Of course, in most relations there are mixtures of trust and control. Each is present to some degree. Nevertheless, it is proper to speak about relations between strangers as structured by rules and procedures because the parties do not know each other well enough to have mutual trust. Trust means confidence in and reliance upon the other to act in accord with moral

principles and rules or at least in accord with his or her publicly manifested principles and rules, whatever they might be. But if the other is a stranger, we do not know whether he or she accepts what we would count as moral principles and rules. We do not know whether he or she is worthy of trust. In the absence of intimate knowledge, or of shared values, strangers resort to rules and procedures in order to establish some control. Contracts between strangers, for example, to supply certain goods, represent instances of attempted control. But contractual relations do not only depend on legal sanctions; they also presuppose confidence in a shared structure of rules and procedures. As Talcott Parsons has noted, "transactions are actually entered into in accordance with a body of binding rules which are not part of the ad hoc agreement of the parties."[18]

Whether medicine is now only a series of encounters between strangers rather than intimates, medicine is increasingly regarded by patients and doctors and by analysts of the profession — such as philosophers, lawyers, and sociologists — as a practice that is best understood and regulated *as if it were* a practice among strangers rather than among intimates. Numerous causes can be identified: First, the pluralistic nature of our society; second, the decline of close, intimate contact over time among professionals and patients and their families; third, the decline of contact with the "whole person," who is now parcelled out to various specialists; fourth, the growth of large, impersonal, bureaucratically structured institutions of care, in which there is discontinuity of care (the patient may not see the same professionals on subsequent visits).[19]

In this situation, Alasdair MacIntyre contends, the modern patient "usually approaches the physician as stranger to stranger: and the very proper fear and suspicion that we have of strangers extends equally properly to our encounters with physicians. We do not and cannot know what to expect of them. ..."[20] He suggests that one possible response to this situation is to develop a rule-based bureaucracy in which "we can confront any individual who fills a given role with exactly the same expectation of exactly the same outcomes. ..." Our encounters with physicians and other health care professionals are encounters between strangers precisely because of our pluralistic society: several value systems are in operation, and we do not know whether the physicians we encounter share our value systems. In such a situation, patient autonomy is "a solution of last resort" rather than "a central moral good." Finally patients have to decide for themselves what will be done to them or simply delegate such decisions to others, such as physicians.

Just as MacIntyre recognizes the value of patient autonomy in our pluralistic society, so John Ladd recognizes the value of the concept of rights among strangers.[21] He notes that a legalistic, rights-based approach to medicine has several important advantages because rules and rights "serve to define our relationships with strangers as well as with people whom we know. ... In the medical context ... we may find ourselves in a hospital bed in a strange place, with strange company, and confronted by a strange physician and staff. The strangeness of the situation makes the concept of rights, both legal and moral, a very useful tool for defining our relationship to those with whom we have to deal."

Rules and rights that can be enforced obviously serve as ways to control the conduct of others when we do not know them well enough to be able to trust them. But all of the models of health care relationships identified above depend on some degree of trust. It is too simplistic to suppose that contracts, which can be legally enforced, do away with trust totally. Indeed, as we have argued, a society based on contracts depends to a very great extent on trust, precisely because not everything is enforceable at manageable cost. Thus, the issue is not simply whether trust or control is dominant, but, in part, the basis and extent of trust.

Trust, at least limited trust, may be possible even among strangers. There may be a presumption of trust, unless the society is in turmoil. And there may be an intermediate notion of "friendly strangers." People may be strangers because of differences regarding values or uncertainty regarding the other's values; they may be friendly because they accept certain rules and procedures, which may ensure that different values are respected. If consensus exists in a pluralistic society, it is primarily about rules and procedures, some of which protect the autonomy of agents, their freedom to negotiate their own relationships.

Physician–Patient Interactions as Negotiations

It is illuminating, both descriptively and prescriptively, to view some encounters and interactions between physicians and patients as negotiations. The metaphor of negotiation has its home in discussions to settle matters by mutual agreements of the concerned parties. While it frequently appears in disputes between management and labor and between nations, it does not necessarily presuppose a conflict of interests between the parties. The metaphor of negotiation may also illuminate processes of reaching agreement regarding the terms of continuing interaction even when the issue is mainly the determination of one party's interests and the means to realize those interests. This metaphor captures two important characteristics of medical relationships: (1) it accents the autonomy of both patient and physician, and (2) it suggests a process that occurs over time rather than an event which occurs at a particular moment.

The model of negotiation can both explain what frequently occurs and identify what ought to occur in physician–patient interactions. An example can make this point: A twenty-eight-year-old ballet dancer suffered from moderately severe asthma. When she moved from New York to Chicago, she changed physicians and placed herself in the hands of a famed asthma specialist. He initiated aggressive steroid therapy to control her asthma, and within several months he had managed to control her wheezing. But she was distressed because her dancing had deteriorated. She suspected that she was experiencing muscle weakness and fluid accumulation because of the steroid treatment. When she attempted to discuss her concerns with the physician, he maintained that "bringing the disease under complete control — achieving a complete remission of wheezes — will be the best thing for you in the long run." After several months of unhappiness and failure to convince the physician of the importance of her personal goals as well as her medical goals, she sought another physician, insisting that she didn't live just to breathe, but breathed so that she could dance.[22]

As in this case — and despite the claims of several commentators — people with medical needs generally do not confront physicians as strangers and as adversaries in contemporary health care. As we suggested earlier, even if they can be viewed as strangers in that they often do not know each other prior to the encounter, both parties may well proceed with a presumption of trust. Patients may approach physicians with some trust and confidence in the medical profession, even though they do not know the physicians before them. Indeed, codes of medical ethics have been designed in part to foster this trust

by indicating where the medical profession stands and by creating a climate of trust. Thus, even if patients approach individual physicians as strangers, they may have some confidence in these physicians as members of the profession as they negotiate the particular terms of their relationship. At the other extreme, some patients may approach physicians as adversaries or opponents. But for negotiation to proceed, some trust must be present, even if it is combined with some degree of control, for example, through legal requirements and the threat of legal sanctions.

The general public trust in the medical profession's values and skills provides the presumptive basis for trust in particular physicians and can facilitate the process of negotiation. But, as we noted earlier, in a pluralistic society, even people who are strangers, i.e., who share very few substantive values, may be "friendly" if they share procedural values. Certain procedural values may provide the most important basis for the trust that is necessary for negotiation; indeed, procedural principles and rules should structure the negotiation in order to ensure equal respect for the autonomy of all the parties.

First, the negotiation should involve adequate disclosure by both parties. In this process of communication — much broader and richer than most doctrines of informed consent recognize — both parties should indicate their values as well as other matters of relevance. Without this information, the negotiation cannot be open and fair. Second, the negotiation should be voluntary, i.e., uncoerced. Insofar as critical illness can be viewed as "coercing" individuals through the creation of fear, etc., it may be difficult to realize this condition for patients with certain problems. However, for the majority of patients this condition is achievable. Third, the accommodation reached through the negotiation should be mutually acceptable.[23]

What can we say about the case of the ballet dancer in the light of these procedural requirements for negotiation? It appears that the relationship foundered not because of inadequate disclosure at the outset, or along the way, but because of the patient's change in or clarification of her values and the physician's inability to accommodate these other values. The accommodation reached at the outset was mutually acceptable for a time. Initially their values and their metaphors for their relationship were the same. The physician regarded himself as a masterful scientist who was capable technically of controlling a patient's symptoms of wheezing. In fact, he remarked on several occasions: "I have never met a case of asthma I couldn't help." The patient, for her part, selected the physician initially for the same reasons. She was unhappy that her wheezing persisted, and she was becoming discouraged by her chronic health problem. Because she wanted a therapeutic success, she selected an expert who would help her achieve that goal. Both the patient and the physician made several voluntary choices. The patient chose to see *this* physician and to see him for several months, and the physician chose to treat asthma aggressively with steroids.

In a short time, the patient reconsidered or clarified her values, discovering that her dancing was even more important to her than the complete remission of wheezing, and she wanted to renegotiate her relationship so that it could be more mutual and participatory. But her new metaphor for the relationship was incompatible with the physician's nonnegotiable commitment to his metaphor which the patient had also accepted at the outset. Thus, the relationship collapsed. This case illustrates both the possibilities and the limitations of the model of negotiation. Even when the procedural requirements are met, the negotiation may not result in a satisfactory accommodation over time, and the negotiation itself may proceed in terms of the physi-

cian's and the patient's metaphors and models of the relationships, as well as the values they affirm.

Autonomy constrains and limits the negotiations and the activities of both parties: Neither party may violate the autonomy of the other or use the other merely as a means to an end. But respecting autonomy as a constraint and a limit does not imply seeking it as a *goal* or praising it as an ideal.[24] This point has several implications. It means, for example, that patients may exercise their autonomy to turn their medical affairs completely over to physicians. A patient may instruct the physician to do whatever he or she deems appropriate: "You're the doctor; whatever you decide is fine." This relationship has been characterized as "paternalism with permission,"[25] and it is not ruled out by autonomy as a constraint or a limit. It might, however, be ruled out by a commitment to autonomy as an ideal. Indeed, commitment to autonomy as an ideal can even be paternalistic in a negative sense; it can lead the health care professional to try to force the patient to be free and to live up to the ideal of autonomy. But our conception of autonomy as a constraint and a limit prevents such actions toward competent patients who are choosing and acting voluntarily. Likewise, maintenance, restoration, or promotion of the patient's autonomy may be, and usually is, one important goal of medical relationships. But its importance can only be determined by negotiation between the physician and the patient. The patient may even subordinate the goal of autonomy to various other goals, just as the ballet dancer subordinated freedom from wheezing to the power to dance.

This view of autonomy as a limit or a constraint, rather than an ideal or a goal, permits individuals to define the terms of their relationship. Just as it permits the patient to acquiesce in the physician's recommendations, it permits the physician to enter a contract as a mere technician to provide certain medical services, as requested by the patient. In such an arrangement, the physician does *not* become a mere means or a mere instrument to the patient's ends. Rather, the physician exercises his or her autonomy to enter into the relationship to provide technical services. Such actions are an expression of autonomy, not a denial of autonomy. If, however, the physician believes that an action requested by the patient — for example, a specific mode of therapy for cancer or a sterilization procedure — is not medically indicated, or professionally acceptable, or in the patient's best interests, he or she is not obligated to sacrifice autonomy and comply. In such a case, the professional refuses to be an instrument of or to carry out the patient's wishes. When the physician cannot morally or professionally perform an action (not legally prohibited by the society) he or she may have a duty to inform the patient of other physicians who might be willing to carry out the patient's wishes. A refusal to be an instrument of another's wishes is very different from trying to prevent another from redefining his or her goals.

Negotiation is not always possible or desirable. It is impossible, or possible only to a limited extent, in certain clinical settings in which the conditions for a fair, informed, and voluntary negotiation are severely limited, often because one party lacks some of the conditions for autonomous choices. First, negotiation may be difficult if not impossible with some types of patients, such as the mentally incompetent. Sometimes paternalism may be morally legitimate or even morally obligatory when the patient is not competent to negotiate and is at risk. In such cases, parents, family members, or others may undertake negotiation with the physician, for example, regarding defective newborns or comatose adults. But health care professionals and the state may have to intervene in order to protect the interests of the patient who cannot negotiate directly. Second, the model of negotiation does not fit situations in which patients are forced by law to accept medical interventions such as compulsory vaccination, involuntary commitment, and involuntary psychiatric treatment. In such situations, the state authorizes or requires treatment against the wishes of the patient; the patient and the physician do not negotiate their relationship. Third, in some situations physicians have dual or multiple allegiances, some of which may take priority over loyalty to the patient. Examples include military medicine, industrial medicine, prison medicine, and university health service. The physician is not free in such settings to negotiate in good faith with the patient, and the patient's interests and rights may have to be protected by other substantive and procedural standards and by external control. Fourth, negotiation may not be possible in some emergencies in which people desperately need medical treatment because of the risk of death or serious bodily harm. In such cases, the physician may *presume* consent, apart from a process of negotiation, if the patient is unable to consent because of his/her condition or if the process of disclosing information and securing consent would consume too much time and thus endanger the patient. Finally, procedural standards are important for certain types of patients, such as the poor, the uneducated, or those with "unattractive medical problems" (e.g., drug addiction, obesity, and hypochondriasis). In such cases, there is a tendency — surely not a universal one — to limit the degree of negotiation with the patient because of social stigmatization. A patient advocate may even be appropriate.

In addition to the procedural requirements identified earlier, there are societal constraints and limits on negotiation. Some actions may not be negotiable. For example, the society may prohibit "mercy killing," even when the patient requests it and the physician is willing to carry it out.[26] Such societal rules clearly limit the autonomy of both physicians and patients, but some of these rules may be necessary in order to protect important societal values. However, despite such notable exceptions as "mercy killing," current societal rules provide physicians and patients with considerable latitude to negotiate their own relationship and actions within that relationship.

If negotiation is a process, its accommodations at various points can often be characterized in terms of the above models — parent–child, friends, partners, contractors, and technician–consumer. Whatever accommodation is reached through the process of negotiation is not final or irrevocable. Like other human interactions, medical relationships change over time. They are always developing or dissolving. For example, when a patient experiencing anginal chest pain negotiates a relationship with a cardiologist, he may not have given or even implied consent to undergo coronary angiography or cardiac surgery if the cardiologist subsequently believes that it is necessary. Medical conditions change, and people change, often clarifying or modifying their values over time. In medical relationships either the physician or the patient may reopen the negotiation as the relationship evolves over time and may even terminate the relationship. For example, the ballet dancer in the case discussed above elected to terminate the relationship with the specialist. That particular relationship had not been fully negotiated in the first place. But even if it had been fully negotiated, she could have changed her mind and terminated it. Such an option is essential if the autonomy of the patient is to be protected over time. Likewise, the physician should have the option to renegotiate or to withdraw from the relationship (except in emergencies), as long as he or she gives adequate notice so that the patient can find another physician.

Notes

1. On metaphor, see George Lakoff and Mark Johnson, *Metaphors We Live By* (Chicago: University of Chicago Press, 1980).

2. See Thomas S. Szasz and Marc H. Hollender, "A contribution to the philosophy of medicine: The basic models of the doctor–patient relationship," *Archives of Internal Medicine* 97 (1956) 585–92; see also Thomas S. Szasz, William F. Knoff, and Marc H. Hollender, "The doctor–patient relationship and its historical context," *American Journal of Psychiatry* 115 (1958) 522–28.

3. For a fuller analysis of paternalism and its justification, see James F. Childress, *Who Should Decide? Paternalism in Health Care* (New York: Oxford University Press, 1982).

4. Eric Cassell, "Autonomy and ethics in action," *New England Journal of Medicine* 297 (1977) 333–34. Italics added. Partnership is only one of several images and metaphors Cassell uses, and it may not be the best one to express his position, in part because he tends to view autonomy as a goal rather than as a constraint.

5. According to Robert Veatch, the main focus of this model is "an equality of dignity and respect, an equality of value contributions." Veatch, "Models for ethical medicine in a revolutionary age," *Hastings Center Report* 2 (June 1972) 7. Contrast Eric Cassell, who disputes the relevance of notions of "equality" and "inequality." *The Healer's Art — A New Approach to the Doctor–Patient Relationship* (Philadelphia: J. B. Lippincott Company, 1976), 193–94.

6. Thomas S. Szasz and Marc H. Hollender, "A contribution to the philosophy of medicine," 586–87. (See Note 2.)

7. See, for example, Paul Ramsey, "The ethics of a cottage industry in an age of community and research medicine," *New England Journal of Medicine* 284 (1971) 700–706; *The Patient as Person: Explorations in Medical Ethics* (New Haven: Yale University Press, 1970), esp. Chap. 1; and Hans Jonas, "Philosophical reflections on experimenting with human subjects: Ethical Aspects of Experimentation with Human Subjects," *Daedalus* 98 (1969) 219–47.

8. Robert Veatch, "Models for ethical medicine in a revolutionary age," 7. (See Note 5.)

9. See Roger Masters, "Is contract an adequate basis for medical ethics?" *Hastings Center Report* 5 (December 1975) 24–28. See also May, "Code and covenant or philanthropy and contract?" in *Ethics in Medicine: Historical Perspectives and Contemporary Concerns*, ed. by Stanley Joel Reiser, Arthur J. Dyck, and William J. Curran (Cambridge, Mass.: The MIT Press, 1977), 65–76.

10. P. Lain Entralgo, *Doctor and Patient,* trans. from the Spanish by Frances Partridge (New York: McGraw-Hill Book Co., World University Library, 1969), 242.

11. Ibid., 197.

12. See Charles Fried, *Medical Experimentation: Personal Integrity and Social Policy* (New York: American Elsevier Publishing Co., Inc., 1974), 76. Our discussion of Fried's position is drawn from that work, *Right and Wrong* (Cambridge, Mass.: Harvard University Press, 1978), Chap. 7, and "The lawyer as friend: The moral foundations of the lawyer–client relation," *The Yale Law Journal* 85 (1976) 1060–89.

13. Immanuel Kant, *The Doctrine of Virtue,* Part 11 of *The Metaphysic of Morals,* trans. by Mary J. Gregor (New York: Harper and Row, Harper Torchbook, 1964), 140.

14. Thomas S. Szasz, William F. Knoff, and Marc H. Hollender, "The doctor–patient relationship and its historical context," 525. See also Robert Veatch, "Models for ethical medicine in a revolutionary age," 5, and Leon Kass, "Ethical dilemmas in the care of the ill: What is the physician's service?" *Journal of the American Medical Association* 244 (1980) 1815 for criticisms of the technical model (from very different normative positions).

15. Veatch, "Models for ethical medicine in a revolutionary age," 7.

16. See Stephen Toulmin, "The tyranny of principles," *Hastings Center Report* 1 (December 1981) 31–39.

17. On trust and control, see James F. Childress, "Nonviolent resistance: Trust and risk-taking," *Journal of Religious Ethics* 1 (1973) 87–112.

18. Talcott Parsons, *The Structure of Social Action* (New York: The Free Press, 1949), 311.

19. On the factors in the decline of trust, see Michael Jellinek, "Erosion of patient trust in large medical centers," *Hastings Center Report* 6 (June 1976) 16–19.

20. Alasdair MacIntyre, "Patients as agents," in *Philosophical Medical Ethics: Its Nature and Significance,* ed. by Stuart F. Spicker and H. Tristram Engelhardt, Jr. (Boston: D. Reidel Publishing Co., 1977).

21. John Ladd, "Legalism and medical ethics," *The Journal of Medicine and Philosophy* 4 (March 1979) 73.

22. This case has been presented in Mark Siegler, "Searching for moral certainty in medicine: A proposal for a new model of the doctor–patient encounter," *Bulletin of the New York Academy of Medicine* 57 (1981) 56–69.

23. Ibid. for a discussion of negotiation. Other proponents of a model of negotiation include Robert A. Burt, *Taking Care of Strangers — The Rule of Law in Doctor–Patient Relations* (New York: Free Press, 1979), and Robert J. Levine, *Ethics and Regulation of Clinical Research* (Baltimore: Urban and Schwarzenberg, 1981).

24. See the discussion in Childress, *Who Should Decide?* Chap. 3.

25. Alan W. Cross and Larry R. Churchill, "Ethical and cultural dimensions of informed consent," *Annals of Internal Medicine* 96 (1982) 110–113.

26. See Oscar Thorup, Mark Siegler, James Childress, and Ruth Roettinger, "Voluntary exit: Is there a case of rational suicide?" *The Pharos* 45 (Fall 1982) 25–31.

Moral Relationships Between Nurse and Client: The Influence of Metaphors

Janet L. Storch, RN, PhD

Metaphors have been commonly used to characterize the nature of the health professional–client relationship, with particular attention to the moral dimensions of that relationship. Metaphors often highlight significant aspects of a relationship, providing us with concrete ways of thinking about the nature of the relationship. However, any metaphor must be used with caution, recognizing that it has the capacity to enlighten, to mislead, and to constrain our thinking. Given the power that metaphors can exert on our practice, critical reflection on how they can shape the moral dimensions of the client–professional relationship is essential.

In this essay, an overview of the types of nurse–client relationships described in the literature through the use of metaphors is provided. The ways in which various metaphors can assist us with or distract us from a clear understanding of our moral agency and our moral duties to our clients/patients are then examined by considering metaphors that are limiting, misguided, or helpful in clarifying the nature of that moral relationship. Finally, a synopsis of key aspects of this special relationship concludes the essay. In an era when health care delivery is beset by a variety of sociopolitical ideologies, it is timely for nursing to embrace metaphors that articulate the values inherent in its practice.

Metaphors and Models to Define Relationships

Before embarking on the discussion, a brief commentary on the use of metaphors is in order. A metaphor is defined as a figure of speech in which one thing is compared to another thing by being spoken of as if it were the other. Although metaphors are commonly used in poetry and in lyrics, as well as in ordinary conversation to embellish discourse, they can be most useful in helping us to see some aspects of life, such as interper-

Janet L. Storch, RN, PhD, Professor School of Nursing, University of Victoria, Victoria, BC.

sonal relationships, in a way that enhances our understanding. Thus, we are directed to see and to think about that relationship in a particular way. That is, metaphors lead us to emphasize certain aspects of the relationship and minimize others. At the same time, metaphors offer alternative views or ways of seeing a relationship. In this way, metaphors can have a powerful influence on our language, on how we think, and on how we come to understand that aspect of life. In many respects, this influence is positive and enlightening. At the same time, this emphasis can lead to a distortion in thinking because it can overemphasize one view at the expense of other equally valid views that become excluded from consideration. That exclusion itself is significant because it allows us to "not see" the whole picture (Morgan, 1997).

Veatch (1972) and Callahan (1988) are two ethicists who have employed metaphors to facilitate understanding of health professional–patient relationships. Several models and metaphors have been identified in health care and health ethics literature. They are captured in the table on page 139 (Table 5.1). Some of these metaphors focus on the comparison of physicians to engineers, to priests, or to contractors (see Veatch, 1972). These metaphors portray medicine as among the first of professions. A more recent discussion, by Emanuel and Emanuel (1992), is based on various approaches in one's relationships with clients rather than on strictly metaphorical comparisons. Consideration of these approaches seems to have been directed towards moving the medical profession forward to keep pace with the changed expectations of the public to be served.

In the discourse about nurse–client relationships that uses metaphorical thinking, there is clearly some "borrowing" of approaches from the literature describing other health professional–patient relationships through model and metaphor. There are also significant contrasts in the types of models and metaphors utilized to understand the nature of the relationship between physicians and patients when compared with those used to characterize nurse–client relationships. In general, nurse–client models and metaphors are more concrete and, therefore, more explicit in their characterization of nursing (e.g., mother, servant). This concreteness can create particular problems for the nursing profession. The nursing profession can be characterized so clearly that images are difficult for the public, other professions, and nurses themselves to shed with ease. It may even be difficult to recognize the distortions the metaphors convey.

Metaphors and Nurse–Client Relationships

It seems unlikely that any other vocation or profession has experienced the diversity of imagery and metaphor that nursing has encountered in the Western world over the past century. Initially the depiction of nursing was through pictures (painted or sketched), often with metaphors as captions (e.g., Angels of Mercy). More recently, the use of written metaphors to describe and analyze nurses and nurse–client relationships has been common. One can only surmise that the penchant for "picturing" the nurse historically is related to a fascination with the female figure. Physicians have also experienced imagery of their roles and relationships with patients, but the images and metaphors of physicians have not been so varied, so gender related, nor so extensive. As noted earlier, the concrete nature of nursing metaphors, such as those depicted in Table 5.1, is also significant. Many of the conclusions about nursing embedded in the minds of readers or viewers have been based upon these metaphors and have been difficult for nursing to overcome. These metaphors are rooted in long-standing historical images.

Historical Images of Professional Nursing

In 1995, the International Council of Nurses, the International Red Cross, and the Red Crescent Museum in Geneva developed an exhibition to capture in images, text, and testimonials the first 30 years (1900–1930) of "... nursing's rise as an intellectual, socially responsible endeavor" (*Profession: Nurse* 1995, p. 11). This exhibition included a wide range of posters, postcards, drawings, paintings, and photographs that depicted nurses and conveyed a sense of the nurse's role and relationship to patients and to society.

The pictures and other material provided images of nurse as mother, sister, friend, lover, guardian angel, or army sergeant. In the accompanying publication, produced by the International Red Cross and Red Crescent Museum, the authors note that these images of nursing (these metaphors of nursing) were widely used during the First World War for purposes of raising funds for the war effort, raising morale, and stimulating patriotic zeal. "A mother figure to all the wounded, the needy and children, a nurse — with or without the red cross or crescent on her uniform — was often perceived as a savior in the glow of fervent patriotism. ... Nurses were viewed as moral figures above all suspicion and were therefore used for propaganda purposes ..." (*Profession: Nurse*, 1995, p. 26).

Following World War I, as the image of the universal mother and guardian angel gave way to post-War realities, nurses began to be depicted as fighters or soldiers who fought the residual ills of the War and epidemics, and worked in communities with social welfare officers to fight social ills.

The World Wars, and wars of the previous century, had a profound influence on the development of nursing. Florence Nightingale's work in founding nursing as a profession was given impetus by the Crimean War. And the influence of military models of health care delivery and hospital organization directed the manner in which nursing unfolded as an independent entity. Only in the latter three decades of the twentieth century has the influence of some of these metaphors begun to fade from view. In fact, some of these historical images or metaphors of nursing continue to have a profound effect on the public's view of nurses, fellow health professionals' understanding of nurse–client relationships, and the views of nurses themselves. Some of these views or perceptions have served to limit the significance of professional nursing.

Limiting Metaphors: Nurse as Parent, Nurse as Servant, Nurse as Friend

Assuming the majority of people hold positive perceptions of parents, and of mothers in particular, the metaphor of *nurse as parent surrogate* or *nurse as mother surrogate* to describe the nurse–client relationship allows us to see some fundamental foundations of that relationship. It is a relationship based upon trust, integrity, promise-keeping, dedication, and nurturance. Taking that metaphor of mother or parent further, one can understand the nurse–client relationship to involve some degree of protection of the client in care, an attempt to help clients gain or regain independence, and a commitment to never abandon a client in need. Inasmuch as this metaphor serves to enlarge understanding about these moral features of the relationship, it is well used.

However, in highlighting some similar characteristics, there can be a tenden-

Table 5.1

MODELS AND METAPHORS IDENTIFIED IN THE LITERATURE

Physician–Patient Relationships and Health Professional–Patient Relationships

VEATCH 1972
1. Engineering
2. Priestly
3. Collegial
4. Contractual

MAY 1975
1. Contract
2. Covenant

BAYLES 1981
1. Agency (Employer)
2. Contract
3. Friendship
4. Paternalistic
5. Fiduciary

CALLAHAN 1988
1. Contract
2. Covenant
3. Advocate
4. Fiduciary

EMANUEL & EMANUEL 1992
1. Paternalistic
2. Informative
3. Interpretive
4. Deliberative

Nurse–Client Relationships

SMITH 1980
1. Nurse as surrogate mother
2. Nurse as technician
3. Nurse as contracted clinician

BROCK 1980
1. Nurse as parent surrogate
2. Nurse as physician surrogate
3. Nurse as healer
4. Nurse as patient advocate or protector
5. Nurse as educator
6. Nurse as contracted clinician

WINSLOW 1984
1. Military metaphor
2. Legal metaphor (Advocacy)

FOWLER 1984
1. Mercantile
2. Indentured Servant
3. Engineering
4. Priestly
5. Collegial
6. Contractual
7. Friendship (Aristotelian)
8. Covenantal

MITCHELL 1990
1. Domestic (Servant)
2. Family (Mother Surrogate)
3. Medical (Physician Extender)
4. Business (Employee)
5. Advocacy (Patient Advocate)
6. Contractual (Contracted Clinician)
7. Friendship (Friend)

cy to overgeneralize. All features of the nurse–client relationship come to be seen as "parenting" or "mothering" relationships. The ways in which this might distort the nature of the relationship are many. Nursing comes to be seen as largely women's work and as a selfless endeavour. Like mothering, nursing then comes to be viewed as something that anyone can do. In making these assumptions, it becomes easy to discount nursing knowledge, skill, and expertise. The "tender loving care" provided by nurses may appear to be just like mother's care and concern, with little more knowledge required than what arises from trying to be caring and helpful to another.

Mitchell (1990) has labeled the mother/parent metaphor a *family metaphor*. She identifies a primary concern within the metaphor of surrogate mother to be found in "... the arrangement of health care services and relationships according to family roles, with the physician as father, nurse as mother, and patients as dependents ..." (page 5). In this scenario the nurse is expected to work (likely harder than anyone else) to maintain harmony in the home, i.e., the hospital. Further, the nurse as helpmate is not accorded power for decision making. This has significant implications for the nurse's ability to exercise his or her moral agency.

The *friendship metaphor* has positive parallels to the family metaphor, including expectations that clients can depend upon nurses and that nurses would value truth-telling and fidelity. It is misleading, however, in that the nurse–client relationship cannot be a relationship of equals, like friendship. Clients are often in a vulnerable state during their health care encounter and there is, by reason of that vulnerability and by reason of the different type and level of knowledge about the client's condition, an asymmetry of power in the healing relationship.

Finally, the *nurse as servant metaphor* adds one level of clarity to the nurse–client relationship, but at the price of potentially serious misconceptions about the relationship. From a positive view, the servant metaphor emphasizes service to others, and in this way captures the moral ideal of service critical to professional roles. In this case, nurses as professionals use their knowledge and skills in service to others. The misleading aspects of the metaphor include the implication that nurses will do anything that needs to be done at work, including domestic work (Mitchell, 1990). This has led to the serious exploitation of nurses in the past and to a significant extent in the present. Nurses' responses to such exploitation have been to establish unions for some protection from the arbitrariness of employers. Through unions they have set limits on the work they are required to do and the times in which they will do it. Nevertheless, in our current era of health care cost constraint, nurses are all too often expected to fill in the gaps when resources are cut.

A serious distortion of the metaphor of nurse as servant is the characterization of the nurse as an *indentured servant* who just "follows orders" (Fowler, 1984). This understanding of the nurse's role and relationship within the health care team led to obedience, in which the nurse cedes his or her moral agency to institutional directives, with the result that both nurse and client suffer. From this indentured servant metaphor, the long history of nurse as handmaiden to the physician has also been prominent. This places the client in a secondary position relative to the nurse–physician, then nurse–client relationship. Indeed, the Nightingale pledge that many nurses took at either capping ceremonies or graduations in times past included the phrase "... with loyalty will I endeavor to aid the physician in his work and devote myself to the welfare of the patient" (Storch, 1982, p. 202). In this sense, devotion to the patient was considered to be realized through loyally aiding the physician (Fowler, 1984). It was not until the middle of the twentieth century that those two commitments (to physician and to patient) were disentangled. By the early 1970s the International Council of Nurses' Code of Ethics stated with unmistaken clarity that "The nurse's primary responsibility is to those people who require nursing care" (Storch, 1982, p. 201). Yet, amongst physicians, health administrators and the public, there are still many who wonder why nurses are not "doing nursing" anymore (e.g., Stein, 1990). Whether their puzzlement is written or stated, the source of concern often can be traced to the query about why nurses are not there to "aid" physicians any longer or to follow orders without question(s).

Misguided Metaphors

Use of the *metaphor of technician* or *nurse as engineer* to describe the nurse–patient relationship emphasizes the task aspect of nursing roles. The strength of this metaphor rests in its emphasis on technical competence. Competence is a highly valued dimension of the nurse–patient relationship since "... caring without knowledge remains simply a matter of good intentions ..." (Falk Raphael, 1996). Unless the nurse meets the level of technical competence to carry out her tasks, "... the whole relationship begins with a lie" (Pellegrino, 1979, p. 48).

However, emphasizing the technical and task aspects of nursing captures only a fraction of nursing knowledge and skill, and the metaphor of technician limits understanding about the work that nurses do. As "re-engineering" of care-giver roles has become fashionable (Schweikhart and Smith-Daniels, 1996), this distortion of role has led to the devaluing of holistic nursing practice and, alarmingly, to simplistic solutions to nursing replacement. Since many can see only the "tasks" nurses do, the rest of nursing work remains invisible. For example, in the giving of a medication,

what is observed is a pill moving from the nurse's hand to the client's mouth. What is unobserved is the nurse's assessment of the client's condition while that simple act is in progress — respirations, pallor, comfort, degree of mobility, ease of swallowing, skin turgor, evidence of edema, etc. — the mental note taken of a plan of care on-course or one in need of modification (based on expert knowledge of the condition, the drug, and environmental stressors). Verbal and nonverbal communication occur in that simple but highly complex interaction. Opportunities arise to engage in client teaching, support, guidance, and reassurance. Perhaps, most important, is the sense of presence the expert nurse brings to the encounter — a way of being with the client that reflects the depth of care and concern, laced with competence to deliver, for that one individual. Thus, the concrete task observed is not the real work of nursing: the real work of nursing requires knowledge and skill that is all but invisible to the observer. The type of care expert nurses provide must begin with considerable investment in the relationship, involves the use of self, and involves attention to the uniqueness of that client.

These same misguided task-oriented conclusions are operative in the *physician extender* and *physician surrogate* metaphors. While there are aspects of medical tasks and medical work that nurses are able to perform, even in performing those tasks nursing work is different. Taking on specific tasks of medicine does not equate to being either a physician extender or a physician surrogate, or a physician for that matter. Nursing roles and relationships are different, with different goals and different processes of care. For example, both physicians and nurses will monitor arterial blood gas results. The physician monitors those results to diagnose cardio-pulmonary dysfunction; the nurse monitors the same results to plan activity, rest, and comfort.

Nursing knowledge increasingly involves many ways of knowing, beyond empirical knowledge and technical skill. It includes knowledge gained through empirics, but also knowledge drawn from ethics, personal knowledge, aesthetics, and sociopolitical knowing (Carper, 1978; White, 1995). Different knowledge and skill lead to different ways of approaching care, and to a different form of nurse–client relationship, including greater attention to "ways of being" in relationship with the clients (Silva, Sorrell and Sorell, 1995).

Helpful Metaphors: Nurse as in a Covenantal Relationship, as Healer, as Advocate

Among the many metaphors applied to nurse–client relationships are several that stand out as characterizing more clearly than others the ideals of what these relationships should be. Use of the metaphor of a *covenantal relationship* emphasizes that nurse and client are "... bound to one another in many ways, not the least of which is morally" (Fowler, 1984, p. 338). As members of a community, and within that community a health care system, nurses are expected to be faithful and to keep their promise of profession, i.e., to use their knowledge and skills to minimize harm and to benefit others.

> A convenantal model calls attention to the reciprocal indebtedness of the public and the profession, suggesting that professional power is a gift from the public to the profession given in exchange for its expertise and orientation to the service of others. (Bernal, 1992, p. 22)

In emphasizing concepts of relatedness and reciprocity, the covenantal model underscores nursing practice priorities of the 1990s.

The image of *nurse as healer* is a long-standing metaphor utilized since the early 1900s to emphasize the healing powers of the nursing presence. Whether a nurse is fully present with a client through the painful journey of being a critically ill patient in ICU or CCU, through an outpatient experience of chemotherapy, or through a long period of rehabilitation at home recovering from a stroke, the professional nurse's ongoing presence can facilitate the individual to move towards restoration and healing. In this way the nurse has a different but complementary role to that of physician.

The *nurse as client advocate* was introduced in the early 1970s and was based on a clearer understanding of nurses' direct accountability (legal and ethical) to clients. Considerable attention in nursing literature (see for example, Donahue, 1978; Abrams, 1978; Curtin, 1979; Gadow, 1980; Kohnke, 1982; Fowler, 1989; Bernal, 1995) has been directed towards identifying the role of advocacy and types of advocacy (e.g., intervening, protecting, informing, supporting, speaking for, coordinating, empowering, etc.) as well as problems for nurses in fulfilling a role as client advocate.

In 1984, Winslow analyzed the shift from a nursing practice based on a military model (characterized by hierarchy and obedience) to one based on a legal model that focused on advocacy for the client in health care. He identified several issues surrounding the nurse as patient or client advocate, including lack of clarity of the concept, the need to revise nursing practice acts to allow for this type of nursing role, the question as to whether clients and their families were prepared to accept advocacy as a nursing role, the potentially adversarial nature of advocacy, and the potential conflicting interests and loyalties inherent in advocacy. Advocacy has served as a powerful metaphor for nursing, although often with only superficial understanding of its real power.

As long as advocacy is confined to legal metaphor it is limiting. However, when it is viewed as "... not simply one more alternative to be added to the list of past and present concepts of nursing ... but as embracing all of them ..." (Curtin, 1979, p. 2), its real meaning is understood. Benner (1994) characterized client advocacy as involving openness and engagement in moral and clinical reasoning. Drawing upon the work of Gadow (1980), who conceptualized "existential advocacy," Benner contrasts the "narrow legal sense of advocacy" (page 49) with a deeper and more meaningful form of advocacy. She describes this type of advocate as one who "stands alongside, who interprets, and understands ..." (page 49) — language congruent with a covenantal relationship. She suggests that this enriched metaphor of client advocacy is manifest in the following way: managing and coordinating services to a client so that all services are directed toward an agreed upon intent to ensure client and family well-being, "... standing in for someone to give them voice ... getting appropriate medical intervention for [clients] ... and presencing and acknowledging loss and grief" with one who is dying (page 51).

These metaphors of nurse in a covenantal relationship, nurse as healer, and nurse as advocate, approach more closely than the previous metaphors the morally significant aspects of the nurse–client relationship. Their emphasis is on the moral commitment of the nurse to be a comforting presence to clients through difficult health situations; to be in relationship with clients; and to intervene, inform, support, and facilitate their empowerment. This emphasis provides insight into the "special" nature of the nurse–client relationship.

What Metaphors Enable Us to See and Learn

Metaphors used to describe the nurse–client relationship can be instructive and they can be limiting. Their limitations include their potential to further devalue nursing knowledge and skill, to perpetuate stereotypical notions of nurse–client and physician–client relationships, to mislead by suggesting equal partnership in that relationship, to perpetuate the task-oriented view of nursing, and to conflate nurse and physician roles. The strength of metaphors applied to nursing rests in the ability to understand more readily the historical shifts in nursing roles and nurse–client relationships and to appreciate both constancy and change in nurse–client relationships over time. Further, metaphors help to articulate the values in nursing practice in an era when roles are under threat from an economic imperative.

The constant themes of the nurse–client relationship accessed through metaphor are relationships based on the moral foundations of trust, integrity, respect, truth-telling, and promise-keeping. These themes are fundamental to nursing. The covenantal metaphor emphasis on reciprocity and connectedness makes more visible the foundation of the relationship. Metaphors have also served a useful purpose in drawing distinctions between medicine and nursing over time. When used with care, metaphors enable us to see and learn much about the nature of nursing and the nature of the nurse–patient relationship. Most importantly, the moral foundations of that relationship can become more visible and less difficult to articulate and defend.

References

The author wishes to thank Dr. Gwen Hartrick, Dr. Patricia Rodney and Dr. Rita Schreiber for their critical review of this essay and for their helpful suggestions.

Abrams, Natalie (1978). "A contrary view of the nurse as patient advocate." *Nursing Forum* 17(3): 258–267.

Bayles, Michael D. (1981). *Professional Ethics.* Belmont: C.A. Wadsworth Publishing Co.

Baylis, Françoise, Downie, Jocelyn, Freedman, Benjamin, Hoffmaster, Barry, and Sherwin, Susan, eds. (1995). *Health Care Ethics in Canada.* Toronto: Harcourt Brace and Company.

Benner, Patricia (1994). "Caring as ways of knowing and not knowing." In *The Crisis of Care* (pp. 42–62). Edited by Susan Phillips and Patricia Benner. Washington D.C.: Georgetown University Press.

Bernal, Ellen W. (1992). "The nurse as patient advocate." *Hastings Center Report* 22(4): 18–23.

Brock, Dan W. (1980). "The nurse–patient relation: Some rights and duties." In *Nursing: Images and Ideals* (pp. 102–124). Edited by Stuart F. Spicker and Sally Gadow. New York: Springer Publishing Co.

Callahan, Joan, ed. (1988). *Ethical Issues in Professional Life.* New York: Oxford University Press.

Carper, Barbara (1978). "Fundamental patterns of knowing in nursing." *Advances in Nursing Science* 1(1): 13–23.

Curtin, Leah (1979). "Nurse as advocate: A philosophical foundation for nursing." *Advances in Nursing Science* 1(3): 1–10.

Donahue, M. Patricia (1978). "The nurse: A patient advocate?" *Nursing Forum* 17(2): 143–151.

Emanuel, Ezekiel J., and Emanuel, Linda L. (1995). "Four models of the physician–patient relationship." In *Health Care Ethics in Canada* (pp. 163–179). Edited by Francoise Baylis et al. Toronto: Harcourt Brace and Company.

Fowler, Marsha (1984). "Ethics and Nursing, 1893–1984: The Ideal of Service, the Reality of History." Doctoral Dissertation, University of Southern California.

——— (1989). "Social advocacy." *Heart and Lung* 18(1): 97–99.

Gadow, Sally (1980). "Existential advocacy: Philosophical foundations of nursing." In *Nursing: Images and Ideals* (pp. 79–101). Edited by Stuart F. Smith and Sally Gadow. New York: Springer Publishing Company.

Kohnke, Mary (1982). *Advocacy: Risk or Reality.* Toronto: C.V. Mosby.

May, William F. (1975). "Code and covenant or philanthropy and contract." *Hastings Center Report* 5(6): 29–38.

Mitchell, Christine (1990). "The nurse–patient relationship: A source of some moral duties." In *Humanities and the Health Professions*, Occasional Papers of the Connecticut Humanities Council, No. 8, 3–16.

Morgan, Gareth (1997). *Images of Organizations.* Thousand Oaks: Sage Publications.

Profession: Nurse, Images 1900–1930 (1995). Geneva: Musée International de la Red Cross et du Red Crescent.

RNABC (1997). *The Role of the Nurse in Advocacy.* Vancouver: Registered Nurses Association of British Columbia.

Schweikhart, Sharon Bergman, and Smith-Daniels, Vicki (1996). "Reengineering the work of caregivers: Roles' redefinition, team structures, and organizational redesign." *Hospital and Health Administration* 41(1): 19–35.

Silva, Mary, Sorrell, Jeanne, and Sorrell, Christine (1995). "From Carper's ways of knowing to ways of being: An ontological shift in nursing." *Advances in Nursing Science* 18(1): 1–13.

Smith, Sheri (1980). "Three models of the nurse–patient relationship." In *Nursing: Images and Ideals* (pp. 176–188). Edited by Stuart F. Spicker and Sally Gadow. New York: Springer Publishing Company.

Stein, Leonard, Watts, D.T., and Howell, T. (1990). "The doctor–nurse game revisited." *New England Journal of Medicine* 60(5): 812–816.

Storch, Janet L. (1982). *Patients' Rights: Ethical and Legal Issues in Health Care and in Nursing.* Toronto: McGraw Hill.

Veatch, Robert M. (1972). "Models for ethical medicine in a revolutionary age." *Hastings Center Report* 2(3): 5–7.

White, Jill (1995). "Patterns of knowing: Review, critique and update." *Advances in Nursing Science* 17(4): 73–86.

Winslow, Gerald R. (1984). "From loyalty to advocacy: A new metaphor for nursing." *Hastings Center Report* 14(3): 32–40.

Further Readings

Bayles, Michael D. "The Professional–Client Relationship." *Professional Ethics.* Belmont, Calif.: Wadsworth, 1981.

Becker, M., and L. Maiman. "Strategies for Enhancing Patient Compliance." *J Community Health* 6 (1980): 113–132.

Buchanan, Allan. "Medical Paternalism." *Philos Pub Affairs* 7 (1978): 370–390.

Callahan, Joan C. "Paternalism and Voluntariness." *Can J Philos* 16:2 (1986): 199–220.

Childress, James I., and Mark S. Siegler. "Metaphors and Models of Doctor–Patient Relationships: Their Implication for Autonomy." *Theoret Med* 5 (1984): 17–30.

Chinen, A. "Modes of Understanding and Mindfulness of Clinical Medicine." *Theoret Med* 9:1 (Feb. 1988): 45–72.

Gordon, Harry H. "The Doctor–Patient Relationship: A Judaic Perspective." *J Med Philos* 8 (1983): 243–255.

Graber, Glenn C. "On Paternalism in Health Care." *Contemporary Issues in Biomedical Ethics.* Eds. John W. Davis, Barry Hoffmaster, and Sarah Shorten. Clifton, N.J.: Humana Press, 1981.

Ingelfinger, Franz. "Arrogance." *N Engl J Med* 303 (1980): 1509.

Katz, Jay. *The Silent World of Doctor and Patient.* Vols. I and II. New York: Free Press, 1984.

Masters, Roger. "Is a Contract an Adequate Basis for Medical Ethics?" *Hastings Center Rep* 5 (Dec. 1975): 24–28.

Percival, Thomas. *Medical Ethics.* Ed. Chauncey D. Leake. Huntington, N.Y.: R.E. Krieger Pub. Co., 1975.

Roach, M.S. *The Human Act of Caring: A Blueprint for the Health Professions.* Ottawa: Canadian Hospital Association, 1987.

Smith, David H., and Lloyd S. Pettegrew. "Mutual Persuasion as a Model for Doctor–Patient Communication." *Theoret Med* 7 (1986): 127–146.

Staum, Martin S., and Donald E. Larson, eds. *Doctors, Patients and Society: Power and Authority in Medical Care.* Waterloo: Wilfrid Laurier Univ. Press, 1981.

Storch, J. *Patients' Rights.* Toronto: McGraw Hill, 1982.

Thomasma, D.C. "Beyond Medical Paternalism and Patient Autonomy: A Model of Physician Conscience for the Physician–Patient Relationship." *Ann of Intern Med* 98:3 (Feb. 1983): 243–247.

CHAPTER 6
INFORMED CONSENT AND THE COMPETENT PATIENT

Introduction

One of the most fundamental principles of Canadian health care theory and law is that, all other things being equal, competent patients have the right to accept or reject any diagnosis, treatment or intervention. The only limitation on this freedom is that the health of other people should not be threatened and that the rights of others should not be infringed. As the old adage has it, "Your right to swing your fist stops where my face begins!"

However, people who make decisions without having appropriate or sufficient information are not in fact choosing freely. The very lack of information constrains their choice. Therefore, in order to exercise their right of choice in a meaningful way, patients have to be informed. Canadian bioethics has tried to capture this insight in the phrase "informed consent." Competent patients have the right to informed consent.

The first reading in this chapter is taken from *Reibl v. Hughes*. This is the classic Canadian legal case on informed consent. In it, the Supreme Court of Canada set out the standards that Canadian health care professionals must follow in order to have a legally valid informed consent from their patients. It begins by recognizing that to be told something and to actually understand it are not necessarily the same thing. It therefore distinguishes between what the patient should be told — this has become known as the *standard of disclosure* — and the level at which the information must be pitched so that the patient can actually understand the information. This has become known as the *standard of comprehension*.

It then says that the appropriate standard of disclosure is not what the ordinary reasonable person would want to know, but what an objective reasonable person *in the patient's particular position* would want to know. As for the level at which the information must be pitched, it says that it must be geared to the level of the particular patient. It should not be assumed that just because people would normally understand the information as it is being provided, therefore *this* patient actually understands it.

The two standards have become known as the *modified objective reasonable person standard of disclosure*, and the *subjective standard of comprehension* respectively. *Reibl v. Hughes* is important not only from a legal perspective. It also captures what would be expected from a deontologically oriented ethical perspective that places primary emphasis on the autonomy of the person. *Reibl v. Hughes* puts more emphasis on patient autonomy than either the relevant U.K.[1] or U.S. cases,[2] and shows that Canadian standards are more stringent and, so to speak, ethically more sensitive than those in these other jurisdictions. The U.K. accepts what is called a professional standard of disclosure. This means that in the U.K., a physician need only disclose what another similarly placed physician would normally disclose. The U.S. accepts an objective reasonable person standard, according to which a physician need only disclose what the ordinary reasonable person would want to know before agreeing to or rejecting the proposed intervention.

Reibl v. Hughes prompted all Canadian provinces to revamp their health care consent legislation. This new legislation — which can readily be accessed by searching the consolidated statutes of the various provinces on the World Wide Web — also makes it very clear that informed consent is not something that is achieved simply by having a patient sign a form. Instead, it is a process that involves information transfer, comprehension and consent. The signed form is merely an indication that the relevant process has taken place. In that sense, current provincial consent legislation constitutes a legal reflection of the ethics of autonomy in health care.

In an analogous vein, Benjamin Freedman reminds us that informed consent is not something abstract, but must be operationalized according to the context in which it is sought. In other words, he raises the question of what informed consent means (or what it should mean) in actual life, and he discusses the concept of responsible decision making and the role of reward or enticement.

Freedman's article is written from an essentially Western perspective. However, Canada is a multicultural society, and Canadian patients differ widely in their familial and cultural embeddings. *Reibl v. Hughes* acknowledged this when it said that the consent process must be adjusted to the reasonable person *in the patient's position*. Insoo Hyun's article focuses on the difficulties that are associated with this: How does one ensure that patients' decisions really reflect their own authentic values instead of being the results of values that have been impressed on them by their families and/or cultures?

As an *addendum*, it should be noted that the phrase "informed consent" is really short for informed consent *or refusal*. Ethically speaking, the two are but different sides of the same coin. This insight has also found legal recognition: specifically, in the 1983 case of *Astaforoff*[3] in the 1990 case of *Malette v. Shulman*[4] and in the 1992 case of *Nancy B.*[5] Finally, consent and refusal extend not only to what is done to the body of the patient but also to any part of the body, to the fluids contained in it, etc. even when these are separated from the body. The Supreme Court made this very clear in 1987 in *R. v. Pohoretsky*,[6] and again in 1988 in *R. v. Dyment*.[7]

Notes

1. See *Freeman v. Home Office* [1987] 1 All ER 1036, and *Sidaway* [1985] AC 871.
2. See *Canterbury v. Spence* (1972), 464 F. 2d; *Cobbs v. Grant*, 502 P. 2d 1.
3. *Re Attorney General of British Columbia et al. and Astaforoff et al.* (1983) 6 C.C.C. (3d) 498 (B.C.C.A.). In this case, the court ruled that even though the prison authorities had a duty to provide the necessities of life to a person in their charge, if that person competently refused such, this refusal had to be respected. It has since become well established that the duty to respect the person's wishes does not cease when the person becomes incompetent.
4. See *infra*, chapter 8.
5. *Nancy B v. Hôtel-Dieu de Québec* [1992] R.J.Q. 361, 86 D.L.R. (4th) 385 S.C.C. Nancy B. was a young woman who was completely paralyzed as a result of Guillaine-Barré Syndrome and hence was completely ventilator dependent. She requested that she be allowed to have her ventilator shut off even though that would lead to her death by suffocation. The court found in her favour; the ventilator was shut off and she died sedated, so that she would not experience the full effect of the suffocation.
6. *R. v. Pohoretsky* (1987), 58 C.R. (3d) 113, 33 C.C.C. (3D) 398 (S.C.C.). In this case the court ruled that taking blood samples without consent or judicial authority violates s. 8 of the Charter.
7. *R. v. Dyment* (1988), 66 C.R. (3d) 348, 45 C.C.C. (3d) 244 (S.C.C.). The Supreme Court ruled that blood taken for medical purposes could not be used without the consent of the person or without due process of law.

Reibl v. Hughes

Supreme Court of Canada, Laskin, C.J.C., Martland, Dickson, Beetz, Estey, McIntyre and Chouinard J.J. October 7, 1980.

LASKIN, C.J.C.: — The plaintiff appellant, then 44 years of age, underwent serious surgery on March 18, 1970, for the removal of an occlusion in the left internal carotid artery, which had prevented more than a 15% flow of blood through the vessel. The operation was competently performed by the defendant respondent, a qualified neurosurgeon. However, during or immediately

---

Reibl v. Hughes, 16 O.R. (2d) 306, 78 D.L.R. (3d) 35, reversed 21 O.R. (2d) 14, 6 C.C.L.T., 227, 89 D.L.R. (3d) 112; reversed [1980] 2 S.C.R. 880, 14 C.C.C.T.I., 114 D.L.R. (3d) 1, 33 N.R., 17.

following the surgery the plaintiff suffered a massive stroke which left him paralyzed on the right side of his body and also impotent. The plaintiff had, of course, formally consented to the operation. Alleging, however, that his was not an "informed consent," he sued for damages and recovered on this ground in both battery and negligence. The trial Judge, Haines J., awarded a global sum of $225,000 [78 D.L.R. (3d) 35, 16 O.R. (2d) 306].

A majority of the Ontario Court of Appeal ordered a new trial on both liability and damages [89 D.L.R. (3d) 112, 21 O.R. (2d) 14, 6 C.C.L.T. 227]. Speaking through Brooke J.A. (Blair J.A. concurring) the Court ruled out battery as a possible ground of liability on the facts of the case. Jessup J.A., dissenting in part, would have ordered a new trial on damages alone, accepting the judgment at trial on liability.

On the hearing of the appeal by this Court, leave to come here having been obtained by the plaintiff, counsel for the defendant respondent agreed to accept the award of damages and limited his contestation to liability, seeking not only to hold the judgment in appeal but a "variation" thereof by way of dismissal of the action. Although, strictly speaking, the claim for a variation should have been made the subject of a cross-appeal, counsel for the appellant took no objection and I see no reason why I should not regularize the claim for dismissal *nunc pro tunc*. Indeed, neither counsel wished to have a new trial, an understandable position when the physical damage suffered took place more than ten years ago. Unless, therefore, there are good reasons to support the order for a new trial on liability alone, the proper course is to determine whether to restore the judgment at trial on either or both grounds upon which it proceeded or whether the defendant should be relieved of liability.

It is now undoubted that the relationship between surgeon and patient gives rise to a duty of the surgeon to make disclosure to the patient of what I would call all material risks attending the surgery which is recommended. The scope of the duty of disclosure was considered in *Hopp v. Lepp*, a judgment of this Court, delivered on May 20, 1980, ... [112 D.L.R. (3d) 67, 22 A.R. 361, [1980] 4 W.W.R. 645], where it was generalized as follows [at p. 81]:

> In summary, the decided cases appear to indicate that, in obtaining the consent of a patient for the performance upon him of a surgical operation, a surgeon, generally, should answer any specific questions posed by the patient as to the risks involved and should, without being questioned, disclose to him the nature of the proposed operation, its gravity, any material risks and any special or unusual risks attendant upon the performance of the operation. However, having said that, it should be added that the scope of the duty of disclosure and whether or not it has been breached are matters which must be decided in relation to the circumstances of each particular case.

The Court in *Hopp v. Lepp* also pointed out that even if a certain risk is a mere possibility which ordinarily need not be disclosed, yet if its occurrence carries serious consequences, as for example, paralysis or even death, it should be regarded as a material risk requiring disclosure.

In the present case, the risk attending the surgery or its immediate aftermath was the risk of a stroke, of paralysis and, indeed, of death. This was, without question, a material risk. At the same time, the evidence made it clear that there was also a risk of a stroke and of resulting death if surgery for the removal of the occlusion was refused by the patient. The delicacy of the surgery is beyond question, and its execution is no longer in any way faulted. (I would note here that in this Court no issue was raised as to the adequacy of post-operative care.) How specific, therefore, must the information to the patient be, in a case such as this, to enable him to make an "informed" choice between surgery and no surgery? One of the considerations weighing upon the plaintiff was the fact that he was about a year and a half away from earning a life-time retirement pension as a Ford Motor Company employee. The trial Judge noted (to use his words) ... that "Due to this tragedy befalling him at the time it did, he was not eligible for certain extended disability benefits available under the collective agreement between the Ford Motor Company of Canada Limited and its hourly employees of 10 years' standing." At the time of the operation, the plaintiff had 8.4 years' service with his employer. He stated in his evidence that if he had been properly informed of the magnitude of the risk involved in the surgery he would have elected to forego it, at least until his pension had vested and, further, he would have opted for a shorter normal life than a longer one as a cripple because of the surgery. Although elective surgery was indicated for the condition from which the plaintiff suffered, there was (as the trial Judge found) no emergency in the sense that immediate surgical treatment was imperative.

This brings me back to the question of the nature of the information provided by the respondent surgeon to the plaintiff and its adequacy in the circumstances. I will deal, in turn, with: (1) the findings and conclusion of the trial Judge on this issue; (2) whether, even on his findings, there was a basis for imposing liability for battery; (3) the assessment made by the Court of Appeal in ordering a new trial; (4) the evidence in the case, which

consisted, in support of the plaintiff's case, mainly of the testimony of the plaintiff and of two neurosurgeons, Dr. Irving Schacter and Dr. Robert Elgie, and portions of the examination for discovery of the defendant and, in support of the defendant's case, the testimony of the defendant and of a neurosurgeon, Dr. William Lougheed, who were the only two witnesses called for the defendant; (5) the duty of disclosure and review of the findings below; and (6) whether causation was established.

...The well-known statement of Cardozo J. in *Schloendorff v. Society of New York Hospital* (1914), 211 N.Y. 125 at p. 129, 105 N.E. 92 at p. 93, that "every human being of adult years and sound mind has a right to determine what shall be done with his own body; and a surgeon who performs an operation without his patient's consent commits an assault, for which he is liable in damages" cannot be taken beyond the compass of its words to support an action of battery where there has been consent to the very surgical procedure carried out upon a patient but there has been a breach of the duty of disclosure of attendant risks. In my opinion, actions of battery in respect of surgical or other medical treatment should be confined to cases where surgery or treatment has been performed or given to which there has been no consent at all or where, emergency situations aside, surgery or treatment has been performed or given beyond that to which there was consent.

This standard would comprehend cases where there was misrepresentation of the surgery or treatment for which consent was elicited and a different surgical procedure or treatment was carried out. See, for example, *Marshall v. Curry*, [1933] 3 D.L.R. 260, 60 C.C.C. 136 (consent given to operation to cure hernia; doctor removes patient's testicle; action in battery); *Murray v. McMurchy*, [1949] 2 D.L.R. 442, [1949] 1 W.W.R. 989

(consent given to a caesarian operation; doctor goes on and sterilizes the patient; doctor liable for trespass to the person); *Mulloy v. Hop Sang*, [1935] 1 W.W.R. 714 (doctor told to repair hand and not to amputate; performs amputation; held liable in trespass); *Winn et al. v. Alexander et al.*, [1940] 3 D.L.R. 778, [1940] O.W.N. 238 (consent given to caesarian; doctor goes further and sterilizes the patient); *Schweizer v. Central Hospital et al.* (1974), 53 D.L.R. (3d) 494, 6 O.R. (2d) 606 (patient consented to operation on his toe; doctor operated on back instead [spinal fusion]; doctor liable for trespass to the person).

In situations where the allegation is that attendant risks which should have been disclosed were not communicated to the patient and yet the surgery or other medical treatment carried out was that to which the plaintiff consented (there being no negligence basis of liability for the recommended surgery or treatment to deal with the patient's condition), I do not understand how it can be said that the consent was vitiated by the failure of disclosure so as to make the surgery or other treatment an unprivileged, unconsented to and intentional invasion of the patient's bodily integrity. I can appreciate the temptation to say that the genuineness of consent to medical treatment depends on proper disclosure of the risks which it entails, but in my view, unless there has been misrepresentation or fraud to secure consent to the treatment, a failure to disclose the attendant risks, however serious, should go to negligence rather than to battery. Although such a failure relates to an informed choice of submitting to or refusing recommended and appropriate treatment, it arises as the breach of an anterior duty of due care, comparable in legal obligation to the duty of due care in carrying out the particular treatment to which the patient has consented. It is not a test of the validity of the consent.

3. The Assessment of the Court of Appeal

Brooke J.A., speaking for the majority of the Court of Appeal, noted, … quite properly, that:

> The duty [of disclosure] to the patient is determined by the Court and the evidence of the expert witnesses, if accepted, is relevant to determining whether or not the defendant has discharged that duty. To be actionable [in negligence] the defendant's failure in his duty of care must cause the plaintiff loss and damage.

He went on to examine the reasons of Haines J. and made the following observations upon that trial Judge's determination: …

> In finding that the plaintiff was left with the impression that the surgery carried no risk of consequence other than those in any surgical procedure I think it must be assumed that the learned trial Judge has rejected the defendant's explanation that the plaintiff was aware of the risk of a stroke as a risk of the surgery. Of some importance, the learned trial Judge makes no specific finding of credibility and indeed does not disbelieve the defendant's evidence that he thought the plaintiff understood the risk. However, the learned trial Judge did not put his judgment simply on the failure to warn, but also on the failure to take sufficient care to discuss the degree of risk. He relied upon the evidence of Dr. Elgie and Dr. Schacter and it is my respectful view that, having regard for the emphasis which the learned trial Judge places upon the statistical details, he has misunderstood the real significance of the evidence of these two doctors.

Drs. Schacter and Elgie appear to have taken a similar approach to the question of explaining the risks of the surgery, but the emphasis is not on statistical detail. Dr. Elgie alone made reference to statistics in discussing the manner in which he would advise his patient when seeking a consent to perform this operation and in this respect his answer was different from that of Dr. Schacter.

Brooke J.A. was highly critical of the use of unexplained statistics which appeared to be directed to the degree of risk involved in the particular surgery. This is what he said in that respect: ...

One need only look at the contrast in the evidence of the statistics quoted by Dr. Hughes and Dr. Elgie to demonstrate the confusion that could arise from their use. When asked in cross-examination, Dr. Hughes' figure as to the incidence of death because of surgery was 4%, which was equal to Dr. Elgie's highest figure where he put the range between 2% and 4%, and with respect to the incidence of stroke causing paralysis or transient weakness, Dr. Hughes put the figure at 10% which was five times Dr. Elgie's lowest figure and almost two and one-half times his highest figure. Taken cumulatively, Dr. Hughes' figure at 14% is more than three times Dr. Elgie's lowest estimate and almost twice his highest. They were really very different. The reason for the difference went unexplained. No one asked the doctors. And yet the trial Judge referred principally in his reasons, and particularly in testing the defendant's conduct, to the statistics recounted by Dr. Hughes, which there was no suggestion the doctor attempted to use. If the difference is based solely or partly on the personal experience

of the surgeons, and there is in the evidence some reason suggested that this may be so, then perhaps the explanation lies in the nature of the cases that each has dealt with and that the chance of survivorship of those undertaken by one was less than the other. If this is so, there may have been good reason not to mention statistics to the patient, but rather to simply contrast his position if he undertakes the surgery with that of not undertaking it and urge him to proceed because of his youth and strength giving some assurance of survivorship. I do not think the evidence justifies the statement made by the learned trial Judge and I would hesitate to lay down any such requirements, for in my view, statistics can be very misleading. The manner in which the nature and degree of risk is explained to a particular patient is better left to the judgment of the doctor in dealing with the man before him. Its adequacy can be simply tested.

I think the Ontario Court of Appeal went too far, when dealing with the standard of disclosure of risks, in saying, as it did in the passage of its reasons just quoted, that "the manner in which the nature and degree of risk is explained to a particular patient is better left to the judgment of the doctor in dealing with the man before him." Of course, it can be tested by expert medical evidence but that too is not determinative. The patient may have expressed certain concerns to the doctor and the latter is obliged to meet them in a reasonable way. What the doctor knows or should know that the particular patient deems relevant to a decision whether to undergo prescribed treatment goes equally to his duty of disclosure as do the material risks recognized as a matter of required medical knowledge.

It is important to examine this issue in greater detail. The Ontario Court of Appeal appears to have adopted a professional medical standard, not only for determining what are the material risks that should be disclosed but also, and concurrently, for determining whether there has been a breach of the duty of disclosure. This was also the approach of the trial Judge, notwithstanding that on the facts he found against the defendant. (Indeed, the trial Judge seems also to have overstated the duty of disclosure. The Court of Appeal, in contrast, seems to have understated it. Generally, the failure to mention statistics should not affect the duty to inform nor be a factor in deciding whether the duty has been breached.) To allow expert medical evidence to determine what risks are material and, hence, should be disclosed and, correlatively, what risks are not material is to hand over to the medical profession the entire question of the scope of the duty of disclosure, including the question whether there has been a breach of that duty. Expert medical evidence is, of course, relevant to findings as to the risks that reside in or are a result of recommended surgery or other treatment. It will also have a bearing on their materiality but this is not a question that is to be concluded on the basis of the expert medical evidence alone. The issue under consideration is a different issue from that involved where the question is whether the doctor carried out his professional activities by applicable professional standards. What is under consideration here is the patient's right to know what risks are involved in undergoing or foregoing certain surgery or other treatment.

The materiality of non-disclosure of certain risks to an informed decision is a matter for the trier of fact, a matter on which there would, in all likelihood, be medical evidence but also other evidence, including evidence from the patient or from members of his family. It is, of course, possible that a particular patient may waive aside any question of risks and be quite prepared to submit to the surgery or treatment, whatever they be. Such a situation presents no difficulty. Again, it may be the case that a particular patient may, because of emotional factors, be unable to cope with facts relevant to recommended surgery or treatment and the doctor may, in such a case, be justified in withholding or generalizing information as to which he would otherwise be required to be more specific.

...

If Canadian case law has so far proceeded on a subjective test of causation, it is in Courts other than this one that such an approach has been taken: see *Koehler v. Cook* (1975), 65 D.L.R. (3d) 766 at p. 767, [1976] W.W.D. 71, and *Kelly v. Hazlett* (1976), 75 D.L.R. (3d) 536 at pp. 565–6, 15 O.R. (2d) 290 at p. 320. The matter is *res integra* here. An alternative to the subjective test is an objective one, that is, what would a reasonable person in the patient's position have done if there had been proper disclosure of attendant risks. The case for the objective standard has been tersely put in the following passage from a comment in 48 N.Y.U.L. Rev. 548 (1973), at p. 550, entitled "Informed Consent — A Proposed Standard for Medical Disclosure":

> Since proximate causation exists only if disclosure would have resulted in the patient's foregoing the proposed treatment, a standard must be developed to determine whether the patient would have decided against the treatment had he been informed of its risks. Two possible standards exist: whether, if informed, the particular patient would have foregone treatment (subjective view); or whether the average prudent person in plaintiff's position, informed of all material risks, would have foregone

treatment (objective view). The objective standard is preferable, since the subjective standard has a gross defect: it depends on the plaintiff's testimony as to his state of mind, thereby exposing the physician to the patient's hindsight and bitterness.

However, a vexing problem raised by the objective standard is whether causation could ever be established if the surgeon has recommended surgery which is warranted by the patient's condition. Can it be said that a reasonable person in the patient's position, to whom proper disclosure of attendant risks has been made, would decide against the surgery, that is, against the surgeon's recommendation that it be undergone? The objective standard of what a reasonable person in the patient's position would do would seem to put a premium on the surgeon's assessment of the relative need for the surgery and on supporting medical evidence of that need. Could it be reasonably refused? Brooke J.A. appeared to be sensitive to this problem by suggesting a combined objective–subjective test.

I doubt that this will solve the problem. It could hardly be expected that the patient who is suing would admit that he would have agreed to have the surgery, even knowing all the accompanying risks. His suit would indicate that, having suffered serious disablement because of the surgery, he is convinced that he would not have permitted it if there had been proper disclosure of the risks, balanced by the risks of refusing the surgery. Yet, to apply a subjective test to causation would, correlatively, put a premium on hindsight, even more of a premium than would be put on medical evidence in assessing causation by an objective standard.

I think it is the safer course on the issue of causation to consider objectively how far the balance in the risks of surgery or no surgery is in favour of under-

going surgery. The failure of proper disclosure pro and con becomes therefore very material. And so too are any special considerations affecting the particular patient. For example, the patient may have asked specific questions which were either brushed aside or were not fully answered or were answered wrongly. In the present case, the anticipation of a full pension would be a special consideration, and, while it would have to be viewed objectively, it emerges from the patient's particular circumstances. So too, other aspects of the objective standard would have to be geared to what the average prudent person, the reasonable person in the patient's particular position, would agree to or not agree to, if all material and special risks of going ahead with the surgery or foregoing it were made known to him. Far from making the patient's own testimony irrelevant, it is essential to his case that he put his own position forward.

The adoption of an objective standard does not mean that the issue of causation is completely in the hands of the surgeon. Merely because medical evidence establishes the reasonableness of a recommended operation does not mean that a reasonable person in the patient's position would necessarily agree to it, if proper disclosure had been made of the risks attendant upon it, balanced by those against it. The patient's particular situation and the degree to which the risks of surgery or no surgery are balanced would reduce the force, on an objective appraisal, of the surgeon's recommendation. Admittedly, if the risk of foregoing the surgery would be considerably graver to a patient than the risks attendant upon it, the objective standard would favour exoneration of the surgeon who has not made the required disclosure. Since liability rests only in negligence, in a failure to disclose material risks, the issue of causation would be in the patient's hands on a subjective test, and would, if his evidence was accepted, result inevitably in liability unless, of course, there was a finding that there was no breach of the duty of disclosure. In my view, therefore, the objective standard is the preferable one on the issue of causation.

In saying that the test is based on the decision that a reasonable person in the patient's position would have made, I should make it clear that the patient's particular concerns must also be reasonably based; otherwise, there would be more subjectivity than would be warranted under an objective test. Thus, for example, fears which are not related to the material risks which should have been but were not disclosed would not be causative factors. However, economic considerations could reasonably go to causation where, for example, the loss of an eye as a result of nondisclosure of a material risk brings about the loss of a job for which good eyesight is required. In short, although account must be taken of a patient's particular position, a position which will vary with the patient, it must be objectively assessed in terms of reasonableness.

...

5. Breach of Duty of Disclosure: The Findings Below Reviewed

In my opinion, the record of evidence amply justifies the trial Judge's findings that the plaintiff was told no more or understood no more than that he would be better off to have the operation than not to have it. This was not an adequate, not a sufficient disclosure of the risk attendant upon the operation itself, a risk well appreciated by the defendant in view of his own experience that of the 60 to 70 such operations that he had previously performed, 8 to 10 resulted in the death of the patients. Although the mortality rate was falling by 1970, the mor-

bidity (the sickness or disease) rate, according to Dr. Hughes, was still about 10%. The trial Judge was also justified in finding that the plaintiff, who was concerned about his continuing headaches and who was found to be suffering from hypertension, had the impression that the surgery would alleviate his headaches and hypertension so that he could carry on with his job. Dr. Hughes made it plain in his evidence that the surgery would not cure the headaches but did not, as the trial Judge found, make this plain to the plaintiff.

The foregoing findings have a basis in the evidence independent of any reliance on so-called statistics which was criticized by the majority of the Court of Appeal. Although Brooke J.A., speaking for the majority, appeared to discount the trial Judge's determinations because the latter made no specific finding on credibility, it is patent to me that the trial Judge's conclusions involved a weighing of the evidence and, hence, a measuring of its relative worth on the issues that he had to decide. There were inconsistencies in the defendant's evidence, as the trial Judge noted in his reasons, and it was for him to reconcile them in arriving at his findings. For example, the defendant said in-chief that he had told the plaintiff of the risk of a stroke during surgery and then said on cross-examination that the risks of the surgery were quite minimal. Again, on cross-examination, he said that he did not tell the patient that there was a risk of a stroke as a result of the surgery at any specific time thereafter, and he returned to an oft repeated statement that the chances of paralysis were greater without an operation than with it. (This was also the only reference by Dr. Lougheed, who testified for the defence, as to the risk involved in submitting to or foregoing the surgery. His evidence was almost exclusively related to post-operative care and whether a re-operation was feasible. He said it was not. However, as I noted earlier, post-operative care was not an issue in this Court.) Moreover, the defendant placed this risk as one within a few years and not within any immediate time. Indeed, when asked in cross-examination whether he told the patient that the surgery carried the risk of a stroke, he answered, "I didn't say that specifically." This was certainly a case in which a trial Judge, here an experienced Judge, was in a better position than an appellate Court or this Court to determine what evidence to accept and what conclusions to draw from it.

In the … reasons of Brooke J.A., speaking for the majority of the Court of Appeal, there are two approaches on the crucial issue whether the defendant apprised the plaintiff of the risk of a stroke from the very operation. In the first … passage, the learned Justice of Appeal appears to have viewed the trial Judge's finding on this question as a finding that the plaintiff was not made aware of that risk. This is clearly a correct assessment of the trial Judge's conclusion. However, Brooke J.A. went on to deal with the case and with the evidence as if there was a partial albeit not a sufficient disclosure of the particular risk, and he proceeded from there into an appraisal of the statistics to which the trial Judge referred and found fault in their use. In the second … passage … Brooke J.A. … ignores the finding of the trial Judge that there was no disclosure of the risks inherent in the surgery itself. In my opinion, there was a failure by the Court of Appeal to address this point directly. In the light of the defendant's own evidence that there was a failure on his part to disclose the risk, even though the plaintiff himself raised the question of the risks he faced on the operating table, I do not see how there could be any doubt of a breach in this respect of the duty of disclosure.

Indeed, the reasons of the Court of Appeal … appear to support the trial Judge's finding that there was no proper disclosure by the defendant of the risk of the surgery itself. Brooke J.A. said this on the question [at p. 119]:

> He [the defendant] did not specifically discuss the questions of death or paralysis as risks of the surgery, his explanation being that he believed the patient was aware of the risk because of questions that he asked when the surgery was being discussed. It was his view that no further detail was necessary.

In this respect then, there would seem to be concurrent findings of fact against the defendant on a central point in case.

There were a number of relevant considerations informing the findings of the trial Judge, about which there was no dispute. First, there was no emergency making surgery imperative. There was no noticeable neurological deficit. The defendant himself placed the risk of a stroke as one off in the future, four to five years. Any immediate risk would be from the surgery and not from foregoing it. Moreover, it must have been obvious to the defendant that the plaintiff had some difficulty with the English language and that he should, therefore, have made certain that he was understood. Finally, there was no evidence that the plaintiff was emotionally taut or unable to accept disclosure of the grave risk to which he would be exposed by submitting to surgery. I do not see in the reasons of the majority of the Court of Appeal any evidentiary basis for challenging the findings of the trial Judge on the defendant's breach of the duty of disclosure. Of course, the medical evidence was relevant to what that duty entailed but, that said, it was for the trier of fact to determine the scope of the duty and to decide whether there had been a breach of the duty. As I have already said, the so-called statistical data used by the trial Judge did not affect the grounds upon which he made his critical findings. The Court of Appeal held, however, that the trial Judge did not examine the issue of causation with the necessary care that this issue required. He did not ignore it, even if he might have gone into it at greater length. The question that remains, therefore, is whether this was a sufficient basis upon which to direct a new trial.

6. Causation

Relevant in this case to the issue whether a reasonable person in the plaintiff's position would have declined surgery at the particular time is the fact that he was within about one and one-half years of earning pension benefits if he continued at his job; that there was no neurological deficit then apparent; that there was no immediate emergency making the surgery imperative; that there was a grave risk of a stroke or worse during or as a result of the operation, while the risk of a stroke without it was in the future, with no precise time fixed or which could be fixed except as a guess of three or more years ahead. Since, on the trial Judge's finding, the plaintiff was under the mistaken impression, as a result of the defendant's breach of the duty of disclosure, that the surgery would relieve his continuing headaches, this would in the opinion of a reasonable person in the plaintiff's position, also weigh against submitting to the surgery at the particular time.

In my opinion, a reasonable person in the plaintiff's position would, on a balance of probabilities, have opted against the surgery rather than undergoing it at the particular time.

Conclusion

I would, accordingly, allow the appeal, set aside the order of the Court of Appeal and restore the judgment at trial. The appellant is entitled to costs throughout.

A Moral Theory of Informed Consent

Benjamin Freedman

Most medical codes of ethics, and most physicians, agree that the physician ought to obtain the "free and informed consent" of his subject or patient before attempting any serious medical procedures, experimental or therapeutic in nature. They agree, moreover, that a proxy consent ought to be obtained on behalf of the incompetent subject. And informed consent is seen as not merely a legal requirement, and not merely a formality: it is a substantial requirement of morality.

Acceptance of this doctrine, however, requires the solution of a number of problems. How much information need be imparted? At what age is a person mature enough to consent on his own behalf? Can prisoners give a "free and informed consent" to be experimented upon? Lurking behind these and similar questions there are more fundamental difficulties. What are the functions of consent for the competent and the incompetent? What is the sense in which the

Benjamin Freedman, "A Moral Theory of Informed Consent," *Hastings Center Report* 5:4 (August 1975): 32–39. Reproduced by permission. © The Hastings Center.

patient/subject must be "free," "informed," and "competent?" It is by way of an approach to these latter questions that I shall attempt to respond to the more specific questions.[1]

I. Consent and the Competent

The negative aspects of the doctrine of informed consent have ordinarily been the focus of attention; difficulties in obtaining the informed consent of the subject/patient render the ethics of experimentation and therapeutic measures questionable. Our common view of informed consent is that, when at all relevant, it represents a minimum condition which ethics imposes upon the physician. It is seen as a necessary condition for medical manipulation, but hardly as a sufficient condition.

The reasons why this is so — why it is not sufficient that an experimenter, for instance, have received informed consent from his subject before proceeding — are quite obvious. The scarcity of medical resources (which includes a scarcity of qualified physician-investigators) forbids us from wasting time upon poorly-designed experiments, or upon experiments which merely replicate well-established conclusions. There seems to be, as well, a limit to the dangers which we (ordinarily) allow subjects to face. We do not, as a matter of policy, think it wise to allow would-be suicides to accomplish their end with the aid of a scientific investigator. Many other reasons could be given for the proposition that a person does not have a right to be experimented upon, even when he has given valid consent to the procedure.

The Right to Consent

But there does seem to exist a positive right of informed consent, which exists in both therapeutic and experimental settings. A person who has the capacity to give valid consent, and who has in fact consented to the procedure in question, has a right to have that fact recognized by us. We all have a duty to recognize a valid consent when confronted with it.

From whence derives this right? It arises from the right which each of us possesses to be treated as a person, and in the duty which all of us have, to have respect for persons, to treat a person as such, and not as an object. For this entails that our capacities for personhood ought to be recognized by all — these capacities including the capacity for rational decision, and for action consequent upon rational decision. Perhaps the worst which we may do to a man is to deny him his humanity, for example, by classifying him as mentally incompetent when he is, in fact, sane. It is a terrible thing to be hated or persecuted; it is far worse to be ignored, to be notified that you "don't count."

If an individual is capable of and has given valid consent, I would argue that he has a right, as against the world but more particularly as against his physician, to have it recognized that valid consent has been given. (The same applies, of course, with still greater force, with regard to *refusals* to consent to medical procedures.) The limited force of this claim must be emphasized: it does not entail a right to be treated, or to be experimented upon. It is a most innocuous right, one which most of us would have little hesitation about granting.

It is, therefore, curious that the literature on informed consent has failed to recognize this right — has, in fact, tacitly denied this right, at least as regards experimentation. In writings on informed consent it seems to have been assumed that if, under certain conditions, it is *doubtful* that valid consent to an experiment has been granted, it is best to "play it safe" ethically. In cases of doubt, we prefer not to take chances: in this case, we will not take a chance upon violating the canons of ethics by experimenting without being certain that the subject has validly consented to the experiment. Since we do not at present know whether a prisoner can give a valid consent, let us not take chances: we call for a moratorium on prison experimentation. Since we do not know at what age a person has the capacity to give a valid consent, we avoid the problem by setting the age of majority at a point where it is beyond doubt that maturity has been attained. If we must err, we shall ensure that we err in being overly ethical.

The establishment of the innocuous right to have valid consent recognized as such eliminates this expedient. Other writers have conceptualized the conflict as one between a right and, at best, a mere liberty. From the patient's point of view, he has a right to have his health protected by the physician, and a mere liberty to be experimented upon. From the physician-investigator's point of view, he has a duty to protect the subject's health, and a mere liberty to experiment upon the subject (contingent, of course, upon obtaining the subject's consent). A recognition of the claims of personhood and autonomy, however, reveals this to be a conflict between rights and duties. The physician-investigator has a duty to recognize consent when validly offered. When the consent is of doubtful validity, therefore, the physician experiences a conflict between two duties. He will not be ethically well-protected by choosing not to experiment, for there exists the possibility — which, as cases are multiplied, becomes a probability — that he is violating a duty in so choosing. Problems in informed consent present us with a dilemma. It is no longer the case that the burden of proof devolves upon the would-be experimenter. The would-be abstainer-from-experiments may have to prove his case as well.

These considerations give us a new point of departure in investigating problems of informed consent. They show us that there is no "fail-safe" procedure which we can fall back upon in cases of doubt. Rather, what is required is an exhaustive examination of each case and issue, to see whether or not a valid consent has in fact been obtained.

When we fail to recognize a valid consent, of course, more is involved than a denial of personhood. Other benefits may be denied as well. Dr. Vernon Mark, for example, maintains that psychosurgery should not be done on prisoners with epilepsy because of the problem in obtaining a voluntary consent from prisoners.[2] But a resolution of this problem has not been shown to be impossible. Surely, the proper thing to do here would be to see whether prisoners can or cannot give valid consent to such a procedure. To remain satisfied with doubts, to fail to investigate this question, complex though it be, results in a denial of medical treatment for the prisoner, as well as representing a negation of the prisoner's human capacities. In depriving prisoners of the opportunity to serve as subjects in medical experiments, there are losses other than those of human respect.[3] Not the least of these is the loss of an opportunity to be of altruistic service to mankind.[4] Even a child feels at times a need to be useful; in promoting a moratorium on prison experimentation we deny prisoners the satisfaction of this psychic need. We should not need a reminder from John Stuart Mill that there are "higher" as well as "lower" pleasures and needs.

The right to have valid consent recognized as such does not indicate that we must experiment on prisoners. What it does indicate is that we have a moral responsibility to investigate in detail the question of whether prisoners can, under certain conditions, validly consent to experimentation. It also requires that we not prevent a researcher from experimenting on the basis of over-scrupulousness. If prisoners *can* give valid consent, we wrong not only the researcher but the prisoner as well by forbidding prison experimentation.

The Requirement of Information

The most common locution for the requirement which I am discussing is "informed consent" — we require "informed consent" to protect a doctor from legal liability resultant from his therapeutic endeavors, or to ensure the "ethicacy" of an experiment. But I believe "informed consent" to be a serious misnomer for what we do, in fact, want medical practice to conform to.

No lengthy rehearsal of the absurdities consequent upon taking the term "informed consent" at face value is necessary. The claim has been made, and repeated with approval, that "fully informed consent" is a goal which we can never achieve, but toward which we must strive. In order to ensure that fully informed consent has been given, it has seriously been suggested that only medical students or graduate students in the life sciences ought to be accepted as subjects for experimentation. *Reductio ad absurdum* examples of "fully informed consent" have been elaborated, in forms which list all the minutiae of the proposed medical procedure, together with all of its conceivable sequelae. With such a view of "informed consent" and its requirements, it is not surprising to find doctors who claim that since they cannot fully inform patients, they will tell them nothing, but instead will personally assume the responsibility for assuring the subject's safety.

In truth, a *reductio ad absurdum* of this view of "informed consent" need not be constructed; it serves as its own *reductio ad absurdum*. For there is no end to "fully informing" patients. When the doctor wishes to insert a catheter, must he commend to the subject's attention a textbook of anatomy? Although this, of course, would not suffice: he must ensure

that the patient understands the text as well. Must he tell the patient the story of Dr. X, that bogey of first-year medical students, who, in a state of inebriation, inserted ("by mistake") his pen-refill instead of the catheter? With, of course, the assurance that *this* physician never gets drunk. ("Well, rarely, anyway.") Must the patient be informed of the chemical formula of the catheter? Its melting point?

The basic mistake which is committed by those who harp upon the difficulties in obtaining informed consent (and by critics of the doctrine) is in believing that we can talk about information in the abstract, without reference to any human purpose. It is very likely impossible to talk about "information" in this way; but impossible or not, when we do in fact talk about, or request, information, we do not mean "information in the abstract." If I ask someone to "tell me about those clouds" he will, ordinarily, know what I mean; and he will answer me, in the spirit in which he was asked, by virtue of his professional expertise as an artist, meteorologist, astronomer, soothsayer, or what-have-you. The meteorologist will not object that he cannot tell you the optical refraction index of the clouds, and therefore that he cannot "fully answer" your question. He knows that you are asking him with a given end in mind, and that much information about the cloud is irrelevant *relative to that purpose*.

That this "abstract information" requirement is not in question in obtaining valid consent is hardly an original point, but it is worth repeating. One of the leading court opinions on human experimentation puts it like this: "...the patient's interest in information does not extend to a lengthy polysyllabic discourse on all possible complications. A mini-course in medical science is not required. ..."[5]

The proper question to ask, then, is not "What information must be given?" That would be premature: we must first know for what purpose information is needed. *Why* must the patient be informed? Put that way, the answer is immediately forthcoming. The patient must be informed so that he will know what he is getting into, what he may expect from the procedure, what his likely alternatives are — in short, what the procedure (and forbearance from it) will mean, so that a responsible decision on the matter may be made. This is the legal stance, as well as, I think, a "common-sensical" stance; as Alexander Capron writes, the information component in valid consent derives in law from the recognition that information is "necessary to make meaningful the power to decide."[6] The proper test of whether a given piece of information needs to be given is, then, whether the physician, knowing what he does about the patient/subject, feels that that patient/subject would want to know this before making up his mind. Outré, improbable consequences would not ordinarily, therefore, be relevant information. Exceptionally, they will be: for example, when there is a small risk of impotence consequent upon the procedure which the physician proposes to perform upon a man with a great stake in his sexual prowess. This is only sensible.

Our main conclusion, then, is that valid consent entails only the imparting of that information which the patient/subject requires in order to make a responsible decision. This entails, I think, the possibility of a valid yet ignorant consent.

Consider, first, the therapeutic context. It is, I believe, not unusual for a patient to give his doctor *carte blanche* to perform any medical procedure which the physician deems proper in order to effect a cure. He is telling the doctor to act as his agent in choosing which procedure to follow. This decision is neither unwise nor (in any serious sense) an abdication of responsibility and an unwarranted burden upon the physician.

We each of us choose to delegate our power of choice in this way in dealing with our auto mechanic or stockbroker.

It may be harder to accept an ignorant consent as valid in the purely experimental context. I think, however, that much of this difficulty is due to our paucity of imagination, our failure to imagine circumstances in which a person might choose to proceed in this way. We might approach such a case, for example, by imagining a Quaker who chooses to serve society by acting as a research subject, but who has a morbid fear of knives and pointed instruments. The Quaker might say to the physician-investigator that he wants to serve science but is afraid that his phobia would overcome his better judgment. He might consequently request that any experiment which would involve use of scalpels, hypodermic needles, and such, be performed without informing him: while, say, he is asleep or unconscious. He might further ask the doctor not to proceed should the experiment involve considerable risk. In such a case, or one similar, we would find an instance of a valid yet ignorant consent to experimentation.

The ostensible differences between the therapeutic and experimental contexts may be resolved into two components: in the therapeutic context it is supposed that the physician knows what the sequelae to treatment will be, which information, by definition, is not available in the experimental situation; and in the therapeutic context the doctor may be said to be seeking his patient's good, in contrast to the experimental context where some other good is being sought. On the basis of these differences it may be claimed that a valid yet ignorant consent is enough permission for therapy, but not for experimentation.

Closer examination, however, reveals that these differences do not necessarily obtain. First, because I believe it would be granted that a valid yet ignorant consent can be given in the "therapeutic-experimental" situation, where a new drug or procedure is being attempted to aid the patient (in the absence of any traditional available therapy). In the therapeutic-experimental situation, as in the purely experimental situation, the sequelae are not known (although of course in both cases some definite result is expected or anticipated). If a valid yet ignorant consent is acceptable in the one, therefore, it must be acceptable in the other.

Secondly, because it is patently not the case that we can expect there to be no good accruing to the subject of an experiment by reason of his participation. There are, commonly, financial and other "tangible" benefits forthcoming (laboratory training, and so on). And it must once again be said that the pleasures of altruism are not negligible. The proposed differences between experimentation and therapy do not stand up, and so we must say that if a valid yet ignorant consent is acceptable in the one it must be acceptable in the other. It must be remembered that this statement only concerns itself with one part of the consent doctrine, which is, itself, only one of the requirements which the ethical experiment must satisfy.

To mention — without claiming totally to resolve — two problems which may be raised at this point: First, it is said that a doctor often does not know what will happen as a consequence of a recommended procedure, and so cannot tell the patient what the patient wants to know. The obvious response to this seems to be right: the physician should, in that case, tell the patient/subject that he does not know what will happen (which does not exclude an explanation of what the doctor expects to happen, and on what he bases this expectation).

Second, it will be objected that the adoption of a requirement such as I propose would forbid the use of placebos and blind experiments. I am not sure that this is so; sometimes it must be the case that the subjects in an experiment may be asked (without introducing artifacts into the results) to consent to an experiment knowing that some will, and some will not, be receiving placebos. Another alternative would be to inform the subjects that the experiment may or may not involve some subjects receiving placebos.[7] I am aware, however, that these remarks are less than adequate responses to these problems.

Our conclusion, then, is that the informing of the patient/subject is not a fundamental requirement of valid consent. It is, rather, derivative from the requirement that the consent be the expression of a responsible choice. The two requirements which I do see as fundamental in this doctrine are that the choice be responsible and that it be voluntary.

The Requirement of Responsibility

What is meant by saying that the choice must be "responsible"? Does this entail that the physician may at any time override a patient's judgment on the basis that, in the physician's view, the patient has not chosen responsibly? Surely not; to adopt such a criterion would defeat the purpose embodied in the doctrine of consent. It would mean that a person's exercise of autonomy is always subject to review.

Still, some such requirement would appear to be necessary. A small child can certainly make choices.[8] Small children can also be intelligent enough to understand the necessary information. Yet surely we would not want to say that a small child can give valid consent to a serious medical procedure.[9] The reason for this is that the child cannot choose *responsibly.*

We are faced with a dilemma. On the one hand, it appears that we must require that the choice be responsible. To require only that the choice be free would yield counter-intuitive results. On the other hand, if we do require that the choice made be a responsible one, we seem to presuppose some body which shall judge the reasonableness of choices; this represents a paternalism which is antithetical to the doctrine of consent. An elderly patient chooses to forgo further life-saving measures. How are we to judge whether or not this choice is a responsible one?

The path between the horns of this dilemma involves saying that the "responsibility" which we require is to be predicated not on the nature of the particular choice, but on the nature of the patient/subject. What we need to know is whether *he* is a responsible man ("in general," so to speak), not whether the choice which has been made is responsible. In this way, we avoid the danger of upholding as "responsible" only those choices which we ourselves feel are good choices. We can and do admit into the community of responsible persons individuals who make choices with which we do not agree.

In this sense, responsibility is a dispositional characteristic. To say that someone is a responsible individual means that he makes choices, typically, on the basis of reasons, arguments, or beliefs — and that he remains open to the claims of reason, so that further rational argument might lead him to change his mind. It is to say that a person is capable of making and carrying through a life-plan — that he is prepared to act on the basis of his choices. It is to say that a person is capable of living with his life-plan; he can live with the consequences of his choices, he *takes responsibility* for his choices.[10] Of course, none of these are absolutes: all responsible people are at times pigheaded, at times short-sighted, at times flighty. That is to say, all responsible men at times act irresponsibly. Should the lack of responsibility persist, of course, to an extreme degree, we may say that the person has left the community of responsible folk.

Voluntarism and Reward

The other requirement of valid consent is that it be given voluntarily. The choice which the consent expresses must be freely made.

We all know some conditions which, if satisfied, make us say that a consent has been given involuntarily. The case which immediately springs to mind occurs when an individual succumbs under a threat: we call this duress or coercion. But the threat need not be overt; and perhaps there need not be a threat at all to render consent involuntary.

Hence, the major problem currently engendered by the requirement of voluntariness. It is typified by the prisoner who "volunteers" for an experiment in the hope or expectation of a reward: significantly higher wages, an opportunity for job training, better health care while involved in the experiment, a favorable report to his parole board. Is the consent which the prisoner offers a voluntary consent? The problem may be stated more generally thus: At what point does reward render consent involuntary?

The problem of reward is particularly difficult, since it involves questions of degree. Is a prisoner's consent involuntary if the reward for his participation in the experiment is a three-month reduction of sentence? Is it relevant here that the prisoner is serving a twenty-year sentence, rather than a one-to-five-year sentence? Does a possible increase in wages from twenty-five cents per hour to one dollar per hour constitute duress? Should we consider the percentage increase, or the increase in absolute value, or the increase in actual value which the seventy-five cent disparity represents in the prison environment?

To some, of course, questions like these have little meaning. They have little meaning to those who are indifferent to the demands of justice and autonomy which the consent doctrine represents, to those who are willing to buy guinea pigs, rather than to reward human beings. And they have little meaning for those who are convinced that prisoners are inherently unfree, and who thus would call for a total cessation of prison experimentation. Each of these positions denies, in an a *priori* fashion, freedom to prisoners; each must be rejected. A recognition of the fact that decisions about consent may be over- as well as under-protective forces us to deal with this sort of question, complex though it may be.

As is so often the case, posing the question in a different way may facilitate response. We have been considering the question of how much reward nullifies the validity of consent, how much reward renders the subject unfree. But is it in fact the case that *reward* is the disruptive factor here?

This problem may be clarified by the following examples. Imagine an upper-middle-class individual, who can provide for his family all of their needs and most of the amenities of civilized life. Let us say that this person is offered one hundred dollars to cross the street — if you like, make it one thousand or ten thousand dollars? He chooses to cross the street. Is his choice *involuntary*? Despite the substantial reward, I think most of us would agree that the consent was freely offered (and would that we should have such problems!).

Consider a person who deeply wants to be an astronaut. He is told that as part of the program he must participate in experiments to determine resistance to high-G conditions. Is his consent to this invalid, involuntary? I think not. We would say, this is part of his job; he should have expected it; and if he can't stand the heat, he should get out of the kitchen. In this vein, consider Evel Knievel, a financially prosperous man, who is offered millions of dollars to perform daredevil stunts. His choice may be bizarre, even crazy: but has his reward rendered it unfree?

Finally, consider a man who is informed by his doctor that he will most likely die unless he has open-heart surgery. His "reward" for consenting is his life; the penalty for not consenting is death. Does this mean this man cannot give the doctor valid consent — morally valid consent — to proceed?

There are two distinctions which, I think, go a long way towards dispelling these problems. First, I think it must be granted that natural contingencies ("acts of God," things which come to pass naturally, those contingencies which we cannot hold anyone responsible for) do not render a person unfree, nor do they render unfree the choices which a person makes in light of those contingencies.[11]

That natural contingencies do not render a man unfree is a point which is apt to be forgotten in the present context. I am not — in the morally relevant sense — lacking in freedom because I cannot, unaided, fly through the air, or live on grass. Nor am I unfree because my heart is about to give out. Nor am I unfree when, recognizing that my heart may give out, I choose to undergo surgery. I may, of course, be so crazed by knowing that I am near death's door that I am in a state of general impotence, and hence must have the choice made for me; but general incompetence is not in question here. The distinction between choices forced by man, and choices forced by nature, is, then, of importance.

The second distinction is between those pressures which are, and those which are not, in Daube's words, "consonant with the dignity and responsibility of free life."[12] I would explain this as follows: there are certain basic freedoms and rights which we possess which *entitle* us (morally) to certain things (or states of affairs). We would all, no doubt, draw up different lists of these rights and freedoms; but included in them would be safety of person, freedom of conscience and religion, a right to a certain level of education, and, for some of us, a right to some level of health care. When the "reward" is such as only to give us the necessary conditions of these rights and freedoms — when all that the reward does is to bring us up to a level of living to which we are entitled, and of which we have been deprived by man — then the "reward," I think, constitutes duress. A reward which accrues to one who has achieved this level, or who can easily achieve it (other than by taking the reward-option), and which hence serves only to grant us "luxury" items, does not constitute duress, and hence does not render choice unfree, no matter how great this reward may be.

The rewards above the moral subsistence level are true rewards. In contrast, we may say (with some touch of metaphor) that the "rewards" which only bring us up to the level to which we were in any event entitled are properly viewed as functioning as *threats*: "Do this, or stay where you are" — when you should not have been "where you are" in the first place.

The astronaut, Evel Knievel, and the upper-middle-class street-crosser are being granted "luxury" items, and hence are capable of giving free consent. But consider a man who will not be admitted to the hospital for treatment unless he agrees to be a subject in an experiment (unrelated to his treatment). Those who feel, as I do, that we are, here and now, morally entitled to medical treatment would agree, I trust, that this illegitimate option coerces the man into agreeing. Or consider a man who has religious scruples against donating blood, who takes his daughter to a hospital for treatment. He is told that the doctors will not treat her unless the family donates a certain amount of blood. His freedom has been nullified: his "consent" to donating blood is morally invalid.[13] Similarly, the college student whose grade is contingent upon his participation in the instructor's psychological experiments is not validly consenting to serve. He is entitled to have his grade based upon his classroom work.

It yet remains to apply this distinction to our original problem, prison experimentation. The application will not be attempted here, for we would first need to be clear in our minds what rights and freedoms a prisoner is entitled to. I would not hesitate to say, though, that when a situation is created whereby a prisoner can only receive decent health care by participating in an experiment, he is being coerced into that experiment. I would have little hesitation in claiming that if subjecting himself to experimentation is the only way in which a prisoner could learn a trade which may be used "outside," then that prisoner is being coerced, his consent is not free. When we take into account the condition of our society, these would seem to be reasonable entitlements for the prisoner. Other rewards — for example, higher pay—may or may not constitute rewards above the moral subsistence level; if they are, then consent in light of these rewards could be freely offered. Perhaps too much has been said already; judgments like these must be made in an individualized fashion, one which is sensitive to the realities of prison life.

Notes

The research for this paper was begun during an internship at the Institute of Society, Ethics and the Life Sciences in the month of June, 1973. I gratefully acknowledge the help of Drs. Daniel Callahan, Marc Lappé, Peter Steinfels, and Robert Veatch, of the Institute, who helped make my internship profitable and enjoyable. My wife Barbara read the manuscript and suggested a number of needed changes.

1. For examples of a similar method applied to different problems, see Thomas I. Emerson, *Toward a General Theory of the First Amendment* (New York: Vintage Books, 1967).

2. "Brain Surgery in Aggressive Epileptics," in *Hastings Center Report*, February 1973.

3. See the insert to Alexander M. Capron's call for a moratorium on prison experimentation, "Medical Research in Prisons," *Hastings Center Report*, June 1973. The insert is a report from *The New York Times*, April 15, 1973, and reads in part: "Ninety-six of the 175 inmates at Lancaster County prison have written to a newspaper here protesting a recent decision by the state to halt all medical experiments on state prisoners. In their letter to the *Lancaster New Era*, they urged that state to allow the research [which] did not harm them and enabled them to pay off their fines and court costs."

4. See Henry K. Beecher, *Research and the Individual: Human Studies* (Boston: Little, Brown, 1970), 56. Professor Beecher notes a study of prison inmates, who, for participation in an experiment involving malaria, received pay but no reduction of sentence. Half of the volunteers cited "altruism" rather than money as their motive for volunteering. Those inmates who did not volunteer "expressed or implied respect for those who did volunteer."

5. *Cobbs* v. *Grant*, 502 P. 2d 1, 11.

6. Alexander M. Capron, "Legal Rights and Moral Rights," in Hilton, *et al.*, eds., *Ethical Issues in Human Genetics* (Plenum Press, 1973), 228.

7. If this sort of explanation were given as a matter of course in *all* experiments, this might still further reduce the problem of artifacts. The remarks, it should be noted, are directed towards medical experiments. By and large, they are inapplicable to, say, experiments in social psychology.

8. The counter-suggestion may be made that children cannot *really* make choices. This would, I think, put too great a weight upon the requirement of voluntarism. We would be recruiting the concepts of choice and volition to do a job which they have not been designed for.

9. I am speaking of course in the moral, not the legal, context. It may be that in an emergency a child may, in the absence of his parents, give legally valid consent.

10. This gives us the link between "responsible" in the dispositional sense explained here, and "responsible" in the blame-sense of the word ("I'll hold you responsible for that.").

11. The *caveat* must be added: natural contingencies do not have, as their *sole* result, the rendering of a person unfree, in the sense which vitiates consent: a man's brain tumor can make the man an idiot, schizophrenia can make a man insane, but these do not so much affect a person's volition as they do disturb his entire psychic structure.

12. David Daube, quoted in Beecher, 146.

13. *In re Gault*, 387 U.S. 1 (1967).

Waiver of Informed Consent, Cultural Sensitivity, and the Problem of Unjust Families and Traditions

Insoo Hyun

Caring for patients from different cultures presents a variety of challenges. One of the most complex centers on a worry that the formal requirements for obtaining informed consent may impose a Western ideal of personal autonomy on some minority patients, especially those who come from cultures that favor what appears to be a family-centered model of decisionmaking over a more individualistic mode.[1] Contrary to the current informed consent standards of full disclosure and patient self-determination, many minority patients may wish to remain uninvolved in the medical decisionmaking process, wanting instead to defer to their families' choices.

In one well-known study published in the *Journal of the American Medical Association*, for instance, researchers reported that elderly Korean Americans and Mexican Americans were less likely than elderly African Americans and European Americans to believe that a patient should be told of a terminal prognosis (35 percent and 48 percent versus 63 percent and 69 percent) and less likely to believe that the patient should make decisions about the use of life-support technology (28 percent and 41 percent versus 60 percent and 65 percent). Elderly Korean Americans (57 percent) and Mexican Americans (45 percent) were said to be more likely than the other two groups to believe that the family and not the patient should make end of life decisions.[2]

Cultural differences like these warn us of a potentially serious problem in the delivery of heath care today: namely, that providers who are unaware of such variable expectations may inadvertently transgress the cultural integrity and personal dignity of some of their minority patients through well-meaning efforts to obtain informed consent in the usual, patient-centered manner—contravening, in the process, the very principle of respect for persons that the doctrine of informed consent was meant to protect.

In response to this concern, some commentators have recommended that providers broaden their view of autonomy to accommodate the cultural values ethnically diverse patients might bring to medical decisionmaking, including a preference to waive their right to informed consent and relinquish decisionmaking authority to their families. Lawrence Gostin has suggested that the medical community can best preserve its overall commitment to personal autonomy by allowing patients to stray from a Western model of independent medical decisionmaking and act in the manner that best accords with their own cultural values.[3] According to this view, providers can help advance this goal by first asking their minority patients which they would prefer: to be informed about their illnesses and involved in making treatment decisions, or to have their families handle these matters for them.[4]

This proposal seems consistent with the medical profession's current norm of allowing variable degrees of patient involvement, as directed by the patient's values. That is, since a patient's right to self-determination includes both the right to decide whether to receive full information and the right to opt out of making treatment decisions altogether, most accept that physicians may be discharged of their duty to fulfill formal consent requirements at the request of their patients.[5] This idea appears to be modified only slightly by the claim that the standard course for obtaining informed consent can be justifiably set aside when patients communicate a *culturally based* desire not to be informed of their diagnosis or prognosis and to have their families make decisions for them.[6]

The call for cultural sensitivity should be lauded for encouraging physicians to consider such diverse sorts of patients' values. Nonetheless, the ethical issues involved in this call are much more complex and difficult than is frequently recognized. They cannot be resolved by merely broadening our view of autonomy.

My chief concern is that this easy solution rests on an inadequate conception of personal autonomy and ignores the possibility that some patients' values might not be *authentic* for them, in the sense of being free of coercive formative influences. This is a serious mistake. In order to act autonomously, one must not simply act on the values one happens to have; one must act on those values that may be called "one's own" in a morally relevant sense.

Call this the *authenticity condition* of individual autonomy. At the very least, this crucial oversight may lead some medical ethicists and health care professionals to an immoderate optimism about how easily one can recognize a patient's waiver of informed consent as a truly autonomous choice. At worst, physicians may unwittingly license the continued control by unjust families of vulnerable and powerless members. Oftentimes, this concern will be especially sharp when the patient is a woman.

My intention here is not to attack any particular cultural group, nor to suggest that all immigrant or minority families have unjust family relationships. Either manoeuver would be presumptuous, if not brazenly offensive. It would be both a moral and a sociological mistake to treat cultural groups as monolithic entities, and to ignore the complex intracultural and intergenerational differences that exist in every community. As Seyla Benhabib warns, philosophers and other theorists must avoid relying on a naive sociology whereby "cultures are presented as hermetic and sealed wholes; the internal contradictions and debates within cultures are flattened out; the different conceptual and normative options which are available to the participants of a given culture and society are ignored."[7] While it is easy to imagine cultures (particularly those we know very little about) as stable, unchanging, and harmonious, in reality cultures are adaptive, open-textured, and permeated with opposing interests.[8] This is a fact we must bear in mind from the very start.

On account of this intracultural variability, then, a careful philosophical examination of the informed consent concerns must look beyond the usual cultural norms of the patient's ethnic community and focus more locally on the dynamics of that patient's family and the circumstances surrounding that patient's desire to relinquish his or her decision-making authority. I recommend this approach because people's views and attitudes toward their inherited traditions are simply too diverse for the complex issues of personal autonomy to be solved by broad appeals to culture. While a patient's ethnic community and cultural heritage certainly often supply many of his or her values, it is a further question whether the patient is acting autonomously when following them.

This last point directs us to the authenticity condition. My aim is to provide a fuller explanation of the authenticity condition, along with an analysis of the general conditions under which a patient's waiver of informed consent would be nonautonomous and ethically problematic, even in certain cases where the patient might actually *want* to defer to the family's wishes.

The Significance of Families

The family is an appropriate unit of analysis from which to begin our present investigation for several reasons. There are four aspects of the family that are directly relevant to the argument I wish to develop, and a quick account of them here will help set up my approach.[9]

First, families are where many cultural traditions are taught, practiced, and internalized, making families powerful social conduits for culture. Although people can absorb cultural influences from many different sources, the routine activities of a family effectively help determine the degree to which a specific cultural heritage becomes embodied in the lives of its members.

Second, through the customs and projects they pass to the young and the manner in which they focus their energies and resources, families also cultivate and sustain what might be regarded as an overall "familial character."[10] Some families, for example, may be said to be more sociable, artistic, religious, traditional, or egalitarian than others, depending on the types of commitments and interests their members share and promote.

Third, in addition to the development of a distinct familial character, it is also largely, and usually, within the bounds of the family that individuals acquire and maintain a subjective sense of identity.[11] A person's self-concept is shaped to a great extent by his or her familial ties and shared histories with loved ones. As Michael Sandell, Alasdair MacIntyre, and other communitarians are fond of saying, people come deeply "embedded" in personal relationships and shared social roles and practices; they are not unconnected, unaffected, individual islands, but sons, daughters, fathers, mothers, and so on.[12]

Last, families are important because they help support some unique and intrinsically valuable ends, such as shared personal affection and a keen sense of emotional enrichment.[13] Families are capable of harboring a degree of love and intimacy rarely found in other segments of society.

An implicit recognition of the importance of the family motivates, in part, the growing tendency among bioethicists to reject individualistic conceptions of autonomy that are not attuned to the lives of real people who are bound together in families. Added to this, of course, is the concern that the standard requirements for obtaining informed consent may run counter to the cultural values of some patients and their families. In light of such issues, some theorists have recommended that we reconceptualize autonomy as the right and ability of persons to act on their values, however dissimilar these values may be from mainstream Western cultural norms.[14]

This would be a welcome change. It would have the happy effect of leaving open the possibility that an autonomous person can choose to act on his more altruistic and socially conscious values rather than a childishly narrow sense of self-regard—provided the former are values he in fact holds. This broader conception of autonomy can also easily accommodate the nonindividualistic values patients from other cultures may bring into the clinic. With this view of autonomy in place, minority patients who value preserving and promoting their families' interests above making their own independent decisions can be given room to act on this value. Furthermore, allowing patients the choice to follow a family-centered decisionmaking style within the context of their own health care is arguably perfectly consistent with the medical profession's standing commitment to personal autonomy.[15]

In short, with a little conceptual manoeuvring, individual autonomy can easily be made more family-friendly. Autonomy would by definition be opposed to family concerns and some patients' cultural values if we were to insist that autonomous persons must act with just their own lives and selfish interests in mind. But there is no reason we must accept such a narrow and egoistic definition of autonomy. What is needed, therefore, is a gestalt shift in our view of individual autonomy, from a focus on rugged individualism to an awareness that there exists a multiplicity of human values on which autonomous persons can act.

Recognizing the Importance of Authentic Values

I believe this renovated conception of personal autonomy, with its space for nonindividualistic values and family-centered medical decisionmaking, is on the right track. It is, however, incomplete in one very important respect. It does not include the authenticity condition—the qualification, in rough and preliminary terms, that those values which guide the actions and decisions of autonomous persons must be authentically "their own" and not the products of wholesale indoctrination or manipulation.[16] This is not a radically new idea, of course; it has been articulated in many well-known literary and philosophical works, from Huxley's *Brave New World* to J. S. Mill's arguments about the subjection of women, to Marx's writings about false consciousness. Despite differences among their accounts, a common lesson these and other authors present is that we must not always take people's values simply as given.

Autonomy theorists must take this warning seriously. Theories of autonomy that ignore the authenticity condition are faced with the embarrassing problem of not being able to rule out as nonautonomous those who have been brainwashed or otherwise had their values surreptitiously programmed for them. This is an unacceptable outcome, since these cases fall under the general category of what philosophers have called *heteronomy*, that is, the circumstance of a person's acting on the laws, or values, of another.

Notice that this outcome cannot be avoided merely by appealing to the individual's ability to reflect critically on her current values, since that ability might itself be malformed. Inauthenticity of the sort I am concerned with here is notoriously difficult for persons to self-diagnose and self-correct. Indeed, this was one of Marx's worries about false consciousness. Furthermore, the differences between autonomous and heteronomous persons can be difficult to detect from a third-person point of view, since these two groups can happen to look and act the same. It is even logically possible that both may be equally reflective and self-scrutinizing.

What remains to distinguish them in these cases is the authenticity condition. This additional stipulation requires us to look into the history of each individual. That is to say, we must first know how a person's values came to be acquired in order to determine whether her actions and decisions that accord with her values are truly autonomous—including her performance of self-reflection. It is in virtue of the authenticity condition, then, that autonomy cannot be read off a person's actions straight away.

Admittedly, everything I have said so far about authenticity may seem to suggest precisely the sort of rugged individualism I agreed we ought to let fade from our view of personal autonomy. How can we say that a person has authentic values in the required sense for autonomy without also presupposing a suspiciously individualistic ideal of the person, namely, that one should strive to make one's inherited values "one's own"?

It is easy to see why some critics might raise these concerns, especially in light of what other philosophers have recently asserted about what I have been calling the authenticity condition. Many autonomy theorists have held that a person's values are not truly "hers" until she has filtered them through a process of critical evaluation.[17] In other words, authentic values are said to have the distinctive feature of having been put through the test of detached self-appraisal, whereby the individual considers which of her inherited values to retain, revise, or reject.

If this is what is required to satisfy the authenticity condition, then autonomy seems possible only for those who have learned to take on an independently minded attitude toward the formation of their values. This character trait appears to embody a particularly rugged individualism. One might imagine here a young adult, in a moment of youthful rebellion, critically challenging the values she has received from her parents and community, like a Cartesian philosopher critically evaluating the epistemic status of her beliefs during a moment of hyperbolic doubt.

Indeed, the chief fault of this view of what authenticity requires is that it must actually *presuppose* autonomy in order to establish it. Insofar as we maintain that a person's having authentic values is a necessary precondition for her acting autonomously, any view of authentic values that demands that they be self-given through a process of critical reflection must already regard that person as autonomous. This explanation sends us on an infinite regress.[18] We need a more tenable view.

An Alternative Approach

Rather than viewing authenticity as the result of a person's critically reflective approval of her values, I believe we should concentrate instead on the social circumstances surrounding her acceptance of these values in the first place. To put the point another way, authenticity is not a matter of what a person *does*, but a matter of the *social context* in which she comes to have her values. Although an individual's ability to think about what is happening to her and how she is being influenced is an important part of being an autonomous person, it cannot stand alone as an adequate means of satisfying the authenticity condition. We must begin with factors that are "external" to the individual's mind and her critical processes if we are to avoid an infinite regress.

The factors I am thinking of here have to do with social restrictions on the options available for one's effective choice. I maintain that a person's values will fail the authenticity condition if she accepted them and holds them because she has suffered serious deprivations of legitimate alternatives and goods that remain open to others in her social milieu. Her values will be authentic only if they lack a causal history in this respect.

Three salient qualifications must be added to my approach: (1) These deprivations must be caused by other persons and not purely by natural circumstances, such as accidental disabilities and other randomly occurring misfortunes. (2) They must be deprivations of choices and goods that are reasonably available to others who are no more able-minded and talented than she. (3) They must not be justly deserved. (I will discuss this third qualification more later.)

These qualifications underscore a key difference between my account of authentic values and the prevalent view. According to the latter, a person's having inauthentic values is lamentable because they could preempt the possibility that she acts autonomously. According to my view, a person's having inauthentic values is lamentable not only for this important reason, but also because this person has been *wronged*. When we say that a person's values are inauthentic, we are not simply noting that they lack a certain characteristic—namely, their having been critically reflected upon. Rather, we are registering a normative complaint about an injustice in that person's life.[19] On the prevalent view, an inauthentic person fails to live up to a philosophical ideal of the individual as a critically self-reflective being. On my view, the fault lies outside the person, falling instead on the morally unjustified and restrictive social circumstances under which she happens to live.

What makes this alternative approach to authenticity especially notable is the fact that the deprivations that produce inauthentic values can occur quite openly. We do not have to imagine fantastic scenarios of widespread hypnosis in order to appreciate the danger of developing inauthentic values. When people are unjustly denied access to alternative and reasonable goods over a long span of time, they normally learn to value the goods that are feasible for them, even if artificially limited. This is a survival skill. It helps diminish the psychological dissonances that accompany injustice. Inequalities of treatment become more bearable if one happens to value what one is able to do instead of fruitlessly pining for what one cannot have.

Other commentators have remarked on this complex psychological coping skill (although they do not explicitly draw the connection to the authenticity condition that I do here).[20] Economist and philosopher Amartya Sen, for example, has observed that most poor and deprived women in rural India do not demand to be as educated and healthy as the Indian men around them because their expectations and hopes have been adapted to fit the life they have always known. What is striking about Sen's report is that the women he mentions often accept as natural and appropriate gross inequalities between men and women with respect to many basic necessities, such as nutrition and health care. There is a sharp disparity between Indian women's self-reported subjective satisfaction with their own level of health and their actual, very poor health status relative to men's.[21]

Furthermore, these women help preserve the unjust and sexist social arrangements around them because they value giving preferential treatment to men and boys—they believe the decisions they make to maintain these gender inequalities are important, and they experience feelings of remorse when they fail to conform to the expected pattern of behavior.[22] The effect, as Sen notes, is that "acute inequalities often survive precisely by making allies out of the deprived. The underdog comes to accept the legitimacy of the unequal order and becomes an implicit accomplice."[23] Yet it is not that these women are unusually naive and dupable; rather, they are unsentimentally pragmatic. They have come to value their way of life because no alternatives remain reasonably open to them. Yet the fact that many of these women do not complain is no indication that they are not deprived. As Sen explains, "It can be a serious error to take the absence of protests and questioning of inequality as evidence of the absence of inequality (or the nonviability of that question)."[24]

Let me posit some general claims. Seriously deprived people have values. And seriously deprived people can be relatively content. Nevertheless, they are wronged. Insofar as their actions stem from inauthentic values, they are autonomous only in appearance. Admittedly, not all seriously deprived people react psychologically to their unjust circumstances by developing inauthentic values; some can be defiant and rebellious relative to others around them. Yet, if the deprivations are systematic enough, especially if they begin at an early stage of life, before one's critical capacities are adequately developed, people can be habituated to view themselves as less capable and deserving than those who are privileged, and can subsequently value the ways of life that are most familiar to them.

Much more can be said about this approach to authenticity than I have space to provide here. Still, this abbreviated account reveals some of its advantages. Here are three.

First, it allows that many different types of people are capable of meeting the authenticity condition, not just deep, critical self-evaluators. People who do not regularly inspect their effective values at a meta-level (probably most of us) can still be autonomous, on the condition that the values they act on have a causal history free of the sort of coercive influences just mentioned.[25] This is not simply a convenient relaxation of the authenticity condition. Nothing prevents people from questioning and revising their values throughout their lifetimes; still, their "starter set" of values, so to speak, must be authentic, as judged by criteria that lie beyond their direct control, if they are to be described as acting autonomously.

Second, by making authenticity a matter of the social context in which a person's values develop rather than a matter of an individual's critical appraisal and choice, we not only avoid the infinite regress, but also the communitarian critique that a person's values are not all completely subject to her own choosing, as some radical forms of liberalism seem to assume. Communitarians are probably right that we absorb many of our identity-constituting values from the community around us; we can still talk about having authentic values in the sense necessary for autonomy.

Third, this approach can help explain why many values that people tend not to question and critically inspect—such as a person's valuing her

opportunities to enjoy artistic expression or outdoor activity—are normally considered authentic. Our presumption of their authenticity might be partly justified by the belief that they probably did not arise as a result of the individual's having been unjustly denied alternative possible goods. Of course, such a presumption could perhaps sometimes be rebutted. But as long as one's values are *in fact* free of unduly restrictive social constraints and (perhaps) are in harmony with their inborn talents and dispositions, they are authentic.

The Problem of Unjust Families and Traditions

Back, then, to the initial problem: many ethnically diverse patients might prefer to transfer their decisionmaking authority to their families and may not want to be informed at all about their diagnoses and prognoses. In fact, the very idea that patients in the United States are expected to understand their conditions and to play a significant role in their own treatment decisions may be completely alien to some.

Health care providers are faced with a daunting task whenever these possibilities present themselves—a much more daunting task than is implied by the response that providers should just broaden their view of autonomy and try to satisfy their patients' expressed preferences to waive informed consent. It is hard to overemphasize the complexities involved in this issue. Here are (minimally) the sort of considerations that must be taken into account. I propose that an individual patient's waiver of informed consent in the sort of cases we have been considering is ethically acceptable provided that the following five conditions are satisfied.

1) In a private conversation with her health care provider, the patient is made aware that she has the right to

informed consent, and that this right need not exclude her family's involvement if she desires it.[26]

2) She clearly expresses a preference to waive completely her right to informed consent and is not pressured or bullied into doing so by her family or anyone else.

[handwritten: how can they determine this??]

3) The patient's value-driven desire to grant her family final decisionmaking authority is authentic, in the sense required by the account above.

4) The family is prepared mentally and emotionally to handle the news of the patient's condition (if it proves serious) and is willing to assume the decisionmaking responsibilities.

5) The family is well-motivated, that is, either the patient's well-being or the common good of the family is identified as the goal of the decision.

The first three conditions ensure that the patient's waiver is autonomous. The last two ensure that the family, just like any other nonpatient decisionmaker, will be an appropriate surrogate authority, with the stipulation that the common good of the family may be included as a legitimate aim of the decision.

Each of these five conditions could be explored further, but I will concentrate on the third—the authenticity condition. I argued that autonomous persons must act on their authentic values—namely, on those values that are formed and held under just circumstances. When considering a patient's desire to transfer all decisionmaking authority to the family, we may be tempted to assume that her wish is authentic in the required sense, especially if the patient appears genuinely happy and eager to waive her right to informed consent in this manner. That is, we may tend to assume that the patient's effective values were not malformed and that she does not now suffer serious deprivations of choice available to other members of her family.

In our pre-reflective thought about the family, it is easy to slip into an idealistic mode in which we envision the family as a cozy sphere of mutual respect and concern wherein the interests, opinions, and happiness of all members are taken seriously by all. But of course this ideal of the family simply does not hold true in many cases, and it can be dangerous to leave this happy vision unchallenged. The reality is that many families today, both Western and non-Western, are unjustly structured: they operate under morally questionable power dynamics and traditions (or interpretations thereof) that fail to honor equally the inherent moral worth of each member. Injustice in the family can range from physical and emotional abuse to less tangible injustices, such as the family's acceptance of sexist attitudes about the proper role of women in society.[27] Simply put, not all family members accept the view that the well-being of each member matters equally.[28]

Plainly the family is crucial for moral education. Children model their behavior according to what they see around them. It is within the family environment that they first learn how to treat others justly or unjustly. It is also where they first form their attitudes toward others in relation to themselves. As Mill once put it, boys who are raised with the belief that being born male instantly makes them more valuable than females come to develop "a sublime and sultan-like sense of superiority" over women.[29]

The four aspects of the family I noted elaborate on this thought: (1) families are where many cultural traditions are passed to the young; (2) families cultivate a familial character by the type of practices that predominate within them; (3) families are where many people develop their sense of identity and self-worth; and (4) families are harbors for love and affection. A family could be said to have an *unjust familial character* if its traditions fail to respect the inherent moral worth of each member equally (an observation connected with the first two aspects of the family). An unjust family is a school for injustice. As Martha Nussbaum succinctly explains, "the family reproduces what it contains."[30]

If the family's unjust practices preponderate and are persistent, they can have (given the third aspect of the family) two significant effects on the young. Those who are privileged by these practices may develop a "sultanlike" self-concept, while the disadvantaged may develop a self-concept inflected by self-doubt and over-dependence on the kindness of others. The implication of the fourth aspect of the family is that the effects of injustice can occur under a shelter of love, harmony, and affection. People can love one another even when they are involved in unjust relationships. And while it may not be a healthy form of love, those who know little else might still experience a strong shared sense of emotional attachment. And this can itself help generate a recurring injustice. As family therapists are well aware, people who come from unjust birth families often find partners who will repeat the same power dynamics.[31]

Now the ingredients are there for the development of inauthentic values. Of course inauthenticity is not *inevitable*, but it is highly likely in such family environments. The deprivations that produce inauthentic values can be especially difficult to resist if there is no reasonable way for one to escape these circumstances, either through divorce or by simply fleeing. Truly vulnerable family members normally do not have opportunities to invest in their own human capital to make their economic survival outside the unjust family a comforting prospect. But perhaps the most significant barrier to leaving unjust family environments is that the person may be unable to see the treatment as unjust.

Inauthenticity is especially likely with patients who occupy subordinate positions and have little or no recognized decisionmaking authority within the family.[32] And although such concerns need not arise only about female family members, historically, of course, women have been subordinated to others both in the West and in the non-Western world.

Of course, I do not mean to suggest that a patient (either Western or non-Western) must *always* be acting inauthentically when she decides to waive her right to informed consent. A recently immigrated patient, for example, may have a variety of reasons for making such a decision, not all of them morally suspicious. She may correctly believe that other family members are simply more knowledgeable than she about the matter, and she may prefer to trust their judgment. She may also prefer to entrust her decisionmaking authority to a family member who has a better command of the English language and who is more comfortable interacting with Western physicians. On the other hand, we may doubt whether a waiver is morally legitimate if the patient simply believes that she does not have the basic right to make decisions for herself.

Remaining Difficulties

Some philosophical and practical difficulties need at least to be flagged. First, one might ask, how are health care providers supposed to know whether a patient's request to defer to her family's medical decisions meets the authenticity condition? How can providers gain access to the sort of personal, historical information necessary to make this determination without being unduly prying, or worse, overly assuming? Getting to know the circumstances of a patient's value formation is more aptly a task for a qualified psychoanalyst than for a health care clinician, particularly given the severe time constraints involved in most clinical provider–patient interactions.

This epistemic problem can perhaps be partly resolved by careful investigation of some of the other considerations that are necessary for an ethically acceptable waiver. The five conditions are interconnected in such a way that an inquiry into one might provide some insight into another. In ascertaining the family's goals for making the patient's medical decisions and understanding the family's actual decisionmaking style, for example, providers might be able to sense whether the family has an unjust familial character.

But suppose it *could* be determined that a patient's waiver is nonautonomous because she is operating with an inauthentic value. What then? Here's a second problem. By denying her wish, providers would be clearly frustrating an adult patient's expressed desire, and perhaps a case can be made about the wrongfulness of just that. Even if patients hold inauthentic values, they may also be quite content. Do we, in Rousseau's memorable phrase, "force them to be free"?[33] It is impossible to imagine how providers could suddenly manage to lift the patient's false consciousness and subsequently offer her adequate social support so that she may freely escape her unjust family environment (assuming she is not being outright abused).

The temptation in many of these cases will be to grant the waiver, and there is at least one interesting philosophical consideration that may support this course. If the patient's decision to waive her decisionmaking authority is truly nonautonomous, then she may also be largely incapable of autonomously making medical choices for herself if denied the waiver. Even after one's unjust social constraints are removed, either temporarily or permanently, one may still feel a habituated inner resistance to making important choices for oneself, at least anytime soon. A case like this might call for others—not unjust family members—to make decisions for the patient's benefit, allowing her to participate in the decision process whenever she is willing to do so. We must admit, however, that we would not be acting here out of our commitment to autonomy in any philosophically accurate sense, but from something else, perhaps beneficence.

Also, doubts may be raised about whether our hypothetical nonautonomous patient would truly *understand* what it means morally to have a right to informed consent—the first condition I identified above for an acceptable waiver of informed consent. Will a quick conversation with her physician impress upon her the understanding that, as a human being, she has the moral right to make decisions for herself, and that this right need not be exercised at the exclusion of her family's morally legitimate interests? Perhaps a provider should just act on good faith that her patient's self-reported understanding of this right is adequate, if only for the reason that the provider has an interest in not sending a misleading message that she does not trust the patient's own judgment. After all, the provider probably would not be able to detect so early in the interaction whether the patient is operating with inauthentic values and an obeisant conception of herself.

I believe this is an unknown that can be better answered after the provider gets acquainted with the family and understands better its internal dynamics. Maybe a second private conversation with the patient would be in order, although the provider's time constraints might militate against that.

Finally, a critic may worry that the general line of argument I have developed is morally imperialistic, insofar as it suggests that all persons from all cultures have a right to personal autonomy. There are, however, serious conceptual limitations to this argument against me. I agree that moral imperialism is wrong.

Furthermore, I submit that moral imperialism is wrong precisely because it forcefully overrides the right people have to decide for themselves how they are going to judge what is moral. In short, it violates their right to act by the lights of their own values—what I have been calling autonomy. As long as the critic and I agree on this basic point, it is conceptually incoherent for him to appeal covertly to this right in arguing against my defense of it. Of course, the critic may object to my interpretation of the authenticity condition, but he needs this condition as I have described it in order to make his conception of autonomy complete.

In summary, the ethical issues of the authenticity condition are extremely complex. While some guidance may be had from the five conditions I laid out for an ethically acceptable waiver of informed consent, actually meeting these requirements is a formidable task. Yet it does not seem overly fastidious to insist that the authenticity condition be borne in mind. If health care providers are truly committed to the principle of respect for persons and the value of personal autonomy broadly defined, they must take seriously the complexities of authenticity.

References

1. No convenient term accurately picks out the subclass of patients I wish to discuss in this article. I hesitantly use the terms "ethically diverse patients" and "minority patients " to refer to those who are typically regarded in the bioethics literature as having a greater cultural tendency to defer to their families' choices concerning their own medical treatments. But a patient need not be an immigrant or an ethnic minority to follow a familial norm such as this, and not all ethnic minorities adhere to a family-centered decisionmaking style.

2. L.J. Blackhall et al., "Ethnicity and Attitudes toward Patient Autonomy," *JAMA* 274 (1995): 820–25. These figures were compiled from interviews with 800 subjects at 31 senior citizen centers in Los Angeles. The age and gender of the hypothetical patient were not specified in the questionnaire for the respondents, thus the importance these details normally have for traditional, non-Western ways of thinking about the good for persons was obscured.

3. See L.O. Gostin, "Informed Consent, Cultural Sensitivity, and Respect for Persons," *JAMA* 247 (1995): 844–45.

4. Blackball et al., "Ethnicity and Attitudes toward Patient Autonomy," 825.

5. For example, the courts have determined that doctors are not liable for failure to disclose resulting from a patient's specific demand not to be informed: *Putensen v. Clay Adams Inc.*, 91 Cal. Rptr. 319, 333 (1970); *Cobbs v. Grant*, 104 Cal. Rptr. 505, 516 (1972); *Arato v. Avedon*, 858 P2d 598, 609 (Cal SCt 1993). For an interesting and sensitive discussion of how physicians might ascertain a patient's level of willingness to be informed, see B. Freedman, "Offering Truth," *Archives of Internal Medicine* 153 (1993): 572–76. For a recent application of Freedman's view to end of life decisionmaking by minority patients, see E. Hern, Jr. et al., "The Difference That Culture Can Make in End of Life Decisionmaking," *Cambridge Quarterly of Healthcare Ethics* 7 (1998): 27–40.

6. Technically, a waiver of informed consent involves two waivers—the waiver of the right to know and the waiver of the right to decide. For all practical purposes, how-

ever, a waiver of the right to know effectively amounts to a waiver of one's right to decide, since without information about his diagnosis or prognosis, a patient cannot make a meaningful decision about treatment.

7. S. Benhabib, "Cultural Complexity, Moral Interdependence, and the Global Dialogical Community," in *Women, Culture, and Development: A Study of Human Capabilities*, ed. M.C. Nussbaum and J. Glover (Oxford: Clarendon Press, 1995), 235–55 at 240.

8. Our common assumptions about cultural homogeneity are further challenged by the observation that—historically—cultural beliefs, practices, and interests have largely been determined and represented by men in positions of power, often at the expense of the group's marginalized members. See Y. Tamir, "Siding with the Underdogs" in *Is Multiculturalism Bad for Women?* ed. J. Cohen, M. Howard, and M.C. Nussbaum (Princeton, N.J.: Princeton University Press, 1999), 47–52; and X. Li, "Gender Inequality in China and Cultural Relativism," in *Women, Culture, and Development,* ed. Nussbaum and Glover, 407–425.

9. The concept of the family is both controversial and open-ended. Because my following arguments do not depend on any single conception of the family, however, I will use the terms "family" and "family members" in their most common senses.

10. 1 borrow this apt phrase from J.L. Nelson's "Taking Families Seriously," *Hastings Center Report* 22, no. 4 (1992), 6–12, at 8–9.

11. S. Minuchen, *Families and Family Therapy* (Cambridge, Mass.: Harvard University Press, 1974).

12. M. Sandel, *Liberalism and the Limits of Justice* (Cambridge: Cambridge University Press, 1982), 52–55; A. MacIntyre, *After Virtue: A Study in Moral Theory* (London: Duckworth, 1981), 204–205. A similar view of the person is outlined in J. Hardwig, "Is There a Duty to Die?" *Hastings Center Report* 27, no. 2 (1997): 34–42. For a discussion of communal views of personhood found in central Africa and Japan, see W. De Craemer, "A Cross-cultural Perspective on Personhood," *Milbank Memorial Fund Quarterly* 61, no. I (1983): 19–34.

13. J.L. Nelson, "Taking Families Seriously," 7–8.

14. E. Pellegrino, "Is Truth Telling to the Patient a Cultural Artifact?" *JAMA* 268 (1992), 1734–35. A similar viewpoint is echoed in T.A. Mappes and J.S. Zembaty, "Patient Choices, Family Interests, and Physician Obligations," *Kennedy Institute of Ethics Journal* 4, no. 1 (1994) 27–46. See also Gostin, "Informed Consent, Cultural Sensitivity, and Respect for Persons," 845; Blackhall et al., "Ethnicity and Attitudes toward Patient Autonomy," 825; and Hern, Jr., et al., "The Difference That Culture Can Make in End of Life Decisionmaking," 36–37.

15. The notion of family-centered decisionmaking is ambiguous. It could mean either that the good of the entire family is prescribed as the aim of the patient's treatment decision (the family-as-beneficiary view) or that the family is customarily taken to be an agent that makes decisions on the patient's behalf (the family-as-decisionmaker view), or some combination of both. I assume the family-as-decisionmaker view, but my argument does not depend on any one interpretation of family-centered decisionmaking. For the ethical complexities involved in family-centered medical decisionmaking, see my "Conceptions of Family-Centered Medical Decisionmaking and Their Difficulties," *Cambridge Quarterly of Healthcare Ethics,* [12:2(2003): 196–200].

16. For a more detailed discussion of the authenticity condition, see my "Authentic Values and Individual Autonomy," *The Journal of Value Inquiry* 35, no. 2 (2001): 195–208. The notion of authenticity I am investigating should be distinguished from more complex interpretations of this term that have been advanced by existentialist schools of thought, which broadly conceive authenticity as either an ideal of human flourishing or a teleological theory of the self.

17. See J. Feinberg, "Autonomy," in *The Inner Citadel,* ed. J. Christman (Oxford: Oxford University Press, 1989), 27–53; S. Benn, *A Theory of Freedom* (Cambridge: Cambridge University Press, 1988); R. Young, "Autonomy and Socialization," *Mind* 89 (1980): 565–76; and R. Young, *Personal Autonomy: Beyond Negative and Positive Liberty* (New York: St. Martin's Press, 1986).

18. In addition to this problem, a strong critical reflection requirement would set too high a standard for autonomy; thus most persons would not qualify as autonomous. See R. Faden and T. Beauchamp, *A History and Theory of Informed Consent* (Oxford: Oxford University Press, 1986), 262–66. See also my "Authentic Values and Individual Autonomy," 199–200.

19. Gerald Dworkin's conception of individual autonomy is sensitive to the sort of concerns I am advancing here, although I do not believe his procedural independence requirement can quite fully capture this normative point. See Dworkin, "Autonomy and Behavioral Control," *Hastings Center Report* 6 (1976): 23–28.

20. A similar view is found in J. Elster's discussion of adaptive preferences — preferences that arise when people unconsciously downgrade their inaccessible options. Elster does not give injustice a central role in the definition, however. See Elster, *Sour Grapes* (Cambridge: Cambridge University Press, 1983).

21. A. Sen, *Commodities and Capabilities* (Amsterdam: North-Holland, 1985).

22. A. Sen, "Gender Inequality and Theories of Justice," in *Women, Culture and Development*, 259–73.

23. A. Sen, "Gender and Co-operative Conflicts," in *Persistent Inequalities: Women and World Development,* ed. I. Tinker (New York: Oxford University Press, 1990), 126.

24. A. Sen, "Gender and Co-operative Conflicts," 126.

25. Having authentic values is a necessary but not sufficient condition for autonomy. Practical rationality, a mature level of understanding, and an epistemic sensitivity to the available facts are other necessary conditions.

26. The Supreme Court defines a waiver as a voluntary and intentional relinquishment of a known right: Miranda v. Arizona, 384 U.S. 436, 475–76 (1966). Thus in order to waive a right to informed consent, the patient must first know that she has it. This right includes both the right to be informed about her medical condition and the right to opt out of treatment altogether.

27. S. Okin, *Justice, Gender, and the Family* (New York: Basic Books, Inc., 1989); X. Li, "Gender Inequality in China and Cultural Relativism," in *Women, Culture, and Development,* ed. Nussbaum and Glover, 407–25, and M.M. Valdes, "Inequality in Capabilities between Men and Women in Mexico," in *Women, Culture, and Development,* ed. Nussbaum and Glover, 426–32.

28. For a discussion of the relationship between conceptions of justice and the idea of moral equality, see R. Dworkin, *Taking Rights Seriously* (London: Duckworth, 1977).

29. J.S. Mill, *The Subjection of Women,* ed. S. Okin (Cambridge: Hackett Publishing Co., 1988), 87.

30. M. Nussbaum, *Women and Human Development* (Cambridge: Cambridge University Press, 1999), 243.

31. Minuchen, *Families and Family Therapy*; and D.G. Dutton, *The Domestic Assault of Women: Psychological and Criminal Justice Perspectives* (Newton, Mass.: Allyn and Bacon Inc., 1988).

32. This point is also mentioned briefly by E. Moazam, "Families, Patients, and Physicians in Medical Decisionmaking: A Pakistani Perspective," *Hastings Center Report* 30, no. 6 (2000): 28–37, at 34.

33. J.J. Rousseau, *The Social Contract* (Baltimore: Penguin Books, 1968).

Further Readings

Akabayashi, A. and M.D. Fetters. "Paying for Informed Consent." *J Med Ethics* 26:3 (2000): 212–214.

Brushett v. Cowan (1990), 3 C.C.L.T. (2d) 195, 69 D.L.R.(4th) 473, 83 Nfld & P.E.I.R. 66, 260 A.P.R.66 (Nfld C.A.)

Donagan, Alan. "Informed Consent in Therapy and Experimentation." *J Med Philos* 2:4 (Dec. 1977): 319.

Downie, J.G., and T. Caulfield. *Canadian Health Law and Policy.* Markham, ON: Butterworths, 1999.

Faden, Ruth R., and Tom L. Beauchamp. *A History and Theory of Informed Consent.* New York and Oxford: Oxford Univ. Press, 1986.

Ingelfinger, Franz J. "Informed (but Uneducated) Consent." *N Engl J Med* 287 (Aug. 31, 1972): 465–466.

Kluge, E.-H. W. *Biomedical Ethics in the Canadian Context*, Chapter 7. Scarborough, ON: Prentice-Hall, 1991.

Kluge E.-H. "Informed Consent in a Different Key: Physicians' Practice Profiles and the Patient's Right to Know." *CMAJ* 160:9 (May 4, 1999): 1321–1322.

Mallary, S.D., B. Gert, and C.M. Culver. "Family Coercion and Valid Consent." *Theoret Med* 7:2 (1986): 123–126.

Mulloy v. HopSang, (1935) W.W.R. 714 (Alberta Supreme Court, App. Div).

Picard, E.I., and G.B. Robertson. *Legal Liability of Doctors and Hospitality in Canada*, Chapter 2, "Consent." 3rd ed. Toronto: Carswell, 1996.

Pinker, S. "Am I My Brother's Keeper? Two Perspectives on Consent." *CMAJ* 165 (2001): 194–195.

Robertson, G.B. "Ontario's New Informed Consent Law." *Health L. J.* (1994).

Somerville, M. *Consent to Medical Care.* Study Paper for the Law Reform Commission of Canada. Ottawa, 1980.

CHAPTER 7
CONSENT AND THE INCOMPETENT PATIENT

Introduction

The paradigm case of informed consent involves a health care professional and someone who is adult, who can understand what is being said and who can react appropriately. However, many times the patient is not competent in that sense. For instance, the patient may be a young child, or someone who is physiologically mature but mentally severely disabled. In these sorts of cases, someone has to make the decision for the incompetent person. But who?

Traditionally, it was assumed that the family or next-of-kin should play that role. With the rise of modern medicine, as the decision-making function was gradually assumed by physicians even in ordinary contexts, it became the practice to let physicians assume the role of decision-makers for incompetent persons. In the last 30 years, the pendulum has once more swung the other way. The family has once again become the primary proxy- or substitute decision-maker.

However, the family may not always function appropriately in this regard. The article by Insoo Hyun, in Chapter 6, discussed some ways that cultural values may influence family decision making in an inappropriate fashion. Moreover, families may also act inappropriately for non-cultural reasons: for example, when they make decisions that are based not on the best interests of the incompetent family member but on the family's own personal preferences and values. The case of *re S.D.*, excerpts from which are reproduced below, illustrates the court's concerns in this regard. By way of contrast, Eike-Henner W. Kluge examines some of the difficulties that attend a purely legally oriented approach to proxy decision making.

As for decision making by children themselves, as was noted a moment ago, the traditional position was that children are by definition incompetent and cannot give (or refuse) consent to health care. However, the last few years have seen a change in this perspective. There are several reasons for this. First, Section 15(1) of the Charter of Rights and Freedoms explicitly prohibits discrimination on the basis of age. Second, Canadian case law has recognized for some time the category of a *mature* or *emancipated minor* who, although under the age of majority, nevertheless is able to make all sorts of decisions—including health care decisions—on her or his own behalf. Third, ethical analysis of the notion of competence and of the right to self-determination has suggested that the ability to make health care decisions does not inherently depend on age but on maturity, the ability to comprehend and reason, and the possession of appropriate values. While younger children may lack these qualities, as they become older this changes and they steadily increase their decision-making capabilities.

These developments have led to a re-evaluation of the legal perspective on decision making by children[1] and to a redrafting of the relevant provincial statutes. Harrison, Kenny, Sidarous and Rowell explore some of the implications of this change. They come to the conclusion that even though a child may not be fully competent, the wishes of the child, if at all possible, should nevertheless be respected.[2] It may be interesting to compare the position on saving the life of a child as stated by the Court in *re S.D.*[3] with the perspective advanced in this article. It may also be interesting to explore how well it accords with the position adopted by the Tri-Council in its Code of Ethical Conduct for Research Involving Humans.[4]

Notes

1. *Re L.D.K.* (1985) R.F.L. (2d) 164. This is a case where the wishes of a 12-year-old to refuse transfusions that were necessary for chemotherapy to be effective were respected. A similar position on the rights of competent children to accept or refuse medical treatment was taken by the courts in *re Y.A.* (19.7.1993) (Nfld. S.C. [Unif. Fam. Ct.]).

2. For another interesting discussion of volitional competence in children, see X. Plaus and B.R. Brissenden, "On adolescence and informed consent," *Health Law in Canada* 14:3 (1994): 68–73.

3. See *infra.*

4. See *infra*, chapter 10.

Re S.D.

The subject of these proceedings is a severely retarded boy approaching 7 years, who shortly after birth suffered profound brain damage through meningi- tis which inflamed the lining of his brain and left him with no control over his faculties, limbs or bodily functions. At the age of 5 months life-support surgery was

---

Re S.D. (1983) 3 W.W.R. 618 (B.C.S.C.).

performed by implanting a shunt which is a plastic tube which drains excess cerebro-spinal fluid from the head to another body cavity from which it is expelled or absorbed.

As perceived by his parents the boy is legally blind, with atrophied optic nerves, partly deaf, incontinent, cannot hold a spoon to feed himself, cannot stand, walk, talk or hold objects. They say that he has no method of communicating with his environment and think he is in pain. The sounds he makes are too soft to be heard from any distance. He is subject to seizures despite anti-convulsant medication. He is restrained by splints which are bandages on his arms to keep his elbows straight so that he cannot chew on his hands and roughly handle his face. Staff carry him from bed to wheelchair, which has a molded "insert" to ensure he is held securely and he is belted in with a hip belt.

This description applies to his condition as it existed when he was a patient in Sunnyhill Hospital before the shunt stopped operating. About 6 weeks ago a blockage in the shunt was detected and the parents gave their consent to remedial surgery but, after a day's reflection, withdrew their consent on the ground that the boy should be allowed to die with dignity rather than continue to endure a life of suffering. They continue to maintain that position.

Because of the parents' refusal the Superintendent of Family and Child Service ... considered this child "in need of protection" and acted ... to apprehend him. ...

Following apprehension, the Superintendent, ... presented a written report to the Provincial Court of British Columbia and asked for an order that the custody of the child be retained by him pending a hearing to determine whether the child was in need of protection. Following 5 days of hearings and a weekend's contemplation and writing, the Provincial Court Judge read in open court a 29-page oral judgment on 14 March 1983 which ordered the Superintendent to return the child to his parents' custody. The Judge identified the issue as:

... who may exercise an incompetent's right to refuse life sustaining treatment if no directive exists and the incompetent is unable to do so?

The Judge appears to have held that this right belongs in the family, in consultation with their medical advisors. Where treatment would serve "only to prolong a life inflicted with an incurable condition" rather than cure or improve the patient's condition, the interest of the state in the preservation of life is overridden by the wishes of the people whose duty it is to make the decision.

Adopting the distinction between treatment that "cures" and treatment that simply "prolongs life where there is no hope of recovery" the Judge found that the shunt revision fell into the latter category.

The Judge found that the shunt revision in S.'s case constituted an "extraordinary surgical intervention," and not "necessary medical attention." Since S. was therefore not deprived of "necessary medical attention" there was no basis for the belief that S. was not a "well-cared-for and loved child," and she concluded that she should order that he be returned to his parents under s.11(2)(b) of the Family and Child Service Act. S.11 sets out the procedure for review of the Superintendent's decision to apprehend a child pending a hearing on the question of whether the child is in need of protection. The Judge also held that the shunt revision would constitute a violation of S.'s right not to be subjected to cruel and unusual treatment under s.12 of the Canadian Charter of Rights and Freedoms. ...

I think that the Superintendent's petition is accurate in contending that the learned Judge:

1) Held that a life saving operation does not amount to necessary medical attention as defined in s.1.

2) Did not consider as paramount the safety and well-being of the child as required in s.2.

3) Held that the shunt revision constituted cruel and unusual punishment under s.12 of the Canadian Charter of Rights and Freedoms.

4) Did not consider s. 7 of the Charter.

By referring to the proceedings in Provincial Court and to the disposition of those proceedings I have done so for narrative reasons only because, as I conceive it, the *parens patriae* jurisdiction of the Supreme Court in this matter takes precedence over the proceedings in Provincial Court and allows this court to act as if the matter came before it in the first instance. Confirmation of this view is contained in s.21 of the Act.

> Nothing in this Act limits the inherent jurisdiction of the Crown, through the Supreme Court, over infants, as *parens patriae*, and the Supreme Court may rescind a permanent order where it is satisfied that to do so is conducive to a child's best interest and welfare.

...

In considering the application of the *parens patriae* jurisdiction I recognize that the central concern is to discover what is in S.'s best interest. This is not a "right to die" situation where the courts are concerned with people who are terminally ill from incurable conditions. Rather it is a question of whether S. has the right to receive appropriate medical and surgical care of a relatively simple kind which will assure to him the continuation of his life, such as it is.

I am satisfied that the laws of our society are structured to preserve, protect and maintain human life and that in the exercise of its inherent jurisdiction this court could not sanction the termination of a life except for the most coercive reasons. The presumption must be in favour of life. Neither could this court sanction the wilful withholding of surgical therapy where such withholding could result not necessarily in death but in a prolongation of life for an indeterminate time but in a more impoverished and more agonizing form.

I do not think that it lies within the prerogative of any parent or of this court to look down upon a disadvantaged person and judge the quality of that person's life to be so low as not to be deserving of continuance.

The matter was well put in an American decision — *re Weberlist* (1974), 360 N.Y.S. (2d) 783, 79 Misc. 2d 753 (N.Y. Co. Ct.), where Justice Asch said at p. 787:

> There is a strident cry in America to terminate the lives of other people — deemed physically or mentally defective. ... Assuredly, one test of civilization is its concern with the survival of the unfittest, a reversal of Darwin's formulation. ... In this case, the court must decide what its ward would choose, if he were in a position to make a sound judgment. ...

This last sentence puts it right. It is not appropriate for an external decision-maker to apply his standards of what constitutes a livable life and exercise the right to impose death if that standard is not met in his estimation. The decision can only be made in the context of the disabled person viewing the worthwhileness or otherwise of his life in its own context as a disabled person — and in that context he would not compare his life with that of a person enjoying normal advantages. He would know nothing of a normal person's life having never experienced it.

...

I respect and have given anxious consideration to the views of the parents. In so doing I must give some weight to the fact that they were divorced in mid-1980 after extended matrimonial discord. Also I must give weight to my conclusion based on the evidence that they thought S. better dead long before the need for the critical decision arose about replacement of the shunt. Despite the evidence of highly qualified professionals, in whom I place great reliance, they are satisfied S. will promptly die if treatment is denied. My finding is that it is by no means a certainty that death will soon follow and a real possibility exists that his life will go on indefinitely but in pain and progressive deterioration. I must reject their assertion that they would consent to the operation if they could be assured that he would thereafter be comfortable and free of pain when at the same time they reject the opinions of competent professionals that such will probably be the case. I believe that their minds are firmly made up and closed shut.

I regret having to make such findings.

Further, I find that the professionals who have been treating and observing S. since late 1982 are better qualified than they are to assess his condition and capacities because they, the parents, have hardly seen him. I do not criticize them for this but simply observe it as a fact.

I cannot accept their view that S. would be better off dead. If it is to be decided that "it is in the best interests of S. that his existence cease," then it must be decided that, for him, non-existence is the better alternative. This would mean regarding the life of a handicapped child as not only less valuable than the life of a normal child, but so much less valuable that it is not worth preserving. I tremble at contemplating the consequences if the lives of disabled persons are dependent upon such judgments.

To refer back to the words of Templeman, L.J., I cannot in conscience find that this is a case of severe proved damage "where the future is so certain and where the life of the child is so bound to be full of pain and suffering that the court might be driven to a different conclusion." I am not satisfied that "the life of this child is demonstrably going to be so awful that in effect the child must be condemned to die." Rather I believe that "the life of this child is still so imponderable that it would be wrong for her to be condemned to die."

There is not a simple choice here of allowing the child to live or die according to whether the shunt is implanted or not. There looms the awful possibility that without the shunt the child will endure in a state of progressing disability and pain. It is too simplistic to say that the child should be allowed to die in peace.

In conclusion I order that interim custody be granted to the Superintendent pending a hearing pursuant to s.13 of the Family and Child Service Act and while in that interim custody the surgical procedure be carried out pursuant to the authority of this court. The matter is remitted to the Provincial Court for the s.13 hearing.

After "Eve": Whither Proxy Decision Making?

Eike-Henner W. Kluge

One of the most difficult situations that physicians may face is one involving an incompetent patient. Normally, following what could be called a fiduciary model of the physician–patient relationship, physicians may feel that they have fulfilled their professional obligation when they have advised the patient of the various pertinent modalities of treatment, expressed an opinion and made a recommendation, and have done all this in language that the patient can and does understand. Whatever decision the patient then makes will be legally and ethically acceptable. If it should not accord with the physician's own better judgement, he or she may of course attempt to reason and persuade but not coerce; and all other things being equal, the physician may not overrule the patient's determination. *Reibl v. Hughes*[1] is very clear on that point. If all else fails and the physician cannot in good conscience accept the patient's decision, there is always the option of referring the patient to another physician and withdrawing from the case.[2] At no point, however, with the exceptions of emergency and therapeutic privilege, is the physician called on to assume the role of proxy decision-maker or to examine the ethical acceptability of the decision itself.

The case of the incompetent patient, however, is different. Here the physician must assume an evaluative role. As frontline workers, so to speak, physicians have to examine the way in which the proxy decision-makers — usually the next-of-kin — make the decision in order to assure themselves that it is the product of reflective consideration and not the off-hand result of a hasty reaction. Furthermore, they must consider the criteria used by the proxy decision-makers in reaching the decision in order to make sure that they do not simply reflect the proxies' own standards, feelings or expectations but rather are ethically appropriate. When there is any doubt, the physician must engage the appropriate administrative or legal channels to prevent what may be an unacceptable exercise of proxy authority.[3]

To some degree, of course, this is a matter of subjective assessment on the part of the physician, but not entirely so. In cases in which the patient was once competent but is competent no longer, the physician will balance the quality of life expected from the various treatment options against the wishes and expectations expressed by the patient when competent in order to assess the reasonableness or acceptability of the particular proxy decision. The testimony of next-of-kin as well as formal and informal data to which the physician may have access will provide invaluable assistance. As to situations in which there is no evidence that the patient expressed preferences when competent, the physician will proceed on the basis of the quality-of-life standards that are currently accepted by the ordinary person, standards that are based not on the concept of social utility (whether defined within the ambit of the immediate family or social grouping or drawn more widely to

Eike-Henner W. Kluge, "After 'Eve': Whither proxy decision making?" Reprinted by permission of the publisher, *Canadian Medical Association Journal*, 137 (October 15, 1987) 715–720.

include society as a whole) but rather on criteria that flow from the concept of the patient as a person. The physician will take into account the distinction between the continuation or sustaining of merely biologic life and support of the patient as a person who has (or retains the capacity for) sapient cognitive awareness and the possibility of meaningful social interaction.[4] Again, while this will involve a certain amount of subjectivity on the part of the physician, it need not and does not occur in complete isolation. Physicians can draw on the more or less standard perception of quality of life that prevails in society and are aided by their sensitivity to the cost of the various treatment options to the patient in purely human terms. Their professional knowledge of the nature and likelihood of the outcomes expected from the various modalities of treatment is invaluable, as is their awareness of what other, competent patients under similar circumstances have decided. Together, all this gives the physician a fairly good idea of what the ordinary reasonable person would decide under similar circumstances and provides a basis against which to measure the proxy decision. And although this sort of approach may present difficulties on occasion, it generally is workable and presents no serious ethical problems.

As to the case of the currently incompetent patient who never has been competent but in all likelihood will become competent in the future — i.e., an otherwise normal child — it, too, does not present the physician with fundamentally new issues. The physician will proceed on the assumption that, all other things being equal, the child's sensible experience and qualitative perception of the world is essentially like that of an adult and that the factor of incompetence involves the cognitive and judgemental plane. It is therefore entirely appropriate for the physician to take into account the child's subjective expressions (insofar as they are present or available) and bal-ance them against the objective standard of what a reasonable person would decide when considering the proxy decision. The function of the proxy is to supply the cognitive and judgemental want of the child. Consequently, if the physician finds that the proxy decision-maker has introduced his or her own nonstandard values in making the decision, the physician must challenge the decision. The situation becomes a little more complicated when the child has given assent in a particular direction, but even here it is not a matter of purely subjective evaluation. The assent must be seen as guiding, although not necessarily determining, depending on the facts of the cases.[5,6] Finally, in all cases of doubt, the courts must be the ultimate forum of appeal.

The Radically Congenitally Incompetent Patient

The case of the congenitally incompetent patient who, so far as medical science can tell, not only is barely at the limits of sapient cognitive awareness but also in all probability will never become competent, is radically different. The sort of balancing of subjective expression against an objective standard that can at least be attempted in other cases seems inappropriate here. This is so not because the patient is not reasonable — no incompetent patient is — but because the presumption on which such balancing is based .may be false in such cases. The quality of life of the radically congenitally incompetent patient may be so fundamentally different from the norm that both the use of the objective standard of what a reasonable person would decide as a balance and the attempt to use the patient's own subjective expression would be untoward. The very significance of the latter may be fundamentally misconstrued because it would be based on the world experience of the physician, someone who fits the norm of the reasonable person. Consequently, there exists a danger that the use of the objective standard would violate the individuality of the patient and that the attempt to circumvent this by using subjective indicators from the patient would be so out of line with his or her actual experience that any treatment decision based on these criteria would be experienced as cruel and unusual treatment.[7,8]

If this is true, the physician who monitors proxy decisions made for radically congenitally incompetent patients is faced with a serious problem: What criteria — indeed, what evaluative approach — ought he or she to apply?

The Stephen Dawson Decision

It was at least in part for this reason that the 1983 British Columbia Supreme Court decision *Re Stephen Dawson*[9] was welcomed by some members of the medical community. The case concerned a 7-year-old boy who had contracted meningitis shortly after birth, suffered severe brain damage and become hydrocephalic and as a consequence was exceedingly retarded, with no control over his faculties or limbs. At 5 months of age a shunt had been inserted and had been revised over the years, and at the time of application to the courts revision was again required. The reason for the court intervention was that the parents, as proxy decision-maker, had initially agreed to the revision, but after taking into account what they considered to be appropriate quality-of-life considerations from the perspective of the ordinary person — considerations involving the capacity for sapient cognitive awareness, the possibility of relatively pain-free and physically comfortable existence, and the potential for meaningful social interaction — and after consultation with a pediatric neurosurgeon they had withdrawn their permission. The superin-

tendent of child welfare for the province intervened, and the matter came to trial in provincial court. The test used by the court to evaluate the parents' decision was whether, under the circumstances, the proposed revision constituted extraordinary treatment. The court decided in the affirmative and held in favour of the parents. On appeal to the British Columbia Supreme Court, the decision was reversed and an order for treatment was made. Stephen subsequently received treatment and continues to live.

It was the reasoning stated by the British Columbia Supreme Court that made the decision so important for the medical community. For the first time in Canadian medicolegal history the courts issued a ruling that explicitly addressed the question of what criteria and approach a proxy decision-maker and a physician should use when dealing with a congenitally incompetent person. Mr. Justice L. McKenzie, who decided the issue, ruled 1) that a congenitally incompetent person does not lose the rights to health care normally enjoyed by other persons simply in virtue of his or her incompetence; 2) that the duty of exercising this right normally rests in the parents as appropriate proxy decision-makers; 3) that their decision-making authority is appropriately challenged when it is not exercised in the best interests of the incompetent person; and 4) that what counts as being in the best interests of the incompetent person must not be determined from the point of view of the objective reasonable person. Rather, 5) it must be determined from the perspective of the incompetent person. As Judge McKenzie put it, "I do not think that it lies within the prerogative of any parent or of this court to look down upon a disadvantaged person and judge the quality of that person's life to be so low as not to be deserving of continuance." Quoting with approval Judge Asch in the U.S. case *In the Matter of*

Eugene Weberlist ("In this case, the court must decide what its ward would choose, if he were in a position to make a sound judgment.") he went on to say:

> This last sentence puts it right. It is not appropriate for an external decision-maker to apply his standards of what constitutes a livable life and exercise the right to impose death if that standard is not met in his estimation. The decision can only be made in the context of the disabled person viewing the worthwhileness or otherwise of his life in its own context as a disabled person — and in that context he would not compare his life with that of a person enjoying normal advantages. He would know nothing of a normal person's life having never experienced it.

In adopting this position, Judge McKenzie was enunciating what had become known as a substituted-judgement approach to proxy decision making for congenitally incompetent persons. As one U.S. commentator put it, proxy decision-makers should try to put themselves as much as possible into the situation of the incompetent person and then decide in the way and from the perspective from which the latter would decide, were he or she able.[10]

The Stephen Dawson case injected an element of clarity into the Canadian context. The Canadian physician faced with the question of how to proceed in these sorts of cases now had definite guidelines on how to interpret "best interests" considerations and evaluate the appropriateness of a particular proxy decision. However, while definitive and clarifying, Judge McKenzie's decision was not without problems, some of which I pointed out at the time.[11] In the context of proxy decision making the most important problem was the concept of a substituted-judgement approach itself. As I said then, the demand that the perspec-

tive of the congenitally incompetent person should constitute the basis of quality-of-life considerations by the proxy decision-maker and that any acceptance or rejection of medical treatment should be grounded on this basis is not only unworkable in practical terms but also and, indeed above all, logically incoherent. If the incompetent person lacks sapient cognitive awareness — or, less severely, if he or she lacks any standards or criteria — then, trivially, neither standards nor criteria can be ascribed to the person. That fact is definitive of the situation in which such people find themselves and characterizes their very nature. It is therefore logically impossible to determine what their wishes are or would be if they could make them known. To proceed otherwise is to do one of two things: to assume that despite this lack they have standards or criteria after all — a flat contradiction — or to project some other standards or criteria into the situation by substitution and thereby treat incompetent people as though they were not incompetent. In either case, however, the very concept of substituted judgement, of viewing the situation from the perspective of the incompetent person, "in its own context," is a fiction.

If this analysis was correct, the position of the physician faced with a congenitally incompetent patient was not improved but rather was worsened by the Stephen Dawson case: uncertainty over how to proceed had indeed been replaced by certainty, but at the price of logical impossibility.

The Case of "Eve"

Then came *Eve v. Mrs. E.*[12] which altered the whole picture. On the facts, the case was entirely different from that of Stephen Dawson. "Eve" was a 24-year-old moderately retarded woman suffering from extreme expressive aphasia. She was described to the courts as an extremely pleasant and affectionate person who, being physically adult, was capable of being attractive to and attracted by men. Her mother, of advancing years, feared that Eve might become pregnant, and since Eve was unable to take care of a child, the mother saw herself faced with the prospect of having to care for Eve's progeny. She found this unmanageable. She also felt that both pregnancy and childbirth would be incomprehensible to Eve. Consequently, acting as proxy decision-maker, she requested that Eve be sterilized.

The court of first instance rejected the request. It ruled that except for clinically therapeutic reasons, parents or other appropriate proxy decision-makers could not give valid proxy consent to such a procedure. On appeal to the Supreme Court of Prince Edward Island, the judgement was reversed and sterilization by hysterectomy was ordered. However, leave was granted to appeal the decision to the Supreme Court of Canada. On Oct. 23, 1986, that court handed down its ruling. It reinstated the trial court's order and rejected sterilization. Mr. Justice La Forest, writing the unanimous decision of the court, gave two reasons. One dealt with the historical nature of the *parens patriae* powers of the court. Here the thrust of Mr. Justice La Forest's deliberations was that these powers could be exercised only in the best interests of the incompetent person, no matter what the position of society or next-of-kin. The second reason was an attempt to clarify the way in which such best interests could be determined. He here focused on the position advanced by the attorneys for Mrs. E. They had argued that as proxy decision-maker Mrs. E. had the duty to exercise Eve's rights for her and had argued further that, indeed, these rights ought to be exercised on the basis of what would be in Eve's best interests. However, they insisted that Eve's best interests could be determined only in a subjective fashion: by approximating as closely as possible the kind of situation in which Eve

found herself and then making the kind of decision that she herself would make. In other words, they reasoned that a "substituted-judgement" approach to the determination of "best interests" would be appropriate "because it places a higher value on the individuality of the incompetent person."[12] Using such an approach, they argued, would result in a decision for sterilization.

For the purposes of this essay, it is irrelevant whether the logic of Mrs. E.'s position is valid. What is important is the court's reaction to the line of reasoning. While accepting the concept of best interests as appropriate, the court roundly rejected the contention that best interests could be appropriately determined with the substituted-judgement approach. In fact, the court brusquely rejected the concept of substituted judgement itself. Substituted judgement, it reasoned, is an attempt to determine what choice the incompetent person would make were he or she able. However, the court stated,[12]

> Choice presupposes that a person has the mental competence to make it. It may be a matter of debate whether a court should have the power to make the decision if that person lacks the mental capacities to do so. But it is obviously a fiction to suggest that a decision so made is that of the incompetent, however much the court may try to put itself in her place. What the incompetent would do if she or he could make a choice is simply a matter of speculation.

Mr. Justice La Forest went on to speak of "the sophistry embodied in the argument favouring substituted judgment" and quoted with approval from *Matter of Eberhardy* (a U.S. case), in which the court had stated:[13]

> We conclude that the question is not choice because it is sophistry to

refer to it as such, but rather the question is whether there is a method by which others, acting on behalf of the person's best interests and in the interests, such as they may be, of the state, can exercise the decision.

Neither the U.S. court nor the Supreme Court of Canada went on to detail such a method. They agreed in their focus on best interests considerations. One thing, however, was clear: by characterizing the substituted-judgement approach as legal "legerdemain," the Supreme Court effectively ruled out the very test enjoined by the Stephen Dawson case.

Of course, it could be argued that all this holds only for sterilization, that it leaves all other cases unaffected. That, however, is unlikely for three reasons. First, it would contradict the very *raison d'être* of Supreme Court decisions. They are, and are supposed to be, models for general types of cases. While *Eve v. Mrs. E.* is representative of sterilization cases, it is also and, indeed, above all representative of a type of case that deals with the problem of proxy decision making for incompetent people. All cases of proxy decision for such people are thereby affected. The fact that the court itself saw it in this light is evidenced by the fact that the precedential cases it considered and cited in reaching its decision were drawn from a whole spectrum of cases proposing medical procedures for incompetent people, not only those advocating sterilization. Second, the fact that the Supreme Court intended its decision to have wider ambit is indicated by the fact that its rejection of substituted judgement is not explicitly directed to sterilization cases. It is couched independently of that issue in response to the argument that a substituted-judgement approach as such "is to be preferred to the best interests test because it places a higher value on the individuality of the

mentally incompetent person."[12] In other words, it was a reply to the argument that because the substituted-judgement approach is the appropriate test for incompetent people in general, it should also be used in this case. It is to this general claim that the court replied in the negative. Its rejection, therefore, has general implications. Finally, there is this to consider. Undoubtedly there are many strands intertwined in this case. However, to construe the rejection of substituted judgement in a limited fashion is to ascribe to the Supreme Court the position that different principles of law and of ethics hold for the very same problem — proxy decision making — in different material cases. Not only would that undermine the very notion of the uniformity of legal and ethical principles, but also it lacks basis in any of the court's dicta.

I suggest, therefore, that *Eve v. Mrs. E.* ought to be seen as having general import. But if that is the case, it presents the Canadian physician with a problem: How to interpret best interests? The fact that the court recalled with approval Lord Eldon's remarks in *Wellesley v. Wellesley* ("It has always been the principle of this court, not to risk damage to children ... which it cannot repair"[12]) may be considered guiding. However, that merely pushes the interpretational uncertainty onto the word "damage." Did the court intend this to apply to physiologic damage only, or did it intend to encompass psychologic, mental and emotional deficit as well as other repercussions? There are indications that it intended the wider construal; for example, it inveighed against a "grave intrusion on the physical and mental integrity of the person"[12] and included "health problems, religious upbringing and protection against harmful association."[12] But we do lack a really explicit statement. The physician is thus once again left in a domain of uncertainty. Only three — negative —

guidelines are clear: physicians may not use a substituted-judgement approach to evaluate the appropriateness of proxy decisions; they may not accept a decision based on the proxy decision-maker's own idiosyncratic standards; and they may not use their own values, standards and expectations.

Attempt at a Resolution

However, both the reasoning advanced in *Re Stephen Dawson* and that given in *Eve v. Mrs. E.* do point in the direction in which more positive criteria may be sought.[14] These stem not from the assumption of equality of life experience, which is the contentious concept, but from the assumption that whatever his or her handicap, the radically and congenitally incompetent patient is still a person. If this assumption is true — and here only incontrovertible evidence of the permanent lack of capability for sapient cognitive awareness can count as an indication to the contrary — that patient has the same panoply of rights as all other persons. More important, it follows that he or she must be treated as a person in all respects. This in turn means that the quality of life that the patient faces in the future as well as the quality at the present time, while it may be admitted to differ in degree of sophistication from that of the competent person, nevertheless cannot be held to differ in kind: no matter what the difference in degree, the quality itself, in its very nature, must be that of a person. This, however, immediately entails that the evaluative criteria that are appropriate in the case of all other persons must be applied here as well. Not, of course, in a straightforward fashion. That would be to ignore the difference in degree between the respective qualities of life. Rather, what it means is that the physician must use the quality of life of an otherwise healthy person with similar type and degree of incompe-

tence as an evaluative baseline and consider the relative changes that would result in that quality under the various treatment options being considered. In this it is appropriate for the physician to take into account the incompetent person's subjective expressions of satisfaction with physical life, the psychologic affect and other attendant factors, and balance these against the likelihood of retention of or improvement in sapient cognitive awareness, the possibility of meaningful social interaction at that level and the cost of the various options to the patient in purely human terms. Let us call this a comparative quality-of-life coefficient. The physician must then do a similar evaluation, with due alteration of detail, for an ordinary competent patient with a similar medical problem to determine what the comparative quality-of-life coefficient would be in his or her case. The physician must then compare the two coefficients. If, on balance, the comparative quality-of-life coefficient for the incompetent patient is the same as or higher than that for the competent patient, and if in the case of the latter the decision would normally be in favour of treatment (or of some specific form of treatment), the decision must be in favour of treatment for the incompetent patient as well. If the proxy decision-maker's decision is against treatment, the physician must oppose it, if necessary through administrative and judicial channels. In all other cases, he or she need not.

This way of approaching the problem provides a procedure that can be implemented in practice. At the same time, however — or perhaps precisely because of this — it allows us to reconcile *Eve v. Mrs. E.* with *Re Stephen Dawson*. For, in this way, Judge McKenzie's injunction to consider the situation of the radically congenitally incompetent person in the "context of the disabled person" can be given an interpretation that avoids the sophistry of substituted judgement while satisfying Mr. Justice La Forest's conclusion that the "best interests" of the person should be guiding.

A Final Problem

At the same time, however, the case of Eve leaves the health care professional with a problem. The considerations that I have sketched are appropriate from the perspective of the incompetent person and under the *parens patriae* powers of the court. Ethically, however, they are insufficient. Medical decisions, after all, are not made in a vacuum, nor can health care decisions be reached in isolation from the overall context in which they must be implemented. The resources that will be involved in health care decisions and their distribution have ineluctable social implications. It is here that *Eve v. Mrs. E.* fails. By being focused narrowly within the *parens patriae* doctrine as traditionally understood, the decision paints an unrealistic picture. The rights of the incompetent person must never be less than those of the competent person solely by virtue of their incompetence, to be sure. However, justice and equality demand that they not be more either. It is ethically unacceptable to engage in reverse discrimination that accords a favoured ethical status to the incompetent person solely by virtue of his or her incompetence. That, however, would in fact occur if the powers of Eve's rights, as captured in the best-interests clause as expressed in the judgement, were to be given automatic precedence over the rights of others; if, in the words of Mr. Justice La Forest, we were to "sympathize with Mrs. E." but insist, as he did, that in cases such as these only the rights of the incompetent person are decisive.[12] The point of *Eve v. Mrs. E.* and analogous court actions surely is to insist that the rights of the incompetent person must be given due weight because incompetent people are persons. That, however, also means that with due alteration of detail their rights must be treated as subject to the same balancing process to which the rights of all other persons are subject under similar conditions. By rejecting the weight of the competing rights of Mrs. E. and the rest of society, Mr. Justice La Forest has created a special class of persons who are immune from the restrictive and balancing considerations that apply to everyone else. This seems to suggest that the physician who monitors proxy decisions for such people must refrain from taking into account the considerations of equity and justice that guide the allocation of resources in all other cases. Not only are the ethics of this highly questionable, but also it may lead to a distributive nightmare.

Notes

1. *Reibl v. Hughes,* 14 CCLT 1 (SCC 1980).
2. *Code of Ethics,* Can Med Assoc, Ottawa, 1978: 15.
3. Dickens, B.: The role of the family in surrogate medical consent. *Health Law Can* 1980; 1 (3): 49–52.
4. Keyserlingk, E.W.: Sanctity of life or quality of life. In *The Context of Ethics, Medicine and Law,* Law Reform Commission of Canada, Ottawa, 1979: 49–72.
5. McCormick, R.A.: Proxy consent in the experimentation situation. *Perspect Biol Med* 1974; 18: 2–20.
6. Ramsey, P.: *The Patient as Person,* Yale U Pr, New Haven, Conn., 1970: 1–58.
7. *Superintendent of Belchertown State School v. Saikewicz,* 370 NE (2d) 417 (Mass 1977).

8. Annas, G.: Reconciling Quinlan and Saikewicz: decision making for the terminally ill incompetent. *Am J Law Med* 1979; 4: 367–396.

9. *Re Stephen Dawson*, 3 WWR 618 (BC SC 1983) reversing 3 WWR 597 (BC Prov Ct 1983).

10. Annas, G.: The incompetent's right to die: the case of Joseph Saikewicz. *Hastings Cent Rep* 1978; 8 (1): 21–23.

11. Kluge, E.-H.W.: In the matter of Stephen Dawson: right v. duty of health care. *Can Med Assoc J* 1983; 129: 815–818.

12. *Eve v. Mrs. E.*, SCC, judgement handed down Oct 23, 1986, SCR 16654.

13. *Matter of Eberhardy*, 307 NW (2d) 881 (Wis 1981).

14. Magnet, J.E., Kluge, E.-H.W.: *Withholding Treatment from Defective Newborn Children*, Brown Legal Pub., Cowansville, PQ, 1985: 3–306.

Involving Children in Medical Decisions

Christine Harrison, Nuala P. Kenny, Mona Sidarous, Mary Rowell

Eleven-year-old Samantha is a bright, loving child who was treated for osteosarcoma in her left arm. The arm had to be amputated, and Samantha was given a course of chemotherapy. She has been cancer-free for 18 months and is doing well in school. She is self-conscious about her prosthesis and sad because she had to give away her cat, Snowy, to decrease her risk of infection. Recent tests indicate that the cancer has recurred and metastasized to her lungs. Her family is devastated by this news but do not want to give up hope. However, even with aggressive treatment Samantha's chances for recovery are less than 20%.

Samantha adamantly refuses her treatment. On earlier occasions she had acquiesced to treatment only to struggle violently when it was administered. She distrusts her health care providers and is angry with them and her parents. She protests, "You already made me give up Snowy and my arm. What more do you want?" Her parents insist that treatment must continue. At the request of her physician, a psychologist and psychiatrist conduct a capacity assessment. They agree that Samantha is probably incapable of making treatment decisions; her understanding of death is immature and her anxiety level very high. Nursing staff are reluctant to impose treatment; in the past Samantha's struggling and the need to restrain her upset them a great deal.

Ethics

Traditionally, parents and physicians have made all medical decisions on

"Involving Children in Medical Decisions" — Reprinted from *CMAJ* 15 Mar 1997; 156(6) pages 825–828 by permission of the publisher. © 1997 Canadian Medical Association.

behalf of children. However, just as the concept of informed consent has developed over the last 30 years with respect to competent adult patients, so new ways of thinking about the role of children in medical decision making have evolved.

Ethical principles that provide guidance in the care of adults are insufficient in the context of caring for children.[1–3] Issues related to the voluntariness of consent, the disclosure of information, capacity assessment, treatment decisions and bereavement are more complex, as is the physician's relationship with the patient and the patient's family.[3,4] Adult models presume that the patient is autonomous and has a stable sense of self, established values and mature cognitive skills; these characteristics are undeveloped or underdeveloped in children.

Although it is important to understand and respect the developing autonomy of a child, and although the duty of beneficence provides a starting point for determining what is in the child's best interest, a family-centred ethic is the best model for understanding the interdependent relationships that bear upon the child's situation.[5] A family-centred approach considers the effects of a decision on all family members, their responsibilities toward one another and the burdens and benefits of a decision for each member, while acknowledging the special vulnerability of the child patient.

A family-centred approach presents special challenges for the health care team, particularly when there is disagreement between parent and child. Such a situation raises profound questions about the nature of the physician–patient relationship in pediatric practice. Integrity in this relationship is fundamental to the achievement of the goal of medicine,[6] which has been defined as "right and good healing action taken in the interest of a particular patient."[7] In the care of adults, the physician's pri-

mary relationship is with the particular capable patient. The patient's family may be involved in decision making, but it is usually the patient who defines the bounds of such involvement. ...

The assumption that parents best understand what's in the interest of their child is usually sound. However, situations can arise in which the parents' distress prevents them from attending carefully to the child's concerns and wishes. Simply complying with the parents' wishes in such cases is inadequate. It is more helpful and respectful of the child to affirm the parents' responsibility for the care of their child while allowing the child to exercise choice in a measure appropriate to his or her level of development and experience of illness and treatment. This approach ... recognizes the child as the particular patient to whom the physician has a primary duty of care ... [and] seeks to harmonize the values of everyone involved in making the decision.[6]

Law

... The patient's right to refuse even life-saving medical treatment is recognized in Canadian law[8,9] and is premised on the patient's right to exercise control over his or her own body.

... In common law and under the statutory law of some provinces patients are presumed capable regardless of age unless shown otherwise; in other provinces an age at which patients are presumed capable is specified.[10] When a child's capacity is in doubt an assessment is required.

In the case of children who are incapable of making their own health care decisions, parents or legal guardians generally have the legal authority to act as surrogate decision-makers. The surrogate decision-maker is obliged to make treatment decisions in the best interest of the child. Health care providers who believe that a surrogate's decisions are not in the child's best interest can appeal to provincial child welfare authorities. The courts have the authority to assume a *parens patriae* role in treatment decisions if the child is deemed to be in need of protection. ... Every province has child welfare legislation that sets out the general parameters of the "best interest" standard. Courts are reluctant to authorize the withholding or withdrawal of medical treatment, especially in the face of parental support for such treatment. ...

Most children fall into one of three groups with respect to their appropriate involvement in decision making.[11,12]... Preschool children have no significant decision-making capacity and cannot provide their own consent. As surrogate decision-makers, parents should authorize (or refuse authorization) on their child's behalf, basing their decisions on what they believe to be in the child's best interest. ...

Children of primary-school age may participate in medical decisions but do not have full decision-making capacity. They may indicate their assent or dissent without fully understanding its implications. Nonetheless they should be provided with information appropriate to their level of comprehension. Although the child's parents should authorize or refuse to authorize treatment, the child's assent should be sought and any strong and sustained dissent should be taken seriously.[13]...

Many adolescents have the decision-making capacity of an adult.[14,15] This capacity will need to be determined for each patient in light of his or her

- ability to understand and communicate relevant information;
- ability to think and choose with some degree of independence;
- ability to assess the potential for benefit, risks or harms as well as to consider consequences and multiple options; and

- achievement of a fairly stable set of values.[16]

Many children and adolescents, particularly those who have been seriously ill, will need assistance in developing an understanding of the issues and in demonstrating their decision-making capacity. Age-appropriate discussions, perhaps with the assistance of teachers, chaplains, play therapists, nurses, psychologists or others skilled in communicating with children, are helpful. ...

Physicians should ensure that good decisions are made on behalf of their child patients. Although the interests of other family members are important and will influence decision making, the child's interests are most important and are unlikely to be expressed or defended by the child himself or herself. Anxious, stressed or grieving family members may need assistance in focusing on what is best for the child. This may be especially difficult when a cure is no longer possible; in such cases a decision to stop treatment may seem like a decision to cause the child's death.

Whether or not the child participates, the following considerations should bear upon a treatment decision concerning that child:

- The potential benefits to the child
- The potential harmful consequences to the child, including physical suffering, psychological or spiritual distress and death
- The moral, spiritual and cultural values of the child's family ...

For Samantha, resuming aggressive treatment will have a serious negative effect on her quality of life. The chances of remission are small, yet a decision to discontinue treatment will likely result in her death. Because death is an irreversible harm, and decisions with serious consequences require a high level of competence in decision making,[17] the capacity required would be very high. It has been determined that Samantha does not have this capacity.

Nevertheless, Samantha is included in discussions about her treatment options, and her reasons for refusing treatment are explored.[18] Members of the team work hard to re-establish trust. They and Samantha's parents come to agree that refusing treatment is not necessarily unreasonable; a decision by an adult patient in similar circumstances to discontinue treatment would certainly be honoured. Discussions address Samantha's and her parents' hopes and fears, their understanding of the possibility of cure, the meaning for them of the statistics provided by the physicians, Samantha's role in decision making and her access to information. They are assisted by nurses, a child psychologist, a psychiatrist, a member of the clergy, a bioethicist, a social worker and a palliative care specialist. ...

Opportunities are provided for Samantha and her family to speak to others who have had similar experiences, and staff are given the opportunity to voice their concerns.

Ultimately, a decision is reached to discontinue chemotherapy and the goal of treatment shifts from "cure" to "care."... Samantha returns home, supported by a community palliative care program, and is allowed to have a new kitten. She dies peacefully.

Notes*

1. Ruddick W. Parents and life prospects. In: O'Neill O., Ruddick W., editors. *Having Children: Philosophical and Legal Reflections on Parenthood*. New York: Oxford University Press; 1979: 124.

2. Nelson, J.L. Taking families seriously. *Hastings Center Report* 1992; 22:6.

3. Hardwig J. What about the family? *Hastings Center Report* 1990; 20(2):5–10.

4. Leikin S. A proposal concerning decisions to forgo life-sustaining treatment for young people. 7 *Pediatr* 1989; 115:17–22.

5. Mahowald M. *Women and Children in Health Care*. New York, Oxford University Press; 1993: 187,189.

6. Hellmann J. In pursuit of harmonized values: patient/parent-pediatrician relationships. In: Lynch A., editor. *The "Good" Pediatrician: An Ethics Curriculum for Use in Canadian Pediatrics Residency Programs*. Toronto: Pediatric Ethics Network; 1996.

7. Pellegrino E.D. Toward a reconstruction of medical morality: the primacy of the act of profession and the fact of illness. 7 *Med Philos* 1979; 4:47.

8. *Malette v. Shulman* [1990], 67 DLR (4th) (Ont CA).

9. Art. II CCQ.

10. Etchells E., Sharpe G., Elliott C., Singer P.A. Bioethics for clinicians 3: Capacity. *Can Med Assoc J* 1996; 155:657–61.

11. Broome M.E., Stieglitz V.A. The consent process and children. *Res Nurs Health* 1992; 15:147–52.

12. Erlen J.A. The child's choice: an essential component in treatment decisions. *Child Health Care* 1987; 1 S. 156–60.

13. Baylis F. The moral weight of a child's dissent. *Ethics Med Pract* 1993; 3 (1):23.

---

* These notes have been renumbered to aid the reader.

14. Weithorn L.A., Campbell S.B. The competency of children and adolescents to make informed treatment decisions. *Child Dev* 1982; 53:1589–98.

15. Lewis C.C. How adolescents approach decisions: changes over grades seven to twelve and policy implications. *Child Dev* 1981; 52:538–44.

16. Brock D.W. Children's competence for health care decision making. In: Kopelman L.M., Moskop J.C., editors. *Children and Health Care: Moral and Social Issues.* Dordrecht (Holland): Kluwer Academic Publishers; 1989: 181–212.

17. Drane J.F. The many faces of competency. *Hastings Center Report* 1985; 15(2): 17–21.

18. Freyer D.R. Children with cancer: special considerations in the discontinuation of life-sustaining treatment. *Med Pediatr Oncol* 1992; 20:136–42.

Further Readings

American College of Physicians. "Cognitively Impaired Subjects." *Ann Intern Med* 111:10 (Nov. 15, 1989): 843–848.

Buchanan, Allen E., and Dan W. Brock. *Deciding for Others: The Ethics of Surrogate Decision Making.* Cambridge and New York: Cambridge Univ. Press, 1989.

Gaylin, W., and R. Macklin, eds. *Who Speaks for the Child? The Problems of Proxy Consent.* New York and London: Plenum Press, 1982.

Keyserlingk, Edward W. *The Unborn Child's Right to Prenatal Care: A Comparative Law Perspective.* Montreal: McGill Legal Studies No. 5, 1984.

Savage, H., and Carla McKague. "Competency and Proxy Decision-Making," H. Savage and Carla McKague, *Mental Health Law in Canada.* Toronto and Vancouver: Butterworths, 1987, 114–124.

Wikler, D. "Paternalism and the Mildly Retarded." *Philos and Pub Affairs* 8 (1979): 337–392.

CHAPTER 8
ADVANCE DIRECTIVES

Introduction

As we have seen in Chapter 6, contemporary ethics maintains — and Canadian law agrees — that everyone has the right to decide whether to accept or reject health care. When someone is unable to exercise that right because of mental disability, lack of capacity, etc., a duly empowered proxy decision-maker will take over the decision-making role. The readings in Chapter 7 outline how this is the case. In most cases, the proxy or substitute decision-maker will make a decision that is in the best interests of the incompetent person, using the objective reasonable person standard: i.e., using the values that an objective reasonable person would use if he or she were in a position similar to that of the incompetent person. This is known as the *objective reasonable person rule*.

However, not all situations that involve incompetent persons are the same. We can distinguish three different kinds: cases where the currently incompetent person was never competent (young children and congenitally incompetent individuals fall into this category); cases where the now incompetent person was previously competent but did not express any wishes about what health care decisions should be made if he or she ever became incompetent; and cases where the currently incompetent person was previously competent and *did* say what should happen to him or her if he or she ever became incompetent and health care decisions had to be made. The objective reasonable person rule applies only in the first two kinds of cases. It does not apply in the third. In the third kind of case, if the wishes were expressed in writing, then the currently incompetent person has executed an *advance directive*. An advance directive is a document that stipulates the nature of the health care that someone would like to receive when they are incompetent and can no longer make such decisions in their own behalf. An advance may also identify the individual who should function as proxy or substitute decision-maker. All Canadian provinces and territories have passed or are in the process of passing laws that validate the legal status of advance directives, that stipulate the specific form that they should take, and that outline the procedures that would have to be followed for recording them. The last, in particular, is important since advance directives are of very little use if emergency response teams are unaware of them, or if they are not part of the patients' records and therefore are inaccessible to the professionals who are looking after the patients. The relevant statutes can be accessed by going to the URLs that are listed at the end of this chapter under *Further Readings*.

On one level, the rationale for advance directives is clear. It centres in the principles of autonomy and equality: the competent person's health care decisions should not lose their force simply because the person has become incompetent. That would constitute discrimination on the basis of disability. However, advance directives themselves may be somewhat problematic. For instance, what should be done if someone is bleeding to death and a simple medical procedure (e.g., a transfusion) would save her life but she has previously expressed the wish — in writing — that she did not want any blood? How does the attending physician know that person has not changed her mind at the last minute? Or that she really meant it? Is letting the patient die compatible with the physician's duty to save lives? The landmark case of *Malette v. Shulman* below addresses these questions. It states that if the *advance directive* is specific to the situation in question and is unambiguous and requires no interpretation, then it must be followed — even if this means that the patient will die.

In an article entitled "Advance Directives: Are They an Advance?" Singer *et al.* take a closer look at advance directives. They suggest some conditions the provincial statutes that give advance directives legal force should meet in order to be ethically acceptable and practically workable. It might be interesting to take a look at the provincial legislation that can be accessed using the URLs at the end of this chapter to see whether the various statutory provisions meet the conditions that are outlined by Singer *et al.*

Also, in light of the article by Harrison, Kenny, Sidarous and Rowell in Chapter 7, which emphasizes the rights of mature children to participate in health care decision-making, it might be interesting to speculate whether mature children below the age of majority should also have the right to make binding advance directives.

Malette v. Shulman

I

In the early afternoon of June 30, 1979, Mrs. Georgette Malette, then age 57, was rushed, unconscious, by ambulance to the Kirkland and District Hospital in Kirkland Lake, Ontario. She had been in an accident. The car in which she was a passenger, driven by her husband, had collided head-on with a truck. Her husband had been killed. She suffered serious injuries.

Malette v. Shulman (1990) 72 O.R. (2d) 417 (C.A.) pp. 17–42.

On arrival at the hospital, she was attended by Dr. David L. Shulman, a family physician practising in Kirkland Lake who served two or three shifts a week in the emergency department of the hospital and who was on duty at the time. Dr. Shulman's initial examination of Mrs. Malette showed, among other things, that she had severe head and face injuries and was bleeding profusely. The doctor concluded that she was suffering from incipient shock by reason of blood loss, and ordered that she be given intravenous glucose followed immediately by Ringer's Lactate. The administration of a volume expander, such as Ringer's Lactate, is standard medical procedure in cases of this nature. If the patient does not respond with significantly increased blood pressure, transfusions of blood are then administered to carry essential oxygen to tissues and to remove waste products and prevent damage to vital organs.

At about this time, a nurse discovered a card in Mrs. Malette's purse which identified her as a Jehovah's Witness and in which she requested, on the basis of her religious convictions, that she be given no blood transfusions under any circumstances. The card, which was not dated or witnessed, was printed in French and signed by Mrs. Malette. Translated into English, it read:

NO BLOOD TRANSFUSION!

As one of Jehovah's Witnesses with firm religious convictions, I request that no blood or blood products be administered to me under any circumstances. I fully realize the implications of this position, but I have resolutely decided to obey the Bible command: "Keep abstaining ... from blood." (Acts 15:28, 29). However, I have no religious objection to use the nonblood alternatives, such as Dextran, Haemaccel, PVP, Ringer's Lactate or saline solution.

Dr. Shulman was promptly advised of the existence of this card and its contents.

Mrs. Malette was next examined by a surgeon on duty in the hospital. He concluded, as had Dr. Shulman, that to avoid irreversible shock, it was vital to maintain her blood volume. He had Mrs. Malette transferred to the X-ray department for X-rays of her skull, pelvis and chest. However, before the X-rays could be satisfactorily completed, Mrs. Malette's condition deteriorated. Her blood pressure dropped markedly, her respiration became increasingly distressed, and her level of consciousness dropped. She continued to bleed profusely and could be said to be critically ill.

At this stage, Dr. Shulman decided that Mrs. Malette's condition had deteriorated to the point that transfusions were necessary to replace her lost blood and to preserve her life and health. Having made that decision, he personally administered transfusions to her, in spite of the Jehovah's Witness card, while she was in the X-ray department and after she was transferred to the intensive care unit. Dr. Shulman was clearly aware of the religious objection to blood manifested in the card carried by Mrs. Malette and the instruction that "NO BLOOD TRANSFUSION!" be given under any circumstances. He accepted full responsibility then, as he does now, for the decision to administer the transfusions.

Some three hours after the transfusions were commenced, Mrs. Malette's daughter, Celine Bisson, who had driven to Kirkland Lake from Timmins, arrived at the hospital accompanied by her husband and a local church elder. She strongly objected to her mother being given blood. She informed Dr. Shulman and some of the other defendants that both she and her mother were Jehovah's Witnesses, that a tenet of their faith forbids blood transfusions, and that she knew her mother would not want blood transfusions. Notwithstanding Dr.

Shulman's opinion as to the medical necessity of the transfusions, Mrs. Bisson remained adamantly opposed to them. She signed a document specifically prohibiting blood transfusions and a release of liability. Dr. Shulman refused to follow her instructions. Since the blood transfusions were, in his judgment, medically necessary in this potentially life-threatening situation, he believed it his professional responsibility as the doctor in charge to ensure that his patient received the transfusions. Furthermore, he was not satisfied that the card signed by Mrs. Malette expressed her current instructions because, on the information he then had, he did not know whether she might have changed her religious beliefs before the accident; whether the card may have been signed because of family or peer pressure; whether at the time she signed the card she was fully informed of the risks of refusal of blood transfusions; or whether, if conscious, she might have changed her mind in the face of medical advice as to her perhaps imminent but avoidable death.

As matters developed, by about midnight Mrs. Malette's condition had stabilized sufficiently to permit her to be transferred early the next morning by air ambulance to Toronto General Hospital where she received no further blood transfusions. She was discharged on August 11, 1979. Happily, she made a very good recovery from her injuries.

II

In June, 1980, Mrs. Malette brought this action against Dr. Shulman, the hospital, its executive director and four nurses, alleging, in the main, that the administration of blood transfusions in the circumstances of her case constituted negligence and assault and battery and subjected her to religious discrimination. ... With respect to Dr. Shulman, the learned judge concluded that the Jehovah's Witness card validly restricted his right to treat the patient, and there

was no rationally founded basis upon which the doctor could ignore that restriction. Hence, his administration of blood transfusions constituted a battery on the plaintiff. The judge awarded her damages of $20,000 but declined to make any award of costs.

Dr. Shulman now appeals to this court from that judgment. Mrs. Malette cross-appeals the judge's dismissal of the action against the hospital and his order with respect to costs.

... I should perhaps underscore the fact that Dr. Shulman was not found liable for any negligence in his treatment of Mrs. Malette. The judge held that he had acted "promptly, professionally and was well-motivated throughout" and that his management of the case had been "carried out in a competent, careful and conscientious manner" in accordance with the requisite standard of care. His decision to administer blood in the circumstances confronting him was found to be an honest exercise of his professional judgment which did not delay Mrs. Malette's recovery, endanger her life or cause her any bodily harm. Indeed, the judge concluded that the doctor's treatment of Mrs. Malette "may well have been responsible for saving her life."

Liability was imposed in this case on the basis that the doctor tortiously violated his patient's rights over her own body by acting contrary to the Jehovah's Witness card and administering blood transfusions that were not authorized. His honest and even justifiable belief that the treatment was medically essential did not serve to relieve him from liability for the battery resulting from his intentional and unpermitted conduct. ...

III

What then is the legal effect, if any, of the Jehovah's Witness card carried by Mrs. Malette? Was the doctor bound to honour the instructions of his unconscious patient or, given the emergency and his inability to obtain conscious instructions from his patient, was he entitled to disregard the card and act according to his best medical judgment?

To answer these questions and determine the effect to be given to the Jehovah's Witness card, it is first necessary to ascertain what rights a competent patient has to accept or reject medical treatment and to appreciate the nature and extent of those rights.

The right of a person to control his or her own body is a concept that has long been recognized at common law. The tort of battery has traditionally protected the interest in bodily security from unwanted physical interference. Basically, any intentional nonconsensual touching which is harmful or offensive to a person's reasonable sense of dignity is actionable. Of course, a person may choose to waive this protection and consent to the intentional invasion of this interest, in which case an action for battery will not be maintainable. No special exceptions are made for medical care, other than in emergency situations, and the general rules governing actions for battery are applicable to the doctor–patient relationship. Thus, as a matter of common law, a medical intervention in which a doctor touches the body of a patient would constitute a battery if the patient did not consent to the intervention. Patients have the decisive role in the medical decision-making process. Their right of self-determination is recognized and protected by the law. As Justice Cardozo proclaimed in his classic statement: "Every human being of adult years and sound mind has a right to determine what shall be done with his own body; and a surgeon who performs an operation without his patient's consent commits an assault, for which he is liable in damages": *Schloendoff v. Society of New York Hospital*, 211 N.Y. 125 (1914).

The doctrine of informed consent has developed in the law as the primary means of protecting a patient's right to control his or her medical treatment.

Under the doctrine, no medical procedure may be undertaken without the patient's consent obtained after the patient has been provided with sufficient information to evaluate the risks and benefits of the proposed treatment and other available options. The doctrine presupposes the patient's capacity to make a subjective treatment decision based on her understanding of the necessary medical facts provided by the doctor and on her assessment of her own personal circumstances. A doctor who performs a medical procedure without having first furnished the patient with the information needed to obtain an informed consent will have infringed the patient's right to control the course of her medical care, and will be liable in battery even though the procedure was performed with a high degree of skill and actually benefitted the patient.

The right of self-determination which underlies the doctrine of informed consent also obviously encompasses the right to refuse medical treatment. A competent adult is generally entitled to reject a specific treatment or all treatment, or to select an alternate form of treatment, even if the decision may entail risks as serious as death and may appear mistaken in the eyes of the medical profession or of the community. Regardless of the doctor's opinion, it is the patient who has the final say on whether to undergo the treatment. The patient is free to decide, for instance, not to be operated on or not to undergo therapy or, by the same token, not to have a blood transfusion. If a doctor were to proceed in the face of a decision to reject the treatment, he would be civilly liable for his unauthorized conduct notwithstanding his justifiable belief that what he did was necessary to preserve the patient's life or health. The doctrine of informed consent is plainly intended to ensure the freedom of individuals to make choices concerning their medical care. For this freedom to be meaningful, people must have the right to make choices that accord with their own values regardless of how unwise or foolish those choices may appear to others. ...

IV

The emergency situation is an exception to the general rule requiring a patient's prior consent. When immediate medical treatment is necessary to save the life or preserve the health of a person who, by reason of unconsciousness or extreme illness, is incapable of either giving or withholding consent, the doctor may proceed without the patient's consent. The delivery of medical services is rendered lawful in such circumstances either on the rationale that the doctor has implied consent from the patient to give emergency aid or, more accurately in my view, on the rationale that the doctor is privileged by reason of necessity in giving the aid and is not to be held liable for so doing. On either basis, in an emergency the law sets aside the requirement of consent on the assumption that the patient, as a reasonable person, would want emergency aid to be rendered if she were capable of giving instructions.

On the facts of the present case, Dr. Shulman was clearly faced with an emergency. He had an unconscious, critically ill patient on his hands who, in his opinion, needed blood transfusions to save her life or preserve her health. If there were no Jehovah's Witness card he undoubtedly would have been entitled to administer blood transfusions as part of the emergency treatment and could not have been held liable for so doing. In those circumstances he would have had no indication that the transfusions would have been refused had the patient then been able to make her wishes known and, accordingly, no reason to expect that, as a reasonable person, she would not consent to the transfusions.

However, to change the facts, if Mrs. Malette, before passing into unconsciousness, had expressly instructed Dr. Shulman, in terms comparable to those set forth on the card, that her religious convictions as a Jehovah's Witness were such that she was not to be given a blood transfusion under any circumstances and that she fully realized the implications of this position, the doctor would have been confronted with an obviously different situation. Here, the patient, anticipating an emergency in which she might be unable to make decisions about her health care contemporaneous with the emergency, has given explicit instructions that blood transfusions constitute an unacceptable medical intervention and are not to be administered to her. Once the emergency arises, is the doctor none the less entitled to administer transfusions on the basis of his honest belief that they are needed to save his patient's life?

The answer, in my opinion, is clearly no. A doctor is not free to disregard a patient's advance instructions any more than he would be free to disregard instructions given at the time of the emergency. The law does not prohibit a patient from withholding consent to emergency medical treatment, nor does the law prohibit a doctor from following his patient's instructions. While the law may disregard the absence of consent in limited emergency circumstances, it otherwise supports the right of competent adults to make decisions concerning their own health care by imposing civil liability on those who perform medical treatment without consent.

The patient's decision to refuse blood in the situation I have posed was made prior to and in anticipation of the emergency. While the doctor would have had the opportunity to dissuade her on the basis of his medical advice, her refusal to accept his advice or her unwillingness to discuss or consider the subject would not relieve him of his obligation to follow her instructions. The principles of self-determination and individual autonomy compel the conclusion that the patient may reject blood transfusions even if harmful consequences may result and even if the decision is generally regarded as fool-hardy. Her decision in this instance would be operative after she lapsed into unconsciousness, and the doctor's con-duct would be unauthorized. To transfuse a Jehovah's Witness in the face of her explicit instructions to the contrary would, in my opinion, violate her right to control her own body and show disrespect for the religious values by which she has chosen to live her life. ...

V

The distinguishing feature of the present case — and the one that makes this a case of first impression — is, of course, the Jehovah's Witness card on the per-son of the unconscious patient. What then is the effect of the Jehovah's Witness card?

In the appellant's submission, the card is of no effect and, as a consequence, can play no role in determining the doc-tor's duty toward his patient in the emer-gency situation existing in this case. The trial judge, the appellant argues, erred in holding both that the Jehovah's Witness card validly restricted the doctor's right to administer the blood transfusions, and that there was no rationally founded basis for ignoring the card. The argument proceeds on the basis, first, that, as a mat-ter of principle, a card of this nature could not operate in these circumstances to pro-hibit the doctor from providing emer-gency health care and, second, that in any event, as a matter of evidence, there was good reason to doubt the card's validity.

The appellant acknowledges that a conscious rational patient is entitled to refuse any medical treatment and that a doctor must comply with that refusal no matter how ill-advised he may believe it to be. He contends, however, to quote from his factum, that "a patient refusing treatment regarded by a doctor as being medically necessary has a right to be advised by the doctor, and the doctor has

a concomitant duty to advise the patient of the risks associated with that refusal." Here, because of the patient's uncon-sciousness, the doctor had no opportunity to advise her of the specific risks involved in refusing the blood transfusions that he regarded as medically necessary. In those circumstances, the appellant argues, it was not possible for the doctor to obtain, or for the patient to give, an "informed refusal." In the absence of such a refusal, the argument proceeds, Dr. Shulman was under a legal and ethical duty to treat this patient as he would any other emer-gency case and provide the treatment that, in his medical judgment, was need-ed to preserve her health and life. In short, the argument concludes, Mrs. Malette's religiously motivated instruc-tions, prepared in contemplation of an emergency, directing that she not be given blood transfusions in any circum-stances, were of no force or effect and could be ignored with impunity.

In challenging the trial judge's find-ing that there was no rationally founded evidentiary basis for doubting the validi-ty of the card and ignoring the restriction contained in it, the appellant puts forth a number of questions which he claims compel the conclusion that he was under no duty to comply with these instruc-tions. He argues that it could properly be doubted whether the card constituted a valid statement of Mrs. Malette's wishes in this emergency because it was unknown, for instance, whether she knew the card was still in her purse; whether she was still a Jehovah's Witness or how devout a Jehovah's Witness she was; what information she had about the risks associated with the refusal of blood transfusion when she signed the card; or whether, if she were conscious, she would refuse blood trans-fusions after the doctor had an opportu-nity to advise her of the risks associated with the refusal.

... I share the trial judge's view that, in the circumstances of this case, the instructions in the Jehovah's Witness card imposed a valid restriction on the emergency treatment that could be provided to Mrs. Malette and precluded blood transfusions.

I should emphasize that in deciding this case the court is not called upon to consider the law that may be applicable to the many situations in which objection may be taken to the use or continued use of medical treatment to save or prolong a patient's life. The court's role, especially in a matter as sensitive as this, is limited to resolving the issues raised by the facts presented in this particular case. On these facts, we are not concerned with a patient who has been diagnosed as terminally or incurably ill who seeks by way of advance directive or "living will" to reject medical treatment so that she may die with dignity; neither are we concerned with a patient in an irreversible vegetative state whose family seeks to withdraw medical treatment in order to end her life; nor is this a case in which an otherwise healthy patient wishes for some reason or other to terminate her life. There is no element of suicide or euthanasia in this case.

Our concern here is with a patient who has chosen in the only way possible to notify doctors and other providers of health care, should she be unconscious or otherwise unable to convey her wishes, that she does not consent to blood transfusions. Her written statement is plainly intended to express her wishes when she is unable to speak for herself. There is no suggestion that she wished to die. Her rejection of blood transfusions is based on the firm belief held by Jehovah's Witnesses, founded on their interpretation of the Scriptures, that the acceptance of blood will result in a forfeiture of their opportunity for resurrection and eternal salvation. The card evidences that "as one of Jehovah's Witnesses with firm religious convictions" Mrs. Malette is not to be administered blood transfusions "under any circumstances"; that,

while she "fully realize[s] the implications of this position," she has "resolutely decided to obey the Bible command"; and that she has no religious objection to "nonblood alternatives." In signing and carrying this card Mrs. Malette has made manifest her determination to abide by this fundamental tenet of her faith and refuse blood regardless of the consequences. If her refusal involves a risk of death, then, according to her belief, her death would be necessary to ensure her spiritual life.

Accepting for the moment that there is no reason to doubt that the card validly expressed Mrs. Malette's desire to withhold consent to blood transfusions, why should her wishes not be respected? Why should she be transfused against her will? The appellant's answer, in essence, is that the card cannot be effective when the doctor is unable to provide the patient with the information she would need before making a decision to withhold consent in this specific emergency situation. In the absence of an informed refusal, the appellant submits that Mrs. Malette's right to protection against unwanted infringements of her bodily integrity must give way to countervailing societal interests which limit a person's right to refuse medical treatment. The appellant identifies two such interests as applicable to the unconscious patient in the present situation: first, the interest of the state in preserving life and, second, the interest of the state in safeguarding the integrity of the medical profession.

VI

The state undoubtedly has a strong interest in protecting and preserving the lives and health of its citizens. There clearly are circumstances where this interest may override the individual's right to self-determination. For example, the state may in certain cases require that citizens submit to medical procedures in order to eliminate a health threat to the community or it may prohibit citizens from engaging in activities which are inherently dangerous to their lives. But this interest does not prevent a competent adult from refusing life-preserving medical treatment in general or blood transfusions in particular.

The state's interest in preserving the life or health of a competent patient must generally give way to the patient's stronger interest in directing the course of her own life. As indicated earlier, there is no law prohibiting a patient from declining necessary treatment or prohibiting a doctor from honouring the patient's decision. To the extent that the law reflects the state's interest, it supports the right of individuals to make their own decisions. By imposing civil liability on those who perform medical treatment without consent even though the treatment may be beneficial, the law serves to maximize individual freedom of choice. Recognition of the right to reject medical treatment cannot, in my opinion, be said to depreciate the interest of the state in life or in the sanctity of life. Individual free choice and self-determination are themselves fundamental constituents of life. To deny individuals freedom of choice with respect to their health care can only lessen, and not enhance, the value of life. This state interest, in my opinion, cannot properly be invoked to prohibit Mrs. Malette from choosing for herself whether or not to undergo blood transfusions.

Safeguarding the integrity of the medical profession is patently a legitimate state interest worthy of protection. However, I do not agree that this interest can serve to limit a patient's right to refuse blood transfusions. I recognize, of course, that the choice between violating a patient's private convictions and accepting her decision is hardly an easy one for members of a profession dedicated to aiding the injured and preserving life. The patient's right to determine her own medical treatment is, however, paramount to what might otherwise be the doctor's obligation to provide needed medical care. The doctor is bound in law by the patient's choice even though that choice may be contrary to the mandates of his own conscience and professional judgment. If patient choice were subservient to conscientious medical judgment, the right of the patient to determine her own treatment, and the doctrine of informed consent, would be rendered meaningless. Recognition of a Jehovah's Witness's right to refuse blood transfusions cannot, in my opinion, be seen as threatening the integrity of the medical profession or the state's interest in protecting the same.

In sum, it is my view that the principal interest asserted by Mrs. Malette in this case — the interest in the freedom to reject, or refuse to consent to, intrusions of her bodily integrity — outweighs the interest of the state in the preservation of life and health and the protection of the integrity of the medical profession. While the right to decline medical treatment is not absolute or unqualified, those state interests are not in themselves sufficiently compelling to justify forcing a patient to submit to nonconsensual invasions of her person. The interest of the state in protecting innocent third parties and preventing suicide are, I might note, not applicable to the present circumstances.

VII

The unique considerations in this case arise by virtue of Mrs. Malette's aim to articulate through her Jehovah's Witness card her wish not to be given blood transfusions in any circumstances. In considering the effect to be given the card, it must, of course, be borne in mind that no previous doctor–patient relationship existed between Dr. Shulman and Mrs. Malette. The doctor was acting here in an emergency in which he clearly did not have, nor could he obtain, her consent to his intervention. His intervention can be supported only by resort to the emergency doctrine which I outlined in Part IV of these reasons.

Under that doctrine, the doctor could administer blood transfusions without incurring liability, even though the patient had not consented, if he had no reason to believe that the patient, if she had the opportunity to consent, would decline. In those circumstances, it could be assumed that the patient, as a reasonable person, would consent to aid being rendered if she were able to give instructions. The doctor's authority to make decisions for his patient is necessarily a limited authority. If he knows that the patient has refused to consent to the proposed procedure, he is not empowered to overrule the patient's decision by substituting his decision for hers even though he, and most others, may think hers a foolish or unreasonable decision. In these circumstances the assumption upon which consent is set aside in an emergency could no longer be made. The doctor has no authority to intervene in the face of a patient's declared wishes to the contrary. Should he none the less proceed, he would be liable in battery for tortiously invading the patient's bodily integrity notwithstanding that what he did may be considered beneficial to the patient.

In this case, the patient, in effect, issued standing orders that she was to be given "NO BLOOD TRANSFUSION!" in any circumstances. She gave notice to the doctor and the hospital, in the only practical way open to her, of her firm religious convictions as a Jehovah's Witness and her resolve to abstain from blood. Her instructions plainly contemplated the situation in which she found herself as a result of her unfortunate accident. In light of those instructions, assuming their validity, she cannot be said to have consented to blood transfusions in this emergency. Nor can the doctor be said to have proceeded on the reasonable belief that the patient would have consented had she been in a condi-

tion to do so. Given his awareness of her instructions and his understanding that blood transfusions were anathema to her on religious grounds, by what authority could he administer the transfusions? Put another way, if the card evidences the patient's intent to withhold consent, can the doctor none the less ignore the card and subject the patient to a procedure that is manifestly contrary to her express wishes and unacceptable to her religious beliefs?

At issue here is the freedom of the patient as an individual to exercise her right to refuse treatment and accept the consequences of her own decision. Competent adults, as I have sought to demonstrate, are generally at liberty to refuse medical treatment even at the risk of death. The right to determine what shall be done with one's own body is a fundamental right in our society. The concepts inherent in this right are the bedrock upon which the principles of self-determination and individual autonomy are based. Free individual choice in matters affecting this right should, in my opinion, be accorded very high priority. I view the issues in this case from that perspective.

VIII

The appellant's basic position, reduced to its essentials, is that unless the doctor can obtain the patient's informed refusal of blood transfusions he need not follow the instructions provided in the Jehovah's Witness card. Nothing short of a conscious, contemporaneous decision by the patient to refuse blood transfusions — a decision made after the patient has been fully informed by the doctor of the risks of refusing blood in the specific circumstances facing her — will suffice, the appellant contends, to eliminate the doctor's authority to administer emergency treatment or, by the same token, to relieve the doctor of his obligation to treat this emergency patient as he would any other. ...

In my opinion, it is unnecessary to determine in this case whether there is doctrine of informed refusal as distinct from the doctrine of informed consent. In the particular doctor–patient relationship which arose in these emergency circumstances it is apparent that the doctor could not inform the patient of the risks involved in her prior decision to refuse consent to blood transfusions in any circumstances. It is apparent also that her decision did not emerge out of a doctor–patient relationship. Whatever the doctor's obligation to provide the information needed to make an informed choice may be in other doctor–patient relationships, he cannot be in breach of any such duty in the circumstances of this relationship. The patient manifestly made the decision on the basis of her religious convictions. It is not for the doctor to second-guess the reasonableness of the decision or to pass judgment on the religious principles which motivated it. The fact that he had no opportunity to offer medical advice cannot nullify instructions plainly intended to govern in circumstances where such advice is not possible. Unless the doctor had reason to believe that the instructions in the Jehovah's Witness card were not valid instructions in the sense that they did not truly represent the patient's wishes, in my opinion he was obliged to honour them. He has no authorization under the emergency doctrine to override the patient's wishes. In my opinion, she was entitled to reject in advance of an emergency a medical procedure inimical to her religious values.

The remaining question is whether the doctor factually had reason to believe the instructions were not valid. ... On my reading of the record, there was no reason not to regard this card as a valid advance directive. Its instructions were clear, precise and unequivocal, and manifested a calculated decision to reject a procedure offensive to the patient's religious convictions. The instructions ex-

cluded from potential emergency treatment a single medical procedure well known to the lay public and within its comprehension. ... The card undoubtedly belonged to and was signed by Mrs. Malette; its authenticity was not questioned by anyone at the hospital and, realistically, could not have been questioned. The trial judge found, "[t]here [was] no basis in evidence to indicate that the card [did] not represent the current intention and instruction of the card holder" [p. 268 O.R., p. 43 D.L.R.]. There was nothing to give credence to or provide support for the speculative inferences implicit in questions as to the current strength of Mrs. Malette's religious beliefs or as to the circumstances under which the card was signed or her state of mind at the time. The fact that a card of this nature was carried by her can itself be taken as verification of her continuing and current resolve to reject blood "fully realiz[ing] the implications of this position."

In short, the card on its face set forth unqualified instructions applicable to the circumstances presented by this emergency. In the absence of any evidence to the contrary, those instructions should be taken as validly representing the patient's wish not to be transfused. If, of course, there were evidence to the contrary — evidence which cast doubt on whether the card was a true expression of the patient's wishes — the doctor, in my opinion, would be entitled to proceed as he would in the usual emergency case. In this case, however, there was no such contradictory evidence. Accordingly, I am of the view that the card had the effect of validly restricting the treatment that could be provided to Mrs. Malette and constituted the doctor's administration of the transfusions a battery.

With respect to Mrs. Malette's daughter, I would treat her role in this matter as no more than confirmatory of her mother's wishes. The decision in this case does not turn on whether the doctor failed to follow the daughter's instructions. Therefore, it is unnecessary, and in my view would be inadvisable, to consider what effect, if any, should be given to a substitute decision, purportedly made by a relative on behalf of the patient, to reject medical treatment in these circumstances.

One further point should be mentioned. The appellant argues that to uphold the trial decision places a doctor on the horns of a dilemma, in that, on the one hand, if the doctor administers blood in this situation and saves the patient's life, the patient may hold him liable in battery while, on the other hand, if the doctor follows the patient's instructions and, as a consequence, the patient dies, the doctor may face an action by dependants alleging that, notwithstanding the card, the deceased would, if conscious, have accepted blood in the face of imminent death and the doctor was negligent in failing to administer the transfusions. In my view, that result cannot conceivably follow. The doctor cannot be held to have violated either his legal duty or professional responsibility towards the patient or the patient's dependants when he honours the Jehovah's Witness card and respects the patient's right to control her own body in accordance with the dictates of her conscience. The onus is clearly on the patient. When members of the Jehovah's Witness faith choose to carry cards intended to notify doctors and other providers of health care that they reject blood transfusions in an emergency, they must accept the consequences of their decision. Neither they nor their dependants can later be heard to say that the card did not reflect their true wishes. If harmful consequences ensue, the responsibility for those consequences is entirely theirs and not the doctor's.

Finally, the appellant appeals the quantum of damages awarded by the trial judge. In his submission, given the findings as to the competence of the treatment, the favourable results, the doctor's overall exemplary conduct and his good faith in the matter, the battery was technical and the general damages should be no more than nominal. While the submission is not without force, damages of $20,000 cannot be said to be beyond the range of damages appropriate to a tortious interference of this nature. The trial judge found that Mrs. Malette suffered mentally and emotionally by reason of the battery. His assessment of general damages was clearly not affected by any palpable or overriding error and there is therefore no basis upon which an appellate court may interfere with the award.

X

In the result, for these reasons I would dismiss the appeal and the cross-appeal, both with costs.

Advance Directives: Are They an Advance?

Advance Directives Seminar Group, Centre for Bioethics, University of Toronto

An advance directive is a document intended to govern the kind of life-sustaining treatment that a competent person will receive if he or she later becomes incompetent.[1] An instruction directive, also called a living will, contains a person's preferences regarding the use of life-sustaining treatments. A proxy directive, also called a durable power of attorney for health care, contains a person's preferences regarding who is to make decisions about life-sustaining treatment on his or her behalf. The two types — instruction and proxy — can be combined into a single document. ...

Should advance directives be supported in principle? If so, how should they be designed? Who should be offered one? When should advance directives be updated? What should be done if patients change their minds? How should implementation be enforced? How should consideration of their use be promoted?

Should Advance Directives Be Supported in Principle?

Arguments in Favour

Five arguments support the use of advance directives. First, because they permit competent people to project their preferences regarding life-sustaining treatment onto situations of future incompetence, advance directives extend

people's autonomy. Studies have found that most patients want to discuss life-sustaining treatment with their physicians[6–9] and that 93% of outpatients and 89% of the public want advance directives.[10] Moreover, making an advance directive is itself an exercise of autonomy — people may benefit from knowing that they have done all they can to decide about treatment issues in the event of incompetence.

Second, advance directives promote the fair treatment of incompetent patients by conveying their prior wishes. Since competent patients have the right to forgo life-sustaining treatments[3,4] justice requires that incompetent patients also have this right and not be treated differently.

Third, advance directives may reduce the emotional anguish to the patient's family members by relieving them of the obligation to make life-or-death treatment decisions or, at least, by assuring them that they are making the decision the patient would have wanted them to make.

Fourth, advance directives may reduce the psychologic distress of health care providers who do not know whether to provide life-sustaining treatment (that patients may not have wanted) or not to provide such treatment (that patients may have wanted).[7–11]

Finally, advance directives may increase physician–patient communica-

Peter Singer, Eileen Ambrosio, Shelley Birenbaum, Arthur Fisher, David Hughes, A.H. Khan, P. Khan, Pat Rundle, John Senn, Ross Upshor, Jo-Ann P. Wilson, Frederick H. Lowy, Eric Meslin, Carol Nash, Nitsa Kohut, Michelle Mullen, Hussein Z. Noorani, Nancy Ondrusek, Sharon Rea, Mehran Sam and Linda R. Shaw. "Advance directives: Are they an advance? — Reprinted from *CMAJ* 15 Jan 1992; 146(2) pages 127–134 by permission of the publisher. © 1992 Canadian Medical Association.

tion. They provide a framework and focus for discussion of medically and ethically relevant issues.

Arguments Against

Seven arguments oppose the use of advance directives.[12] First, people who have become incompetent, such as those in a persistent vegetative state, are greatly changed from when they were competent, and the decisions they would make if they could communicate might be different. It may be inappropriate to project the autonomous wishes of competent people onto future situations of incompetence.

Second, justice does not require equal treatment of groups that vary in morally relevant ways. Competent patients are fully autonomous; incompetent patients are not. This may represent a morally relevant difference.

Third, people change their minds and may forget to change their directives, in which case care may be provided that the patient does not want or would adamantly reject if he or she could.

Fourth, most advance directives are biased toward refusal of treatment. If vulnerable groups are selectively encouraged to complete them, directives may become an instrument of discrimination. Moreover, it might be assumed that patients who have not completed a directive want life-sustaining treatment to be provided.

Fifth, policies on advance directives may restrict patients' rights. In the United States some states allow only patients who are terminally ill to complete advance directives, and some exclude artificial feeding from the types of treatments that may be contained in an advance directive.

Sixth, advance directives may lead to inappropriate choices if situations arise that the person did not foresee or consider. There may be a medical advance that would restore the person to full health. Conversely, treatment may be futile in a

particular situation, and yet the person requested it in the directive when the hopelessness of the situation was not apparent.

Finally, by substituting a written form for physician–patient dialogue, advance directives may undercut the goal of informed consent — extensive and open discussion between patients and health care professionals.

Balancing the Arguments

There are arguments of autonomy and justice that support and oppose the use of advance directives. The remaining arguments in favour — families' emotional anguish, the distress of health care professionals and improved communication — reflect anecdotal experience but will require empirical validation. The remaining arguments against — changing preferences, the biased design of advance directive forms, applicability to patients who are not terminally ill, inappropriate treatment choices and undermining of the patient–health care professional dialogue — are practical issues of implementation. We conclude that although advance directives may be desirable in principle, if they are not carefully designed and implemented they may have undesirable effects in practice.

How Should Advance Directives Be Designed?

Refusals of or Requests for Life-sustaining Treatments?

Some instruction directives permit patients only to refuse, not to request, life-sustaining treatment. ... The Medical Directive[13] permits patients to decline or request life-sustaining treatment and has options that include "undecided" and "I want a therapeutic trial."[13]... Since the goal is to record for the future the preferences of competent patients, it seems unreasonable to offer advance directives that provide only for refusal. Advance directives should permit patients to refuse or request life-sustaining treatment.

Treatment Preferences or General Life Values?

Instruction directives can focus on preferences or values. By preference we mean a specific choice of the use of life-sustaining treatments in identified clinical situations. The Medical Directive permits its patients to choose or refuse 11 specific treatments in four specified clinical situations.[13] By value we mean a person's attitudes toward various aspects of human life such as physical and mental functioning, pain, social interaction, other elements of quality of life and medical technology. Another directive, the Values History,[14] contains a series of questions about "attitude toward life" and "personal relationships."

Value-based directives may be easier for patients to complete, because they do not require a knowledge of health problems or medical treatments. However, preference-based directives may be easier for health care professionals to interpret and implement because they provide more explicit directions regarding treatment. It is difficult to know how to balance these conflicting goals. Since values and preferences represent fundamentally different, but complementary, approaches, instruction directives should contain both these components.

Instruction or Proxy Directive?

It is difficult to design instruction directives to anticipate all possible clinical situations. Proxy directives avoid this problem by allowing the proxy to make an informed choice based on the clinical circumstances, but not everyone has a potential proxy he or she can trust. Because instruction and proxy directives complement one another we recommend that patients be offered both in one document. People who do not want to consider the use of life-sustaining treatments and prefer to entrust someone else with decision-making authority should complete only the proxy component. People without proxies whom they trust should complete only the instruction component.

Can a Specific Advance Directive Be Recommended?

Many advance directive documents are currently available and have been developed by a number of bodies. ... We cannot recommend any one document over another since empirical data would be needed for comparison: Which directive is preferred (and why) by patients, families and health care providers? Which is most likely to ensure that patients receive the care they request when they become incapacitated? Such questions are in urgent need of research. Who should be offered an advance directive?

Who Should Be Offered an Advance Directive?

Advance directives could be offered not only to people who have requested information about them but also to the public, patients admitted to hospital, patients who have specific target conditions, and people who are making or updating their testamentary wills. (By "offering" we mean systematically providing information about and the opportunity to complete an advance directive with assistance when necessary.)

Information about advance directives and even the forms themselves could be distributed with drivers' licences, health cards, income tax returns and census questionnaires, at post offices or through mass mailing. Information could also be provided through special toll-free telephone numbers. The main advantage of this approach is that it would reach all those who might need life-sustaining treatment; for example, young adults admitted to hospital unconscious after a motor vehicle accident. Moreover, it would meet an egalitarian standard of justice, since all citizens would be offered the opportunity to complete a directive. The disadvantage is that language, literacy and educational barriers may prevent many people from understanding the directives and completing them appropriately.

Advance directives could be offered to all patients at the time of hospital admission, as required by the patient self-determination provisions of 1990.[2] An advantage of this approach is that patients admitted to hospital are more likely than members of the public to need advance directives. Many patients have conditions with foreseeable clinical courses, and discussions can be focused on the life-sustaining treatments that they might need; the choices are not as hypothetical and abstract as they are for healthy people. There are several drawbacks: discussions might be distressing to sick patients; advance directives cannot be completed by patients who are incompetent at the time of admission; patients in the midst of a medical emergency may not understand the choices being offered; the hospital environment is potentially coercive, and if facilities are obliged to offer advance directives the different versions developed may prove to be a problem if the patient is subsequently transferred to another facility.

Another group to be offered advance directives could be patients with specific illnesses. Such patients could be chronically or terminally ill or have such illnesses as early Alzheimer's disease, acquired immunodeficiency syndrome, end-stage renal disease or amyotrophic lateral sclerosis. The advance directive would embody a considered and authentic choice since patients would be in the situation to which their instructions apply. Because these patients have likely already considered their death, their completing a directive may not be distressing and may provide comfort by returning to them control over the future course of treatment. Moreover, such patients may be the most receptive to advance directives. They are likely to have a relationship with a physician who can raise the topic of life-sustaining treatment in a sensitive manner and at an appropriate time. On the other hand, an advance directive may distress some patients, especially in emergencies, when there is only limited time to consider the choice. Health care providers may not want to raise the issue of advance directives because of the time involved, the lack of reimbursement or the emotional stress of such discussions. The criteria for target groups may be difficult to define, and identifying an already vulnerable group of patients as being in need of advance directives could be considered discriminatory.

People who are making or updating their wills (testators) could be offered an advance directive. In this way a large number of people would be reached. Testators are already thinking about their death and so are likely to be receptive to discussing such issues. The lawyers involved often have their clients' trust, a detailed knowledge of their personal affairs and experience in discussing intimate and delicate matters with them. They are also experienced in recognizing people whose competence is likely to be challenged, so that such clients can be referred for medical or psychiatric assessment and their competence documented convincingly in case of a later challenge. One disadvantage of offering these people an advance directive is the implicit suggestion that a will concerning disposal of property is of equal importance to a will concerning "disposal" of a person's life and that they can be dealt with through a similar process. Another is that without the assistance of a physician, lawyers often cannot properly draft or discuss specific instruction directives.

Patients who are chronically or terminally ill are most likely to become incompetent and therefore have the most urgent need for an advance directive. People making or updating their wills are already thinking about death and so may be more receptive. We do not claim that these are the only groups to whom advance directives should be offered or that physicians and lawyers are the only people who should be offering them.

When Should Advance Directives Be Updated?

Advance directives should be updated when people change their minds about their choices. Moreover, a policy of regular updating may increase the confidence of health care professionals and families that they are following the patients' most current wishes. An adequate advance directive process must have some mechanism whereby changes can be easily incorporated and made known to all involved parties.

How often and under what circumstances people change their minds regarding the content of their advance directive is an empirical question. Four studies have examined the stability of preferences for life-sustaining treatment. Everhart and Pearlman[15] found that for critically ill patients these preferences at the time of discharge from an intensive care unit and 1 month later were stable. Silverstein and associates[16] reported that patients with amyotrophic lateral sclerosis changed their preferences over a 6-month period. Emanuel and collaborators found that on average the durability over 6 to 12 months of patients' preferences regarding situation-treatment choices in the Medical Directive was 87%. Teno, Mor and Fleishman[17] found moderate stability over 1 year of the preferences of patients with human

immunodeficiency virus infection (m = 0.16 to 0.35).

We believe that updating should be done when there is a change in the patient's clinical status (improvement or deterioration), when the patient is admitted to a health care facility, when it is deemed appropriate by the physician or lawyer and when there is a major event such as divorce, death of a spouse, birth of children or move to a new jurisdiction. In addition, for patients in institutions, advance directives should be considered part of the medical record in the same way details of medication are; as such, they would be subject to review on a semi-annual or annual basis.

It is probably unnecessary to set fixed periods after which advance directives are automatically null and void. A lesson from the decision in the Malette case[20] is that when people complete a directive their preferences will now be taken seriously. Linking advance directives to other documents (e.g., a driver's licence) may ensure that people review their directives regularly. However, they should be informed at the time they complete an advance directive that it is not cast in stone, that if they change their mind they should change their directive and that all those who are aware of the earlier directive should be informed of the change.

What Should Be Done if Patients Change Their Minds?

When patients complete advance directives they are, presumably, competent. When they change their minds later they may be competent or they may not. (The terms "competent" and "incompetent" are the subjects of considerable philosophic, medical and legal discussion[18,19] that is beyond the scope of this article.)

If a competent patient is able to communicate a preference that is contradictory to the one in the advance directive physicians should honour the later preference. Informed consent is a process and not an event, and patients have the right to change their minds. Safeguards should ensure that the patient did not change his or her mind under duress, but there is no reason to be more suspicious of changes of preference than of advance directives themselves. ...

A patient who is incompetent and able to communicate is controversial. Some members of our group held that the patient's last competent wish, not the wish expressed during the state of incompetence, should be followed regardless of whether the patient had recently declined a previously requested treatment or recently requested a previously declined treatment. The rationale is the overriding priority of autonomy as embodied in the advance directive. Others argued that the physician should act generally in favour of preserving life. If the patient initially declined treatment but later requested it, then treatment should be given. If the patient initially requested treatment but later declined it, then, again, treatment should be given. The rationale is that in the face of contradictory evidence about the patient's authentic wishes the physician should err in favour of preserving life because wrongful death is worse than wrongful life.[20] If time permits, we recommend broad consultation with the family, other health care professionals and possibly institutional ethics committees or consultants.

Since the patient who is incompetent and unable to communicate is unable to express a change in preference, this situation, too, is more theoretic than practical.

How Should Implementation Be Enforced?

A recent study by Danis and colleagues[21] has shown that 75% of patients received the type of care that they requested in an advance directive. Was this rate of compliance too low, too high, or just right? How should compliance with patients' advance directives be enforced? We considered three mechanisms: legislation, case law and a system of graded referral through ethics committees and administrative tribunals. (The problem of conscientious objection to a patient's treatment has been addressed elsewhere.[22,23])

First, compliance with advance directives could be enforced through sanctions contained in provincial legislation and buttressed by federal legislation, including the Criminal Code and the Canadian Charter of Rights and Freedoms. ... The perceived benefits of legislative sanctions depend on one's view of the problem that advance directives attempt to address. If one believes that patients' preferences are usually unknown but if they were known health care professionals would act in good faith to carry them out, then legislative sanctions are unnecessary. If one believes that even if patients' preferences were known, health care professionals would not follow them, then legislative sanctions are necessary.

There are potential hazards to legislative sanctions. Patients' directives may be followed even if there is evidence that the patient had changed his or her mind, perhaps as a result of the clinical circumstances. Sanctions may deter health care professionals from offering advance directives to their patients because they fear that they will be forced to follow the poorly considered or inauthentic wishes of the patients who complete them. Finally, health care professionals are generally skeptical of legal solutions to patient care problems, and the presence of heavy-handed legislative sanctions may cause them to abandon the entire project of advance directives.

Some would argue that legislation that recognizes advance directives without ensuring that they will be followed is unnecessary. However, a clear benefit of such legislation is its symbolic value: the message that society approves of advance directives. Legislation would likely promote the use of these documents. It would dispel the concerns of health care professionals regarding the legality of advance directives. (It could also provide immunity from civil prosecution or disciplinary action for physicians who follow patients' advance directives.) It would offer an opportunity for public education through the news media as the proposed legislation is debated in provincial legislatures or the federal parliament.

Second, compliance with advance directives could be enforced solely by the common law and the courts. However, the adversarial nature of the courtroom is not well suited to the human problems of the hospital or clinic, and family lawyers increasingly realize that conflicts are best resolved outside the courts. Moreover, if all cases of disagreement were referred to the courts, an already burdened system would be overloaded. Access to the court system requires financial resources that many families may not possess.

Finally, compliance could be enforced by graded referral, which occupies a middle ground between legislative sanctions and common-law solutions. Legislation could establish a process of selective referral of cases in which the health care professional wishes to deviate from or seek clarification about the patient's advance directive or in which there is conflict between providers and family members regarding its implementation. Such a system would operate at three levels. First, cases involving conflict would be referred to the institutional ethics committee.[24] Second, cases not thus resolved would be referred to a professional disciplinary board or multidisciplinary administrative tribunal. (The advantage of a professional disciplinary board administered by licensing bodies ... is that these bodies are already in place

and have a mandate to protect the public; the advantage of creating an administrative tribunal is that it would be constituted specifically to address the problem of advance directives.) Third, decisions made by the administrative tribunal or disciplinary body could be appealed to the courts. Such appeal procedures are well established.

Neither legislative sanctions nor common-law solutions alone satisfactorily address the problem of noncompliance with patients' advance directives. We recommend legislation without sanctions for noncompliance in addition to a system of graded referral of individual cases.

How Should Consideration of the Use of Advance Directives Be Promoted?

There are no published data on how many Canadians have completed advance directives. U.S. surveys have shown that 9% of people in Wisconsin[25] and 15% of Americans overall[26] have completed such documents. How can more people be given the opportunity to consider the use of advance directives? (By "considering their use" we mean offering people the opportunity to complete advance directives; a public policy focusing solely on encouraging people to complete them might foster coercion and violate the principle of self-determination on which advance directives are based.)

Consideration of the use of advance directives could be promoted by public education, professional education, policy in health care facilities, legislation and remuneration. Public education (which may include advertisements in the media) should not be used merely to direct or encourage people to complete a directive but also to inform them of the problem that such directives seek to address, their purpose, the main types of directives, the procedures for completing them and where people can turn for further information.

The professional education of health care providers, lawyers and all other counsellors on advance directives complements public education. Health care professionals should be aware of the legal status of advance directives, the need to raise the topic of directives at an appropriate time, effective methods of communication during their completion and the limitations of advance directives. Lawyers should understand the clinical situations and life-sustaining treatments involved and the need to refer clients for further discussion of their health to their physicians. Professional organizations whose members are called on to assist people to complete advance directives should make educational programs on this topic available to their members.

It may be appropriate for facilities to develop a policy of making advance directives available to patients, especially if the facility also provides education for health care providers. Only education can ensure that there are staff trained to assist patients to complete directives and that physicians and other members of the health care team are prepared to implement the directives appropriately when they come into effect.

Legislation recognizing the validity of advance directives could ensure that the documents are legally binding and protect physicians and other health care providers from civil liability for following them. (The Criminal Code should also be amended to protect them from criminal liability.) If the legal validity of advance directives is confirmed, physicians may be more willing to recommend them to their patients and the public more willing to complete them.

Remuneration of health-care professionals for time spent discussing advance directives may encourage their use. It is likely that under provincial health care insurance plans at present, such discussions qualify for remuneration as routine office visits or counselling. However, if advice on directives were an item in the fee schedule, more physicians might be encouraged to offer it. (The perception may remain that when there is a financial incentive, patients may be coerced into completing advance directives.) Remuneration of lawyers will tend to be driven more by client demand than by public policy. However, policy-makers should encourage publicly funded legal clinics to provide clients with advance directives; in addition, they should include advance directives among the services for which legal-aid remuneration is available and encourage private legal service plans (like those provided by unions) to include advance directives among the services offered.

Public and professional education is necessary to facilitate the introduction of advance directives. Legislation, institutional policies and remuneration all play a role in clarifying the official status of these documents and encouraging their use. Asked to pick a single best strategy, we prefer public education. A combined strategy that makes use of several or all of the options may be even better. For example, public education would be more effective if the legal validity of advance directives were established and health care providers were educated about advance directives, so that patients requesting them could be accommodated. Despite the focus on legislation in the public debate, other steps are necessary to promote the appropriate use of advance directives.

Conclusions

1. In principle, advance directives are a valuable method for people to express their preferences about life-sustaining treatment.

2. In design, directives should permit refusal of and requests for life-sustaining treatment. Instruction direc-

tives should be framed in terms of specific treatment preferences and general life values. Combined directives are preferable to instruction or proxy directives alone. No specific directive can be recommended.

3. Advance directives should be offered to anyone who requests them. Chronically or terminally ill patients will need them most, and clients who are making or updating their testamentary wills may be receptive to the idea of completing one.

4. Advance directives should be updated on the person's request, when there is a change in clinical status or admission to a health care facility, when deemed appropriate by a physician or lawyer and when the person undergoes a major life change. Those completing a directive should be advised to revise it if their preferences for life-sustaining treatment or the identity of the proxy decision-maker changes.

5. If competent people change their preferences, the most recently expressed wishes should be followed. If incompetent patients change the preferences expressed while they were competent, it is questionable whether the physician should follow the original wishes or those that would preserve the patient's life.

6. Advance directives should be enforced through a system of graded referral of controversial cases to institutional ethics committees, administrative tribunals or professional disciplinary boards and the courts.

7. Consideration of the use of advance directives should be promoted through public and professional education, health facility policy, legislation and remuneration.

... Other important questions remain: How will advance directives be made transportable, that is, made available when they are needed? Which people are best placed to give advice about advance directives?

Are advance directives an advance? We believe that they are. However, as we realized and as will become apparent when advance directives are more broadly used, they contain many limitations. Having identified and addressed some of these limitations, we hope that the introduction of advance directives in Canada will proceed with due caution.

Notes[*]

1. Singer P.A., Siegler M. Elective use of life-sustaining treatments. In Stollerman G.H. (ed): *Advances in Internal Medicine,* vol 36. Yr Bk Med Pubs, New York, 1991: 57–79.

2. Omnibus Budget Reconciliation Act, 1990 (U.S. Public Law 101-508), s 42069 4751.

3. *Cruzan v. Director, Missouri Department of Health* (1990), II 0 SCt 2841.

4. *Attorney-General of B.C. v. Astaforoff*, 6 CCC, 3d 498 (BCCA 1983).

5. *Malette v. Shulman* (1990), 72 OR (2d) 417 (Ont CA).

6. Lo B., McLeod G.A., Saika G.: Patient attitudes to discussing life-sustaining treatment. *Arch Intern Med* 1986; 146: 1613–1615.

7. Shmerling R.H., Bedell S.E., Lilienfeld A. *et al.*: Discussing cardiopulmonary resuscitation: a study of elderly outpatients. *J Gen Intern Med* 1988; 3: 317–321.

8. Frankl D., Oye R.K., Bellamy P.E.: Attitudes of hospitalized patients toward life-support: a survey of 200 medical patients. *Am J Med* 1989; 86: 645–648.

---

[*] These notes have been renumbered to aid the reader.

9. Gamble E.R., McDonald P.J., Lichstein P.R.: Knowledge, attitudes and behavior of elderly persons regarding living. *Arch Intern Med* 1991; 151: 277–280.

10. Emanuel L.L., Barry M.J., Stoeckle J.D. *et al.*: Advance directives for medical care—a case for greater use. *N Engl J Med* 1991; 324: 889–895.

11. Pellegrino E.D., Thomasma D.C.: *For the Patient's Good—The Restoration of Beneficence in Health Care*, Oxford U Pr, New York, 1989: 136–147.

12. Fisher R.H., Meslin E.M.: Should living wills be legalized? *Can Med Assoc J* 1990; 142: 23–26.

13. Emanuel L.L., Emanuel E.J.: The Medical Directive: a new comprehensive advance care document. *JAMA* 1989; 261: 3288–3293.

14. Lambert P., Gibson J.M., Nathanson P.: The Values History: an innovation in surrogate medical decision making. *Law Med Health Care* 1990; 3: 202–212.

15. Everhart M.A., Pearlman R.A.: Stability of patient preferences regarding life-sustaining treatments. *Chest* 1990; 97: 159–164.

16. Silverstein M.D., Stocking C.B., Antel J. *et al.*: Amyotrophic lateral sclerosis and life-sustaining therapy: patients' desires for information, participation in decision making, and preferences for life-sustaining therapy. *Mayo Clin Proc* 1991; 66: 906–913.

17. Teno J., Mor V., Fleishman J.: Stability of preferences among patients with HIV-related disease [abstr]. *Clin Res* 1991; 39: 632A.

18. Weisstub D.N.: *Enquiry on Mental Competency, Final Report.* Queen's Printer for Ontario, Toronto, 1990.

19. Appelbaum P.S., Grisso T.: Assessing patients' capacities to consent to treatment. *N Engl J Med* 1988; 319: 1635–1638.

20. Singer P.A., Lowy F.H.: Refusal of life-sustaining treatment: the Malette case and decision-making under uncertainty. *Ann R Coll Physicians Surg Can* 1991; 24: 401–403.

21. Danis M., Southerland L.I., Garrett J.M. *et al.*: A prospective study of advance directives for life-sustaining care. *N Engl J Med* 1991; 324: 882–888.

22. *Making Health Care Decisions: A Report on the Ethical and Legal Implications of Informed Consent in the Patient–Practitioner Relationship*, vol 1. President's Commission for the Study of Ethical Problems in Medicine and Biomedical and Behavioral Research, Washington, 1982.

23. Miles S.H., Singer P.A., Siegler M.: Conflicts between patients' wishes to forgo treatment and the policies of health care facilities. *N Engl J Med* 1989; 321: 48–50.

24. Singer P.A., Pellegrino E.D., Siegler M.: Ethics committees and consultants. *J Clin Ethics* 1990; I: 263–267.

25. Shapiro R.S., Tavill F., Rivkin G. *et al.*: Living will in Wisconsin. *Wis Med J* 1986; 85: 17–23.

26. Harvey L.K., Shubat S.C.: *Physician and Public Attitudes.* Am Med Assoc, Chicago, 1989: 113.

Further Readings

Childress, James F. *Who Should Decide? Paternalism in Health Care.* Oxford and New York: Oxford Univ. Press, 1982.

Emanuel, Ezekiel J., and Linda L. Emanuel. "Living Wills: Past, Present and Future." *J Clin Ethics* 1:1 (Spring 1990): 9–19.

Hackler, C., R. Moseley and D.E. Vawter, eds. *Advance Directives in Medicine.* New York: Praeger, 1989, 141–145.

Kuhse, Helga. *The Sanctity of Life Doctrine in Medicine: A Critique.* Oxford: Clarendon Press, 1987.

Law Reform Commission of Canada, Working Paper 46. *Omission, Negligence and Endangering.* Ottawa: Law Reform Commission, 1985.

Law Reform Commission of Canada, Report 20. *Euthanasia, Aiding Suicide and Cessation of Treatment.* Ottawa: Minister of Supply and Services, 1983.

Maguire, Daniel, *Death by Choice.* New York: Doubleday, 1974.

Nova Scotia Medical Consent Act, 1988, c.14, s.1.

Picard, Ellen, and Gerald Robertson. *Legal Liability of Doctors and Hospitals in Canada.* Toronto: Carswell, 1996.

Rosner, F. *Modern Medicine and Jewish Law.* New York: Yeshiva University, 1972.

Schmeiser, Douglas A. "Living Wills and Medical Treatment of the Terminally Ill." *Health Mgt Forum* 2:3 (Fall 1989): 32–37.

Society for the Right to Die. *Handbook of Living Will Laws.* New York: Society for the Right to Die, 1987.

Selected Provincial Government Web Sites for Advance Directives

Alberta Personal Directives Act R.S.A. 2000, c. P-6: **http://www.canlii.org/ab/sta/csa/20030217/r.s.a.2000c.p-6/whole.html**

British Columbia Representation Agreement ct [RSBC 1996], Chapter 405: **http://www.qp.gov.bc.ca/statreg/stat/R/96405_01.htm**

Manitoba Health Care Directives Act, C.C.S.M. c. H27 (1992): **http://www.canlii.org/mb/sta/ccsm/20030910/c.c.s.m.c.h27/whole.html**

New Brunswick: *An Act to Amend the Infirm Persons Act*, Chapter 45: **http://www.gnb.ca/0062/acts/BBA-2000/Chap-45.pdf**

Newfoundland Advance Health Care Directives Act, SNL1995 CHAPTER A-4.1: **http://www.gov.nl.ca/hoa/sr/**

Nova Scotia Medical Consent Act, Chapter 279, Revised Statutes of Nova Scotia, 1989: **http://www.gov.ns.ca/legi/legc/statutes/medcons.htm**

Ontario Health Care Consent Act: **http://192.75.156.68/DBLaws/Statutes/English/96h02_e.htm**

Prince Edward Island Consent to Treatment and Health Care Directives Act, Revised Statutes of Rpicne Edward Island Chapter C-7.2: **http://www.gov.pe.ca/law/statutes/pdf/c-17_2.pdf**

Quebec: *Civil Code of Quebec*, S.Q., 1991, c. 64. Title 2 chapter 1 s 1.11: **http://www.canlii.org/qc/sta/csqc/20030530/c.c.q./part1.html**

Saskatchewan Health Care Directives and Substitute Health Care Decision Makers Act, Chapter H-0.001 (1997) as amended by the Statutes of Saskatchewan, 2000, c.A-5.3: **http://www.canlii.org/sk/sta/cssk/20030227/s.s.1997c.h-0.001/whole.html**

CHAPTER 9
INFORMATION AND MEDICAL TREATMENT

Introduction

The readings in Chapters 6, 7 and 8 deal with some of the major issues that are central to informed consent when providing health care. They focus mainly on the nature and amount of information necessary to making a truly informed choice, with the extent to which we are free to choose what shall happen to us, and with the rights and duties of those who make decisions on our behalf. In that sense, the selections in these chapters focus mainly on what might be called *external information*: on information about outside factors that are essential to making an informed choice. However, the significance of that external information — its implications on a particular occasion — very much depends on the health status of the individual whose health care is supposed to be determined by that choice. For instance, information about the effectiveness of a particular antibiotic means one thing for persons who are immunocompromised, something else for persons who are simply suffering from an uncomplicated infection with no co-morbidities, and something still different for people who are allergic to that particular type of antibiotic. Therefore, in order to be able to make a truly informed choice — to be able to give a truly informed consent — we have to know more than merely the various treatment options that are open to us. We also have to know our own health status and profile.

However, in most cases we can get this sort of knowledge only if we have access to our own health records. That is to say, in most cases we can get this picture only from the records that detail the medically relevant findings that health care professionals — and especially physicians — have made about our health. Patient-rights groups have therefore maintained for some time that since informed consent is not really possible when patients do not know their own health care records, patients should have the right to see their records and to have copies made of them if they so wish.

Traditionally, the organizations that represent health care professionals — in particular, the Canadian Medical Association — have tended to resist this. Among other things, they have argued that these records were never

222

intended for patients, only for the attending physician or for other physicians, and, following the line that a little knowledge is a dangerous thing, they have gone on to say that patients don't know enough about how to interpret these health care records, and therefore would jump to the wrong conclusions. They have also argued that patients might actually be harmed by finding out what is in their records. Physicians cannot allow this to happen. After all, the primary obligation of physicians is to look out for the welfare of their patients. Finally, they have maintained that the patient record belongs to the physicians because it is the physicians who originated it.

If the courts are any indication, Canadian society does not agree with this. We find a graphic illustration of this in the New Brunswick case of *McInerney v. MacDonald*, excerpts from which are included below. This case stipulates that, under normal circumstances, a patient does indeed have the right of access to her or his records. The court's stance on this matter is part of the evolving societal insistence on individual autonomy — an insistence that appears to reflect a deontological ethical perspective.

At the same time, the case does not address a major issue that has been worrying health care professionals ever since the matter was decided by the courts: What if the records contain confidential information about *other* people? Then there is the question about third-party access: For instance, what if a patient gives a lawyer or an insurance company authorization to have access to her or his records? Do the patients really understand what this means? Especially in the case of insurance companies? Should health care professionals worry about this? Should health care institutions? Also, physicians sometimes give pharmaceutical companies access to their patients' records in order to allow the companies to conduct pharmaceutical research. Is this ethically appropriate? *McInerney v. MacDonald* does not address such questions. It may be interesting to explore them in light of the readings in the preceding chapters. (The readings in Chapter 10 may also be relevant in this regard.)

The article by Howard Brody (a physician) deals with an entirely different issue but one that also falls under the heading of information: Health care professionals sometimes deliberately mislead their patients — for example, when they lead their patients to believe that the prescriptions they give them or the treatments they recommend are causally effective for the patients' conditions when actually this is not the case. Sometimes there appear to be good practical reasons for doing this. For instance, when there is nothing physiologically wrong with the patients yet the patients *feel* ill; or, when there is no known treatment that is causally effective, yet there is a chance that the simple fact of prescribing something or of doing something will have a beneficial effect. In these and similar cases, the physicians may be banking on what is known as the *placebo effect* to make the patients feel better or even to produce a cure. That is, they may be hoping that the *psychosomatic effect* of doing something will help the patients. In these cases, information is supplied in a misleading fashion — *but with the best interests of the patient in mind*. And then there is the case of the addict who is convinced that no method of treatment will help.

The physician gradually weakens the injection of morphine with a saline solution — and after a while the patient is completely weaned. Are practices like this unethical? Brody looks at some of the issues that are involved in these and similar cases. His focus is the use of placebos in the therapeutic setting. The issue of placebo use in experimental contexts is explored further by Charles Weijer in Chapter 10, in his article "Placebo Trials and Tribulations." It forms a useful companion piece to Brody's discussion.

McInerney v. MacDonald

The judgement was delivered by Mr. Justice La Forest. ...

The central issue in this case is whether in the absence of legislation a patient is entitled to inspect and obtain copies of his or her medical records upon request. ...

The appellant raises two issues in this appeal: (1) Are a patient's medical records prepared by a physician the property of that physician or are they the property of the patient? (2) If a patient's medical records are the property of the physician who prepares them, does a patient nevertheless have the right to examine and obtain copies of all documents in the physician's medical record, including records that the physician may have received which were prepared by other physicians? ...

I am prepared to accept that the physician, institution or clinic compiling the medical records owns the physical records. This leaves the remaining issue of whether the patient nevertheless has a right to examine and obtain copies of all documents in the physician's medical records. ...

Of primary significance is the fact that the records consist of information that is highly private and personal to the individual. It is information that goes to the personal integrity and autonomy of the patient. ... [S]uch information remains in a fundamental sense one's own, for the individual to communicate or retain as he or she sees fit. ...

A physician begins compiling a medical file when a patient chooses to share intimate details about his or her life in the course of medical consultation. The patient "entrusts" this personal information to the physician for medical purposes. ... [C]ertain duties do arise from the special relationship of trust and confidence between doctor and patient. Among these are the duty of the doctor to act with utmost good faith and loyalty, and to hold information received from or about a patient in confidence. ... When a patient releases personal information in the context of the doctor–patient relationship, he or she does so with the legitimate expectation that these duties will be respected. ...

The fiduciary duty to provide access to medical records is ultimately grounded in the nature of the patient's interest in his or her records. As discussed earlier, information about oneself revealed to a doctor acting in a professional capacity remains, in a fundamental sense, one's own. The doctor's position is one of trust and confidence. The information conveyed is held in a fashion somewhat akin to a trust. While the doctor is the owner of the actual record, the information is to be used by the physician for the benefit of the patient. The confiding of the information to the physician for medical purposes gives rise to an expectation that the patient's interest in and control of the information will continue. ...

The trust-like "beneficial interest" of the patient in the information indicates that, as a general rule, he or she should have a right of access to the information and that the physician should have a corresponding obligation to provide it. The patient's interest being in the information, it follows that the interest continues when that information is conveyed to another doctor who then becomes subject to the duty to afford the patient access to that information.

There is a further matter that militates in favour of disclosure of patient records. As mentioned earlier, one of the duties arising from the doctor–patient relationship is the duty of the doctor to act with utmost good faith and loyalty. If the patient is denied access to his or her records, it may not be possible for the patient to establish that this duty has been fulfilled. As I see it, it is important that the patient have access to the records for the very purposes for which it is sought to withhold the documents, namely, to ensure the proper functioning of the doctor–patient relationship and to protect the well-being of the patient. If there has been improper conduct in the doctor's dealings with his or her patient, it ought to be revealed. The purpose of keeping the documents secret is to promote the proper functioning of the relationship, not to facilitate improper conduct.

Disclosure is all the more important in our day when individuals are seeking more information about themselves. It serves to reinforce the faith of the individual in his or her treatment. The ability of a doctor to provide effective treatment is closely related to the level of trust in the relationship. A doctor is in a better position to diagnose a medical problem if the patient freely imparts personal information. The duty of confidentiality that arises from the doctor–patient relationship is meant to encourage disclosure of information and communication between doctor and patient. In my view, the trust reposed in the physician by the patient mandates that the flow of information operate both ways. ...

While patients should, as a general rule, have access to their medical records, this policy need not and, in my mind, should not be pursued blindly. The related duty of confidentiality is not absolute. ... For example, "there may be cases in which reasons connected with the safety of individuals or of the public, physical or moral, would be sufficiently cogent to supersede or qualify the obligations prima facie imposed by the confidential relation." Similarly, the patient's general right of access to his or her records is not absolute. The patient's interest in his or her records is an equitable interest arising from the physician's fiduciary obligation to disclose the records upon request. As part of the relationship of trust and confidence, the physician must act in the best interests of the patient. If the physician reasonably believes it is not in the patient's best interests to inspect his or her medical records, the physician may consider it necessary to deny access to the information. ... In my view, the onus properly lies on the doctor to justify an exception to the general rule of access. ...

If a physician objects to the patient's general right of access, he or she must have reasonable grounds for doing so. Although I do not intend to provide an exhaustive analysis of the circumstances in which access to medical records may be denied, some general observations may be useful. I shall make these in a response to a number of arguments that have been advanced by the appellant and in the literature for denying a patient access to medical records. These include: (1) disclosure may facilitate the initiation of unfounded lawsuits; (2) the medical records may be meaningless; (3) the medical records may be misinterpreted; (4) doctors may respond by keeping less thorough notes; and (5) disclosure of the contents of the records may be harmful to the patient or a third party.

The argument that patients may commence unfounded litigation if they are permitted to examine their medical records is not a sufficient ground for withholding them. ... Denial of access may actually encourage unfounded lawsuits. If a lawsuit is started, a patient can generally obtain access to his or her records under rules of civil procedure relating to discovery of documents. Thus, if a patient strongly wishes to see his or her records, one way of achieving this result is to commence an action before ascertaining whether or not there is a valid basis for the action. ...

The arguments that the records may be meaningless or that they may be misinterpreted do not justify non-disclosure in the ordinary case. If the records are, in fact, meaningless, they will not help the patient but neither will they cause harm. It is always open to the patient to obtain assistance in understanding the file. ... If it is possible that the patient will misconstrue the information in the record (for example, misinterpret the relevance of a particular laboratory test), the doctor may wish to advise the patient that the medical record should be explained and interpreted by a competent health care professional. ...

The concern that disclosure will lead to a decrease in the completeness, candour and frankness of medical records, can be answered by reference to the obligation of a physician to keep accurate records. A failure to do so may expose the physician to liability for professional misconduct or negligence. It is also easy to exaggerate the importance of this argument. ...

Non-disclosure may be warranted if there is a real potential for harm either to the patient or to a third party. This is the most persuasive ground for refusing access to medical records. However, even here, the discretion to withhold information should not be exercised readily. Particularly in situations that do not involve the interests of third parties, the court should demand compelling grounds before confirming a decision to deny access. ... Non-disclosure can itself affect the patient's well-being. If access is denied, the patient may speculate as to what is in the records and imagine difficulties greater than those that actually exist. In addition, the physical well-being of the patient must be balanced with the patient's right to self-determination. Both are worthy of protection. ...

Since I have held that the tangible records belong to the physician, the patient is not entitled to the records themselves. Medical records play an important role in helping the physician to remember details about the patient's medical history. The physician must have continued access to the records to provide proper diagnosis and treatment. Such access will be disrupted if the patient is able to remove the records from the premises.

Accordingly, the patient is entitled to reasonable access to examine and copy the records, provided the patient pays a legitimate fee for the preparation and reproduction of the information. Access is limited to the information the physician obtained in providing treatment. It does not extend to information arising outside the doctor–patient relationship. ...

The Lie That Heals: The Ethics of Giving Placebos

Howard Brody

The 170-year-long debate in the medical literature about the ethics of prescribing placebos in medical therapeutics needs to be reevaluated in light of recent placebo research and improved understanding of the placebo effect as an integral part of the doctor–patient relationship. It has traditionally been assumed that deception is an indispensible component of successful placebo use. Therefore, placebos have been attacked because they are deceptive, and defended on the grounds that the deception is illusory or that the beneficent intentions of the physician justify the deception. However, a proper understanding of the placebo effect shows that deception need play no essential role in eliciting this powerful therapeutic modality; physicians can use nondeceptive means to promote a positive placebo response in their patients.

The debate over whether it is ethical for physicians to prescribe placebos for patients has surfaced at intervals in the medical literature since the 19th century. Because traditional oaths and codes of ethics are silent on this issue, physicians taking a stand on placebo use have been unable to appeal to authority and have been prompted to develop original and often highly creative moral arguments. Although these arguments deserve review simply as an often-neglected feature of medical history, they also require critical reexamination in light of two recent developments. The first is the awakening of experimental interest in the placebo effect, and a gradual reconceptualization of placebo phenomena to recognize their pervasiveness as part of medical practice.[1] The second is the emphasis in contemporary medical ethics of individual rights and patient autonomy in the doctor–patient relationship,[2–4] leading to the rejection of many paternalistic assumptions previously thought to justify medical deception.[5]

Placebos and the Placebo Effect

"An empiric oftentimes, and a silly chirurgeon, doth more strange cures than a rational physician ... because the patient puts his confidence in him," Robert Burton wrote in 1628,[6] showing that at least by Renaissance times physicians appreciated the power of the imagination and expectation to change bodily states and to cure disease. In 1785 Benjamin Franklin led a commission to investigate Mesmer's animal magnetism and, in a series of elegant experiments, showed that the subjects' imagination was the most important factor in explaining the bizarre effects and miraculous cures attributed to that practice.[7] Physicians were not reluctant to take advantage of this phenomenon by prescribing medications thought to be pharmacologically inert when no specific remedy was indicated. Thomas Jefferson wrote to Dr. Casper Wistar in 1807, "One of the most successful physicians I have ever known, has assured me, that he used more of bread pills,

H. Brody, "The lie that heals: the ethics of giving placebos," *Annals of Internal Medicine* 1982; 97: 112–118.

drops of colored water, and powders of hickory ashes, than of all other medicines put together."[8]

The contemporary era of placebo research began with the adoption of the double-blind controlled trial as the standard experimental method in the 1940s; subsequent findings on the placebo effect have been reviewed extensively.[1,9–13] Whenever a supposedly inert treatment is used in an experimental situation, 30% to 40% of subjects can be expected to show some benefit from the placebo treatment.[9] The pattern of the response to placebo typically resembles the pharmacologic findings of active drug responses.[14] In one study of the effect of both clofibrate and placebo on cholesterol level and cardiovascular mortality, those control subjects who reliably took their placebos showed lower cholesterol and reduced mortality compared with their less compliant counterparts.[15] Placebo response is not limited to the patient's subjective experience; placebos alter laboratory values and other measures of objective physiologic change.[16] Although placebos are commonly thought of primarily as pain relievers, virtually all potentially reversible symptoms and diseases that have been investigated in double-blind studies show some response to placebo — including diabetes,[17] angina pectoris,[18] and malignant neoplasms.[19] Placebos can also cause many of the same side effects seen with active medication.[20,21] For all these reasons it is impossible to use placebo response to distinguish between a real, organic symptom and a symptom that is "all in the patient's head," although the myth to the contrary still persists.[22]

From an early focus on attempting to elucidate the "personality type" of persons who react to placebos (which failed in part because the same person may respond or fail to respond to placebo in different circumstances),[9] attempts to understand placebo phenomena have shifted to a broader approach to factors in the doctor–patient relationship, in the overall situational context, and in the cultural background.[23–29] It has become more clear that whatever happens when a patient gets better after ingesting a sugar pill also happens to some degree whenever the patient receives a pharmacologically potent treatment within a supportive healing relationship; that at least some of the symptom relief that follows administration of the active treatment arises from emotional and symbolic factors. That is, the placebo effect pervades much of medical practice even when no placebo has been used.

For example, when meprobamate, phenobarbital, and placebo were administered blindly to anxious patients, the two pharmacologically active drugs were clearly superior to placebo when administered by a physician who had confidence in the drugs' efficacy and who was viewed by the subjects as supportive; the drugs and placebo showed no difference when administered by a less supportive and more skeptical physician. Subjects of the first physician also showed more overall symptom relief.[30] It is reasonable to suspect, then, that when the family physician prescribes decongestants for a viral upper respiratory infection, some of the patient's symptom relief is due to the pharmacologic action of the drug, but some is also due to the emotional support of the doctor–patient relationship, the doctor's confirmation and legitimization of the illness, and the reassurance that the symptoms do not represent something more serious than a bad cold.

Definitions

The expanded concept of the placebo effect just described makes it undesirable to have the definition of "placebo effect" totally dependent on the definition of "placebo." The following definitions may serve satisfactorily for our purposes: The placebo effect is the change in the patient's condition that is attributable to the symbolic import of the healing intervention rather than to the intervention's specific pharmacologic or physiologic effects; a placebo is a form of medical therapy, or an intervention designed to simulate medical therapy, that is believed to be without specific activity for the condition being treated, and that is used either for its symbolic effect or to eliminate observer bias in a controlled experiment. It is worth recalling here that although the sugar pill is cited as the paradigm case of placebo use, any medical treatment, including such diverse techniques as surgery[31] and biofeedback[32] can function as a placebo.

Another useful distinction uses the terms "pure" and "impure" placebos. A pure placebo, such as a lactose pill or a saline injection, is totally without pharmacologic potency. An impure placebo has some pharmacologic properties, but these are not relevant to the current circumstances and the treatment is used solely for its psychologic effect. Common examples are thyroid, vitamin B12, and penicillin, when used in patients who do not have hypothyroidism, pernicious anemia, or bacterial infections, respectively.

Placebos and Deception

Jefferson said of the use of bread pills and drops of colored water in 1807, "It was certainly a pious fraud."[8] Subsequent writers, including physicians, philosophers, and scientists, have adopted widely divergent positions on the ethics of giving placebos.[33] All authorities, however, are agreed on one point — if there is an ethical problem in therapeutic use of placebos, the problem is that of deception. This agreement in turn arises from a shared assumption about how placebos are typically used in clinical practice, which will be called here the "traditional use" of placebos. In the traditional use, the physician administers a treatment known to him or her to be without pharmacologic potency; but the physician either tells

or allows the patient to believe that the treatment has such potency. It is further assumed in the traditional-use model that the patient's false belief in the potency of the treatment is essential for the placebo effect to occur.[34–36]

Enough has already been said about the recently expanded concept of the placebo effect to call the traditional-use model into question on several counts. However, the bulk of the medical literature on the ethics of placebos accepts this model as a given. Hence, to do justice to most of the arguments offered by physicians for and against placebo use, the traditional-use model must form the point of departure. In a subsequent section, the ethical position that results from replacing the traditional model with the expanded concept will be considered.

It will be most convenient to survey first the arguments offered against placebo use, as these assume that deception is generally wrong, and that it is just as wrong (if indeed not worse) when encountered in medicine as when encountered elsewhere in life. Next, arguments in favor of placebo use can be investigated to see how successfully they defuse the deception issue.

Arguments Against Placebos

It is standard in modern writings on medical ethics to oppose placebo use because it represents a specific instance of the more general issue of patient deception.[2,3,5,37,38] The value of avoiding deception is grounded in the more basic values of the autonomy and dignity of the individual patient. The basic idea is that of moral reciprocity. We generally wish that other people treat us in a manner that shows their respect for us as persons; and this entails that they not use manipulation or deception on us, even if they judge the results to be for our own good. If we are to regard our patients as our moral equals and to respect their dignity as persons, we are similarly prohibited from practicing deception or manipulation on them.

This line of reasoning is most at home in the context of a deontologic or duty-based ethical theory. Deception is condemned because it violates an *a priori* moral rule — *a priori* because the rule appeals to the very nature of our beings (that is, persons deserving respect) rather than to the good or bad consequences of our actions. Appeal to duty and to moral rule has always been a popular mode of argument. Thus one medical editor[39] wrote in 1885, "Physicians … cannot always tell the plain truth to a patient without injuring him. It should be the rule of … life, however, to be straightforward and candid. Therefore, we say that placebos should be … rarely, if ever, prescribed." Describing the characteristics of the trustworthy and virtuous physician, the writer concluded, "We venture to say that such a man would not find it necessary to keep a polychromatic assortment of sugar pills in his closet."

This commentator explicitly rejects an argument from consequences — at times, indeed, being truthful may injure patients. But more basic than negative consequences is the *a priori* "rule of … life," which in the 19th century was closely tied to concepts of virtue and gentlemanly conduct, and hence truthfulness.

Other physicians, however, have been uncomfortable with *a priori* appeals and have preferred a utilitarian mode of argument, demanding to be shown that placebo use, generally applied, would lead to a net increase in unhappiness over happiness for all concerned. Among many adopting a utilitarian stand, the most articulate and forceful was Richard C. Cabot, best known today as originator of the clinicopathologic conferences of the Massachusetts General Hospital, but in his day an innovative writer on medical ethics as well as on medicine, and holder of the Chair of Professor of Social Ethics

at Harvard University in addition to his medical appointment.[40] Cabot[41] rejected an *a priori* approach to issues of truth and falsehood — "you will notice I am not now arguing that a lie is, in itself and apart from its consequences, a bad thing" — but felt that the negative consequences of placebo use condemned the practice. The obvious short-range consequence occurred when the patient discovered the deception and lost trust in the physician. True, it was probable in any single case that the physician would not be found out; but Cabot[41] rejoined, "Is it good for us as professional men to have our reputations rest on the expectation of not being found out?"

But Cabot[41] was much more concerned about the long-range consequences of creating unhealthy public attitudes toward medicine and medications:

The majority of placebos are given because we believe that the patient will not be satisfied without them. He has learned to expect medicine for every symptom and without it he simply won't get well. True, but who taught him to expect a medicine for every symptom? He was not born with that expectation. He learned it from an ignorant doctor who really believed it. … It is we physicians who are responsible for perpetuating false ideas about disease and its cure … and with every placebo that we give we do our part in perpetuating error, and harmful error at that.

Cabot elsewhere[42] stated even more bluntly, "Placebo giving is quackery." He concluded[41] that in general the negative consequences of placebo use outweighed the positive; but that placebos could be justified in some rare cases:

No patient whose language you can speak, whose mind you can approach, needs a placebo. I give placebos now and then … to Armenians and others with whom I cannot communicate, because to refuse to give them would create more misunderstandings, a falser impression, than to give them. The patient will think that I am refusing to treat him at all; but if I can get hold of an interpreter and explain the matter, I tell him no lies in the shape of placebos.

Another more recent commentator reflected on both the occasional justification for giving placebos, and the rarity with which such a case ought to arise: "Some patients are so unintelligent, neurotic, and inadequate as to be incurable, and life is made easier for them by a placebo." Then, paraphrasing an earlier commentator,[43] he concluded: "It has been said that the use of placebos is in inverse ratio to the combined intelligences of patient and doctor."[44]

In assessing the consequences of placebo use as a general policy, one should note the tendency of deception to multiply itself, and the need to cover up for the original lie. Prescribing placebos now involves insuring the complicity of the nurse, the pharmacist, and all other parties to the prescription. There is also the problem of setting a fee for the placebo prescription — if too high, then someone will appear to be making an unjustified profit from deception; if too low, the deception may inadvertently be discovered. It may be more for such mundane reasons and not out of any increased ethical insight that the use of totally inert medicines like lactose pills has declined once physicians stopped dispensing their own drugs. In more recent times, fear of lawsuits may also have played a role.

Arguments for Placebos

Deceptive or not, placebos have in fact been widely administered by practicing physicians, and to many the fascinating power of the body to respond to purely symbolic interventions seemed too potent a therapeutic tool to pass up. A number of commentators have tried to give a formal justification for placebo use. Once again, two general moral approaches have been used. For the deontologist, the force of the moral rule against deception cannot be denied; so it must be argued either that the deception rule does not properly apply to the placebo case, or that other moral rules may mitigate it. The utilitarian may calculate all the good consequences attributable to placebos, and argue (or assume) that these outweigh the evils of deception. For each of these attempts at justification, however, the placebo opponents have had a ready and generally persuasive reply.

First, one may forthrightly deny that placebo use need involve deception by the physician. This position, while occasionally alluded to,[45] is seldom stated explicitly in the medical literature; but it is frequently encountered in debate and discussion among physicians. It is usually argued that if the physician tells the patient that a sugar pill is morphine or penicillin, he is guilty of an outright and unethical lie. But if he administers the pill with a noncommittal statement, such as, "This pill will make you feel much better," he has not deceived the patient; any false beliefs result from the patient's deceiving himself and are not the moral responsibility of the physician: "should a patient become suspicious ... the therapist need only give an honest evasion, rather than a lie."[36]

Richard Cabot[41] attacked this and other arguments defending medical practices that mislead the patient by stating, *"a true impression*, not certain words literally true, is what we must try to convey." By way of fleshing out Cabot's objection, it may be acknowledged that what counts as deception may be dependent on the norms and expectations associated with particular social settings. For instance, when we go to the theater and see Mark Twain reading from *Huckleberry Finn*, we do not consider ourselves to have been deceived when we discover he is a cleverly made-up actor. We may then ask whether the clinical setting is one of those special social situations where creating a false impression by deliberate misdirection does not count as deception. Cabot appears to have assumed that a patient may reasonably expect in that setting that, if a drug or other treatment is given, it is selected for its pharmacologic potency for the patient's condition. It also seems reasonable to assume that the patient will not expect that the physician will specifically name the treatment — the patient is accustomed to receiving pills alluded to by the physician merely as "an antibiotic" or "a decongestant," but these remedies are still assumed by the patient to be pharmacologically potent. One may then conclude that if the physician prescribes an inert pill and conceals this from the patient by verbal misdirection, he has violated these legitimate patient expectations and is guilty of deception; the special nature of the clinical setting gives no license for creating a false impression in this manner.

Legal backing[46] for Cabot's argument comes with the characterization of the physician–patient relationship as a fiduciary one, in which one party assumes a special responsibility to look out for the best interests of the other. "Where a person sustains toward others a relation of trust and confidence, his silence when he should speak, or his failure to disclose what he ought to disclose, is as much a fraud in law as an actual affirmative false representation."[47]

Still, the physician is not responsible for false beliefs the patient may bring into the encounter, if the physician has taken no action to cause those beliefs;[48,49] how far the physician's duty extends to dispel those false beliefs, if they do not lead directly to health-threatening behavior, is an interesting ethical question in itself. What is the physician's duty toward the patient who arrives with a firmly entrenched belief in the therapeutic and preventive powers of vitamins, and asks the physician to recommend a good daily vitamin supplement? This patient harbors a false belief, and energetic and prolonged discussion from the physician might mitigate or dispel it. But this reeducation seems hardly worth the effort, given the low probability of harm and the (presumed) low readiness of the patient to assimilate the new information. Thus the postulated duty not to create false beliefs in the patient by one's words or actions need not imply a more onerous duty to seek out and dispel all the false beliefs the patient may have acquired elsewhere.

Second, the placebo advocate may admit that placebos as traditionally used involve deception, but still insist that this use is ethically justified. Social practice recognizes a class of deceptions called white lies, which are felt to be essentially harmless because of their innocuous content and benign motivation.[50] Even if the special circumstances of medical practice do not automatically permit out-and-out deception, it still seems to be the case that many partial truths or euphemisms are appropriate. For example, proper supportive care of the cancer patient seeking some hope to mitigate the frightening diagnosis calls for a somewhat slanted presentation emphasizing the potential gains from therapy, not merely for a listing of the 5-year survival statistics.

But a problem in including placebos in the category of white lies is that what counts as a white lie is fairly well demarcated by social convention; otherwise anyone uttering a falsehood, however blatant, could excuse his act by claiming it was "only a white lie." Members of society are thus in effect forewarned about this practice and, if they choose to ask their friends how their new hats or ties look on them, they can be said to have given at least implied consent to any white lie that results. By contrast, the traditional-use model assumes that knowledge of the lie will be restricted to the medical profession, lest placebos lose their effectiveness with wider publicity. Recipients of the so-called white lie are therefore systematically excluded from any knowledge of the existence of this practice, and they have no opportunity to challenge questionable uses of placebo deception by reference to generally accepted social norms and limits. This would make placebo use morally suspect in a way that the usual white lies are not.

Leslie[51] attempted to justify placebo deception in a similar fashion: "There is a fine line of distinction between the words, *deception* and *deceit* ... deceit implies blameworthiness whereas deception does not necessarily do so. ..." Leslie emphasized the benign intent of the physician and offered as an analogy a magician practicing sleight of hand to entertain an audience. But Bok[50] has emphasized that the supposedly benign intent of the person doing the lying, and the expected value of the resulting benefits, often look very different from the perspective of the person being lied to. The audience choosing voluntarily to witness the magician's performance can weigh for themselves the degree of deception, the intent, and the value of the benefits; the patient in the traditional-use model of placebos is denied this opportunity. (It may in fact be argued that the magic show is not "deception" at all, as any reasonably well informed person knows what goes on at such events and is not fooled in any substantive way.) Thus, Leslie is either merely asserting that some deceptions are justified and others are not, without giving any arguments to prove that placebos belong in the justified category; or else his "fine line" between deception and deceit is so fine as to escape attention altogether.

All this discussion of justified and unjustified deception, however, may seem pointless to the pragmatic physician who adopts the traditional use of placebos merely because it can benefit the patient. By this pragmatic view, either the physi-

cian's duty not to deceive is of no moral concern at all, or else it is far outweighed by the much stronger duty to benefit the patient — a duty which, Veatch[38] has argued, has dominated the so-called Hippocratic ethical tradition in medicine to the unwarranted exclusion of other, equally rational moral considerations. This view has gained added impetus since the recent wave of research described above, showing the extent and frequency of placebo responses. The pragmatic approach has been further bolstered by research linking the placebo response to endorphins.[52] Because endorphins function primarily in analgesia, and because, as was noted above, the placebo response is not limited to pain, this endorphin research really provides a very limited account of the physiologic means by which placebos may exert their effects. But to the uncritical medical mind, the identified biochemical basis for some placebo responses has somehow made the whole placebo issue suddenly respectable. (Shapiro[53] discovered in an informal survey that negativism toward placebo use among physicians correlated with greater age, private rather than academic practice, and nonparticipation in clinical research.)

In this setting, the placebo advocate may attribute, rightly or wrongly, several false beliefs to the person who argues against placebo use. The opponent of placebos may be thought to believe: that placebos really do not work, or work only for a limited number of medical conditions; that some pharmacologically active remedy exists for all conditions, so that the doctor who prescribes a placebo is automatically withholding the "correct" drug; or that any treatment that works by psychologic mechanisms is thereby inferior to a treatment that works by biochemical means. As we saw, ethical concern over placebos does not depend on any of these false assumptions, yet placebo opponents are still sometimes labeled as if their arguments ran contrary to modern scientific medicine. It may have been a mistaken attribution of these false beliefs that led a distinguished investigator of the placebo response[54] to characterize as "oft-quoted but fatuous" one of the better recent papers[55] offering arguments of the sort first used by Cabot.

One could, of course, offer a utilitarian counter-attack to Cabot[41] and contend that he had miscalculated the likelihood and the severity of the various consequences of placebo use. But any balanced view of the pros and cons makes this a remote possibility. First, if past studies are reliable, only 30% to 40% of patients will respond to placebo positively. Second, even though lactose can be expected to have fewer toxic effects than active drugs, placebo side effects and even addiction do periodically occur. Finally, even if one rejects these considerations, one is still left with the long-range consequences Cabot predicted — a public conditioned to look for the cure for all ills in a bottle of medicine, and to neglect prevention and a healthy lifestyle in favor of a medical quick fix.

But most pragmatic authors do not even attempt a balanced utilitarian consideration. If anything, they are content with a crude risk-benefit ratio: Anything that benefits the patient is good; placebos have been shown in scientific trials to benefit patients; therefore, placebos should be used, at least in selected sorts of cases. A frequent hidden assumption is that the only harm worth considering in this crude pragmatic calculus is direct physical harm such as that due to a toxic drug reaction. Less tangible harms — risks to doctor–patient trust, unhealthy views about drug-taking, and decreased opportunity for the patient to make choices about his own care — are simply left out of the equation.[34,36,43,56-65] The nature of the risk-benefit calculus is further illustrated by those authors who list specific contraindications or limitations for placebo use,[33,34,51] for instance, the concern that overuse of placebos will lead to diminished diagnostic vigilance[57] or that the placebo-treated patient will

be more resistant to definitive psychotherapy.[66]

Placebo use may thus be cautiously endorsed because of its success, without raising ethical qualms:

> I knew a surgeon years ago who thought nothing of performing an oblique lower right quadrant incision, then suturing without entering the abdominal cavity in patients who had emotional problems manifested by pain in the abdomen. His results were excellent and as one might expect his operative mortality and morbidity were exceptionally low. ... Certainly this is not common and I doubt whether anyone else would have done such procedures. However, I am certain that thousands of appendectomies and hysterectomies are done yearly as placebos. In retrospect, though at the time I was horrified at what he had done, and still am aware of the possible grave consequence, I am inclined to admire his courage.[63]

The unnecessary-surgery argument indicates that the less scientifically inclined physician may inadvertently use therapy that actually can benefit the patient only through the placebo effect. One may then argue that it is better for the physician to use a pure placebo rather than an impure placebo. Prescribing pure placebos at least promotes full knowledge (for the physician, at least) of the approach being taken; impure placebos promote unscientific medicine and expose the patient to increased risk of toxic reactions.[43,57,60]

> If deception is involved in the case of the pure placebo, it applies to only one person, namely, the patient, for the physician knows that the agent is devoid of all but psychotherapeutic properties. But when we use [an impure placebo] there is the danger

of deceiving two people. ... The doctor may come to think that the agent has potency when, in fact, it has none. That danger is real. ...[67]

Other authors are vaguely concerned about the deception issue but feel it to be merely a semantic problem: "If placebo therapy is regarded as a form of deception, then, of course, an ethical dilemma arises.... What is needed is a redefinition of placebo or nonspecific effects in psychologic or psychotherapeutic terms."[27] "If we give patients a placebo as an honest psychotherapeutic device, we can be considered fulfilling [our] primary responsibility."[63] But just because a substance is used for its symbolic properties does not eliminate the possibility of morally blameworthy deception:

> We like to think that our patients bring us their symptoms and problems for our consideration, expecting thoughtful and honest advice. With ... the declining influence of the Church, the doctor's value to the community as an impartial and educated adviser has become as important as the priest's used to be. The placebo is a form of deception and a betrayal of trust equivalent to the sale of bottles of ditch-water as water of the River Jordan.[44]

There is, however, another form of defense for placebos that does not look at a weighing of the good and bad consequences, but rather at the nature of the implied expectations in the doctor–patient relationship. Placebo use is unjustified if the patient's proper expectation is "that the physician will give me the chance to be informed about the treatment"; but not if the expectation is "that the physician will choose on my behalf the treatment most likely to help." Thus it is argued that placebo use "does not amount to deception of the patient who trusts the doctor to order whatever he considers is most likely to be of benefit."[45]

There is nothing illogical about an expectation that gives the physician this extensive a blank check. But it is unlikely that most patients have such an expectation, at least in modern times, and specifically in relation to placebos. On the contrary, the indignation with which most people respond on learning they have received placebos surreptitiously is strong evidence against any widespread acceptance of this much paternalism. An individual patient, of course, may negotiate such an arrangement with his or her physician; but that hardly justifies the blanket attribution of paternalistic expectations to patients generally.

An Alternative Position: Placebo Effect Without Deception

Of all the positions above, opposition to placebo use unless there are especially strong extenuating circumstances in a specific case is ethically most sound; the other positions either evade the deception issue or fail to disarm its legitimate force. But one must recall that all of these arguments assume the traditional-use model, which holds that the deception is an essential ingredient for successful placebo treatment. The considerations noted at the beginning of this paper, however, based on newer placebo research and appropriate redefinition of the terms "placebo effect" and "placebo," point the way to an effective separation of deception and the placebo effect in clinical practice. Once deception is eliminated (and not merely glossed over) the ethical problem is defused.

One excellent and commonplace example of nondeceptive use of placebos occurs in properly designed double-blind research with informed consent. The research subject is ignorant as to whether he or she is actually receiving placebo or the experimental drug; but he or she has been fully informed of the experimental design, about the use of placebos in the study, and about the risks and benefits associated with the design. If free consent is given based on that information, no deception has occurred and all the criteria for ethical research have been met. Unfortunately there are a few experiments, more commonly occurring in social science research, where deception about the nature of the experimental design is essential if the data are to be valid. Whether and with what consent arrangements such studies may be ethically conducted requires additional analysis.[68]

The first empirical rejection of the traditional-use model of the placebo response was a nonblind placebo trial.[69] Thirteen of 14 psychiatric outpatients with somatic symptoms who completed a week's trial of sugar pills, having been openly informed that they were sugar pills and that many patients experienced relief with such medication, experienced objective symptom reduction. Such a study, of course, has severe limitations, and this work has not been replicated. But a more recent survey of placebo therapeutics gives several case reports of successful placebo therapy in patients who were openly informed that they were receiving pharmacologically inert substances.[70] Furthermore, Norman Cousins,[71] in describing the response of his mysterious connective tissue disease to a combination of high-dose ascorbic acid, laughter, and positive thinking, commented, "It is quite possible that this treatment — like everything else I did — was a demonstration of the placebo effect." Here is anecdotal testimony that a well-informed patient may be aware of the mental or symbolic effect of a therapy and still experience major bodily changes.

Whereas possibilities for nondeceptive use of placebos are theoretically intriguing and are of some limited clinical applicability, the nondeceptive use of the placebo effect has much more important practical implications, because some element of the placebo effect exists in every clinical encounter even when no placebo is used.[1,23,25,28,29] An analysis of the symbolic elements of the physician–patient relationship suggests that a clinical approach that makes the illness experience more understandable to the patient, that instills a sense of caring and social support, and that increases a feeling of mastery and control over the course of the illness, will be most likely to create a positive placebo response and to improve symptoms.[24,26,29] Empirical support for this thesis is provided by a study of the effect of the anesthesiology pre-operative visit on postoperative pain. The control group received a standard visit whereas the experimental group received teaching about the nature of postoperative pain, advice on simple techniques to avoid pain and increase relaxation, and reassurance that back-up medication was available from the nurses. The experimental group required half as much pain medication and were able to be discharged an average of 2 days earlier. These investigators[72] — who used no inert substances and who committed no deceptions on the subjects — described their results as illustrating "a placebo effect without a placebo." Once clinicians realize the extent to which simple information and encouragement can elicit a positive placebo response and thus supplement the pharmacologic effects of any active medication, the perceived need to use deception or inert medication in clinical practice ought to be markedly diminished.

Conclusion

The placebo, as traditionally used, could be called the lie that heals. But a satisfactory understanding of the nature of the placebo effect shows that the healing comes not from the lie itself, but rather from the relationship between healer and patient, and the latter's own capacity for self-healing via symbolic and psychological approaches as well as via biological intervention.

For some time medical science has looked almost exclusively at technical means of diagnosis and treatment; the doctor–patient relationship that forms the setting for their application has been naïvely viewed as a noncontributory background factor, relegated to the amorphous realm of the "art of medicine," or simply ignored. In this setting, the placebo effect has inevitably been viewed as a nuisance variable, interfering with our ability to elicit "clean data" from clinical trials; and deception in medicine has been seen either as an unimportant side issue or as a tolerated means toward another end. But, as the doctor–patient relationship is rediscovered as a worthy focus for medical research and medical education, the placebo effect assumes center stage as one approach to a more sophisticated understanding of this relationship.[73] Deception is avoided, as ethically inappropriate and as a threat to the long-term stability of the relationship; and clinicians turn to alternative, nondeceptive ways to elicit positive placebo responses in all patient encounters at the same time that they apply the most appropriate medical technology.

Notes

1. Brody, H. *Placebos and the Philosophy of Medicine*. Chicago: University of Chicago Press; 1980.

2. Beauchamp, T.H., Childress, J.F. *Principles of Biomedical Ethics*. New York: Oxford University Press; 1979.

3. Brody, H. *Ethical Decisions in Medicine*, 2nd ed. Boston: Little, Brown & Co.; 1981.

4. Buchanan, A. Medical paternalism. *Philosophy and Public Affairs*. 1978;7:370–90.

5. Reiser, S.J. Words as scalpels: Transmitting evidence in the clinical dialogue. *Ann Intern Med*. 1980;92:837–42.

6. Burton, R. *The Anatomy of Melancholy*. New York: Empire State Book Co.; 1924:168.

7. *Report of Dr. Benjamin Franklin and Other Commissioners Charged by the King of France with the Examination of the Animal Magnetism, As Now Practised at Paris*. London: J. Johnson; 1785. Fabin's Bibliotecha Americana, microcard #25 579.

8. Ford P.L., ed. *The Writings of Thomas Jefferson*. Vol. IX. New York: Putnam; 1898:78–85.

9. Beecher, H.K. The powerful placebo. *JAMA*. 1955;159:1602–6.

10. Kurland, A.A. Placebo effect. In: Uhr, L., Millar, J.G., eds. *Drugs and Behavior*. New York: John Wiley; 1960:156–65.

11. Berg, A.O. Placebos: A brief review for family physicians. *J Fam Pract*. 1977;5:97–100.

12. Shapiro, A.K., Morris, L.A. The placebo effect in medical and psychological therapies. In Garfield, S.L., Bergin, A.E., eds. *Handbook of Psychotherapy and Behavior Change*. 2nd ed. New York: John Wiley; 1978.

13. Turner, J.L., Gallimore, R., Fox, C. *Placebo: An Annotated Bibliography*. Available from: UCLA, Neuropsychiatric Institute, Center for the Health Sciences, 760 Westwood Plaza, Los Angeles, CA 90024.

14. Lasagna, L., Laties, V.G., Dohan, J.L. Further studies on the "pharmacology" of placebo administration. *J Clin Invest*. 1958;37:533–7.

15. The Coronary Drug Project Research Group. Influence of adherence to treatment and response of cholesterol on mortality in the Coronary Drug Project. *N Engl J Med*. 1980;303:1038–41.

16. Wolf, S. Effects of suggestion and conditioning on the action of chemical agents in human subjects — the pharmacology of placebos. *J Clin Invest*. 1950;29:100–9.

17. Singer, D.L., Hurwitz, D. Long-term experience with sulfonylureas and placebo. *N Engl J Med*. 1967;277:450–6.

18. Benson, H., McCallie, D.P. Angina pectoris and the placebo effect. *N Engl J Med*. 1979;300:1424–9.

19. Klopfer, B. Psychological variables in human cancer. *J Projective Techniques*. 1957;21:331–40.

20. Wolf, S., Pinsky, R.H. Effects of placebo administration and occurrence of toxic reactions. *JAMA*. 1954;155:339–41.

21. Honzak, R., Horackova, E., Culik, A. Our experience with the effect of placebo in some functional and psychosomatic disorders. *Activitas Nervosa Superior*. 1972;14:184–5.

22. Goodwin, J.S., Goodwin, J.M., Vogel, A.V. Knowledge and use of placebos by house officers and nurses. *Ann Intern Med*. 1979;91:106–10.

23. Modell, W. *The Relief of Symptoms*. Philadelphia: WB Saunders; 1955.

24. Adler, H.M., Hammett, V.B.O. The doctor–patient relationship revisited: An analysis of the placebo effect. *Ann Intern Med*. 1973;78:595–8.

25. Benson, H., Epstein, M.D. The placebo effect: A neglected asset in the care of patients. *JAMA*. 1975;232:1225–7.

26. Cassell, E.J. *The healer's art: A new approach to the doctor–patient relationship*. Philadelphia: J.B. Lippincott; 1976.

27. Gallimore, R., Turner, J.L. Contemporary studies of placebo phenomena. In: Jarvik, M.E., ed. *Psychopharmacology in the Practice of Medicine*. New York: Appleton-Century-Crofts; 1977:45–57.

28. Silber, T.J. Placebo therapy: The ethical dimension. *JAMA*. 1979;242:245–6.

29. Brody, H., Waters, D.B. Diagnosis is treatment. *J Fam Pract*. 1980;10:445–9.

30. Uhlenhuth, E.H., Canter, A., Neustadt, J.O., Payson, H.E. The symptomatic relief of anxiety with meprobamate, phenobarbital, and placebo. *Am J Psychiatry*. 1959;115:905–10.

31. Beecher, H.K. Surgery as placebo: A quantitative study of bias. *JAMA*. 1961;176:1102–7.

32. Stroebel, E.F., Glueck, B.C. Biofeedback treatment in medicine and psychiatry: An ultimate placebo? *Semin Psychiatry*. 1973;5:379–93.

33. Shapiro, A.K. Attitudes toward the use of placebos in treatment. *J Nerv Ment Dis*. 1960;130:200–9.

34. Abramowitz, E.W. The use of placebos in the local therapy of skin diseases. *NY State J Med*. 1948;48:1927–30.

35. Hofling, C.K. The place of placebos in medical practice. *GP*. 1955;11(6):103–7.

36. Fischer, H.K., Dlin, B.M. The dynamics of placebo therapy: A clinical study. *Am J Med Sci*. 1956;232:504–12.

37. Simmons, B. Problems in deceptive medical procedures: An ethical and legal analysis of the administration of placebos. *J Med Ethics*. 1978;4:172–81.

38. Veatch, R.M. *A Theory of Medical Ethics*. New York: Basic Books; 1981.

39. Placebos. *Med Record*. 1885;27:576–7.

40. Burns, C.R. Richard Clarke Cabot and reformation in American medical ethics. *Bull Hist Med*. 1977;51:353–68.

41. Cabot, R.C. The use of truth and falsehood in medicine: An experimental study. *Am Med*. 1903;5:344–9.

42. Cabot, R.C. The physician's responsibility for the nostrum evil. *JAMA*. 1906;47:982–3.

43. Platt, R. Two essays on the practice of medicine. *Lancet*. 1947;253:305–7.

44. Handfield-Jones, R.P.C. A bottle of medicine from the doctor. *Lancet*. 1953;265:823–5.

45. Placebo therapy. *Practitioner*. 1964;192:590.

46. Brody, H. The physician–patient contract: Ethical and legal aspects. *J Legal Med*. 1976;4:25–30.

47. *Perkins v. First National Bank of Atlanta*. 143 SE 2d 474: Georgia; 1975.

48. McDermott, J.F. A specific placebo effect encountered in the use of dexedrine in hyperactive child. *Am J Psychiatry*. 1965;121:923–4.

49. Cassel, C., Jameton, A.L. Power of the placebo: A dialog on principles and practice. *Art of Medication*. 1980;1(3):22–7.

50. Bok, S. *Lying: Moral Choice in Public and Private Life*. New York: Pantheon; 1978.

51. Leslie, A. Ethics and the practice of placebo therapy. *Am J Med*. 1954;16:854–62.

52. Levine, J.D., Gordon, N.C., Fields, H.L. The mechanism of placebo analgesia. *Lancet*. 1978;2:654–7.

53. Shapiro, A.K. The use of placebos: A study of ethics and physicians' attitudes. *Psychiatry in Med*. 1973;4:17–29.

54. Lasagna, L. The powerful cipher. *The Sciences*. 1980;20(20):31–2.

55. Bok, S. The ethics of giving placebos. *Sci Am*. 1974;231(5):17–23.

56. Carter, A.B. The placebo: Its use and abuse. *Lancet*. 1953;265:823.

57. The humble humbug [Editorial]. *Lancet*. 1954;267:321.

58. Wayne, E.J. Placebos [Abstract]. *Br Med J*. 1956;2:157.

59. Lasagna, L. Placebos. *Sci Am*. 1956;193(7):68–71.

60. Koteen, H. Use of a "double-blind" study investigating the clinical merits of a new tranquilizing agent. *Ann Intern Med*. 1957;47:978–89.

61. Atkinson, E.C. Dummy tablets [letter]. *Br Med J*. 1958;1:1478.

62. Branson, H.K., Ward, R. The place of the placebo in geriatric nursing. *Hosp Management*. 1964:98(6):34, 37.

63. Shure, N. The placebo in allergy. *Ann Allergy*. 1965;23:368–76.

64. Thrift, C.B., Traut, E.F. Further studies on placebo management of skeletal disease. *Ill Med J*. 1966;129:683–5.

65. Sicé, J. Evaluating medication [Letter]. *Lancet*. 1972;2:651.

66. Salfield, D.J. The placebo. *Lancet*. 1953;265:940.

67. Wolff, H.G., DuBois, E.F., Cattell, M., et al. Conferences on therapy: The use of placebos in therapy. *NY State J Med*. 1946;46:1718–27.

68. Soble, A. Deception in social science research: Is informed consent possible? *Hastings Cen Rep*. 1978;8(October):40–6.

69. Park, L.C., Covi, L. Nonblind placebo trial: An exploration of neurotic outpatients' response to placebo when its inert content is disclosed. *Arch Gen Psychiatry*. 1965;12:336–45.

70. Vogel, A.V., Goodwin, J.S., Goodwin, J.M. The therapeutics of placebo. *Am Fam Physician*. 1980;22(1):105–9.

71. Cousins, N. Anatomy of an illness (as perceived by the patient). *N Engl J Med*. 1976;295:1458–63.

72. Egbert, L.D., Battit, G.E., Welch, C.E., Bartlett, M.K. Reduction of postoperative pain by encouragement and instruction of patients. *N Engl J Med*. 1964;270:825–7.

73. Jensen, P.S. The doctor–patient relationship: Headed for impasse or improvement? *Ann Intern Med*. 1981;95:769–71.

Further Readings

Burack, J.H., A.L. Back, and R.A. Pearlman. "Provoking Nonepileptic Seizures: The Ethics of Deceptive Diagnostic Testing." *Hastings Center Rep* 27:4 (July–Aug. 1997): 24–33.

Halpern S.D., and J.H. Karlawish. "Placebo-Controlled Trials Are Unethical in Clinical Hypertension Research." *Arch Intern Med*. 160:20 (Nov. 13, 2000): 3167–3169.

Harrington, A., ed. *The Placebo Effect: An Interdisciplinary Exploration*. Cambridge, MA: Harvard Univ. Press, 1999.

Howe, E.G. "Deceiving Patients for Their Own Good." *J of Clin Ethics* 8:3 (Fall 1997): 211–216.

Jospe, M. *The Placebo Effect in Healing*. Lexington, MA: Health, 1978.

Kluge, E.-H.W. "Placebos: Some Ethical Considerations." *CMAJ* 142:4 (1990): 293–295.

Lipkin, M. "Suggestion and Healing." *Perspectives in Biology and Medicine* 20 (1984): 121–126.

Macklin, R. "The Ethical Problems with Sham Surgery in Clinical Research." *N Engl J Med*. 341:13 (Sept. 23, 1999): 992–996.

Mallary, S.D., B. Gert, and C.M. Culver. "Family Coercion and Valid Consent." *Theoret Med* 7:2 (June 1986): 123–126.

Markus, A.C., "The Ethics of Placebo Prescribing." *Mt Sinai J Med* 67:2 (Mar. 2000):140–143.

Parks, L.C., and L. Covi. "Non-blind Placebo Trials." *Arch Gen Psych* 124 (1965): 334–345.

Rushton, C.H. "Placebo Pain Medication: Ethical and Legal Issues." *Pediatric Nursing* 21:2 (Mar.–Apr. 1995): 166–168.

Shapiro, A.K., and E. Shapiro. *The Powerful Placebo: From Ancient Priest to Modern Physician*. Baltimore, MD: Johns Hopkins Univ. Press, 1997.

Spiro, H.K. *Doctors, Patients and Placebos*. New Haven: Yale Univ. Press, 1986. 33.

Welie, J.V.M. "Placebo Treatment." *Encyclo of App Ethics*, Vol. 3. Ed. R. Chadwick. San Diego, Calif.: Academic Press, 1998. 493–502.

CHAPTER 10
RESEARCH AND EXPERIMENTATION INVOLVING COMPETENT PERSONS

Introduction

Patients expect their health care providers to prescribe validated therapies with known outcomes and well-documented side effects. However, sometimes this is not possible if there are no established protocols; sometimes the only thing the professional can do is recommend something that is innovative or experimental in nature. In this sort of situation, we are dealing with what is usually referred to as *therapeutic experimentation*. Here the primary aim is to benefit the patient. Therapeutic experimentation raises a distinctive set of issues that centre around questions like: How should the experimental or innovative protocol be presented? How much information should be disclosed? May the treating health care professional also be the person who has designed the experimental protocol? May the patient ever be deceived about the situation? Does experimentation with competent patients require protocols different from experimentation with incompetent patients such as the mentally challenged, the demented elderly or young children? What about people who are dying — are they really capable of giving free consent when they may well be grasping at straws? What about randomization in clinical trials — or the use of placebos?

These questions become especially difficult when the primary aim of a particular protocol is not to advance the welfare of the patient but to advance knowledge — in other words, when we are dealing with *non-therapeutic* research or experimentation. Non-therapeutic experimentation is necessary because it is one of the few ways in which medicine can increase its knowledge base and develop new treatment modalities.

In the popular mind, the phrases "human experimentation" and "research on human subjects" are closely associated with the atrocities that were committed by German and Japanese physicians on captive populations before and during World War II. As violations of basic ethics, these experiments rival anything that has been done to human beings in the name of science. However, German and Japanese physicians were not the only ones who performed unethical human experiments. In the U.S., there was the infamous *Tuskeegee Experiment* — the longest-running experiment in medical history (1932–1972) whose aim was to identify the effects of untreated syphilis — and the *Willowbrook Study* in the 1970s, which involved deliberately infecting mentally challenged children with hepatitis in order to see whether gamma globulin would constitute a beneficial treatment. In Canada, there was the brainwashing experiment conducted by Dr. Cameron and his colleagues at the Allen Memorial Institute of McGill University in the 1950s for the CIA, and the chemical warfare experiments performed on Canadian soldiers at Suffield, Alberta, in the 1940s.

Collectively, these experiments, when they became known, evoked a storm of condemnation. To prevent such atrocities from ever being committed again, codes of experimental ethics were formulated. The first code of research and experimental ethics was the so-called *Nuremberg Code*. It was formulated in 1948 and subsequently refined and updated by the World Medical Association in 1964 in its *Declaration of Helsinki* (revised in 1975, 1983, 1989 and 1996). In 1996, the WHO, going beyond merely medical experiments, formulated the *Guidelines for Good Clinical Practice for Trials on Pharmaceutical Products*, and in 1997 the Council of Europe passed the *Convention on Human Rights and Biomedicine*. These codes were intended to govern research and experimentation in both the private and the public sector. They provided — and still provide — the standards against which the conduct of researchers is measured on the international stage. Nowadays, most countries also have their own bodies that formulate more detailed research ethics standards, and no granting agency will provide funds for, and no reputable scientific journal will publish the results of, any research that does not meet the standards that are contained in these codes.

In Canada, the standards for federally funded projects involving research with human subjects were originally set by the Medical Research Council of Canada.[1] However, it soon became obvious that research with human beings could not be readily divided into medical as opposed to engineering or socially oriented research: the areas frequently overlap. Consequently, in the 1990s, the Medical Research Council of Canada, the Natural Sciences and Engineering Research Council of Canada, and the Social Sciences and Humanities Research Council of Canada formed a combined working group and developed an integrated set of guidelines. After years of consultation, these guidelines were published in 1996. They were amended, updated and published in 1999 as the Tri-Council Policy Statement *Ethical Conduct for Research Involving Humans*. The guidelines that are contained in this Policy Statement are binding on all publicly funded research institutions in Canada. They are usually administered by institutional ethics committees, whose job it is to vet research protocols and to ensure that the guidelines are stringently followed. Major portions of the

Tri-Council Policy Statement are reproduced below. The Policy Statement reasserts the fundamental principle of complete disclosure that was already enunciated by the courts in *Halushka v. The University of Saskatchewan*. Relevant excerpts from that case are also included in this chapter, because it is one of the few legal cases in North America that deals with consent and disclosure in the experimental/research setting.

However, sometimes the very design of a particular piece of research makes it impossible to disclose all relevant information to the research subjects, and therefore makes it impossible to achieve informed consent. For example, this may be the case when psychological attitudes are being studied and the research subjects would not give a genuine response if they knew what exactly was being investigated. Another example is in clinical trials, when testing the effectiveness of new drugs. Here, placebo controls are used. That is, the research subjects are divided into two groups, one of whom is given the drug to be tested, and the other is given, not the active agent, but instead an inert agent or placebo — but the subjects are not told which they are being given. In fact, sometimes even the professionals who actually administer the drug are blinded as to whether, in a given case, they are administering the active agent or the placebo. These are called double-blind placebo controlled trials. The reason for this sort of research design is that it has the greatest chance of eliminating subjective responses from the research subjects and of preventing observational bias on the part of the researchers themselves. However, this seems to violate informed consent. While it may be scientifically justified, is this ethical? Further, the Tri-Council Guidelines clearly state that "[t]he use of placebo controls in clinical trials is generally unacceptable when standard therapies or interventions are available for a particular patient population." Charles Weijer takes a look at the implications of all of this for psychiatric research as it is actually being practised, focusing on placebo use in particular. It may be interesting to ask whether his concerns have relevance to other areas of clinical research.

The last selection in this chapter deals with an issue that is assuming ever greater importance today. As medical research is becoming more expensive and universities are less and less able to support it on their own, they are increasingly turning to pharmaceutical companies and to industry for funding. A common adage has it that whoever pays the piper calls the tune. This is certainly true in the private sector. Does it also apply in the academic research setting? Some pharmaceutical companies seem to think so, as the case of Nancy Olivieri amply illustrates.[2] Dr. Olivieri, a hematologist at the University of Toronto and Toronto's Hospital for Sick Children, was conducting two studies sponsored by Apotex on deferiprone (hydroxypyridin-4-one) as a possible treatment for thalassemia. Apotex owns the patent on deferiprone. Dr. Olivieri discovered that deferiprone could exacerbate the liver damage caused by thalassemia. She felt compelled to communicate this finding directly to the participants in the study, and to alert the scientific community by publishing her findings in the *New England*

Journal of Medicine. Apotex, who denied the validity of her findings, demanded that she adhere to her confidentiality agreement with the company, and it discontinued the studies. Apotex also threatened legal action. In 1999, a report commissioned by the academic tenure and freedom committee of the Canadian Association of University Teachers exonerated Dr. Olivieri. It found that the University of Toronto, which apparently was expecting a large donation from Apotex, did not do its best to defend Dr. Olivieri, and concluded that her academic freedom was violated when Apotex stopped the trials and threatened legal action if she went public with her fears about the drug.[3]

The Olivieri case throws into relief certain fundamental questions: How much control — if any — should corporations who fund university-based research exercise? Does corporate funding undermine the integrity of academic medical research? Is there some other method for dealing with the chronic shortfall of academic funds without running the risk of another "Olivieri case"? Lewis *et al.* explore these and related questions, and indicate the direction in which a viable accommodation might be reached.

Notes

1. Medical Research Council of Canada, *Guidelines on Research Involving Human Subjects* (Ottawa: Minister of Supply and Services, 1987).

2. For a Web site founded by Dr. Olivieri and colleagues, see "Doctors for Research Integrity" **http://www.doctorsintegrity.org**

3. Thompson, J., Baird, P., Downie, J. "Report of the Committee of Inquiry on the Case Involving Dr. Nancy Olivieri, the Hospital for Sick Children, the University of Toronto, and Apotex, Inc." October 26, 2001. **http://www.dal.ca/~jgdownie/coi/index.html**

Tri-Council Policy Statement

Ethical Conduct for Research Involving Humans

Article 1.1
(a) All research that involves living human subjects requires review and approval by an REB in accordance with this Policy Statement, before the research is started, except as stipulated below.

(b) Research involving human remains, cadavers, tissues, biological fluids, embryos or foetuses should also be reviewed by the REB.

Source: *Tri-Council Policy Statement: Ethical Conduct for Research Involving Humans*, 1998, Interagency Advisory Panel on Research and Ethics. Reproduced with permission of the Minister of Public Works and Government Services Canada, 2003.

(c) Research about a living individual involved in the public arena, or about an artist, based exclusively on publicly available information, documents, records, works, performances, archival materials or third-party interviews, is not required to undergo ethics review. Such research only requires ethics review if the subject is approached directly for interviews or for access to private papers, and then only to ensure that such approaches are conducted according to professional protocols and to Article 2.3 of this Policy.

(d) Quality assurance studies, performance reviews or testing within normal educational requirements should also not be subject to REB review.

Article 1.2 The institution in which research involving human subjects is carried out shall mandate the REB to approve, reject, propose modifications to, or terminate any proposed or ongoing research involving human subjects which is conducted within, or by members of, the institution, using the considerations set forth in this Policy as the minimum standard.

Article 1.3 The REB shall consist of at least five members, including both men and women, of whom:

(a) at least two members have broad expertise in the methods or in the areas of research that are covered by the REB;

(b) at least one member is knowledgeable in ethics;

(c) for biomedical research, at least one member is knowledgeable in the relevant law; this is advisable but not mandatory for other areas of research; and

(d) at least one member has no affiliation with the institution, but is recruited from the community served by the institution.

Article 1.4

(a) REBs shall be established by the highest levels of the institution, and

cover as broad a range of research as is consistent with manageable workloads. Departmental REBs normally are not acceptable (except as discussed below for review of undergraduate research within course requirements). A multiplicity of REBs with small workloads within the same institution should be avoided.

(b) Large institutions may find it necessary to create more than one REB, usually to cover different areas of research. The jurisdiction of each REB should be clearly defined by the normal processes of governance within the Institution, and a mechanism should be established to coordinate the practices of all REBs within the Institution.

(c) Small institutions may wish to explore regional cooperation or alliances, including the sharing of REBs.

Article 1.5

(a) The REB shall satisfy itself that the design of a research project that poses more than minimal risk is capable of addressing the questions being asked in the research.

(b) The extent of the review for scholarly standards that is required for biomedical research that does not involve more than minimal risk will vary according to the research being carried out.

(c) Research in the humanities and the social sciences which poses, at most, minimal risk shall not normally be required by the REB to be peer reviewed.

(d) Certain types of research, particularly in the social sciences and the humanities, may legitimately have a negative effect on public figures in politics, business, labour, the arts or other walks of life, or on organizations. Such research should not be blocked through the use of harms/

benefits analysis or because of the potentially negative nature of the findings. The safeguard for those in the public arena is through public debate and discourse and, *in extremis*, through action in the courts for libel.

Article 1.6 The REB should adopt a proportionate approach based on the general principle that the more invasive the research, the greater should be the care in assessing the research.

Article 1.7 REBs shall meet regularly to discharge their responsibilities.

Article 1.8 Minutes of all REB meetings shall be prepared and maintained by the REB. The minutes shall clearly document the REB's decisions and any dissents, and the reasons for them. In order to assist internal and external audits or research monitoring, and to facilitate reconsideration or appeals, the minutes must be accessible to authorized representatives of the institution, researchers and funding agencies.

Article 1.9 REBs shall meet face-to-face to review proposed research that is not delegated to expedited review. REB review shall be based upon fully detailed research proposals or, where applicable, progress reports. The REB shall function impartially, provide a fair hearing to those involved and provide reasoned and appropriately documented opinions and decisions. The REB shall accommodate reasonable requests from researchers to participate in discussions about their proposals, but not be present when the REB is making its decision. When an REB is considering a negative decision, it shall provide the researcher with all the reasons for doing so and give the researcher an opportunity to reply before making a final decision.

Article 1.10 Researchers have the right to request, and REBs have an obligation to provide, reconsideration of decisions affecting a research project.

Article 1.11
(a) In cases when researchers and REBs cannot reach agreement through discussion and reconsideration, an institution should permit review of an REB decision by an appeal board, provided that the board is within the same institution and its membership and procedures meet the requirements of this Policy. No *ad hoc* appeal boards are permitted.

(b) The Councils will not entertain any appeals of REB decisions.

Article 1.12 If an REB is reviewing research in which a member of the REB has a personal interest in the research under review (e.g., as a researcher or as an entrepreneur), conflict of interest principles require that the member not be present when the REB is discussing or making its decision. The REB member may disclose and explain the conflict of interest and offer evidence to the REB provided the conflict is fully explained to the REB, and the proposer of the research has the right to hear the evidence and to offer a rebuttal.

Article 1.13
(a) Ongoing research shall be subject to continuing ethics review. The rigour of the review should be in accordance with a proportionate approach to ethics assessment.

(b) As part of each research proposal submitted for REB review, the researcher shall propose to the REB the continuing review process deemed appropriate for that project.

(c) Normally, continuing review shall consist of at least the submission of a succinct annual status report to the REB. The REB shall be promptly notified when the project concludes.

Article 1.14 Research to be performed outside the jurisdiction or country of the institution which employs the researcher shall undergo prospective ethics review both (a) by the REB within the researcher's institution; and (b) by the appropriate REB, where such exists, which has authority in the country or jurisdiction where the research is to be done.

Article 2.1

(a) Research governed by this Policy (see Article 1.1) may begin only if (1) prospective subjects, or authorized third parties, have been given the opportunity to give free and informed consent about participation, and (2) their free and informed consent has been given and is maintained throughout their participation in the research. Articles 2.1(c), 2.3 and 2.8 provide exceptions to Article 2.1(a).

(b) Evidence of free and informed consent by the subject or authorized third party should ordinarily be obtained in writing. Where written consent is culturally unacceptable, or where there are good reasons for not recording consent in writing, the procedures used to seek free and informed consent shall be documented.

(c) The REB may approve a consent procedure[1] which does not include, or which alters, some or all of the elements of informed consent set forth above, or waive the requirement to obtain informed consent, provided that the REB finds and documents that:

   i. The research involves no more than minimal risk to the subjects;

   ii. The waiver or alteration is unlikely to adversely affect the rights and welfare of the subjects;

   iii. The research could not practicably be carried out without the waiver or alteration;

   iv. Whenever possible and appropriate, the subjects will be provided with additional pertinent information after participation; and

   v. The waivered or altered consent does not involve a therapeutic intervention.

(d) In studies including randomization and blinding in clinical trials, neither the research subjects nor those responsible for their care know which treatment the subjects are receiving before the project commences. Such research is not regarded as a waiver or alteration of the requirements for consent if subjects are informed of the probability of being randomly assigned to one arm of the study or another.

Article 2.2 Free and informed consent must be voluntarily given, without manipulation, undue influence or coercion.

Article 2.3 REB review is normally required for research involving naturalistic observation. However, research involving observation of participants in, for example, political rallies, demonstrations or public meetings, should not require REB review since it can be expected that the participants are seeking public visibility.

Article 2.4 Researchers shall provide, to prospective subjects or authorized third parties, full and frank disclosure of all information relevant to free and informed consent. Throughout the free and informed consent process, the researcher must ensure that prospective subjects are given adequate opportunities to discuss and contemplate their participation. Subject to the exception in Article 2.1(c), at the commencement of the free and informed consent process, researchers or their qualified designated representatives shall provide prospective subjects with the following:

(a) Information that the individual is being invited to participate in a research project;

(b) A comprehensible statement of the research purpose, the identity of the researcher, the expected duration and nature of participation, and a description of research procedures;

(c) A comprehensible description of reasonably foreseeable harms and benefits that may arise from research participation, as well as the likely consequences of non-action, particularly in research related to treatment, or where invasive methodologies are involved, or where there is a potential for physical or psychological harm;

(d) An assurance that prospective subjects are free not to participate, have the right to withdraw at any time without prejudice to pre-existing entitlements, and will be given continuing and meaningful opportunities for deciding whether or not to continue to participate; and

(e) The possibility of commercialization of research findings, and the presence of any apparent or actual or potential conflict of interest on the part of researchers, their institutions or sponsors.

Article 2.5 Subject to applicable legal requirements, individuals who are not legally competent shall only be asked to become research subjects when:

(a) the research question can only be addressed using the identified group(s); and

(b) free and informed consent will be sought from their authorized representative(s); and

(c) the research does not expose them to more than minimal risks without the potential for direct benefits for them.

Article 2.6 For research involving incompetent individuals, the REB shall ensure that, as a minimum, the following conditions are met:

(a) The researcher shall show how the free and informed consent will be sought from the authorized third party, and how the subjects' best interests will be protected.

(b) The authorized third party may not be the researcher or any other member of the research team.

(c) The continued free and informed consent of an appropriately authorized third party will be required to continue the participation of a legally incompetent subject in research, so long as the subject remains incompetent.

(d) When a subject who was entered into a research project through third-party authorization becomes competent during the project, his or her informed consent shall be sought as a condition of continuing participation.

Article 2.7 Where free and informed consent has been obtained from an authorized third party, and in those circumstances where the legally incompetent individual understands the nature and consequences of the research, the researcher shall seek to ascertain the wishes of the individual concerning participation. The potential subject's dissent will preclude his or her participation.

Article 2.8 Subject to all applicable legislative and regulatory requirements, research involving emergency health situations shall be conducted only if it addresses the emergency needs of individuals involved, and then only in accordance with criteria established in advance of such research by the REB. The REB may allow research that involves health emergencies to be carried out without the free and informed consent of the subject or of his or her authorized third party if ALL of the following apply:

(a) A serious threat to the prospective subject requires immediate intervention; and

(b) Either no standard efficacious care exists or the research offers a real possibility of direct benefit to the subject in comparison with standard care; and

(c) Either the risk of harm is not greater than that involved in standard efficacious care, or it is clearly justified by the direct benefits to the subject; and

(d) The prospective subject is unconscious or lacks capacity to understand risks, methods and purposes of the research; and

(e) Third-party authorization cannot be secured in sufficient time, despite diligent and documented efforts to do so; and

(f) No relevant prior directive by the subject is known to exist. ...

Article 3.1 Subject to the exceptions in Article 1.1(c), researchers who intend to interview a human subject to secure identifiable personal information shall secure REB approval for the interview procedure used and shall ensure the free and informed consent of the interviewee as required in Article 2.4. As indicated in Article 1.1(c), REB approval is not required for access to publicly available information or materials, including archival documents and records of public interviews or performances.

Article 3.2 Subject to Article 3.1 above, researchers shall secure REB approval for obtaining identifiable personal information about subjects. Approval for such research shall include such considerations as:

(a) The type of data to be collected;

(b) The purpose for the which the data will be used;

(c) Limits on the use, disclosure, and retention of the data;

(d) Appropriate safeguards for security and confidentiality;

(e) Any modes of observation (e.g., photographs or videos) or access to information (e.g., sound recordings) in the research that allow identification of particular subjects;

(f) Any anticipated secondary uses of identifiable data from the research;

(g) Any anticipated linkage of data gathered in the research with other data about subjects, whether those data are contained in public or personal records; and

(h) Provisions for confidentiality of data resulting from the research.

Article 3.3 If identifying information is involved, REB approval shall be sought for secondary uses of data. Researchers may gain access to identifying information if they have demonstrated to the satisfaction of the REB that:

(a) Identifying information is essential to the research; and

(b) They will take appropriate measures to protect the privacy of the individuals, to ensure the confidentiality of the data, and to minimize harms to subjects;

(c) Individuals to whom the data refer have not objected to secondary use.

Article 3.4 The REB may also require that a researcher's access to secondary use of data involving identifying information be dependent on:

(a) The informed consent of those who contributed data or of authorized third parties; or

(b) An appropriate strategy for informing the subjects; or

(c) Consultation with representatives of those who contributed data.

Article 3.5 Researchers who wish to contact individuals to whom data refer shall seek the authorization of the REB prior to contact.

Article 3.6 The implications of approved data linkage in which research subjects may be identifiable shall be approved by the REB.

Article 4.1 Researchers and REB members shall disclose actual, perceived or potential conflicts of interest to the REB. REBs should develop mechanisms to address and resolve conflicts of interest.

Article 5.1
(a) Where research is designed to survey a number of living research subjects because of their involvement in generic activities (e.g., in many areas of health research or in some social science research such as studies of child poverty or of access to legal clinics) that are not specific to particular identifiable groups, researchers shall not exclude prospective or actual research subjects on the basis of such attributes as culture, religion, race, mental or physical disability, sexual orientation, ethnicity, sex or age, unless there is a valid reason for doing so.
(b) This article is not intended to preclude research focused on a single living individual (such as in a biography) or on a group of individuals who share a specific characteristic (as in a study of an identifiable group of painters who happen to be all of one sex, colour or religion, or of a religious order which is restricted to one sex).

Article 5.2 Women shall not automatically be excluded from research solely on the basis of sex or reproductive capacity.

Article 5.3 Subject to the provisions in Articles 2.6 to 2.8, those who are not competent to consent for themselves shall not be automatically excluded from research

which is potentially beneficial to them as individuals, or to the group that they represent.

Article 6 (None)

Article 7.1 Phase I non-therapeutic clinical trials shall undergo both stringent review and continuous monitoring by an REB independent of the clinical trials sponsor.

Article 7.2 In combined Phase I/II clinical trials, researchers and REBs shall carefully examine the integrity of the free and informed consent process. Where appropriate, the REB may require an independent monitoring process.

Article 7.3 REBs shall examine the budgets of clinical trials to assure that ethical duties concerning conflict of interest are respected.

Article 7.4 The use of placebo controls in clinical trials is generally unacceptable when standard therapies or interventions are available for a particular patient population.

Article 8.1 The genetics researcher shall seek free and informed consent from the individual and report results to that individual if the individual so desires.

Article 8.2 The researcher and the REB shall ensure that the results of genetic testing and genetic counselling records are protected from access by third parties, unless free and informed consent is given by the subject. Family information in databanks shall be coded so as to remove the possibility of identification of subjects within the bank itself.

Article 8.3 Researchers and genetic counsellors involving families and groups in genetic research studies shall reveal potential harms to the REB and outline how such harms will be dealt with as part of the research project.

Article 8.4 Genetics researchers and the REB shall ensure that the research protocol makes provision for access to genetic counselling for the subjects, where appropriate.

Article 8.5 Gene alteration (including "gene therapy") that involves human germ-line cells or human embryos is not ethically acceptable. Gene alteration for therapeutic purposes and involving human somatic cells may be considered for approval.

Article 8.6 Though the banking of genetic material is expected to yield benefits, it may also pose potential harms to individuals, their families and the groups to which they may belong. Accordingly, researchers who propose research involving the banking of genetic material have a duty to satisfy the REB and prospective research subjects that they have addressed the associated ethical issues, including confidentiality, privacy, storage, use of the data and results, withdrawal by the subject, and future contact of subjects, families and groups.

Article 8.7 At the outset of a research project, the researcher shall discuss with the REB and the research subject the possibility and/or probability that the genetic material and the information derived from its use may have potential commercial uses.

Article 9.1 Researchers shall obtain free and informed consent from the individual whose gametes are to be used in research.

Article 9.2 In research, it is not ethical to use in research ova or sperm that have been obtained through commercial transactions, including exchange for service.

Article 9.3 It is not ethically acceptable to create, or intend to create, hybrid individuals by such means as mixing human and animal gametes, or transferring somatic or germ cell nuclei between cells of humans and other species.

Article 9.4 It is not ethically acceptable to create human embryos specifically for research purposes. However, in those cases where human embryos are created for reproductive purposes, and subsequently are no longer required for such purposes, research involving human embryos may be considered to be ethically acceptable, but only if all of the following apply:
(a) The ova and sperm from which they were formed are obtained in accordance with Articles 9.1 and 9.2;
(b) The research does not involve the genetic alteration of human gametes or embryos;
(c) Embryos exposed to manipulations not directed specifically to their ongoing normal development will not be transferred for continuing pregnancy; and
(d) Research involving human embryos takes place only during the first 14 days after their formation by combination of the gametes.

Article 9.5 It is not ethically acceptable to undertake research that involves ectogenesis, cloning human beings by any means including somatic cell nuclear transfer, formation of animal/human hybrids, or the transfer of embryos between humans and other species.

Article 10.1 Research proposing the collection and use of human tissues requires ethics review by an REB. Amongst other things, the researcher shall demonstrate the following to the REB:
(a) That the collection and use of human tissues for research purposes shall be undertaken with the free and informed consent of competent donors;
(b) In the case of incompetent donors, free and informed consent shall be by an authorized third party;

(c) In the case of deceased donors, free and informed consent shall be expressed in a prior directive or through the exercise of free and informed consent by an authorized third party.

Article 10.2 For the purpose of obtaining free and informed consent, researchers who seek to collect human tissue for research shall, as a minimum, provide potential donors or authorized third parties information about:

(a) The purpose of the research;

(b) The type and amount of tissue to be taken, as well as the location where the tissue is to be taken;

(c) The manner in which tissue will be taken, the safety and invasiveness of acquisition, and the duration and conditions of preservation;

(d) The potential uses for the tissue including any commercial uses;

(e) The safeguards to protect the individual's privacy and confidentiality;

(f) Identifying information attached to specific tissue, and its potential traceability; and

(g) How the use of the tissue could affect privacy.

Article 10.3

(a) When identification is possible, researchers shall seek to obtain free and informed consent from individuals, or from their authorized third parties, for the use of their previously collected tissue. The provisions of Article 10.2 also apply here.

(b) When collected tissue has been provided by persons who are not individually identifiable (anonymous and anonymized tissue), and when there are no potential harms to them, there is no need to seek donors' permission to use their tissue for research purposes, unless applicable law so requires.

Notes

1. Article 2.1(c) was adapted from *Protection of Human Subjects*, U.S. Dept. of Health & Human Services, Title 45; *Code of Federal Regulations, Part 46.116(d)*.

Halushka v. University of Saskatchewan et al.

Saskatchewan Court of Appeal, Woods, Brownridge and Hall, J.J.A. May 4, 1965

HALL, J.A.:
... The respondent reported to the anaesthesia department at the University Hospital and there saw the appellant Wyant. The conversation which ensued concerning the proposed test was related by the respondent as follows:

Doctor Wyant explained to me that a new drug was to be tried out on the Wednesday following. He told me that electrodes would be put in my both arms, legs and head and that he assured me that it was a perfectly safe test it had been conducted many times before. He told me that I was not to eat anything on Wednesday morning, that I was to report at approximately nine o'clock, then he said it would take about an hour to hook me up and the test itself would last approximately two hours, after the time I would be given fifty dollars, pardon me, I would be allowed to sleep first, fed and then given fifty dollars and driven home on the same day.

The appellant Wyant also told the respondent that an incision would be made in his left arm and that a catheter or tube would be inserted into his vein.

The respondent agreed to undergo the test and was asked by the appellant Wyant to sign a form of consent. ... The respondent described the circumstances surrounding the signing ... saying:

> He then gave me a consent form, I skimmed through it and picked out the word "accident" on the consent form and asked Doctor Wyant what accidents were referred to, and he gave me an example of me falling down the stairs at home after the test and then trying to sue the University Hospital as a result. Being assured that any accident that would happen to me would be at home and not in the Hospital I signed the form.

The test contemplated was known as "The Heart and Blood Circulation Response under General Anaesthesia," and was to be conducted jointly by the appellants Wyant and Merriman, using a new anaesthetic agent known commercially as "Fluoromar." This agent had not been previously used or tested by the appellants in any way.

The respondent returned to the University Hospital on August 23, 1961, to undergo the test. The procedure followed was that which had been described to the respondent and expected by him, with the exception that the catheter, after being inserted in the vein in the respondent's arm, was advanced towards his heart. When the catheter reached the vicinity of the heart, the respondent felt some discomfort. The anaesthetic agent was then administered to him. ... Eventually the catheter tip was advanced through the various heart chambers out into the pulmonary artery where it was positioned. ...

At 12:25 the respondent suffered a complete cardiac arrest.

The appellants Wyant and Merriman and their assistants took immediate steps to resuscitate the respondent's heart by manual massage. To reach the heart an incision was made from the breastbone to the line of the arm-pit and two of the ribs were pulled apart. A vaso-pressor was administered as well as urea, a drug used to combat swelling of the brain. After one minute and thirty seconds the respondent's heart began to function again. ...

In ordinary medical practice the consent given by a patient to a physician or surgeon, to be effective, must be an "informed" consent freely given. It is the duty of the physician to give a fair and reasonable explanation of the proposed treatment including the probable effect and any special or unusual risks. ...

In my opinion the duty imposed upon those engaged in medical research ... to those who offer themselves as subject for experimentation ... is at least as great as, if not greater than, the duty owed by the ordinary physician or surgeon to his patient. There can be no exceptions to the ordinary requirements of disclosure in the case of research as there may well be in ordinary medical practice. The researcher does not have to balance the probable effect of lack of treatment against the risk involved in the treatment itself. The example of risks being properly hidden from a patient when it is important that he should not worry can have no application in the field of research. The subject of medical experimentation is entitled to a full and frank disclosure of all the facts, probabilities and opinions which a reasonable man might be expected to consider before giving his consent. The respondent necessarily had to rely upon the special skill, knowledge and experience of the appellants, who were, in my opinion, placed in the fiduciary position. ...

Although the appellant Wyant informed the respondent that a "new drug" was to be tried out, he did not inform him that the new drug was in fact an anaesthetic of which he had no previous knowledge, nor that there was risk involved with the use of an anaesthetic. Inasmuch as no test had been previously conducted using the anaesthetic agent "Fluoromar" to the knowledge of the appellants, the statement made to the respondent that it was a safe test which had been conducted many times before, when considered in the light of the medical evidence describing the characteristics of anaesthetic agents generally, was incorrect and was in reality a non-disclosure.

The respondent was not informed that the catheter would be advanced to and through his heart but was admittedly given to understand that it would be merely inserted in the vein in his arm. While it may be correct to say that the advancement of the catheter to the heart was not in itself dangerous and did not cause or contribute to the cause of the cardiac arrest, it was a circumstance which, if known, might very well have prompted the respondent to withhold his consent. The undisclosed or misrepresented facts need not concern matters which directly cause the ultimate damage if they are of a nature which might influence the judgment upon which the consent is based.

The explanation ... given by the appellant Wyant to the respondent could be misleading and could well serve to distract the respondent from a proper appraisal of his position. ...

The appeal is dismissed with costs.

Placebo Trials and Tribulations

Charles Weijer

The most divisive debate within psychiatric research today involves the proper role of placebo controls in clinical trials that test the effectiveness of new drugs. Canada's *Tri-Council Policy Statement* carefully defines the conditions under which placebo controls may be used legitimately.[1] Article 7.4 stipulates that "[t]he use of placebo controls in clinical trials is generally unacceptable when standard therapies or interventions are available for a particular patient population." This is not an idiosyncratic position. Indeed, the most recent revision of the *Declaration of Helsinki* (paragraph 29) similarly prohibits the use of a placebo control when effective therapy exists for the medical condition being studied.[2] But ethical guidelines are only as good as their application in practice. Are Canada's researchers, research institutions and government abiding by these requirements?

"Placebo trials and tribulations" — Reprinted from *CMAJ* Mar 2002; 166(5) pages 603–604 by permission of the publisher. © 2002 Canadian Medical Association.

Unfortunately, at least in some cases, it appears that the answer is no. Consider the following ongoing clinical trial for which I served as an external reviewer for a local research ethics board (REB). The study is a multicentre, randomized controlled trial comparing a new selective serotonin reuptake inhibitor, paroxetine, and placebo in the treatment of major depressive disorder. Given the existence of proven, effective treatment for major depressive disorder,[3] the local REB concluded that the use of a placebo control was inappropriate and, in accordance with the *Tri-Council Policy Statement* and paragraph 29 of the *Declaration of Helsinki*, rejected the study. The local REB's decision placed it in the minority of Canadian REBs that had considered the same study: 16 other REBs approved the protocol for use by 19 investigators.[4]

In order to explain this disparity, each of the many levels of Canada's regulatory system that is designed to protect research subjects must be examined. The first level of protection for research subjects is provided by the clinical investigator and by each subject's own physician. When may the responsible physician offer trial enrolment to her or his patient? Clinical equipoise provides the most widely accepted answer to this question.[5] According to this concept, there must exist at the start of the trial a state of honest, professional disagreement in the community of expert clinicians as to the preferred treatment. Under these circumstances a state of clinical equipoise is said to exist, and the physician may offer trial enrolment to his or her patients legitimately.

Placebo controls may be used when there is no available treatment for a disorder, or when an adjunctive treatment is being tested, so that all participants receive the standard treatment.[6] Second-generation treatments, however, must be tested against the best available therapy.[6] In the case of depression, the effec-tiveness of drug treatment is well established.[3] In such cases, the scrupulous clinician cannot offer participation in a placebo-controlled trial ethically to his or her patients.[3]

The second level of protection for Canada's research subjects is the research institution, be it a university or hospital. Research institutions that receive funds from the Canadian Institutes of Health Research, the Natural Sciences and Engineering Research Council or the Social Sciences and Humanities Research Council must uphold the ethical standards for research laid out in the *Tri-Council Policy Statement*.[1] Lack of compliance may be associated with serious consequences: "The Councils will consider funding (or continued funding) only to individuals and institutions which certify compliance with this policy regarding research involving human subjects."[1] The REB's role is to ensure that research meets the standards set by the *Policy Statement*.

The protocol described earlier was approved by REBs from a number of Canada's leading universities and their teaching hospitals. This suggests a lack of clarity on a national level regarding the need for adherence to the *Tri-Council Policy Statement*. The funding councils themselves may have perpetuated this state of affairs. To date, the councils have failed to caution or suspend funding to any institution for failing to adhere to the *Policy Statement*.

The third level of protection for Canada's research subjects is the government. All research for the licensing of new drugs, including the protocol described here, is conducted under the aegis of Health Canada's Therapeutic Products Directorate (TPD), which was part of the Therapeutic Products Programme (TPP) until April 2001. The TPD does not officially endorse the *Tri-Council Policy Statement*. Rather, new drug research must comply with the guidelines of the International

Conference on Harmonization (ICH), an international standard-setting body for the licensing of new drugs.[7,8] Obviously, any discrepancy between ICH guidelines and the *Policy Statement* will translate into a double standard for Canadian research subjects.

Further problems are posed by the fact that the ICH documents give conflicting guidance about the conduct of placebo-controlled trials. At one point, ICH guidelines take a relatively permissive stance on the use of placebo controls, allowing them when effective treatment exists as long as subjects are not exposed to the risk of death or permanent morbidity (Section 2.1.3).[7] At another point, however, ICH guidelines require that "[c]linical trials should be conducted in accordance with ... the Declaration of Helsinki ..."(Section 2.1) and, thus, prohibit the same trials that other ICH guidelines permit.[8] Clearly, this regulatory conflict must be resolved.

The TPD relies on arm's-length review by the REBs to ensure that research is conducted ethically. In some cases, these REBs are not affiliated with any institution (and as such are not bound by the *Tri-Council Policy Statement*) and charge for ethics review. These "for profit" REBs are neither accredited by government nor are they subject to government oversight despite the obvious conflict of interest posed by "for profit" ethics review.[9] At least 2 of the REBs that reviewed the protocol described here are "for-profit" REBs.[4]

The TPD must itself avoid the appearance of conflict of interest. After the local REB rejected the protocol under discussion, it received a copy of a letter from the then TPP written to a project manager at a research centre and forwarded by a researcher at the same centre that stated the following:

> We believe judicious use of placebo controlled trials to establish unequivocally the efficacy of a new drug, together with a compre-

hensive risk management protocol and appropriate informed consent, is ethical. To use an inconclusive trial design when a conclusive trial design is possible, is unethical.[10]

REB review must be independent and it was, therefore, inherently improper for the TPP to tell an REB what is ethical. The facts of this case are problematic for 2 reasons. First, whether a particular practice is ethical or not is a matter set forth in national and international guidelines to be interpreted by REBs. The TPP should not have promulgated idiosyncratic views. Second, though the letter from the TPP made its way to the REB indirectly and the TPP may not have been aware of the investigator's intention to so distribute it, the TPP ought to have made it clear that this action by the investigator was inappropriate and should have reassured the REB that the TPP had no intention of interfering with the REB review process. I raised this issue in a letter to the TPP's then Acting Director General, Dr. Robert Peterson, dated Sept. 27, 2000.[11] I wrote, "For the TPP to attempt to influence the decision of a particular REB, or for it to even appear to do so, is a violation of proper procedure, and undermines the REB's role as a societal mechanism to protect Canadians in research."[11] To date, I have not received a reply.

The placebo-controlled trial is a litmus test for the adequacy of Canada's regulatory system for research. The case discussed here reveals the need for change at all levels. Clinician investigators must reaffirm their commitment first and foremost to the well-being of their patients. REBs must follow the ethical guidance given by the *Tri-Council Policy Statement*. The funding councils must enforce these standards. Finally, the TPD must formally adopt the *Policy Statement* to ensure that all Canadians who give of themselves to further research are afforded the highest level of protection.

References*

1. Canadian Institutes of Health, Natural Sciences and Engineering Research Council of Canada, and Social Sciences and Humanities Research Council of Canada. *Tri-council policy statement: ethical conduct for research involving humans.* Updated 2000 Nov 21. Available: **www.pre.ethics.gc.ca/english/ policystatement/policystatement.cfm** (accessed 2002 Jan 23).

2. World Medical Association. *Declaration of Helsinki.* 2000. Available: **www. wma.net/e/policy/b3.htm** (accessed 2002 Jan 23).

3. Whooley MA, Simon GE. Managing depression in medical outpatients. *N Engl J Med* 2000;343(26):1942–50.

4. E-mail correspondence from Roopa Ganapathy, AstraZeneca, to Helen Begin, St. Joseph's Health Care, Hamilton, Ont., re approval given by ethics boards. 2001 June 18.

5. Freedman B. Equipoise and the ethics of clinical research. *N Engl J Med* 1987; 317: 141–5.

6. Weijer C. Placebo-controlled trials in schizophrenia: Are they ethical? Are they necessary? *Schizophr Res* 1999;35:211–8.[Medline]

7. International Conference on Harmonisation of Technical Requirements for Registration of Pharmaceuticals for Human Use. ICH Harmonised Tripartite guideline: choice of control group and related issues in clinical trials (E10). 2000.

8. International Conference on Harmonisation of Technical Requirements for Registration of Pharmaceuticals for Human Use. ICH Harmonised Tripartite guideline: guideline for good clinical practice (E6). 1996.

9. Lemmens T, Freedman B. Ethics review for sale? Conflict of interest and commercial research review boards. *Milbank Q* 2000;78:547–84.

10. Letter from Dr. Siddiki Mithani, Manager, Clinical Trials & Special Access Programme, Health Canada, Ottawa, to Ms. Lorelei Audas, Project Manager, Queen Elizabeth II Health Sciences Centre, Halifax, re placebo-controlled trials. 2000 Aug 15.

11. Letter from Dr. Charles Weijer, Dalhousie University, Halifax, to Dr. Robert Peterson, Acting Director General, Therapeutic Products Programme (TPP), Health Canada, Ottawa, re TTP policy concerning placebo-controlled trials. 2000 Sept 27.

---

*URLs were revised in April 2004 from the original source for inclusion in this book.

Dancing with the Porcupine: Rules for Governing the University–Industry Relationship

Steven Lewis, Patricia Baird, Robert G. Evans, William A. Ghali, Charles J. Wright, Elaine Gibson, Françoise Baylis

Universities have long been involved in the creation and evaluation of pharmaceutical products. In its best form, academic participation in drug-related science both spurs innovation and, through the disinterest and skepticism that are hallmarks of the academic mission, provides a check on the premature enthusiasms of industry. In this commentary we examine the logic and behaviour of the pharmaceutical industry in pursuit of its interests and propose rules to govern university–industry partnerships that reflect the public interest.

The duty of universities is to seek truth. The duty of pharmaceutical companies is to make money for their shareholders. Drug companies that fail to do so go out of business. Universities that subordinate the disinterested search for truth to other ends lose credibility and their claim to a privileged status in society. If either abandons its fundamental mission, it ultimately fails. At times, institutional imperatives are bound to conflict.[1,2]

Research can either serve or subvert the public interest. Its findings may advance knowledge and support useful innovation, or be filtered and twisted to support prejudices or gain commercial advantage. The capacities and integrity of researchers, and their universities, can be enhanced or corrupted in the process. Some partnerships are united by an open-minded

quest for discovery; others are unholy alliances whereby researchers and universities become handmaidens of industry. Whatever ethical bed we make, we lie in.

There is abundant evidence that many such partnerships place industry imperatives above both the public interest and the fundamental ethos of the university. The evidence includes major variation in disclosure requirements,[3] insufficient protection of the right to publish in a timely fashion[4] and researchers having financial interests in companies potentially affected by the outcomes of their research.[5] The creation of the Canadian Institutes of Health Research (CIHR) and its renewed commitment to excellence and expanded capacity for innovation and discovery have created unprecedented health research opportunities in Canada. With what ethical compass will Canada chart its health research course?

The outcome will depend on 3 key players: the federal government and its agencies, the universities, and industry. The recent history of government policy is a 3-part drama. In the late 1980s the federal government concluded that increased drug research and development by the private sector in Canada would contribute to the economy. Second, multinational drug companies indicated that their expansion of research and development activities in their Canadian

"Dancing with the porcupine: rules for governing the university–industry relationship,"
Reprinted from *CMAJ* 18 Sept 2001; 165(6) pages 783–785 by permission of the publisher.
© 2001 Canadian Medical Association.

branches would be contingent on favourable patent protection legislation. Third, in return for extending patent protection, the government exacted a commitment from industry to invest 10% of sales in Canadian-based research.

The Medical Research Council of Canada[6] (MRC, the forerunner of the CIHR) and many faculty members and universities supported these measures. The MRC budget declined for 3 consecutive years beginning in 1995/96 and was essentially frozen during most of the decade.[6] Elsewhere, spending on health research rose significantly, most notably in the United States, where federal funding alone doubled in real terms during the 1990s.[7] Science became more complex, expensive and competitive. To offset the severe restraints imposed on public funding of universities as part of the war on government deficits in Canada during the 1990s, researchers and universities had to look elsewhere for funding. Enter industry.

In 2000, "business enterprise," which was almost exclusively the pharmaceutical industry (although Statistics Canada does not break down the figures), accounted for about 43% of gross domestic expenditures on research and development in the health field (the amount includes $350 million from foreign sources spent on business enterprises in Canada, which we assume to be industry dollars).[8] Universities and teaching hospitals received $161 million from industry, which was more than the amount from provincial governments combined and over half the amount received from federal sources (largely the MRC–CIHR). Aside from being a major player on campus, industry exerts considerable influence on public policy by virtue of the $900 million it spends in-house on research and development.

What does industry expect for its $161 million invested in universities and teaching hospitals? Drug companies have a fiduciary duty to exploit the intellectual talent and ethical credibility of universi-

ties to advance their interests. The proximate goal is the publication of positive results of trials of new drugs, or evaluations that show that certain drugs are better than their competitors' products. The ultimate goal is sales. Negative findings often, and predictably, create an unhappy industry partner. Common sense suggests that universities must be vigilant about protecting their own, fundamentally different culture and orientation.

To date, they have not been. The new money and activity exploded onto the scene with inadequate oversight and no standardization of rules or mechanisms to resolve disputes. The results: some highly publicized aggressions,[9] tarnished institutional reputations, one-sided marriages of convenience, and who knows how much unhelpful drug therapy and increased cost.

Unsettling incidents of this nature have occurred throughout the world.[10] These are not impersonal and civil corporate disagreements; they often involve intimidating tactics by industry that profoundly affect researchers' lives and careers. Canadian cases, the details of which we do not recount for reasons of space, include the Bristol–Myers Squibb lawsuit against the Canadian Coordinating Office on Health Technology Assessment (CCOHTA) to suppress its statin report,[11] and the AstraZeneca legal threat against McMaster University researcher Anne Holbrook for her review of medications for stomach disorders (personal communication 2001). Regardless of the outcome of these cases, industry harassment consumes time and energy (and in the CCOHTA case, 13% of its budget, for legal fees) and creates unease; these are of course the intended effects.

In other cases, the financial clout of industry may influence academic behaviour more subtly, or at least appear to do so. Witness the withdrawal of an offer of employment to Dr. David Healy by the Centre for Addictions and Mental Health (CAMH) in Toronto shortly after he made a speech critical of Prozac, whose manufacturer, Eli Lilly, donated $1.55 million to the CAMH in 2000.[12–14] There is no evidence of direct involvement by Eli Lilly in this decision, but the company did withdraw corporate funding of The Hastings Center after its journal published a series of articles critical of antidepressant prescribing practices.[15]

Such cases demonstrate yet again that, when public and private interests conflict, at least some companies will fiercely protect their shareholders' interests. If the drugs they hoped would be breakthroughs turn out to be "me-toos," they must market them at the highest possible price in order to recoup the development costs, which can exceed US$100 million. If one company's drug is the therapeutic equivalent of other companies' drugs, it is obliged to try to persuade doctors, pharmacists and the public that its drug is actually better. In this, they are identical to car manufacturers and brewers of beer.

These inevitabilities demand prudent engagement. The warrant for prudence is not that something *will* go wrong; it is simply that something *may* go wrong, and *has* gone wrong in several cases. The intimidation and lawsuits are only the tip of the iceberg. Far more prevalent and insidious is the correlation between industry funding and research that shows a positive therapeutic effect.[16] In a landmark article, researchers found that industry-sponsored studies of calcium-channel antagonists are more likely to be supportive of that therapy than independently funded research.[17] Similar findings emerged from a review of economic analyses of new oncology drugs.[18] The positive skew is not dependent on such high-risk and brazen strategies as falsification of data; it is achievable by framing the questions and the design of studies to increase the probability of a positive result.

Industry funding creates an incentive to promote the positive and suppress the negative. When drug companies control publication of results or simply delay unwelcome findings, truth is partially disclosed and therefore compromised. And if researchers' laboratories and career prospects depend on renewed industry funding, their interests may begin to align with those of their paymasters. Unhappily, disinterested scholarly editorial practices often exacerbate rather than counteract this bias,[19–21] reaffirming Francis Bacon's observation that "the human intellect ... is more moved and excited by affirmatives than negatives."[19]

What is to be done? We propose the rules in Box 1 as a starting point for governing partnerships. The rules need an institutional home. One option would vest responsibility with the Association of Universities and Colleges of Canada. Health research is but a subset of all research, and the university, not its parts or affiliates, should be the institution of record. Any tendency for the health sciences to develop ethical standards in isolation must be resisted. "Academic separatism" flies in the face of the multidisciplinary and interdisciplinary collaboration that is heavily promoted as essential to the advancement of knowledge. Even more centrally, the university must not duck its responsibility to govern activities in its well-funded peripheries, including teaching hospitals.

Is a coordinated, national approach necessary? On the basis of the evidence to date, universities and researchers cannot be expected to protect their (and by extension the public's) interests with uniform sophistication and vigour.[22] Some US commentators have proposed precisely our form of remedy.[23] In May [2001] the US National Bioethics Advisory Commission called for federal legislation to create the National Office for Human Research Oversight to oversee all research involving human subjects, including the definition, disclosure and management of conflict of interest.[24]

Not infrequently, universities encounter challenges, veiled in the language

Box 1

PROPOSED RULES FOR GOVERNING UNIVERSITY–INDUSTRY RELATIONSHIPS

- A standard, Canada-wide contract governing university–industry relationships, enshrining the right of the academic to disclose potentially harmful clinical effects immediately, and publish freely after a modest interval.

- Guidelines to determine whether a proposed industry–university project is of sufficient intellectual originality and interest to qualify as academic activity. If the project does not qualify, it should be defined as a service or consulting contract and should be priced and managed as such.

- Mandatory filing of all university–industry agreements and contracts with the overseeing body, and registration of all clinical trials.

- Mandatory written debriefing signed by all parties at the conclusion of every university–industry agreement, to be filed with the provost or equivalent of the university and the overseeing body, with a hearings process to resolve disputes.

- A certification and rating system for industry that assesses such areas as scientific integrity, observance of contracts, commitment to intellectual freedom, degree of interference in the conduct of research and appropriateness of financial arrangements.

- A surtax levied on all university–industry contracts, the proceeds from which would help both to fund a core office and its oversight activities and to cover the costs of defending researchers against industry harassment or formal litigation as vigorously as the Canadian Medical Protective Association protects doctors against medical malpractice claims.

- The appointment of an ombudsperson to whom researchers and industry can refer concerns about partnerships.

- Participation in and endorsement of the refined and expanded set of rules based on these general principles and structures by all agencies funding health research.

of increased accountability, to their freedom of inquiry and expression. The claim that proposed constraints would be fatal to the academic mission becomes hypocrisy if universities allow industry to define the nature of inquiry, dictate methods and shackle expression. An industry–university contract is a transaction, and our proposed rules are designed principally to protect the university's most precious commodity: intellectual integrity.

We are not asking academic researchers to forswear all interactions with industry. We are merely proposing rules for exercising due diligence to protect the essence of academic inquiry. A positive effect of the proposed rules would be voluntarily improved industry behaviour, with enlightened companies adopting honourable codes of conduct that in time may mitigate the wariness and cynicism that recent aggressions have doubtless engendered.

Some bargains are Faustian, and some horses are Trojan. Dance carefully with the porcupine, and know in advance the price of intimacy.

Acknowledgment

Dr. Ghali is supported by a Population Health Investigator Award from the Alberta Heritage Foundation for Medical Research and by a Government of Canada Research Chair in Health Services Research.

Competing interests: None declared.

References*

1. Press E, Washburn J. The kept university. *Atlantic Monthly* 2000;285. **www. theatlantic.com/issues/2000/03/press.htm** (accessed 2001 Aug 20).

2. Weatherall D. Academia and industry: increasingly uneasy bedfellows. *Lancet* 2000;355:1574.

3. Van McCrary S, Anderson CB, Jakovljevic J, Khan T, McCullough LB, Wray NP, et al. A national survey of policies on disclosure of conflicts of interest in biomedical research. *N Engl J Med* 2000;343:1621–6.

4. Cho MK, Shohara R, Schissel A, Rennie D. Policies on faculty conflicts of interest at US universities. *JAMA* 2000;284:2237–8.

5. Lo B, Wolf LE, Berkeley A. Conflict-of-interest policies for investigators in clinical trials. *N Engl J Med* 2000;343:1616–20.

6. Medical Research Council of Canada. *Report of the president 1999–2000.* Ottawa: Canadian Institutes of Health Research; 2000. Cat no MR1-2000. Available (in pdf format): **www.cihr-irsc.gc.ca/e/publications/report9900_e.pdf** (accessed 2001 Aug 20).

7. Meeks RL. *Federal R&D funding by budget function: fiscal years 1999–2001, special report.* Arlington (VA): National Science Foundation, Division of Science Resources Studies; 2001. Report no NSF 01-316.

8. *Estimates of total expenditures on research and development in the health field in Canada, 1988 to 2000.* Ottawa: Statistics Canada; 2001. Cat no. 88F0006XIE01006.

9. Hailey D. Scientific harassment by pharmaceutical companies: time to stop. *CMAJ* 2000;162(2):212–3. Available: **www.cmaj.ca/cgi/content/full/162/2/212**

10. Morgan S, Barer ML, Evans RG. Health economists meet the fourth tempter: drug dependency and scientific discourse. *Health Econ* 2000;9:659–67.

11. Skolnick AA. Drug firm suit fails to halt publication of Canadian health technology report. *JAMA* 1998;280:683–4.

12. Boseley S. Bitter pill. *Guardian Weekly* 2001;164(22):23.

13. Hospital denies that withdrawal of MD's job offer was related to drug-company funding. *CMAJ* 2001;164(13):1879. **www.cmaj.ca/cgi/content/full/164/13/1879**

14. Lead donor Eli Lilly Canada launches education centre. In: *Foundation progress report winter 2000.* Toronto: Centre for Addiction and Mental Health; 2000. Available: **www.camh.net/foundation/newsletters/foundation_news_winter2000.html** (accessed 2001 Aug 20).

---

* Some of the URLs were revised in April 2004 from the original source for inclusion in this book.

15. Kaebnick G. What about the report? *Hastings Cent Rep* 2001;31(2):16–7.

16. Davidson RA. Source of funding and outcome of clinical trials. *J Gen Intern Med* 1986;1:155–8.

17. Stelfox HT, Chua G, O'Rourke K, Detsky AS. Conflict of interest in the debate over calcium-channel antagonists. *N Engl J Med* 1998;332:101–6.

18. Friedberg M, Saffran B, Stinson TJ, Nelson W, Bennett CL. Evaluation of conflict of interest in economic analyses of new drugs used in oncology. *JAMA* 1999;282:1453–7.

19. Dickersin K. The existence of publication bias and risk factors for its occurrence. *JAMA* 1990;263:1385–9.

20. Easterbrook PJ, Berlin JA, Gopalan R, Matthews DR. Publication bias in clinical research. *Lancet* 1991;337:867–72.

21. Naylor CD. Meta-analysis and the meta-epidemiology of clinical research. *BMJ* 1997;315:617–9.

22. Boyd EA, Bero LA. Assessing faculty financial relationships with industry: a case study. *JAMA* 2000;284:2209–14.

23. Hall ZA, Scott C. University–industry partnership. *Science* 2001;591:553.

24. National Bioethics Advisory Commission. *Ethical and policy issues in research involving human participants*. Rockville (MD): The Commission; 2001 May 18. Recommendations available: **http://www.georgetown.edu/research/nrcbl/ nbac/human/overvol2.html**

Further Readings

Beecher, H.K. "Ethics in Clinical Research." *N Engl J Med* 274 (1966): 1354–1360.

Beecher, H.K. *Experimentation in Man.* Springfield, Ill.: Charles C. Thomas, 1959.

Clark, P.A. "The Ethics of Placebo-Controlled Trials for Perinatal Transmission of HIV in Developing Countries." *J of Clin Ethics* 9:2 (Summer 1998): 156–166.

Cassell, J., and A. Young. "Why We Should Not Seek Individual Informed Consent for Participation in Health Services Research." *J Med Ethics* 2002 Oct;28(5):313–317.

Cohen, C. "Medical Experimentation on Prisoners." *Perspectives in Biology and Medicine.* 21:3 (Spring 1978): 357–372.

Dickens, B. "What Is a Medical Experiment?" *CMAJ* 113 (Oct. 4, 1975): 635–639.

Donagan, A. "Informed Consent in Therapy and Experimentation." *J Med Philos* 2:4 (1977): 307–329.

Freedman, B., C. Weijer, and K.C. Glass. "Placebo Orthodoxy in Clinical Research. I: Empirical and Methodological Myths." *J of Law and Med Ethics.* 24:3 (Fall 1996): 243–51.

Freedman, B., K.C. Glass, and C. Weijer. "Placebo Orthodoxy in Clinical Research. II: Ethical, Legal, and Regulatory Myths." *J of Law and Med Ethics* 24:3 (Fall 1996): 252–259.

Iltis A. "Biomedical Research Ethics." *J Med Philos* 27:5 (Oct. 2002): 515–22.

Katz, Jay. *Experimenting with Human Beings.* New York: Russell Sage Foundation, 1972.

Kluge, E.-H. W. *Biomedical Ethics in the Canadian Context*, Chapter 7. Scarborough, ON: Prentice-Hall, 1991.

Macklin, R. "The Ethical Problems with Sham Surgery in Clinical Research." *N Engl J Med* 341:13 (Sept. 23, 1999): 992–996.

National Commission for the Protection of Human Subjects of Biomedical and Behavioral Research. *The Belmont Report: Ethical Principles for the Protection of Human Subjects of Research, pub. no. 78-0012.* Washington, D.C.: U.S. Government Printing Office, 1978.

Nuremberg Code. *The Trials of War Criminals before the Nuremberg Military Tribunal.* Washington, D.C.: U.S. Government Printing Office, 1948.

Reynolds T, "The Ethics of Placebo?Controlled Trials." *Ann of Intern Med* 133:6 (Sept. 19, 2000): 491.

Somerville, M.A. "A Postmodern Moral Tale: The Ethics of Research Relationships." *Nature Reviews: Drug Discovery* 1 (2002): 316–320.

Spurgeon, D. "Report Clears Researcher Who Broke Drug Company Agreement," *Brit Med J* 323 (2001): 1085.

Stevens, P.E., and P.K. Pletsch. "Informed Consent and the History of Inclusion of Women in Clinical Research." *Health Care Women Int* 23:8 (Dec. 2002): 809–819.

Weijer C., and K.C. Glass. "The Ethics of Placebo-Controlled Trials." *N Engl J Med* 346:5 (Jan. 31, 2002): 382–383.

Weijer, C. "Research Involving the Vulnerable Sick." *Account Res* 7:1 (1999): 21–36.

———. "The Ethical Analysis of Risk." *J of Law and Med Ethics* 28:4 (Winter 2000): 344–61.

CHAPTER 11
RESEARCH AND EXPERIMENTATION INVOLVING PERSONS WITH DIMINISHED COMPETENCE

Introduction

It is difficult to act as proxy decision-maker in the ordinary therapeutic setting. The problems are compounded when the treatment that is suggested is experimental or innovative in nature. Nevertheless, sometimes there is no choice but to involve incompetent subjects in experimental protocols. The factors that make them incompetent may be the very reason why the protocol is developed in the first place. For instance, young children differ from adults not simply because they are younger, smaller and know less. In many cases, their organs function differently from those of adults — or even those of older children. This is important when prescribing medications. One cannot simply scale down the dosage proportionally on the basis of size and body-weight. The pharmacokinetic function of the drug, the metabolization processes, etc. may be quite different. Therefore, young children really are the only subjects on whom we can find out how a drug works on young children.

Similar remarks apply to people who suffer from organic psychiatric diseases — or the elderly. There are conditions that strike mainly elderly persons. Alzheimer's disease is a good example; the disease typically leaves the stricken individual incompetent. Therefore, such a person cannot meet the ordinary standards of informed consent. Yet to exclude this population group from research and experimentation is to exclude precisely the group about whom we need data if we are going to be able to develop appropriate methods of treatment.

The first article, by D. J. Manning, a pediatrician who deals with proxy consent on a constant basis, takes a look at the informed consent process as it has evolved over the last few years, with its emphasis on autonomy. He identifies what he sees as the difficulties this causes in the emergency pediatric setting. He suggests that deviating from standard proxy decision-making protocols by introducing an opting-out scheme may not only advance the welfare of the child and spread the burden of research more fairly, but, paradoxically enough, lead to a more informed and authentic proxy decision-making process.

The article by Mahendra looks at the special problems that are faced by medical researchers dealing with patients suffering from dementia. As he points out, this issue has been thrown into focus by an increasingly aging population among whom dementia is more common than other age groups. Not unexpectedly, Mahendra raises the problem of how to gain consent for the research. However, he also points out another important issue: Should we not also ask ourselves about the purpose of doing the research in the first place? Is it morally justified to pursue research into dealing with and arresting a pathology without paying attention to the quality of life to be led by those who survive — in this case, the elderly? With due alteration of detail, the same question can be raised about research on the health problems of any compromised population.

Presumed Consent in Emergency Neonatal Research

D. J. Manning

Introduction

Neonatal research exposes inherent conflicts between the obligation to evaluate the efficacy and safety of new treatments, justice in recruiting subjects, and respect for autonomy in protecting subjects. Recent controversies highlight these conflicts. Conroy *et al* reported that 90% of drugs prescribed in a neonatal intensive care unit had not been evaluated adequately, and called for more controlled trials to remedy this.[1] At the same time, an inquiry was announced following parents' claims that their newborn babies had been enrolled in a trial of continuous negative pressure ventilation for respiratory distress syndrome (RDS) without their consent. Yet the published report of this trial stated that parents consented to inclusion of their baby between two and four hours after birth.[2]

In this paper, I outline the potential harms caused by conventional methods of seeking consent for emergency neonatal research. I argue that, in circumstances which demand this research, reasonable understanding and voluntariness are likely to be severely compromised. Thus, adequately informed consent cannot be obtained. I propose an alternative approach, whereby presumed parental consent is sought antenatally, with scope for opting out. I argue that this approach, compared to conventional seeking of consent, would lessen parental distress, might increase recruitment and would acknowledge the severe impediments to autonomy experienced by parents of sick neonates.

Since research ethics committees usually require that persons asked to consent have at least 24 hours to deliberate, I define emergency research as research in circumstances when intervention must take place within 24 hours.

Journal of Medical Ethics 2000; 26: 249–253. With permission from the BMJ Publishing Group.

In many relevant neonatal scenarios such as resuscitation, surfactant treatment, comparing modes of respiratory support, cerebral protection in neurologically damaged babies, and treatment of neonatal seizures, much less time is available. Research in these situations is thus subject to severe time constraints on the process of obtaining consent.

In the past 30 years, respect for autonomy has overtaken beneficence as the most important ethical consideration governing medical research.[3] It is reflected in ethics codes such as the Declaration of Helsinki, which attaches great importance to obtaining consent for clinical research. When a potential research subject is competent to evaluate information about the nature and purpose of a trial, has enough time to deliberate, and is free from coercion, adequately informed consent can be obtained. Since the neonate is not autonomous, consent for trial inclusion is sought from one or both parents.

Problems with Current Methods of Seeking Consent from Parents of Sick Neonates

A) *Parental Distress Is Exacerbated*

The parents may be frightened by the unexpected onset and progression of preterm labour, and may have witnessed resuscitation attempts before hurried admission of their baby to the neonatal unit. In another common scenario (and a topical area of research) a full term baby has suffered hypoxic-ischaemic damage in labour, again needing resuscitation and urgent admission, and in consequence suffers respiratory failure or brain injury. In either case the parents may feel guilty and responsible for the mishap, or they may blame the hospital staff. The mother may be in pain, exhausted or experiencing the cognitive effects of analgesic or anaesthetic drugs.

Seeking consent for entry into a trial may aggravate the parents' distress. In the same breath as giving them worrying news about their baby's condition, to add further worrying information about possible risks of alternative treatments, to add the burden of seeking consent, and to ask them to read and sign a legalistic consent form, risks increasing their suffering. They may be further worried by the frank admission of the uncertainty that demands the research in the first place, and disappointed if their baby is randomised to control treatment.[4,5] If these actions hurt the parents without promoting substantial understanding of the research, they are being used as means to an end, the only beneficiary being the investigator, who has been seen to follow standard procedures.

These concerns have been borne out in practice. Parents of surviving babies enrolled in the recent United Kingdom extracorporeal membrane oxygenation (ECMO) trial completed structured interviews detailing their experiences.[6] Subjects were full term babies who had become very ill, often unexpectedly, in the first few hours of life. Information about their illness, and the nature and purpose of the trial comparing ECMO to conventional ventilation for respiratory failure, had to be given in these first hours. The decision whether or not to consent had to be made quickly. Parents described graphically their sense of fear and haste as they recalled being approached, sometimes disturbed from sleep, to discuss possible trial entry. Many perceived the doctor's requesting consent for trial entry as implying preference for the new treatment. They were then angry or distressed if their baby was randomised to conventional treatment. These were the recollections of parents of survivors. Those of the parents whose babies died are unlikely to be better.

B) Adequate Explanation of the Trial, and of Randomisation, Is Not Possible

Grave doubt has been cast on whether the recent delivery of a very ill baby permits reasonable parental understanding of the nature and purpose of emergency research, and autonomous authorisation for inclusion.[7] Again, the experience of parents of babies in the ECMO trial bears this out. Parents reported widely differing interpretations of randomisation. Some understood it as a means for rationing access to the new treatment, and some as a solution to difficult clinical decision making. Few understood the true purpose of randomisation.

While the circumstances of recruitment to the ECMO trial might have compromised rational deliberation, similar problems were reported in trials conducted in much less fraught circumstances. Harth and Thong reported parental perceptions of, and attitudes to, consent in a trial of an anti-asthma drug.[8] In this trial, the children were older and clearly less sick than babies in the ECMO trial. The parents received a telephone interview and written information at least one week before the child's initial evaluation. None the less, only a minority grasped the full purpose of randomisation. While 97% of parents understood the need to determine drug efficacy, only 13% appreciated the need to determine drug safety too. Many parents underestimated possible drug risks. More than 40% of parents perceived the requirement of a signed consent form, far from protecting the research subjects, as a mechanism for protecting the investigators from litigation. The authors concluded that careful adherence to consent procedures, even in non-emergency research, did not guarantee substantial comprehension by the parents. While more could possibly be done to improve the process of communication and obtaining consent in less fraught situations and when time permits,[9] it is difficult to see how substantial understanding can be improved in emergency neonatal research.

C) Voluntariness Is Compromised

Parents may also suffer constraints on voluntariness, another essential component of consent. Hewlett argued that the experience of illness, the accompanying psychological responses and the vulnerability of hospitalised patients all threaten voluntariness in clinical research.[10] These factors can overwhelm the parents of sick neonates. Harth and Thong suggested that psychological factors influence parents' decisions to enrol children in research, and compromise a rational decision to consent.[11] They reported that parents who consented to their children entering the trial of anti-asthma treatment described above were less well-educated, had less social support, and displayed more health-seeking behaviour than those parents who refused. Silverman voiced similar concerns in reporting that clinical research in the United States has been conducted more often on impoverished minorities than on the more privileged.[12] Walterspiel related how, when recruiting preterm subjects for a clinical trial, he found himself avoiding parents whom he felt were more likely to ask concerned questions.[13] If these experiences are generalisable, voluntariness as well as information processing is likely to be severely compromised in research on the sick neonate.

Other ethical problems arise if there are substantial psychosocial differences between parents who consent to, and those who refuse, recruitment of their babies. Psychosocial adversity worsens the neurodevelopmental outcome for very preterm babies. If babies from deprived families are included disproportionately in trials, the outcomes may not be generalisable to the whole population. Also, justice dictates that the burden of clinical research should be borne fairly by all social groups.

Therefore, the conventional process of seeking consent poses great problems in emergency neonatal research. It may aggravate the parents' distress. This distress, and the time constraints, compromise substantial understanding and authorisation, and thus respect for autonomy. Selection bias is likely, the results may not be generalisable and on utilitarian grounds, the research may therefore be unethical. Potential over-representation of the socially deprived is unjust. Can these problems be resolved?

Alternative Approaches — Waiver of Consent in Adult Emergency Research

Similar problems have arisen in seeking consent for emergency research in adults, for example in resuscitation medicine. In particular, the subjects may be incompetent, and there may not be enough time to contact relatives. A consensus meeting of critical care researchers in 1994 concluded that circumstances arose when subject or proxy consent in emergency research could not be obtained and that patients were vulnerable, not only to research risks, but also to being deprived of potentially beneficial therapy.[14]

The United States Food and Drug Administration (FDA) acknowledged this dilemma, and has produced guidelines for circumstances where consent may be waived in emergency research.[15] Criteria for considering a waiver include the following. The subjects must have a life-threatening illness which precludes their ability to give consent. Determination of the safety and efficacy of a new intervention is necessary. Appropriate animal and preclinical studies must support a reasonable expectation that the intervention will benefit the subjects, and that associ-

ated risks are reasonable given the severity of the illness and known risks of standard treatment. Representatives of the communities where the research will be conducted must have been consulted, and public disclosure must occur before starting the trial. The trial results must be reported publicly on completion. These latter requirements are important in emphasising the societal context of clinical research; the community has a stake, and must be consulted. The FDA also acknowledged the case for presumed consent.

Presumed Consent in Neonatal Research

Many of these criteria also apply to emergency neonatal research, and Morley advocated a similar approach with neonates.[16] He suggested some alternatives to conventional consent, including antenatal notification of a particular trial, and seeking antenatal consent from parents in the event of their baby meeting the inclusion criteria. The problem with such a specific request is that an individual baby is unlikely to meet the criteria for inclusion in a given trial. More broadly, parents could be advised during antenatal care that the hospital is engaged in neonatal research, and that this includes emergency evaluation of new treatments in, for example, very preterm babies, or those suffering perinatal brain damage. The information given could emphasise the difficulty of obtaining conventional consent in an emergency. It could be given to parents in less hurried and fraught circumstances than after delivery of a sick baby. Presumed consent could then cover several trials of emergency treatments in circumstances which precluded conventional consent. It should be supplemented by informing parents as soon as practical after birth that their baby is involved in the trial, and by regular meetings with them during their baby's involvement to share information and answer their questions — the concept of "continuing consent."

What are the criticisms of this approach? Autonomy is overridden in that consent to a specific intervention is bypassed. For the reasons outlined above, however, exercise of substantial autonomy may be impossible in emergency neonatal research. Another concern is that prospective parents may pay little heed to trial information given antenatally, assuming that their baby is unlikely to be affected. Some may ignore it altogether, and arguably in these events presumed consent is a fiction. These problems could be minimised by careful attention to communicating the information antenatally. This is likely to be less problematic than postnatal disclosure to the few parents whose babies become sick. Antenatal disclosure might be harmful in adding to parental worry and distress. Again this could be minimised by presenting the information sensitively. In an era of high parental expectation, to acknowledge that some babies are born early or unexpectedly ill, and need emergency care, is not inappropriate. Prospective discussion of research could also be beneficial in giving parents the message that research is an essential aspect of health care, including the evaluation of new treatments.

Opting Out

In contrast to conventional methods for seeking consent, in an opt out system the parents' consent would be presumed following antenatal discussion as outlined above, unless they had objected. The parents could opt out antenatally, or after inclusion of their baby in a trial, and if so the baby would receive conventional treatment. Modi argued that such a system would lessen the distress caused by seeking consent from parents of sick neonates.[17] It might be kinder in that it

removes at least some of the burdens of weighing the technical and emotive aspects of research, as well as the burden of having to decide whether or not to consent. Evidence supports this hypothesis. Zupancic *et al* reported that a significant minority of parents would prefer to have their doctor advise them on whether to include their baby in neonatal research than have to decide themselves.[18]

Not only might an opt out system be kinder, it might also increase recruitment, and thus generate valuable knowledge earlier. This benefit has twice been reported in low-risk, non-emergency research in children. Using an opt out system, Mutch and King reported 97% uptake for a project aimed at identifying disability, compared to 79% recruitment using the traditional opt in approach.[19] Rogers *et al* reported similar findings in a trial of primary care follow up for disadvantaged infants.[20] They also reported that mothers included via the opt out system scored significantly higher than the conventional consent group in recall and understanding of study purpose and methods. Kennedy *et al* reported that in Belgium a system of presumed consent for organ donation, with opting out, increased the yield of organs by 55% in 5 years.[21] Fewer than 2% of the population opted out, and fewer than 10% of bereaved families objected to organ removal, compared to 20–30% in the rest of Europe. The authors speculated that one reason for the social acceptance of the system was the moral benefit of sparing grieving relatives the burden of deciding about organ donation at a time of great psychological distress. This scenario is analogous to that of the frightened parents of a critically ill baby asked to consent to inclusion in a trial. The moral benefits of increased recruitment and sparing the parents further distress might equally apply.

Whether opting out would share the research burden more fairly is not known. Deliberation in less fraught circumstances antenatally might mitigate the psychological factors shown to influence parental participation in research, but this has not been tested in practice.

Criticisms of the opt out approach are similar to those of presumed consent, in particular that autonomy is overridden. Does the low opt out rate for organ donation outlined by Kennedy *et al* reflect this?[21] Do subjects fail to exercise their opt out right by default, rather than autonomously? This is a valid theoretical concern. It may be allayed by good communication of the problems and issues antenatally. The greater understanding reported for parents using the opt out approach suggests that satisfaction, rather than ignoring the opt out opportunity, was responsible for the increased recruitment reported.[21] Again, regular discussion with the parents while their baby continues to be involved in the study would offset the bypassing of autonomy. It would also help restore autonomy to the parents by offering more time for information sharing, and giving them the chance to withdraw their baby from the trial.

Adequately informed parental consent should still be sought for non-therapeutic or non-urgent research in babies, for example in nutritional therapy or developmental interventions. Whether or not therapeutic and non-therapeutic research are qualitatively different, there are moral differences between emergency and non-urgent research. In the latter, the parents' autonomy is not usually constrained by the distress of delivering a critically ill baby, and there will usually be much more time to evaluate information on the nature and purpose of the study, to deliberate, and to consent or refuse. Thus, conventional methods of seeking consent, including allowing at least 24 hours for parents to deliberate, should still be used for non-urgent research.

The Symbolic Importance of Consent to Trial Inclusion

Several authors have noted the paradox that a higher standard of consent is demanded for evaluation of new treatments in controlled trials than for trying such treatments unsystematically on clinical hunch. Lantos argued that, while controlled evaluation is safer than unsystematic introduction of a new treatment, the rigorous demand for consent for trial entry has symbolic significance.[22] Including a patient in a trial changes the doctor–patient relationship. The patient is being used as a means to an end, and the investigator's goal extends beyond the best interests of that patient to include benefits to society. Even if this is true, the distinction from clinical practice is more apparent than real. The surgeon who publishes a case report, or outcomes and complications of an uncontrolled series of operations (such as ECMO), uses his experience with individual patients as a means to the end of advancing clinical knowledge in the same way as the researcher. The controlled trial is ethically more justifiable, however, than the uncontrolled series, as it is more likely to clarify the efficacy and safety of a new treatment, interim data analysis is more likely to identify unanticipated adverse effects, and the risks of these materialising are minimised by randomisation. There is indeed evidence of an "inclusion benefit" of partaking in controlled trials. Reported previously in adult trials, this was also seen in a placebo-controlled trial of anti-thrombin therapy in neonatal RDS.[23] Babies randomised to placebo had a significantly shorter mean duration of ventilation than eligible non-randomised babies. Possible explanations include adherence to protocols reviewed rigorously by peers and ethics committees, the Hawthorne effect (the influence on performance of being observed closely), superior data analysis and interim monitoring of results. Whatever the explanations, Lantos acknowledged that the better outcomes of inclusion in a trial challenge the symbolic significance of the absolute requirement for consent.[22]

Research and the Community

The FDA requirement that the community be consulted before consent is waived for emergency research is important in acknowledging the increasing role for society in debating dilemmas in medical ethics. It might eventually facilitate research, as lay consultation may emphasise that research, rather than clinical judgment alone, is the ethically required norm for evaluating new treatments. Rigorous peer and ethics committee review could provide adequate safeguards of the interests of subjects. Kremers *et al* reported early experience in community consultation in resuscitation research.[24] They advertised the trial extensively in their community, and held a public meeting as part of the consultation process. The attendance was small, and all present supported the research. The authors acknowledged that further efforts might be needed to inform the public in order to elicit a broader perspective of response. None the less, their experience is encouraging and suggests that the public may support emergency research as an essential clinical responsibility. This approach could equally apply to the problem of emergency neonatal research.

Summary and Conclusions

Society must acknowledge the conflicting ethical demands for research in the sick neonate. It must reconcile the competing requirements for controlled trials of new treatments, considerations of justice and respect for autonomy. Recent experience emphasises the difficulty of obtaining consent from parents of sick neonates. Current methods for obtaining this are deontologically unsound in underestimating constraints on the parents' autonomy, and in effect serving to protect the investigator. From a utilitarian viewpoint, they risk the harms of increasing the distress of vulnerable parents and, by selection influences, obtaining results which may not be generalisable. The burden of research may be borne disproportionately by more vulnerable and deprived families. A system of presumed consent, with opting out, for including sick neonates in appropriate trials would overcome some of these ethical problems. It would respect autonomy in acknowledging the difficulties of obtaining informed consent in emergency neonatal research. It might reduce selection bias, thus producing more generalisable conclusions, and might be more equitable. Experience with opting out in non-urgent research, and in organ donation, suggests that recruitment might increase, thus generating knowledge earlier than with conventional methods. Given current concerns about neonatal research, the lack of adequate licensing of drugs used in the neonate, and the need to evaluate emergency treatments, such as neuroprotection in asphyxiated neonates,[25] this debate must take place urgently.

References

1. Conroy S, McIntyre J, Choonara L. Unlicensed and off label drug use in neonates. *Archives of Disease in Childhood* 1999;90:FI42–5.

2. Samuels MP, Raine J, Wright T, Alexander JA, Lockyer K, Spencer SA, *et al.* Continuous negative extrathoracic pressure in neonatal respiratory failure. *Pediatrics* 1996;99:1154–60.

3. Rothman DJ. Ethics and human experimentation. Henry Beecher revisited. *New England Journal of Medicine* 1987;317: 1195–9.

4. Perlman NB, Freedman JI, Abramovitch R, Whyte H, Kirpalani H, Perlman M. Informational needs of parents of sick neonates. *Pediatrics* 1991; 88:512–8.

5. Allmark P. Should Zelen pre-randomised consent designs be used in some neonatal trials? *Journal of Medical Ethics* 1999;25:325–9.

6. Snowdon C, Garcia J, Elbourne D. Making sense of randomisation: responses of parents of critically ill babies to random allocation of treatment in a clinical trial. *Social Science and Medicine* 1997;45:1337–55.

7. Mason S. Obtaining informed consent for neonatal randomised controlled trials — an elaborate ritual? *Archives of Disease in Childhood* 1997;76:FI43–5.

8. Harth SC, Thong YH. Parents' perceptions and attitudes about informed consent in clinical research involving children. *Social Science and Medicine* 1995;40:1573–7.

9. van Stuijvenberg M, Suur MH, de Vos S, Tjiang GCH, Steyerberg EW, Derksen-Lubsen G, et al. Informed consent, parental awareness, and reasons for participating in a randomised controlled trial. *Archives of Disease in Childhood* 1998;79:120–5.

10. Hewlett S. Consent to clinical research — adequately voluntary or substantially influenced? *Journal of Medical Ethics* 1996;22:232–7.

11. Harth SC, Thong YH. Sociodemographic and motivational characteristics of parents who volunteer their children for clinical research: a controlled study. *British Medical Journal* 1990;300:1372–5.

12. Silverman WA. The myth of informed consent in daily clinical practice and in clinical trials. *Journal of Medical Ethics* 1989;15:6–11.

13. Walterspiel JN. Informed consent: influence on patient selection among critically ill premature infants. *Pediatrics* 1990;85:119–21.

14. Informed consent in emergency research. Consensus statement from the Coalition Conference of Acute Resuscitation and Critical Care Researchers. *Journal of the American Medical Association* 1995;273:1283–7.

15. Adams JG, Wegener J. Acting without asking: an ethical analysis of the Food and Drug Administration waiver of informed consent for emergency research. *Annals of Emergency Medicine* 1999;33:218–23.

16. Morley C. Consent is not always practical in emergency treatments. *British Medical Journal* 1997;314:1480.

17. Modi N. Clinical trials and neonatal intensive care. *Archives of Disease in Childhood* 1994;70:F231–2.

18. Zupancic JA, Gillie P, Streiner DI, Watts JI, Schmidt R. Determinants of parental authorization for involvement of newborn infants in clinical trials. *Pediatrics* 1997; 99,1:117. URL: **http://www.pediatrics.org/ggi/content/full/99/l/e6**

19. Mutch I, King R. Obtaining parental consent — opting in or opting out? *Archives of Disease in Childhood* 1985;60:979–80.

20. Rogers CG, Tyson JE, Kennedy KA, Broyles S, Hickman JR. Conventional consent with opting in versus simplified consent with opting out: an exploratory trial for studies that do not increase patient risk. *Journal of Pediatrics* 1999;132:606–11.

21. Kennedy I, Sells RA, Deer AS, Guttmann RD, Hoffenberg R, Lock M, et al. The case for "presumed consent" in organ donation. *Lancet* 1998;351:1650–2.

22. Lantos JD. The "inclusion benefit" in clinical trials. *Journal of Pediatrics* 1999;134:130–1.

23. Schmidt B, Gillie P, Caco C, Roberts J, Roberts R. Do sick newborn infants benefit from participation in a randomized clinical trial? *Journal of Pediatrics* 1999;134:151–5.

24. Kremers MS, Whisnant DR, Lowder I, Gregg L. Initial experience using the Food and Drug Administration guidelines for emergency research without consent. *Annals of Emergency Medicine* 1999;33:224–9.

25. Edwards AD, Azzopardi D. Hypothermic neural rescue treatment: from laboratory to cotside? *Archives of Disease in Childhood* 1998;79:F88–91.

Some Ethical Issues in Dementia Research

B. Mahendra

The future extent of the problems to be posed by old age and senile dementia is not in dispute. Dementia refers to an acquired condition in which memory, intellect and personality are adversely affected, often but not necessarily in a progressive and irreversible way. Ninety per cent of cases of dementia occur in the senile population and about 10 per cent of the patients are pre-senile. The dividing line between senile and pre-senile groups is the age of 65, a purely arbitrary distinction traceable, it is alleged, to Bismarck who decided that State old age pensions should be payable at that age. The causes of dementia are several, dementia merely being the common endpoint of several pathological processes. Though senile dementia accounts for by far the most cases with over 700,000 patients in England and Wales, there are small but significant numbers of other kinds of demented patients — for instance about 5,000 sufferers with dementia due to Huntington's chorea —

and many of these often raise special problems of their own.

About 80 per cent of cases of dementia are beyond the scope of any reasonable prospect of cure and most dementing illnesses, in particular those due to Alzheimer's disease and multi-infarct vascular disease, tend to reduce life expectancy to a fraction of that to be expected in the healthy of the same age.

In the 20 per cent or so of cases who present with a picture of dementia and expect to be treated, there is at least a possibility that pathology, if not chronology, may be reversed and the sick old patient returned to society as a healthy old person. Straightaway, we are faced with the question of whether or not it is permissible to do research into dementia in the elderly.

Obvious though it may be, one has to emphasise that research into dementia is quite distinct from research into ageing. The problems of the *normal* aged in the population have become well known, especially since their numbers have begun to

Journal of Medical Ethics 1984; 10: 29–31. With permission from the BMJ Publishing Group.

change the demographic balance. The wider question, it is legitimate to ask, is whether it is justifiable to seek to transfer scarce resources in order to reverse sickness and prolong life by researching a group of patients who, when they are freed of pathology, may well, in contemporary society, expect in general to experience hardship and a certain measure of rejection by younger people.

If the elderly were invariably able to lead their lives with satisfaction and dignity in the absence of sickness, there would be no difficulty in urging that our energies be directed towards the pursuit of such knowledge and its application. But in a situation such as the one that obtains it might be felt that the traditional scientific belief in dispassionately pursuing any subject of interest may have to be tempered by the realisation that simply freeing people of pathology can raise other ethical problems. As in numerous other clinical situations the wider question of the quality of life to be enjoyed by the patient, or his counterpart when rendered free of illness, must be taken into consideration. Also, though the milieu of the elderly might already be considered unpromising it is a sobering thought that when the fruits of current research come to be consumed, the expectation must be, at present, that the socioeconomic circumstances of the elderly will have worsened and the quality of their existence become so much the grimmer.

It might be argued, therefore, that the researcher into dementia, before he becomes too carried away in his enthusiasm for errant molecules in synapses, has a moral duty to engage the younger members of society and confront them with the fact that it is not enough to assuage their consciences by sanctioning research into one of the more serious illnesses of old age while continuing to choose to turn away from the larger issue of social provision for the elderly population.

Sound clinical research begins with precise diagnosis utilising all available investigatory tools. For the most part, investigations on demented patients, including clinical assessment, psychometric evaluation, electroencephalograph (EEG) recordings, most blood-flow techniques and computerised tomography, are noninvasive and are accepted without controversy. Unfortunately, in our present state of knowledge, the diagnosis of the most important cause of dementia, Alzheimer's disease, is possible only by cerebral biopsy and by subsequent histological and, to a lesser extent, histochemical study. Any invasion of the brain arouses profound suspicion. Though the procedure for brain biopsy has a small but definite risk of complication, the objection and opposition to the operation is not so much this risk but perhaps the emotional difficulty on the part of patients, relatives and doctors in accepting an assault on this last great bastion of human anatomy. In this respect the issues are similar to the problems associated with electroconvulsive therapy (ECT), though the latter is part of therapy, the former part of diagnosis. With ECT, the possibility of aggravating underlying brain lesions and of producing memory impairment is also a small but definite risk to be weighed against the generally accepted efficacy of the procedure on severe, chronic and intractable cases of depressive illness. But the generally cautious and selective use of ECT these days has not damped very much the lively controversy that has surrounded this procedure, which has now been in use some fifty years and, again, the criticisms are not always based on real and calculable risks but on the grounds of "assault" on the patient's mind and dignity by this largely empirical procedure.

When it comes to cerebral biopsy, can the real risks of the operation on a given patient justifiably be set against the real risks of failure to gain precise knowledge of groups of patients by not performing it? Undoubtedly, at present, a diagnosis of Alzheimer's disease is likely to be only of academic interest as far as the individual patient is concerned. However, there is much work going on into the illness. When and if potentially therapeutic agents become available there can be little doubt that a reversal of the symptoms of the illness will only be successful if treatment is carried out immediately after early diagnosis. Current interest is focused on memory difficulties with histochemical correlates which need to be detected and countered by replacement chemicals. When this form of chemical treatment might become fully established and available is uncertain; but if the experimental drugs are not used on trial patients with early symptoms — subject, of course, to the usual ethical considerations applicable to clinical trials — there probably will not be any prospect for development of this treatment. Similar considerations apply to other potential treatments. However, the later stages of dementia, involving intellectual deficits and personality disorganisation as well, are not at present thought to be reversible.

Further, some 20 per cent of demented patients are treatable by conventional management of the causes of their dementing state. It is possible to argue with some conviction in this context that a negative biopsy result (meaning that the cause of the dementia is not Alzheimer's disease) may add extra impetus to the further search for a treatable cause. We know that Alzheimer's disease is not only one of the commoner causes of dementia, but also that it is one of those that is at present untreatable; on the other hand, if a biopsy does not reveal Alzheimer's disease, the chances that the cause is a less common but perhaps therapeutically more promising condition greatly improve. In these circumstances, it might be thought that ethical pressures would be in the direction of performing an early biopsy. Moreover, as Torack [1] has discussed, a normal biopsy result may afford a more favourable

prognosis than any pathological result, even when the dementia is of comparable severity. (This may seem confusing, but dementia is a clinical evaluation; the biopsy refers to a technical procedure. It is possible to be demented with a known cause, unknown cause or even with normal "pathology" on biopsy.) If it is agreed that there is a moral duty to inform patients fully of the implications of their illness, it may be argued there is a strong case for low risk brain biopsy in the search for relevant information about that illness.

Before any procedure is undertaken there is an assumption of consent, implied or explicitly given, on the part of the patient. Consent implies a rational mind capable of understanding the issues and possessed of the judgement necessary to consent. Unfortunately, among the cardinal features of the dementia syndrome are loss of insight, intellect and judgement. The very features which are of clinical interest are those the patient is deprived of when called upon to give consent. Except in the earliest stages of the illness the patient probably has little capacity to give fully considered consent to any procedure which the investigator wishes to undertake and, as the illness proceeds, this capacity is reduced even further to the point that a rational decision cannot reasonably be expected from a patient. In the later, and terminal, stages of dementia, consent regarding, say, autopsy and removal of the brain can only be obtained from relatives who will also be called upon to approve serial investigatory procedures, the first of which might have been done when the patient was in reasonably full possession of his or her faculties. In an effort to overcome this difficulty, the idea has been mooted of the "penultimate will" through which the patient, at the time of diagnosis (assuming it is relatively early in the course of the illness), makes his relatives the guardians of his body for the rest of his life. In theory, this would seem an admirably simple solution. In practice, it is most likely that intolerable pressure would be put on most relatives who might come to feel the term "executors" had taken on an unintended meaning. In these circumstances, the research worker will have to pay even greater heed to and be even more aware of the ethical implications of his activities and procedures if he is not to exploit a delicate situation.

These observations would apply in the main to the numerically large number of patients with senile dementia. An important pre-senile dementia, Huntington's chorea, presents special ethical difficulties for both clinician and research worker. Huntington's chorea is transmitted by an autosomal dominant genetic mechanism. Though the risk of disease varies with age the illness usually does not manifest until late adult life or middle age, by which time a third affected generation from the initial patient might already have been conceived. There is no certain method yet of determining carrier status, and any advice that might be given about the chance of developing the illness and hence the prospects for marriage and child-bearing can only inadequately be based on probabilities. Nonetheless, several tests have been used, and continue to be devised and used, to detect the carrier state, and surveys in Britain, the USA and Australia[2–4] have shown that 77 per cent to 84 per cent of subjects "at risk" or related to Huntington's chorea patients wish to be informed, when an effective test becomes available, whether or not they are carriers. A question in these circumstances is whether in the absence of effective curative or palliative treatment of this seriously distressing illness the whole truth should be revealed to these subjects. Perry,[5] a distinguished researcher into the condition, has said there is no justification for doing so. He says "I suggest that pending development of an effective form of treatment, scientists who perform pre-clinical tests on persons at risk should ensure that the results of individ-ual tests are not made available to those tested." He also believes that there is little evidence that the incidence of Huntington's chorea has been reduced by any preventive measures taken so far. "I wonder ..." Perry says "whether the non-directive approach towards genetic counselling that is now fashionable will ever succeed in reducing the incidence of Huntington's chorea ... I suggest that there is nothing inherently unethical in providing directive genetic counselling to persons at risk ... Directive counselling need not be authoritarian." This strikes one as being a slightly naive attitude. In being directive, the physician is surely being authoritarian, if only in the sense of exploiting his authority. There is also a lack of consistency in Perry's argument. On the one hand physicians are being urged to be conscious of their fallibility and helplessness and conceal the whole truth from subjects and yet, on the other, they are being advised to exert their authority to order the lives of healthy people in case the latter turn out to be affected and pass on the delinquent gene.

It seems extremely unlikely, in the light of the evidence from several countries, that subjects who submit themselves to tests will agree to go away empty-handed when the results become available to the investigators. Whether there is ethical justification under any circumstances for deliberately depriving subjects of knowledge that has been obtained by doing tests on their bodies is questionable. And whether an authoritarian — that is what it will be in practice — ban on the activities of individuals on grounds of probability is likely to be ethically justified (or effective) is moot.

One approach is to discuss the issues with persons "at risk" *before* the tests are undertaken. The nature of Huntington's chorea makes most relatives perfectly aware at first hand of the consequences of having the disease and if the subject opts out of a situation which might bring him face to face with a fateful future it is likely to be a well-considered decision.

The full extent of the ethical problems surrounding dementia may only be realised when senile dementia becomes, as it threatens to in the remaining years of this century, one of the main public health problems. On the other hand, and ironically, the sheer extent of the problem may well ease some of the ethical difficulties with which we are preoccupied today. The morality and ethics of birth control and abortion once preoccupied people to an inordinate degree and led to repressive attitudes on the part of those in authority. The realisation that strictures on birth control and abortion were incompatible both with increasing personal freedom and with the need for population limitation helped change attitudes. It is possible that realistic appraisal of a situation likely to arise in the fairly near future could exert a similar influence on our consideration of the ethical issues in dementia.

Acknowledgement

The author is supported by the Wellcome Trust.

References

1. Torack RM. Adult dementia: history, biopsy, pathology. *Neurosurgery* 1979;4,5: 434–442.

2. Barette J, Marsden CD. Attitudes of families to some aspects of Huntington's chorea. *Psychological Medicine* 1979;9:327–336.

3. Stern R, Eldridge R. Attitudes of patients and their relatives to Huntington's disease. *Journal of Medical Genetics* 1975;12:217–223.

4. Teltcher B, Polgar S. Objective knowledge about Huntington's disease and attitudes towards predictive testing of persons at risk. *Journal of Medical Genetics* 1981;18:31–39.

5. Perry TL. Some ethical problems in Huntington's chorea. *Canadian Medical Association Journal* 1981;125:1098–1100.

Further Readings

In the Matter of Kristie Lee F, P.C.C. (F.D.) Ontario (1072/88).

Berghmans, R.L. "Advance Directives for Non-therapeutic Dementia Research: Some Ethical and Policy Considerations." *J of Med Ethics* 24:1 (Feb. 1998): 32–7.

High, D.M., "Research with Alzheimer's Disease Subjects: Informed Consent and Proxy Decision Making." *J Am Geriatr Soc* 40:9 (Sept. 1992): 950–957.

Malone, R.P., and G.M. Simpson. "Use of Placebos in Clinical Trials Involving Children and Adolescents." *Psych Ser* 49:11 (Nov. 1998): 1413–1414, 1417.

McCormick, R. "Proxy Consent in Experimentation Situations," *Perspect in Biol and Med* 18:1 (1974).

Picard, E.I., and G.B. Robertson. *Legal Liability of Doctors and Hospitals in Canada*, Chapter 2, "Consent." Toronto: Carswell, 1996.

Pinker, S. "Am I My Brother's Keeper? Two Perspectives on Consent." *CMAJ* 165 (2001): 194–195.

Ramsey, P. *The Ethics of Fetal Research.* New Haven: Yale Univ. Press, 1975.

Superintendent of Belchertown State School v. Saikewicz, 370 N.E. (2d) C 417 (Mass. S.C. 1977).

Singer, P.A., and S. Choudhry. "Ontario's Proposed Consent Laws: 1. Consent and Capacity, Substitute Decisions, Advance Directives and Emergency Treatment." *CMAJ* 146 (1992): 829–832.

Wasserstrom, R. "Ethical Issues Involved in Experimentation on the Non-Viable Human Foetus," National Commission for the Protection of Human Subjects of Biomedical and Behavioral Research, *Appendix: Research on the Foetus* (1975) DHEW No. (05): 76–128.

Weijer, C. "Research Involving the Vulnerable Sick." *Account Res* 7:1 (1999): 21–36.

CHAPTER 12
PERSONHOOD

Introduction

Until fairly recently, the distinction between being a person and being a member of the species *homo sapiens* was of interest only to philosophers and theologians. It was generally assumed that any living human being was a person, and *vice versa*. Not only our traditions but also our criminal law reflect this fact.[1]

Three recent developments in health care have challenged this assumption. First, medical technology, such as respirators, dialysis machines, etc., was developed to the point that people could be kept alive considerably beyond the time when they otherwise would have died. However, in many cases, the people who were thus saved were left in a permanent vegetative coma because their higher brain centres had been destroyed. These individuals were therefore biologically alive but without any possibility of return to sentient cognitive awareness. In fact, in some cases, not only were their higher brain centres destroyed but in fact the whole brain — and yet for a time their bodies could be kept alive. The question arose whether these individuals were still persons. The thrust of the question was sharpened by the scarcity of medical resources. People therefore began to ask whether it was ethically appropriate to spend scarce resources to sustain someone who was only biologically alive when doing so would deprive others of appropriate and possibly beneficial health care.

A second development that influenced and expanded the debate was the advent of transplantation. It soon became evident that organs from living donors had a much lower rejection rate than organs from cadavers. This increased the pressure to examine the validity of the distinction between being biologically alive only, and being alive as a person.

Finally, the distinction between humanity and personhood was pressed when abortion became a public issue, and when the federal government attempted to draft an abortion law that would satisfy the multicultural and multi-religious makeup of Canadian society.[2] This pushed the debate about personhood to the very beginning of human life, i.e., it forced an examination of the question of whether a human being is a person from conception on, or whether personhood is acquired at some later stage. Some people saw a correlation between birth and death, and began to argue that the question of when someone is dead is really the question of when someone is *no longer* a person, and that this question could not ethically be divorced from the question of when someone is *already* a person. They maintained that whatever notion of personhood was ultimately developed, and however it was related to the concept of a human being, it would have to be applicable in a consistent fashion in both cases.

The selections below give an indication of the range of considerations that have been raised in the course of the debate. The case of *Re A. (in utero)*, which is reproduced in part below, specifically deals with the question of whether the courts may force a drug-addicted and pregnant woman to take appropriate steps to safeguard the welfare of her foetus, or whether this amounts to an unjustified infringement of her right to security of the person? However, in order to deal with the issue properly, the court had to consider the status of the human foetus. Is a foetus *in utero* a person in the eyes of the law? Because if the foetus is a person, then the courts have a duty to protect it. Although the case dates from 1990, it still reflects current Canadian law. Is this law, as it stands, ethically defensible? Should legal and ethical personhood be judged according to the same criteria?

On the issue of when someone is *no longer* a person, the case of *R. v. Kitching and Adams* is the classic Canadian legal case. It endorses what has become known as a *whole brain* criterion. Roland Puccetti, who is a philosopher, pushes the envelope by asking whether individuals who are in a permanent vegetative state are still persons. These individuals do not meet the whole-brain criterion, yet they no longer have any capacity for sentient cognitive awareness. The issue is especially important in light of the chronic shortage of health care resources and the cost involved in keeping these individuals biologically alive. Issues such as resource allocation, right to health care, etc. that were dealt with in preceding chapters here become relevant.

Finally, the article by Gareth Jones explores the question of whether there really is a parallel between *not yet* being a person and being a person *no longer.* Jones casts the issue in terms of *brain birth* and *brain death* — and suggests that the parallel might not be as close as some people think. If he is correct, does this mean that there cannot be a single set of criteria for being a person?

Notes

1. Outside the criminal context, the law is not quite so consistent. Women were not recognized as legal persons in Canada until 1929, when the Privy Council of Great Britain extended that recognition by stating that the word "person" contained in the *British North America Act* extended to women as well as men. It is interesting to note that in this sense, children are still not recognized as persons.

2. Bill C-43, *An Act Respecting Abortion*, November 3, 1989.

Re A. (in utero)

...

Two issues must be addressed: (1) is there any authority in the court to intervene to protect the foetus in the manner sought by the Society? (2) is there any jurisdiction in the court to proceed to make an ex parte interim order of the nature sought by the Society? ...

In *M. (B.)*, ... Proudfoot J. of the British Columbia Supreme Court concluded at p. 283 R.F.L.:

> From the evidence before me of the physical problems that a baby born drug-addicted has to endure, it would be incredible to come to any other conclusion than that a drug-abused baby is born abused.

In *Re Brown*, supra, Judge Stortini adopted a comment by a psychiatrist to the following effect [p. 323 R.F.L.]:

> Every child should have certain basic rights such as: the right to be wanted, the right to be born healthy, the right to live in a healthy environment, the right to such basic needs as food, housing and education, and the right to continuous loving care.

It should be noted, however, that in both of the above cases, the judicial comments noted above related to children who had been born at the time the respective actions had been commenced. ...

I have reviewed the provisions of the *Child and Family Services Act*, 1984. I, unlike Judge Kirkland, cannot find anything in the definition of "child" (s. 3(1)

Item 6 "child") or in the declaration of principles set out in s. 1, or any other provision in the Act which would accord to the foetus any status as a person or right to protection under the Act. This is especially so since the legislature has repealed s. 6(2)(g) of the *Child Welfare Act*, R.S.O. 1980, c. 66 [repealed and replaced by the *Child and Family Services Act*, 1984, s. 208] which earlier provided that:

> 6(2) Every society shall be operated for the purposes of:
>
> ...
>
> (g) assisting the parents of children born or likely to be born outside of marriage and their children born outside of marriage ...

Nowhere does the phrase "children ... likely to be born" appear in the present *Child and Family Services Act*, 1984.

I note that in *Re Baby R.* (1988), 30 B.C.L.R. (2d) 237, 53 D.L.R. (4th) 69, 15 R.F.L. (3d) 225 (S.C.), Mr. Justice Macdonell concluded [at p. 234 R.F.L.] that under the *Family and Child Service Act* of British Columbia (S.B.C. 1980, c. 11), there was "nothing to be found in it that assists in expanding the definition of 'child' [s. 1] to include an unborn child". He reversed a judgment of a lower court upholding the apprehension of an unborn child.

In *Tremblay v. Daigle*, [1989] 2 S.C.R. 530, 62 D.L.R. (4th) 634, 102 N.R. 81, 27 Q.A.C. 81, at pp. 569–570 S.C.R., the Supreme Court expressly approved of the judgment of Macdonell J. in *Re Baby R.*

(U.F.C.) 75 O.R. (2d) 82 [1990] O.J. No. 1347 Action No. C/766/90.

In *Dehler v. Ottawa Civic Hospital* (1979), 25 O.R. (2d) 748, 14 C.P.C. 4, 101 D.L.R. (3d) 686, 3 L. Med. Q. 141 (H.C.J.) [affd (1980), 29 O.R. (2d) 677, 117 D.L.R. (3d) 512 (C.A.)] Robins J., as he then was, concluded at p. 757 O.R.:

> Since the law does not regard an unborn child as an independent legal entity prior to birth, it is not recognized as having the rights the plaintiff asserts on its behalf or the status to maintain an action. A foetus, whatever its stage of development, is recognized as a person in the full sense only after birth. In the law of torts or property, in cases involving inheritance or pre-natal injury, a foetus would have no rights if stillborn. Only upon live birth can rights acquired during gestation be asserted. ... In short, the law has set birth as the line of demarcation at which personhood is realized, at which full and independent legal rights attach, and until a child *en ventre sa mére* sees the light of day, it does not have the rights of those already born.

Finally, he stated at p. 761 O.R.:

> The question of when life begins is one which has perplexed the sages down the corridors of time. In my respectful view, even if the theological, philosophical, medical and jurisprudential issues involved in it could be answered in a court-room, the answer would be beside the point in so far as this lawsuit is concerned. Accepting as fact the conclusion the plaintiff seeks to establish by testimony at trial, that is, that a foetus is a human being from conception, the legal result obtained remains the same. The foetus is not recognized in law as a person in the full legal sense.

I find, therefore, that there is no jurisdiction in this court to grant the relief claimed by the applicant. ...

The question still remains as to whether the court must remain passive in light of the apparent facts of this case which indicate that unless the mother obtains proper pre-natal care and proper medical care on the delivery of the foetus, there may be irreparable harm visited upon it.

This case is considerably different from those cases which have dealt with the foetus' rights to be protected from a mother's decision to abort her pregnancy: see *Dehler v. Ottawa Civic Hospital*, supra, and *Tremblay v. Daigle*. ... This is not an instance where a court would presume to force upon a woman the obligation to bear an unwanted child. The mother in this case has made a decision to bear the child full term. In fact, the child is now at full term. The society seeks some type of order to require the mother to take proper precautions to ensure the child has a proper birth in light of the evidence that that may not happen.

While I agree with the conclusion of Mr. Justice Robins in the Dehler case that a "foetus is not recognized in law as a person in the full legal sense," having regard to the age of the foetus in this case, he or she has developed virtually all the attributes of a person in law, without in fact being one. As such, the foetus in this case may truly be likened to a person under a disability, and perhaps deserving of some protection.

It also seems to me that the mother, having opted to give life to the foetus, and having raised it to full term, has a duty to ensure that the balance of her pre-natal care and the child's birth be effected in a proper manner, having regard to her apparent medical problems. This is simply a reflection of the mother's natural duty in such circumstances.

The applicant now submits that I exercise my *parens patriae* powers vested ... in order to protect the foetus. ...

However tempted I might be to intervene under the court's paternalistic powers, I reluctantly conclude that I cannot do so. The essence of the *parens patriae* power is that the court is empowered to take steps to protect the child or the foetus, in the place of the parent. But here the child is actually inside of the mother. It is, therefore, impossible in this case to take steps to protect the child without ultimately forcing the mother, under restraint if necessary, to undergo medical treatment and other processes, against her will. I believe that the *parens patriae* jurisdiction is just not broad enough to envisage the forcible confinement of a parent as a necessary incident of its exercise. Even if it were, however, the court should be very wary about using its powers in such instances, as its routine exercise could possibly lead to some abuse of pregnant mothers. ...

I respectfully agree with the judge below in this case that to accept such jurisdiction and yet to apply the principle that it is the interest of the child which is to be predominant is bound to create conflict between the existing legal interests of the mother, and those of the unborn child and that it is most undesirable that this should occur.

Next, I think that there would be insuperable difficulties if one sought to enforce any order in respect of an unborn child against its mother, if that mother failed to comply with the order. I cannot contemplate the court ordering that this should be done by force, nor indeed is it possible to consider with any equanimity that the court should seek to enforce an order by committal.

There is no doubt that the state has an interest in protecting those foetuses that mothers have decided to bring to full term, but the means and criteria for their protection had best be left to the legislature or Parliament and not to the discretion of the judiciary.

This motion is dismissed.

R. v. Kitching and Adams

Matas J.A. (dissenting in part) (Monnin J.A. concurring): — The appellants, Adams and Kitching, were charged with causing the death of D. G. Junor by means of an unlawful act, thereby committing manslaughter. They were convicted on the charge after a trial before Hunt J. and a jury, and were sentenced to penitentiary for five years and four years respectively. This is an appeal from conviction and sentence.

Around midnight, 23rd July 1975, Junor was seen at the Vibrations Discotheque, a bar attached to the St. Charles Hotel in Winnipeg. Junor ordered a drink, and shortly after was seen sitting in a chair with his feet up on another chair, his head slouched forward and his chin resting on his chest. (It became known later that Junor had a blood alcohol reading of 267 milligrams per 100 millilitres of blood.)

(1976) 6 W.W.R. 697 (Manitoba Court of Appeal).

One of the waiters employed at the Vibrations tried to rouse him but was unsuccessful.

Within a few minutes Junor was taken outside by two men and dropped onto the concrete sidewalk. A cab driver stationed near the hotel saw the manoeuvre and said that when Junor was dropped, his face hit the sidewalk, making a sound which was described as: "a squishy sound, like, say a tomato hitting against concrete."

...

An ambulance was called. On arrival, the ambulance attendant examined Junor, did not detect any sign of life and tried resuscitative procedures. Junor was taken to the Health Sciences Centre, with the procedures being continued. On arrival at the hospital, shortly after 1:00 a.m. on 24th July, Junor was examined by Dr. Donan, the resident in charge of the intensive care unit. Dr. Donan noted that the patient had no respiration, pulse, or activity of the heart. Seven minutes after continued resuscitative procedures, a pulse was obtained and respiration was restored. Junor was admitted to the intensive care unit. During the early morning he was attached to a respirator and to several monitoring devices.

At 7:00 a.m. on 24th July, Dr. Tweed, an anaesthetist, examined Junor and found he was deeply unconscious, totally unresponsive to voice or deep painful stimulation and with no significant neurological signs. When removed from the respirator he breathed spontaneously but his breathing was shallow and inadequate. Dr. Tweed diagnosed a brain injury. At 11:30 p.m., the same day, Dr. Tweed found, in summary, that Junor had a complete absence of function at any level of his brain and that his outlook for recovery was hopeless.

Dr. A. J. Gomori, a neurologist, was called in as a consultant and he examined Junor in the early afternoon of 24th July and at 11:00 a.m. on 25th July. On the second examination, Dr. Gomori found that Junor was unable to breathe on his own, there was no evidence of response to external painful stimuli and there were no reflexes; Dr. Gomori could not detect any brain stem function; all of this indicated "brain death" and no chance of any recovery.

In the early afternoon of 25th July Junor suffered a cardiac arrest, which normally would have ended his life. However, Junor's bodily functions were maintained until his kidneys could be removed for transplant purposes. The purpose of maintaining the bodily functions, latterly, was to preserve Junor's organs, not his life. After removal of the kidneys the artificial respirator was turned off; the EKG, monitoring the heart, continued to show electrical activity for 13 minutes.

The formal death certificate was completed upon removal of the kidneys.

Dr. J. R. Taylor, a pathologist, conducted an autopsy on the morning of 26th July 1975. He said there were two major findings: two hairline fractures of the base of the skull and extensive degenerative changes within the brain itself. The injuries to the skull and brain were consistent with a fall. According to Dr. Taylor, the principal injury was "the brain lesion, the total and absolute death of the brain." Dr. Taylor summarized his findings as follows:

Well, as I have said at the time of autopsy I found several things. He had an absence of kidneys for one thing. Incidently [*sic*] he had evidence of highly bronchial pneumonia. Thirdly, he had, and most significantly to my mind, he had evidence of severe and irreversible brain injury at the time of death. How that injury came about can be interpreted in one of two ways. At least, but primarily, it was I think due to a blow which was sufficient to crack his skull. It was sufficient to produce subarachnoid hemorrhage, and it might, but I can't prove this, it might have been sufficient at the time to have damaged this man's brain. It could have damaged the hypothalamus, or some other part of the brain. At the time of autopsy all I can suggest is one of two pathways of this finding of the final condition of the brain. Either it was caused at the time of the initial injury or the death of the brain was a result of a sequence of events starting with the injury and the brain swelling, compression of blood vessels, and from the compression of the blood vessels to the death of the brain, with the same final end result. At the time of autopsy it is not possible to say when or which pathway this man took. I think it would require other evidence of the state of his nervous system, the function especially of his hypothalamus at the time that he was admitted, to be able to elucidate and at this point I cannot expand on that factor.

The jury heard detailed evidence from all the doctors who were called by the Crown on the several tests given Junor and his progressive medical condition; as well, there was an exhaustive exploration of the difficult criteria for determining death and the basis for use of those criteria.

...

The question of the cause of death was left to the jury for their decision. They obviously decided, after weighing all the evidence, including the extensive medical testimony, and the judge's charge, that Junor had died as a result of acts of appellants. In my view, the learned trial judge, if anything, gave more credence than was warranted to the defence that death was caused by the doctors, in respect of the transplant.

O'Sullivan J.A.: — Counsel for the accused argued that their clients should

not be convicted of manslaughter because there was a possibility on the evidence that the deceased, Mr. Junor, was killed not as a result of the acts of the accused, but as a result of the acts of doctors at Health Sciences Centre in Winnipeg, who removed the deceased's kidneys and shut off a life-supporting ventilator.

The actions of the accused took place on 24th July 1975 about 1:00 a.m., when Mr. Junor was dropped on the sidewalk while being taken out of the Vibrations.

On 25th July 1975, at about 1:00 p.m., the deceased's heart was beating spontaneously and his lungs were breathing with the help of a ventilator.

At that time the deceased's body was taken to an operating room and both kidneys were removed for potential transplantation.

About 2:10 p.m., following removal of the kidneys, the ventilator was shut off. The heart continued to beat on its own for 13 minutes. Then the heart stopped beating.

It was only after the kidneys were removed that Dr. W. A. Tweed certified the death of Mr. Junor. No one at Health Sciences Centre had pronounced him dead before the removal of the kidneys.

The contentions of counsel raise far-reaching questions of law relating to death, its definition, and the time of death.

By traditional criteria, there is no question that Mr. Junor was alive when his kidneys were removed. Traditionally, both law and medicine have been unanimous in saying that it is not safe to pronounce a man dead until after his vital functions have ceased to operate. The heart has always been regarded as a vital organ.

Since the introduction of organ transplantation, however, many physicians and moralists have sought to establish new and different criteria for determining the time and the fact of death.

It is apparent that the fresher the kidneys, the better chance the recipient will have. It is apparent that in the case of a heart transplant there is no use transplanting a dead heart. The heart must be alive if the recipient of it is to have any chance of life. The problem facing medicine and society in recent years is: How do you get a living heart out of a dead body? If a person is not dead until after his heart ceases to function, it is practically impossible to imagine a successful heart transplant except by taking a living heart out of a still living person. But this is abhorrent to the conscience of many people.

So a substantial body of medical opinion has come forward with the suggestion that the concept of death itself should be redefined.

Some have said, if a man is "as good as dead," we will call him "dead" and then there will be no ethical problem about taking out his vital organs.

Some doctors have said that a person is as good as dead, and is therefore dead, if he is in such a condition that it can be predicted with confidence that he will never again be able to be restored to meaningful life.

Others have advanced the proposition that death is not an event but a process and when the process of death reaches a stage where a doctor is of the opinion that the process is irreversible the person should be declared dead.

Dr. Tweed advanced this view in this case before the jury and the learned trial judge appears to have adopted it for he said to the jury, "It appears that death is a process, not an event, as I stated earlier."

This is a most controversial statement, at variance with centuries of religious tradition. It is a statement vigorously disputed in many medico-legal books, for example, in Gray's *Attorneys' Textbook of Medicine*, (3d) 1975 (Supp.), vol. 1B, para. 29.11. Religion has taught us that death is an event. Dying may be a process, but death is an event. Except for some small sects, such as those in Rumania, who believe that death is a process during which the soul is in a state of suspended animation (hence, perhaps

residing in vampire bats), the overwhelming weight of religious teaching all over the world is that the moment of death occurs when the soul leaves the body. This is true not only of Christians, who believe in the personal immortality of the individual soul and the immediacy of judgment after death, but also of eastern religions which believe in the transmigration of souls at the moment of death.

Furthermore, by common consent, it has been held by all civilized people that no one, for however laudable a purpose, has the right to dispatch a dying man so as to hasten his death. Most moralists agree that it is not wrong to withhold extraordinary treatment to prolong the life of a dying man. It is not wrong to let him die. But directly to dispatch him by cutting out his heart or his lungs or his kidneys is contrary to every principle of civilized morality, as held by large numbers of citizens.

Another large body of medical opinion, I think the most substantial body, accepts the fact that death is an event and not a process. They say that the criteria for "defining" death are really criteria for determining the manifestations of death. It is true that the fact of death is manifested where all the vital signs, including heartbeat, have ceased. But, they say, it is equally true that the fact of death is manifested if all activity of the brain has ceased for a sufficient period of time. If the brain of a man is dead, then it is safe to say that the whole man is dead. It is the activities operated through the brain which differentiate man from an animal. If the brain is dead, he is dead.

This approach has gained widespread support not only among doctors but among moralists as well and has received legislative recognition in some states and in the Province of Manitoba.

This opinion does not proceed on the principle that if a man will surely die, then it is safe to call him already dead. It operates on the principle that, if a man's brain is dead, he is dead.

The trouble is that it is not always obvious when brain death occurs. There are well documented cases where a man's brain has shown absolutely no sign of activity for two days or more and yet he has recovered and survived. This is particularly so where a man has ingested large quantities of central nervous system depressants such as barbiturates.

There has been a great deal of debate about this subject and the debate is likely to go on for some time.

Many eminent physicians, including an ad hoc committee of doctors of Harvard University, have established certain criteria for determining brain death. Among the requirements are flat EEGs taken 24 hours apart. The possibility of barbiturate consumption being excluded, they say that if there is no sign of brain activity during a 24-hour period, it is then safe to say that the brain is dead and hence that the man is dead.

In the case of the deceased, Mr. Junor, the Harvard criteria were not followed. Twenty-four hours before the kidney transplant there was evidence of brain stem activity. Neither were the criteria proposed by Cornell University doctors followed.

Faced with the difficulties inherent in establishing universally acceptable criteria for determining brain death, many doctors have said that the safe course is to have at least two doctors certify death before allowing removal of vital organs.

Thus, a world assembly on medicine held in Australia in 1968 said, "If transplantation of an organ is involved, the decision that death exists should be made by two or more physicians, and the physician determining the moment of death should in no way be immediately concerned with the performance of the transplantation."

Many hospitals have regulations requiring such certificates of death prior to removal of vital organs. According to the evidence, the Health Sciences Centre has no such protection for potential donors.

These questions are important and they may have to be considered by the courts some day. In my opinion, however, they were not properly before the court in the case before us.

The legal and ethical implications of the conduct of doctors are no doubt under constant and careful review by peer review committees, by the Colleges of Physicians and Surgeons, and by others.

I think it is regrettable that the doctors at Health Sciences Centre were subjected to the lengthy questioning in this case. I do not think that the trial in this case, or in cases similar to it, affords a suitable forum for discussing these important questions.

I think that counsel for the accused proceeded on a fundamental misconception of the law. They assumed that, if it could be shown that death resulted in this case from the removal of the kidneys, then the accused should be acquitted because there would be a reasonable doubt that they had been the cause of death.

The assumption underlying counsel's conduct in this case is that there can be only one cause of death. I think the law is that the conduct of a defendant in a criminal trial need not be shown to be the sole or "the effective" cause of a crime. It is sufficient if it is a cause. ...

I think the authorities are clear that there may be two or more independent operative causes of death.

Without in this case criticizing the doctors of Health Sciences Centre or suggesting that they were guilty of any improper conduct, I am of the opinion that their conduct was irrelevant to the questions before the jury. Even if it could be shown that the actions of the doctors constituted an operative cause of Mr. Junor's death — and I emphasize that I do not suggest that the evidence would support such a conclusion — still that would not exonerate the accused unless the evidence left a reasonable doubt that the accused's actions also constituted an operative cause of the deceased's death.

On that question, the evidence was overwhelming. Whether or not the kidneys had been removed, the deceased could not have lasted more than a short period of time even with artificial assistance.

The jury had to decide not whether the doctors were ethical or not but simply, did the accused cause the death of the deceased by unlawful means? The question of causation was put to the jury plainly; they decided that the accused did cause the death. The evidence was overwhelmingly in favour of their verdict.

On the matters raised by defence counsel on the subject of conviction, I am in substantial agreement with the reasons of my brother Matas.

I would not say, however, that the learned trial judge answered the jury's question satisfactorily. Although he said that criminal negligence was not the jury's major problem, it is obvious, I think, that the jury had directed its mind toward the possibility of finding the accused liable on the basis of their criminal negligence. I think the trial judge left the jury with the impression that they could convict the accused of manslaughter if they concluded that the accused caused death not by

unlawful act but by criminal negligence.

The accused were acting in the course of a duty. Their actions amounted to the unlawful act of assault only if they used more force than was reasonably necessary.

A wanton and reckless disregard for the deceased's safety might have made the accused guilty of manslaughter by criminal negligence but they were not charged with that.

Had the charge been worded suitably, this distinction would not have been material. But the Crown chose to charge only manslaughter by unlawful act. Why the Crown did so we do not know. But the Crown is bound by the charge it brings. Otherwise the accused might be convicted of that of which they have had no proper notice.

Nevertheless, I am prepared to apply the provisions of s. 613(1)(*b*)(iii) because I am satisfied that the jury could not, as reasonable men, have done otherwise than find the accused guilty of manslaughter by unlawful act.

...

Does Anyone Survive Neocortical Death?

Roland Puccetti

A person is dead when an irreversible cessation of all that person's brain functions has occurred. The cessation of brain functions can be determined by the prolonged absence of spontaneous cardiac and respiratory functions.

— Law Reform Commission of Canada Working Paper 23 (1979, pp. 58–59)

An individual with irreversible cessation of all functions of the entire brain, including the brain stem, is dead.

— *Defining Death,* President's Commission ([15], p. 162)

"Does Anyone Survive Neocortical Death?" by Roland Puccetti. *Death: Beyond Whole-Brain Criteria,* Richard M. Zaner, ed. (1988), pp. 75–90. Reprinted by permission of Kluwer Academic Publishers.

One day on a very cold morning, I started the engine of my car without opening the garage door, then retreated to the kitchen to let it warm up. At that moment there was a long distance phone call from my publisher, and I spent a half hour haggling over the terms of a contract. Upon returning to the garage I found there, alongside the car, my dog Fido. Of course I immediately opened the automatic door and carried him outside into the fresh air. When I saw he wasn't breathing I pressed rhythmically on his chest cavity, and sure enough his heart and lungs started to respond. But still he did not wake up, so I took him to the vet's on the way to the university. The vet said Fido appeared to be comatose as a result of carbon monoxide poisoning, and advised that I prepare myself for the worst. He said it seemed the dog would not recover consciousness because the top of the brain was destroyed, although the brain stem must be intact, since Fido could breathe unaided. What should I do?

Now suppose I told you that I did the following. I took Fido home, made a special bed for him, shaved his body and fitted him with diapers, learned to feed him intravenously and nasogastrically, and arranged to have him turned in his bed often so he would not develop pressure sores. Evenings I would watch TV alongside Fido, stroking his warm body and listening to his breathing, though never again did he go for a walk with me, fetch the newspaper, bark, or do anything dogs normally do.[1] Would you think I am a rational person? Or worse, suppose I asked the vet to put Fido down for me and he replied that he couldn't do that to a comatose canine capable of spontaneous breathing, *because the law forbade it.* Would you think this a rational society?

If your answers to those questions are, as I think they would be, resoundingly negative, then presumably the main reason for your negative response

is simply that my ministrations would do *no good* for Fido, who has permanently lost consciousness even if he is nonapneic; for the same reason, *no harm* can be done to him by stopping his breathing. In other words, a permanently unconscious dog is, for all practical purposes, a dead dog anyway.

Now change the above apocryphal story in just one detail. Instead of it being Fido on the garage floor, it is my neighbor's infant son, little Bobby. I rush him to a children's hospital, but with the same result. Now could what was agreed to be irrational behavior in Fido's case become rational in Bobby's case? That a human life is much more valuable and worth preserving at all costs is completely irrelevant, since we agreed before that the main consideration was simply that one can do neither good nor harm to an irreversibly comatose being, and that should hold true independently of his species identity.

Yet, and this is what I find amazing, a great number of otherwise very able people in the legal and health professions think just the opposite. But before we examine their arguments, let us get one point absolutely straight. No matter what your calling, any position you adopt on this issue is going to be a *philosophical* stand. For the question we are addressing here is quintessentially philosophical: namely, *what constitutes* (in this world anyway, to avoid begging religious questions) *personal death?* This does not mean a poll of professional philosophers will settle the matter, for by that standard the Earth must have been flat in the Middle Ages, before it became spherical again in the Renaissance. Nevertheless, you cannot offer argument as to when a person may be safely considered dead without doing philosophy. The question, of course, is whether you are doing philosophy well or badly. I begin with an example of what I consider bad philosophizing on this subject.

I. Walton on Cerebral vs. Encephalic Death

In his recent book, Douglas N. Walton asks why proponents of the cerebral or neocortical criterion of brain death are not even more selective.

> The reply (that it is the cerebrum which mediates cognitive activity in the brain) is still not entirely satisfactory. However, it seems equally plausible to say that mental activity of the higher cognitive sort takes place essentially in the cerebral cortex, the thin membraneous [sic] substance that forms a mantle over the cerebrum. Why include the lobes of the cerebrum under the cortex if lower parts of the midbrain or the cerebellum and brain stem are excluded? ... [The cerebral death advocate] might argue that it is safer to include the whole cerebrum, because there is a possibility of indeterminacy or error. But then, if tutiorism (chancing error to be on the safe side) is brought in, why not be even safer and take into account the whole-brain ([18], p. 50)?

To which one can counter: if it is better to err on the side of safety, why not wait until complete somatic death (including, e.g., cartilage cells in the knee) occurs, thereby foregoing organ transplantation? The reason cerebral death includes the lobes of the cerebrum beneath the cortical surface is that these are composed of association fibers (white matter) that interconnect neocortical motor and sensory areas (grey matter); if these are selectively destroyed (e.g., in asphyxiation), the result is a shattered self with isolated conscious functions [5]. If, on the other hand, the neocortical surface is itself selectively destroyed, which as we shall see is the case with apallic syndrome, that is sufficient to obliterate all conscious functions.

The case for excluding other subcortical structures mentioned by Walton in passing has nothing at all to do with tutiorism anyway. The midbrain is of course just the top of the brain stem, where the superior and inferior colliculi trigger orientating reflexes related, respectively, to sources of visual and auditory stimuli: such reflexive responses do not require conscious mediation, as we all know from finding ourselves turned towards an abrupt movement in the peripheral visual field, or in the direction of a sudden sound, before such stimuli register in consciousness. If a brain structure does its job unconsciously, then there is no reason to think its integrity in a comatose patient is evidence of residual conscious functions. Similarly with the cerebellum, which preorchestrates complex bodily movements, and under therapeutic electrode stimulation does not yield clear sensations [3]. The cerebellum probably also stores learned subroutines of behavior, like swimming or typing: precisely the kinds of things you do better when not concentrating on them. Why then is it necessary for the cerebellum to be dead in order to have a dead person on your hands?

Yet Walton seems to think that everything above the level of C^1 [i.e., above a particular cellular level in the cerebellum] directly contributes to a conscious mental life. His attitude seems to be that if something moves, it must or at least might have a life of its own, with its own kind of feeling. For example, of the pupillary reflex mediated by the lower brain stem he says:

> The pupillary reflex could, for all we know, indicate some presence of feeling or sensation even if the higher cognitive faculties are absent. Even if we cannot resolve the issue with the precision we would like and, indeed, just because of that, we

should be on the safe side. ... Following my tutiorist line of argument, it is clear that we cannot rule out the possibility that brain stem reflexes could indicate some form of sensation or feeling, even if higher mental activity is not present ([18], p. 69).

The statement fairly reeks of superstition. As we all know, when the doctor flashes his penlight on the eye, we do not feel the pupil contract, then expand again when he turns the light off. If not, then why in the world does Walton suppose that a deeply comatose patient feels anything in the same testing situation? The whole point of evolving reflexes like this, especially in large-brained animals that do little peripheral but lots of central information processing, is to shunt quick-response mechanisms away from the cerebrum so that the animal can make appropriate initial responses to stimuli *before* registering them consciously. If one could keep an excised human eye alive *in vitro* and provoke the pupillary reflex, the way slices of rat hippocampus have been stimulated to threshold for neuronal excitation, would Walton argue that the isolated *eye* might feel something as its pupil contracts?[2]

Apparently he would, since in his view the entire encephalon must be safely dead to justify a finding of personal death. The spinal cord, he agrees, presents no obstacle to a determination of death, because of the relative sparsity of its neurons and its accessibility to tactile stimuli exclusively. I quote:

The upshot is that brain death should include the whole-brain but nothing more. I would add that specially if we emphasize the element of reflective selfconsciousness or awareness ... the tactile stimuli accessible from the spinal cord need not be thought significant if, in the absence of a brain, there is no possibility of awareness of these

stimuli. The presence of a tactile reflex by itself need not indicate mental activity or consciousness ([18], p. 75).

But what is sauce for the goose is sauce for the gander. Why does a pinprick in the foot or hand, provoking a withdrawal reflex in that limb because of residual electrical activity in the spinal arc nerve pathways, count as a tactile sensation in the case of a cerebrally dead patient, but not in the case of an encephalically dead one? For consider: there is no such thing as a non-localized tactile sensation; to the question "Where did the accused touch you on your person?" there always is and must be a fairly specific answer. Even a statement like "I felt the spring sun warm my body all over, like a gentle kiss," is in a sense localized: it refers to all the skin surface on one side of the body, that facing the sun. Now what brain mechanism localizes sensations of touch? Surely it is the somatosensory strip posterior to the Rolandic fissure in both cerebral hemispheres (Brodmann's area 3), which is clearly gone in the cerebrally dead patient. No localization, no tactile sensation: thus Walton's unconcern for spinal cord–mediated nerve impulses from the skin surface is logically extendable to the entire subcortical architecture of the brain.

Walton nevertheless expresses deep puzzlement over this matter, and in fact at times comes perilously close to committing the Fallacy of Ad Ignorantiam. For example, wondering whether perception or awareness might not occur in the absence of higher cognitive functions, he writes:

It is hard to know how to define exactly what is meant by "higher cognitive faculties," so it is hard to be sure that we mean by this phrase something that definitely excludes all types of perception that might persist in deeper parts of the brain ([18], pp. 75–76).

But surely ignorance of whether a statement is true does not imply that we know it is false; the admitted complexity of the human brain does not carry with it the imputation that we cannot say *some* things about it with confidence. One thing I feel reasonably confident in stating is that sensations are not experienced without recruitment of populations of neurons in the grey matter on the cerebral cortical surface. And it is easy to see why this is so: the phylogenetic novelty of *neo*cortex is due to brain expansion in primates beginning about 50 million years ago to accommodate increasing intelligence, for where else could new cell layers appear but on the outer surface of the brain [9]? That being the case, sensation migrated there as well, and although deeper structures certainly contribute complexly to the sentient input, this is not transduced as sensation until, at a minimum, some 10,000 neurons are provoked to discharge on the surface of at least one cerebral hemisphere at the same time [16]. It is also plain why the contribution of subcortical mechanisms to this input does not itself implicate conscious perception. If it did, we would have sensations in *seriatum:* a baseball leaving the pitcher's hand would be seen as arriving by the hitter several times in succession as neural impulses course from retina to optic chiasm to geniculate body through the optic radiation to primary visual cortex in the occipital lobe. From an evolutionary viewpoint, that would be a recipe for disaster.

Walton makes the claim that, to be on the safe side, "we should presume that the whole-brain is required to produce mental activity" ([18], p. 74). Normally, of course, that is true, but from this it would hardly follow that, when the ultimate neuronal destination of neural input is no longer there, or is dead, sensations still occur. We can liken this proposal to having an express elevator that whisks passengers from the ground floor to executive offices on the top floor. If a nuclear strike blows off the top floor, it would be unreasonable to suppose that you could nevertheless conduct your business at still-standing intermediate floors. What Walton is doing is confusing the normally necessary contribution of subcortical mechanisms to sensation with the sufficient condition of neocortical functions. In the case of the primary visual system in man this is indisputable: destruction of Brodmann's area 17 alone, say by shrapnel wounds, brings permanent total blindness [7]; whereas a peripherally blind person with intact visual cortex can be induced to experience visual sensations by direct electrode stimulation of that grey matter [2].

Probably the sensation we worry most about in irreversibly comatose patients is *pain*. Now Walton may know that depth electrode stimulation intended to relieve intractable "central" or "thalamic" pain (where the pain is not localized at all), indicates that there are discrete "pain centers" in the thalami [14,17], and these are certainly subcortical structures that could survive neocortical death. Would this fact not tend to show that such patients might nevertheless experience pain, in line with Walton's tutioristic cautions?

Such a suggestion would be, I think, doubly wrong. It is wrong, first, because it incorporates an excessively *homuncular* view of the relation between brain structures and conscious experience. The "little men in the thalami getting pain messages" picture is absurd: it is *we* who get the pains, not those structures. And it is wrong, secondly, because if the firing of thalamic pain centers by itself gave rise to pain experience, then it surely follows that if we could excise this tissue, keep it alive *in vitro,* stimulate it electrically to threshold for discharge and record the neurons' discharging, we would have to say that there is pain going on *in the vat!* Anyone who would believe this is beyond reason.

II. People as Brain Stems

I want now to consider a specific case of neocortical death without brain stem death, in order to show the utter futility of acting on the stand Walton defends. There are many cases like this one, and in some, somatic survival subsequent to cerebral destruction far surpasses the present case.[3] Nevertheless, the case history here is remarkably complete. I give it *in extenso* so that I cannot be accused of glossing over some crucial fact [8].

Case 8. The patient (Th. Sv.) was a female who had been born in 1936. In July 1960, at the age of 24, she suffered severe eclampsia during pregnancy with serial epileptic attacks, followed by deep coma and transient respiratory and circulatory failure. In the acute phase, Babinski signs were present bilaterally and there was a transitory absence of pupillary, corneal and spinal reflexes. A left-sided carotid angiogram showed a slow passage of contrast medium and signs of brain edema. An EEG taken during the acute phase did not reveal any electrical activity. The EEG remained isoelectric for the rest of the survival time (seventeen years). After the first three to four months the patient's state became stable with complete absence of all higher functions.

Examination ten years after the initial anoxic episode showed the patient lying supine, motionless, and with closed eyes. Respiration was spontaneous, regular and slow with a tracheal cannula. The pulse was regular. The systolic blood pressure was 75-100 mm. Hg. Severe flexion contractures had developed in all extremities. Stimulation with acoustic signals, touch or pain gave rise to primitive arousal reactions including eye-opening, rhythmic movement of the extremities, chewing and swallowing, and withdrawal reflexes. The corneal reflex was present on the left side. When testing was done on the right side, transient horizontal nystagmus movements were elicited. Pupillary reflexes were present and normal on both sides. On passive movements of the head, typical vestibulo-ocular reflexes were elicited. The spinal reflexes were symmetrical and hyperactive. Patellar clonus was present bilaterally. Divergent strabismus was found when the eyes were opened (by the examiner). Measurement of the regional cerebral blood flow on the left side (ten years after the initial anoxic episode) showed a very low mean hemisphere flow of 9 ml/100g/ min. The distribution of the flow was also abnormal, high values being found over the brain stem. The patient's condition remained essentially unchanged for seven more years and she died seventeen years after the anoxic episode after repeated periods of pulmonary edema.

Autopsy showed a highly atrophic brain weighing only 315 grams. The hemispheres were especially atrophied and they were in general transformed into thin-walled yellow-brown bags. The brain stem and cerebellum were sclerotic and shrunken. On the basal aspect some smaller parts of preserved cortex could be seen. ... Microscopically the cerebral cortex was almost totally destroyed with some remnants of a thin gliotic layer and underneath a microcystic spongy tissue with microphages containing iron pigment. The basal ganglia were severely destroyed, whereas less advanced destruction was found in the subfrontal basal cortex, the subcallosal gyrus, ... the thalamus and hypothalamus, and in the subicular and entorhinal areas. In the cerebellum the Purkinji cells had almost completely disappeared and were replaced by glial cells. The granular layer was partly destroyed. The cerebellar white matter was partly demyelinated. In the brain stem some neurons had disappeared and a diffuse gliosis was found. Several cranial nuclei remained spared. The long sensory and motor tracts were completely demyelinated and gliotic, whereas transverse pontine tracts remained well myelinated ([8], pp. 196–198).

This clinical picture, confirmed by the autopsy findings, is known in the literature as "neocortical death without brain stem death," or more recently and appropriately, as "the apallic syndrome," for its characteristic feature is precisely destruction of the paleum, that cortical mantle of grey matter covering the surface of the cerebrum or telencephalon. As it happens, neurons composing the paleum are the most vulnerable to oxygen deprivation during transient cardiac arrest or, as in the above case, asphyxiation. Whereas in encephalic or whole-brain death, therefore including the brain stem that monitors respiration (which in turn provokes cardiac activity), the patient can be sustained on a ventilator for only up to a week in adults and two weeks in children before cardiac standstill, the apallic patient breathes spontaneously and demonstrates cephalic reflexes (also brain stem mediated), so that if fed nasogastrically or intravenously and kept free from infection, he or she can sustain somatic life for years or even decades after losing the top of the brain.

I said "somatic life," for without a paleum, the basis for a conscious and hence a personal life in this world is gone forever. But then what are we doing supplying intensive care to apallic syndrome patients? For surely the quality of life in a patient like Th. Sv. during all those seventeen years differed not one jot from the quality of life of someone buried underground for seventeen years. It was zero. Permanent unconsciousness is permanent unconsciousness whether the condition is associated with a body that lives by virtue of being able to breathe spontaneously or not. To deny this is to elevate spontaneous breathing to a principle of human life, something I find incredible. Yet this is actually the emerging consensus of the medico-legal community in North America, as indicated by my earlier quotations from the Reform Commission's Report in Canada for 1979, and the U.S. President's Commission's Report of 1981. Are there any good arguments to support this astonishing attitude?

The President's Commission goes out of its way to justify regarding a whole-brain dead person sustained on a respirator as a dead person whose organs are therefore freely transplantable, whereas cerebrally dead persons are still to be considered alive and requiring heroic maintenance procedures. Listen to this passage:

> While the respirator and its associated medical techniques do substitute for the functions of the intercostal muscles and the diaphragm, which without neuronal stimulation from the brain cannot function spontaneously, they cannot replace the myriad functions of the brain stem or of the rest of the brain. The startling contrast between bodies lacking *all* brain functions and patients with intact brain stems (despite severe neocortical damage) manifests this. The former lie with fixed pupils, motionless except for the chest movements produced by their respirators. The latter can not only

breathe, metabolize, maintain temperature and blood pressure, and so forth, *on their own* but also sigh, yawn, track light with the eyes, and react to pain or reflex stimulation ([15], p. 35).

One is tempted to cry out: *So what?* I can not only breathe, metabolize, maintain temperature and blood pressure, *on my own*, but also sigh, yawn, and react to reflex stimulation (such as the patellar reflex) when in a deep, dreamless sleep. Admittedly I cannot track light with my eyes, or react to a pinprick in the foot, without awakening, but that is because, with an intact reticular formation and intact primary visual system, the light I am tracking causes visual sensations, and with an intact somatosensory strip, a pinprick in the foot wakes me up because I feel it as such. The apallic syndrome patient *can* do both these things without awakening, of course, because those neocortical structures are permanently missing. In fact, he or she cannot do *anything* consciously anymore, because there is no one home in that head to wake up.[4]

This consideration seems to make no difference to members of the President's Commission, who then go on to say:

It is not easy to discern precisely what it is about patients in this latter group that makes them alive while those in the other category are not. It is in part that in the case of the first category (i.e., absence of all brain functions) when the mask created by the artificial medical support is stripped away what remains is not an integrated organism but "merely a group of artificially maintained subsystems." Sometimes, of course, an artificial substitute can forge the link that restores the organism as a whole to unified functioning. Heart or kidney transplants, kidney dialysis, or an iron lung used to replace physically impaired breathing ability in

a polio victim, for example, restore the integrated functioning of the organism as they replace the failed function of a part. Contrast such situations, however, with the hypothetical of a decapitated body treated so as to prevent the outpouring of blood and to generate respiration: continuation of bodily functions in that case would not have restored the requisites of human life ([15], pp. 35–36).

But what *are* the requisites of human life according to the President's Commission? Evidently they are the ability to breathe spontaneously, demonstrate cephalic reflexes, regulate body temperature, metabolism, and blood pressure, etc.: in other words, *to perform unaided the janitorial functions of the Central Nervous System, which requires no conscious direction or reflection whatsoever.* Thus by the standards of the Commission, a hypothetical decapitated human body treated so as to prevent the outpouring of blood, but with brain stem left intact so that these janitorial functions are performed unaided, qualifies as a live person with all the requisites of human life, whereas if someone lops off the stem and substitutes a mechanical respirator in its place, the patient becomes a dead person thereby. Again, what is the difference in quality of life, or even prospects for the quality of life, in the two cases? And again the answer seems undeniable: none whatever.

To sum up: either human life is rooted in brain stem function or it is rooted in the capacity for personal experience. If the former, then all vertebrate species are on an equal footing and what counts in medical ethics is just long-term organic functioning independently of our capacity to intervene. If the latter, then there is no ethically relevant difference in the status of encephalically and cerebrally dead people: they have both lost the neocortical basis of an ongoing personal life. The only surprising fact to come out of the apallic syndrome is, or should be, that corpses are really of two kinds: the vast majority that cannot breathe unaided, and a small minority that nevertheless can do this. Apneic or nonapneic, a corpse is still a corpse.

III. The Diagnostic Problem

In a still more recent writing Walton [19] returns to defense of the whole-brain criterion of death. He begins by restating his earlier scepticism about our ability to avoid negative error in diagnosis of the apallic syndrome. He says:

> However, physicians have not yet developed or tested proven, certainly safe criteria for the apallic syndrome or other so-called "vegetative states" more highly localized in dysfunction than whole-brain death. For the present, tutioristic reasoning dictates cleaving to criteria for whole-brain death ([19], p. 270).

I do not know what Walton understands by "certainly safe" criteria for diagnosis of apallic syndrome; since the practice of medicine is an empirical science, there is always room for error. However, an accumulation of diagnostic results like those given in the case of Th. Sv. seems strongly conclusive. If one can safely exclude the possibility of hypothermia or intoxication with a CNS depressive, which drastically lowers oxygen requirements of the neocortex, a repeated finding of diminished cerebral blood flow, to less than 20% of normal, is itself powerful evidence of pallial destruction. In fact, Lassen *et al.* [10] reported firm correlations between increases in blood flow to specific regions of the cortex of patients in the waking, conscious state when problem solving, and also a significant overall increase in blood flow to the cerebrum as a whole of about 10 per cent

during such activity. It therefore seems exceedingly unlikely that any kind of conscious experience is going on in a brain with use for less than a fifth of normal blood flow.[5]

However, with the advent of Positron Emission Tomography, all reasonable grounds for doubt can be removed. In PET scanning, the uptake of oxygen and particularly glucose in selective subregions of cerebral cortex can be measured and displayed in color on a video screen: yellow or green for normal metabolic activity, blue or purple for low or no uptake. Although as of a couple years ago the PET scan had apparently not been used to confirm a diagnosis of apallic syndrome [4], nothing could be safer, easier or more certain: the entire surface of the brain would be displayed in blue or purple. While such deep subcortical structures as the brain stem itself are not visualizable using the PET scan [11], the absence of apnea is by itself evidence of the integrity of the stem. So much for Walton's concerns about negative error in diagnosing apallic syndrome.

IV. Seeds of Doubt

Before leaving Walton's contrary stand on this issue, I want to reply to two further points he makes in that more recent defense of the whole-brain criterion. Neither is really very important, but they illustrate the tendency in philosophical debate to sow confusion among your opponents by almost any means at hand.

First, Walton says that even in the face of a repeated isoelectric EEG, where there is not death of the whole-brain, there can be *restoration* of cortical activity through reactivation of the brain stem arousal system. The imputation, of course, is that cortical destruction may itself be reversible. Where there is breath there is always hope.[6]

But Walton refers to only one case [6]. And he does not go on to say that the patient, victim of a motorcycle fall, was treated with electrode stimulation for only 19 days following five months' akinetic mutism, gave only partial signs of arousal, and at no time recovered spontaneous motor activity, leading to abandonment of the treatment. If this patient *had* recovered consciousness, then he could not have been correctly diagnosed as a case of post-traumatic apallic syndrome, for the fact is that no one, after age 16 or so, sprouts new central neurons. The failure in this case to secure sustained arousal is indeed confirmation of post-traumatic pallial destruction, and remains, sadly, incurable.

Walton's second fresh point in the debate alludes to findings by Lorber (reported in [12]), that some people recovered from infantile hydrocephaly, thus growing up with severely reduced cerebral hemispheres, can nevertheless function well: an example being that of a university student, IQ 126, who gained first-class honors in mathematics. This Walton takes to be evidence that the neocortex is neither the sole seat of consciousness nor, perhaps, crucial to the return of conscious functions.

One wants to scream aloud a commonplace of clinical psychopathology: When neural plasticity enters the picture, all bets are off! The neural plasticity of the infant brain allows a lot less than the normal quantity of grey matter to take over a wide range of functions that are usually diffused in greater brain space. This is strikingly and uncontroversially demonstrated in complete hemispherectomy for infantile hemiplegia, where control of the whole body (except for distal finger movements in the arm contralateral to the missing half brain) is found in adulthood [1]. Furthermore, as Epstein has said (quoted in [12]), hydrocephalus is principally a disease of the *white* matter of the brain (the cerebral ventricles, swelled by overproduction of cerebrospinal fluid, disrupt the axons of association fibers around them). It is pre-

cisely the *sparing* of nerve cells in the grey matter, even in severe cases of hydrocephalus, that explains the retention of conscious functions and high-performance IQs.

To summarize against Walton on both these points, *for those who have a normal history of neocortical development*, the integrity of the neocortex is essential to the continuance of a mental, and hence a personal, life. It follows from this that pallial destruction is equivalent to personal demise, and this has nothing to do with a residual capacity for spontaneous respiration. Thus both the wholly brain dead and the cerebrally dead patient are dead people, and it is only superstition to make a vital dichotomy between them.

V. Ethical Considerations

Many who have followed me so far would nevertheless balk at the problem of disposing of human remains capable of breathing spontaneously. They would say that active intervention to stop the breathing prior to preparation for burial is not only presently illegal (laws can be changed, and already have, to facilitate organ harvesting), but morally murder; and it is often argued that passive (by the non-continuance of treatment) as opposed to active euthanasia is the more humane course.

Both these replies miss the point. You can stab a corpse, but you cannot *kill* it, for it is already dead whether breathing or not. If neocortical death is agreed to constitute personal death, then a firmly diagnosed apallic syndrome patient is in no better or worse situation than the encephalically dead patient sustained on a respirator, whom we all agree is dead though still breathing artificially. Similarly, "euthanasia" means "mercy killing," but one cannot be merciful to a cadaver, for cadavers are beyond pain and indeed all further experience of this world. Indeed, if it were *my* nonapneic remains causing the problem, I want to insist in advance that the breathing be stopped, for by treating my body as if *I* were still alive, hospital personnel would be stripping me of human dignity: it is enough to have others change your diapers in the first years of life.[7]

Someone might suggest that the difference between defenders of the whole-brain criterion and defenders of the neocortical standard is that they envisage different logical subjects: the former taking that to be a still living, spontaneously breathing human *body*, the latter a *mind* now gone from this world. But if this were just a verbal dispute, it ought

not to matter much to the disposal problem in a more enlightened age. But in fact it does matter. Those taking the first view would have to say to enquiring relatives and friends, "He's still alive but permanently unconscious, so we're going to let him die of dehydration, starvation, or infection, whichever comes first." Whereas those taking the second view, which is my own, would logically respond in words like these: "She's dead but her body is still breathing, so we're going to stop the breathing and prepare her body for burial."

Needless to say, the latter formulation seems to me less cruel.

Notes

1. He might, however, occasionally wag his tail. Apparently this is spinal cord mediated, as dogs coming out of anesthesia often wag their tails. I owe this suggestion to John Fentress.

2. Of course no such contraction would occur, since the pupillary reflex is brain stem mediated; the point is strictly hypothetical.

3. McWhirter gives the following case: "The longest recorded coma was that undergone by Elaine Esposito (b. Dec. 3, 1934) of Tarpon Springs, Florida. She never stirred after an appendectomy on Aug. 6, 1941, when she was 6, in Chicago, Illinois, and she died Nov. 24, 1978 aged 43 years 357 days, having been in a coma for 37 years 111 days" ([13], p. 37).

4. Conversely, selective damage to the brain stem alone can produce a similar result, for without input from the brain stem's reticular activating system, untouched neocortical cells cannot be alerted to incoming stimuli and the patient never wakes up. In the apallic syndrome the lines, so to speak, are still up but no one is home; whereas with brain stem lesions sparing cells that monitor respiration, there is someone home but permanently slumbering because the lines are down. In either case a personal life in this world has ended, so the same remarks made in the section of this paper entitled "Ethical Considerations" will apply. It is perhaps confusion of the necessary contribution of the brain stem reticular formation to achieving conscious awareness with conscious awareness itself that motivates superstitious attitudes towards the apallic syndrome.

5. D. H. Ingvar has recently reported that cerebral blood flow in apallic patients has been measured using Xenon 133 gas inhalation and 254 scintillators that monitor oxygen and glucose uptake in as many square centimeters of superficial cerebral cortex on each side of the head. The video display is uniform: dark blue or purple on the entire screen, indicating little or no uptake of blood, because "these patients have no neocortex to supply with blood" (Ingvar, in a Symposium organized by the Faculty of Medicine, University of Montreal, entitled "Two Hemispheres: One Brain," on May 18, 1984).

6. An anatomist once suggested to me that there is hope for eventual restoration of cortical activity in experiments where embryonic fetal tissue has been successfully transplanted into homologous lesioned areas of the adult rat brain. While this may be encouraging with regard to treatment of, say, expressive aphasia, I do not see how one could hope to replace an entire neocortex that way; surely the survivor of such an operation would not be the original person.

7. This point was originally supplied by a former student of mine who has nursed apallic syndrome patients (name withheld).

Bibliography

1. Basser, L. S.: 1962, "Hemiplegia of Early Onset and the Faculty of Speech with Special Reference to the Effects of Hemispherectomy," *Brain* 85, 427–460.
2. Brindley, G. A. and Lewin, W. S.: 1968, "The Sensations Produced by Electrical Stimulation of the Visual Cortex," *Journal of Physiology* 196, 479–493.
3. Cooper, I. S. et al.: 1974, "The Effect of Chronic Stimulation of Cerebellar Cortex on Epilepsy in Man," in I. S. Cooper, M. Riklan and R. S. Snider (eds.), *The Cerebellum, Epilepsy, and Behavior*, Plenum Press, New York and London, pp. 119–171.
4. Feindel, W.: 1982, Personal Communication.
5. Geschwind, N. et al.: 1968, "Isolation of the Speech Area," *Neuropsychologia* 6, 327–340.
6. Hassler, R. et al.: 1969, "Behavioural and EEG Arousal Induced by Stimulation of Unspecific Projection Systems in a Patient with Post-traumatic Apallic Syndrome," *Electroencephalography and Clinical Neurophysiology* 27, 306–310.
7. Holmes, G.: 1945, "The Organization of the Visual Cortex in Man," *Proceedings of the Royal Society* (Biology) 132, 348–361.
8. Ingvar, D. H. et al.: 1978, "Survival After Severe Cerebral Anoxia, with Destruction of the Cerebral Cortex: The Apallic Syndrome," *Annals of the New York Academy of Sciences* 315, 184–214.
9. Jerison, H. J.: 1973, *Evolution of the Brain and Intelligence*, Academic Press, New York and London.
10. Lassen, N. A. et al.: 1978, "Brain Function and Blood Flow," *Scientific American* 239, 62–71.
11. LeBlanc, M.: 1983, Personal Communication.
12. Lewin, R.: 1980, "Is Your Brain Really Necessary?" *Science* 210, 1232–1234.
13. McWhirter, N. D.: 1984, *Guinness Book of World Records*, Bantam, New York.
14. Melzack, R.: 1973, *The Puzzle of Pain*, Penguin, London.
15. President's Commission for the Study of Ethical Problems in Medicine and Biomedical and Behavioral Research: 1981, *Defining Death: Medical, Legal, and Ethical Issues in the Determination of Death*, U.S. Government Printing Office, Washington, D.C.
16. Puccetti, R.: 1981, "The Case of Mental Duality: Evidence from Split-brain Data and Other Considerations," *The Behavioral and Brain Sciences* 4, 92–123.
17. Sem-Jacobsen, C.: 1968, *Depth-Electrographic Stimulation of the Human Brain and Behavior*, Thomas, Springfield, Illinois.
18. Walton, D. N.: 1980, *Brain Death: Ethical Considerations*, Purdue University Press, West Lafayette, Indiana.
19. Walton, D. N.: 1981, "Epistemology of Brain Death Determination," *Metamedicine* 2, 259–274.

The Problematic Symmetry Between Brain Birth and Brain Death

Gareth Jones

Introduction

In the 30 years since the designation of brain death as a new criterion for death, attention has been directed towards the central role of the nervous system in a number of areas of ethical decision-making. The notion that there exists a neurological end-point to human life has led to efforts at defining a neurological starting-point. This latter quest has led to the concept of brain birth (or brain life), signifying the converse of brain death.[1-3] Nevertheless, many scientific and ethical queries remained.[4,5]

The quest for a neurological marker of the first events of human life owes its impetus to the perceived symmetry between processes at the beginning and end of life. Burgess and Tawia write: "If conscious experiences ... are the aspect of our lives we value when we *look forward*, considerations of symmetry *dictate* that we first acquire a capacity for what we most value in our lives when we first become conscious.[5] They view the beginning of consciousness as the beginning of "cortical life." A concrete expression of this trend has been provided by Sass, who advocates the legal protection of "personal life (animate life) from the beginning of brain functioning (brain life) to its end (brain death)."[6]

Yet brain birth describes a progressive phenomenon which is leading somewhere new, whereas brain death describes the final point of an existence.[7,8] The contrast between these two states is striking, with brain birth centring around a discovery concerning personhood and brain death around a definition,[7] and with the *order* of neural embryogenesis standing against the *disorder* of neural death.[4,9] The symmetry argument also simplifies brain death criteria by overlooking the most appropriate definition of brain death, either loss of function of the whole brain (destruction of the cerebral hemispheres plus brain stem, or brain stem alone since this is a precursor of whole brain death), or irreversible loss of higher brain functions (total loss of consciousness and awareness, loss of cognitive faculties, representing widespread destruction of the cerebral hemispheres). This is a distinction between a *vitalist* interpretation, with its emphasis on biological integration, and a *personalist* interpretation, stemming from the significance of sentience or consciousness for the existence of persons. The contrast is between "mere human biological life" and "being alive as a person."[10]

Unfortunately, brain death has generally provided an undefined context for discussions regarding how best to describe events at the beginning of life. For instance, it is not clear what definition of brain death is being used in symmetry-based arguments. This gap is a far more serious one than generally realized, and the debate on brain birth can be taken much further by exploring its dimensions alongside those of brain death.

Journal of Medical Ethics 1998; 24: 237–242. With permission from the BMJ Publishing Group.

Brain Death — Fundamental Concepts

Whole Brain Definition

The Harvard criteria for a permanently nonfunctioning brain pointed to total and *irreversible* loss of functioning of the *whole* brain.[11] A flat electroencephalogram (EEG) was recommended as a confirmatory test.

Whole brain death refers to the irreversible cessation of function of both the brain stem and higher parts of the brain, including the cerebral hemispheres, although in the United Kingdom it refers to the brain stem alone, on the assumption that loss of brain stem functions is rapidly followed by cessation of function of the higher parts of the brain. In other words, brain stem death is seen as synonymous with death of the individual, since loss of functions associated with the brain stem results in the individual ceasing to function as an independent biological unit.[12]

From this it follows that death does not occur until both the brain as a whole and the body as a whole are irreversibly dysfunctional. This is a biological concept, and death is recognized as having taken place without any reference to a capacity for self-consciousness or personhood. However, in spite of the brain as a whole being considered dead, isolated functions may continue within the brain, and cellular activity in localized regions of the brain may also remain intact.[13,14]

Although proponents of a whole brain definition allegedly use the entire brain as their criterion of death, the identification of a higher brain function, such as sentience, tends to emerge as an essential feature. For some, a whole brain definition is an unstable compromise between the deaths of persons and organisms.[15] It has to be asked whether individuals with intact integrative functions (signifying an intact brain stem), but without the marks of personhood (damage to the cerebral hemispheres) are

previous paper

alive in any meaningful sense. Some writers do not think so, arguing that the life that continues after destruction of the cerebral hemispheres (neocortex) is no more than metabolic activity, equivalent to that of a disembodied human organ or cell surviving in vitro.[16]

Higher Brain Definition

A higher brain definition refers to destruction of the cerebral hemispheres alone, with retention of brain stem function. A move in this direction is a move away from utilizing criteria shared with other animals to a definition focusing on functions characteristic only of humans. Interest centres on the irreversible loss of higher brain functions, such as the capacity for consciousness, and the capacity for remembering, judging, reasoning, acting, enjoying and worrying. If these are regarded as characteristic of human existence and of our meaning as human persons, they may be regarded as the sole functions of ultimate importance when defining brain death.[17] What counts as a living human being is the presence of the capacity for both organic and mental functioning, rather than the persistence of isolated brain stem reflexes following destruction of the cerebral hemispheres. The centrality of the person lies at the heart of the higher brain definition, and this in turn, focuses attention on our humanness and on those responsibilities lying at the core of human community.

Complexity of Brain Death

These definitions of brain death highlight the complexity of death, the variety of factors to be considered, and the range of neurobiological and philosophical components to be taken into account.[18]

For many people, there is a difference between death of the body and death of the brain (regardless of the definition employed). However, bodily life is still life, but is this meaningful life in a human sense? It is tempting to conclude that the meaningfulness of an individual's existence is open to question once irreversible higher brain death is definitely diagnosed: that individual life is at an end, the irreversibility of the condition eliminating any potential for future relationships, for self-awareness, or for plans of any description. On the other hand, the opposite perspective is succinctly expressed by Lamb: "Life without conscious experience may be meaningless, possibly futile, but it does not amount to death."[19]

These considerations are relevant for those of brain birth. When can an embryo/fetus be said to be alive in any meaningful sense? Is it at the first glimmerings of a nervous system (neural plate/neural tube), at the first signs of the potential for consciousness/sentience (cerebral hemispheres recognizable/initial manifestation of localized EEG activity), or when there is sufficient structural organization for the nervous system to function in a coordinated manner (EEG activity characterized by little electrocerebral silence)? Is it possible to translate perspectives on brain death directly into considerations of brain birth? If this is done, different characteristics will emerge as relevant.

Brain Birth

The concept of brain birth has featured in attempts to elucidate a moral point-of-demarcation, prior to which experimental procedures may be undertaken on human embryos but after which they are forbidden.[6–20] Numerous writers have attempted to pinpoint what they regard as the biological substratum for personal life,[5,21–23] with attention on development of the cerebral cortex and on identifying the first moments of conscious experience. Some have set this at 25–40 days gestation.[24] For others, eight weeks gestation represents the point at which the

brain is capable of consciousness. From this point onwards, the "biography" of the individual has begun;[25] alternatively, this level of brain activity signifies the emergence of a person,[22] makes possible an holistic level of life,[21] leads to affective recognisability by other people,[26] or denotes the beginnings of sentience.[27,28]

Goldenring,[2] who originally proposed the "brain-life theory," based his view on evidence that the subcortical brain comes into being as an organized unit at five weeks, with cerebral hemispheres differentiating at seven weeks, and EEG activity commencing at eight weeks. According to the brain-life theory, a human being is alive whenever a functioning human brain is present. Thus, the commencement of EEG activity is seen as the starting point for human (personal) existence, since it marks integration of the brain as a whole.[3] The attractiveness of this theory stems from an apparent symmetry between the beginning and end of human existence, using the converse of brain death as a model for thinking about the initiation of coordinated neural activity.

Others have sought a much later beginning. Gertler[20] proposed 22–24 weeks gestation, on the basis that the neocortex begins producing EEG waves at this time. Underlying this proposal is the view that human cognition is the beginning of cognitive capability and the point at which protection of personhood should begin. In similar fashion, Burgess and Tawia[5] defined a functioning brain as one where there is identifiable activity of the kind that normal adult brains (cortices) indulge in. They argue that what is required is a critical minimum level of structural organisation, with functional components present and mature enough to perform. On the basis of EEG readings, they conclude that a fetus becomes conscious at 32–36 weeks gestation.

The significance of EEG activity for this discussion is unmistakable. The earliest very localized EEG activity appears at ten weeks,[29] with more generalized activity at 22–23 weeks gestation. This activity, however, is discontinuous, with long periods of electrocerebral silence, a characteristic of the immature nervous system.[30,31] Premature infants with gestational ages less than eight months have long periods during which the EEG shows no activity. Gradual changes in EEG characteristics occur over the first few years of postnatal life, until adult patterns predominate around age seven or eight years.[9]

Also relevant here is the issue of fetal awareness, which has been placed at not earlier than 26 weeks gestation by a 1997 working party of the Royal College of Obstetricians and Gynaecologists.[32] According to this working party, this is the minimum stage of structural development necessary to confer awareness upon the developing fetus, with structural integration of peripheral nerves, spinal cord, brain stem, thalamus, and cerebral cortex.

In view of the above, can any one notion of brain birth encapsulate the state of development or maturity over a 30-week period? This represents 75 per cent of gestation, from early in the embryonic period to late in the fetal period. Such a vast time period is too crude to prove convincing embryologically, and is too diffuse to prove helpful ethically.

Critique of Brain Birth

Apart from this consideration, the brain birth concept is not universally accepted. For Moussa and Shannon,[7] it is neither a defensible nor useful notion, since it is a metaphysical concept. The dependence placed on the physical maturity of one bodily system implies that metaphysical status can be inferred from scientific data — a notion that Moussa and Shannon strongly reject. For them, personhood is a social and moral construct and, they contend, biological realities neither guarantee the presence of, nor constitute the definition of, a person. According to these authors, a functioning nervous system is a presupposition only of physical activity, with an *integrated* nervous system being required for intellectual activity. As others have suggested, scientific criteria have a role in helping direct our moral gaze, demonstrating when a nervous system exists with sufficient material complexity to embody those capacities judged morally pertinent.[33] The tenor of these sentiments points towards a definition of brain birth modelled on a higher brain definition of death — if such a definition is even contemplated at the beginning of life.

In terms of scientific criteria, the dominant feature of the developing brain is the laying down of different systems at different times, and the coordination of these systems relatively late in development.[4] Some developmental sequences can only begin once the preceding sequence has been completed, some sequences occur relatively late in fetal life, while others are not completed until after birth. Consequently, if brain birth is placed early, numerous phases of development will not even have been initiated. Hence, if the concept is to be used, it would seem preferable to place it at a time when most developmental sequences have started,[4] once again pointing to a definition based on a higher brain definition of brain death.

Is There More Than One Definition of Brain Birth?

Apart from any problems with the concept of brain birth, a crucial question is whether a unitary concept is an oversimplification. If there are two definitions of brain death, are there two definitions of brain birth?

The whole brain definition of death refers to the loss of major brain regions, including the brain stem. Is there a parallel at the beginning of life? Employing the appearance of brain stem functioning as one's criterion, brain birth would be placed at around 6–8 weeks gestation. I shall refer to this as *brain birth I*, which is a vitalist interpretation, with its emphasis on biological integration and its stress on mere human biological life. In contrast, a second definition may be determined by the beginning of consciousness at 24–36 weeks gestation. This is *brain birth II*, which parallels the personalist overtones of the higher brain definition of death, with a sufficiently well-developed neural organization to serve as the substratum from which self-consciousness and personal life subsequently emerge.

Do these two clearly delineated definitions of brain birth promote an understanding of the significance of early developmental events? In a developmental sequence, brain birth I always precedes brain birth II, while in a degenerative process at the end of life a higher brain definition of death (cortical/cerebral death) may or may not precede whole brain (brain stem) death. This variability is unavoidable, since degenerative processes lack the inbuilt sequence of developmental milestones. One of the defining features of whole brain death in adults is a lack of consciousness and an inability to feel pain. Symmetry with the brain death concept suggests that brain birth I should demarcate the beginning of the period when the fetus begins to develop sensation and feel pain, but as yet, the answer to this problematic question remains unclear.[34–36] Rudimentary sensation seems to occur long before the stage when the nervous system can keep the fetus alive, but until a greater understanding of this process can be achieved, there exist no specific developmental milestones that establish the moment when a fetus becomes brain-alive in this sense.[37] Even brain birth II is surrounded by ambiguity, although neural integration and the potential for consciousness, as depicted by cerebral cortical development, point to a relatively mature nervous system.

The realization that two separate timings of brain birth are feasible enlarges the horizons of the debate, but at present fails to solve fundamental queries at the neurobiological level. This is even more pronounced for ethical questions, since we are left with major uncertainty whether brain birth I and/or brain birth II have moral significance. Levels of uncertainty look set to increase when serious debate is undertaken on the possible repercussions of techniques that stimulate nonembryonic cells into totipotency, provide them with primitive human nervous systems but fail to allow the development of any additional "human" characteristics. What impact would such scientific work have on the notion that brain birth signifies moral value?

A Continuum from Life to Death

If brain life is taken as a notional indicator of brain function, it is possible to use two pathways to trace brain life. One pathway represents normal development, from fertilization, through fetal and embryonic stages, to the child/adult, at which point brain life is at a maximum. The other is a pathological one, working in reverse, and tracing various pathological states as they depart from brain life at its maximum, with dementia and the persistent vegetative state (PVS)/anencephaly representing increasing decrements until death of the individual occurs. When the various definitions of brain death are superimposed upon these pathways, possible parallels can be explored between normal development on the one hand and pathological deviations from the normal on the other. In this way, it is possible to compare (in a tentative fashion) the degrees of brain life evidenced by those designated as being dead using a whole brain definition in contrast to a higher brain definition, as well as by anencephalics and those in a PVS. Against this background, and using what is known of brain death, the next step is to ask when a brain can be said to come into existence.

Using a higher brain definition, the answer lies somewhere in the vicinity of 24–36 weeks (brain birth II). If this is the case, the parallelism postulated here raises the question whether the embryo/fetus at all stages prior to about 22 weeks gestation can be meaningfully referred to as "brain dead". This is a possibility if a brain birth concept based on a higher brain definition of death is accepted. However, the terminology is confusing since it is difficult to appreciate how something can be dead when it has never lived. In addition, the developing nervous system *is developing into* "something," whereas the adult brain that is now non-functioning previously *was* "something". The problems of lack of symmetry remain. A "preconscious" nervous system is fundamentally different from a "post-conscious" nervous system; the *potential* of the first differs significantly from the *memories* represented by the second.

An alternative is to adopt a whole brain definition of death as the model on which to base a definition of brain birth (brain birth I). Taking this approach, brain birth is placed at around 6–8 weeks gestation, when the nervous system is still at a relatively early stage of development, and the neuromuscular system is sufficiently developed for spontaneous fetal movements to occur.[32] While this is feasible, such early neural development does not constitute a brain-like organization in biological terms.

Even brain birth does not signify the first beginnings of the nervous system. This happens with the appearance of the neural plate (18 days gestation), and

then more obviously with the slightly later appearance of the neural tube (closing around 27 days). These early stages in nervous system development do not generally feature in discussions of brain birth, although they may be utilized in connection with the significance of the primitive streak or even with the onset of consciousness.

In conclusion, although it is possible to place the two-week embryo, eight-week embryo, 36-week fetus, term fetus, newborn infant and child on a continuum, it is doubtful whether the biological interest elicited by this is matched by ethical significance. Even if an eight-week embryo is considered to display less brain life than, say, an adult in a PVS or an adult with dementia, one cannot conclude from this that an embryo at this stage of development has more of the characteristics of brain death than does either of these adult groups. Definitions of death apply specifically to those who are dying, not to those who are developing. Development and degeneration are not interchangeable. The problems encountered with translating brain death into neural system development serve to highlight the questionable foundation on which the entire edifice of the brain life concept is constructed.

Definitions of death are not purely biological, but are informed by moral judgments. While their base is, in part, biological, the character of the definitions owes more to ethical, social, and religious values. This applies also to the beginning of human life: hence my suspicions regarding the validity of the brain birth concept. Its biological base is significantly more fragile than that of brain death, and, as a result, far more is demanded of its ethical and social underpinnings. Brain death is proving a helpful concept, despite the fact that its dimensions remain open to debate and interpretation. Brain birth, even in its dual form discussed here, continues to be elusive.

Acknowledgement

Thanks to Barbara Telfer and Robyn Harris for their many contributions to my thinking on this topic.

References

1. Brody B. The morality of abortion. In: Beauchamp TL, Walters L, eds. *Contemporary issues in bioethics.* Belmont, CA: Wadsworth, 1982:240–50.

2. Goldenring JM. Development of the fetal brain [letter]. *New England Journal of Medicine* 1982;307:564.

3. Goldenring JM. The brain-life theory: towards a consistent biological definition of humanness. *Journal of Medical Ethics* 1985;11:198–204.

4. Jones DG. Brain birth and personal identity. *Journal of Medical Ethics* 1989;15:173–8.

5. Burgess JA, Tawia SA. When did you first begin to feel it? — locating the beginning of human consciousness. *Bioethics* 1996; 10:1–26.

6. Sass H-M. The moral significance of brain-life criteria. In: Beller FK, Weir R.F, eds. *The beginning of human life.* The Netherlands: Kluwer Academic Press, 1994:57–70.

7. Moussa M, Shannon TA. The search for the new pineal gland: brain life and personhood. *Hastings Center Report* 1992;22:30–7.

8. Moussa M, Shannon TA. Brain metaphysics [letter]. *Hastings Center Report* 1993;23:45–6.

9. Jones DG. *Manufacturing humans.* Leicester: Inter-Varsity Press, 1987.

10. Engelhardt HT. Some persons are humans, some humans are persons, and the world is what persons make of it. In: Spicker SF, Engelhardt HT, eds. *Philosophical medical ethics: its nature and significance.* Dordrecht, Holland: Reidel Publishing, 1975:183–94.

11. Ad Hoc Committee of the Harvard Medical School to Examine the Definition of Brain Death. A definition of irreversible coma. *Journal of the American Medical Association* 1968;205:337–40.

12. Pallis C. Whole-brain death reconsidered — physiological facts and philosophy. *Journal of Medical Ethics* 1983;9:32–7.

13. Bernat JL, Culver CM, Gert B. On the definition and criterion of death. *Annals of Internal Medicine* 1981;94:389–94.

14. Grigg MM, Kelly MK, Celesia GG, Ghobrial MW, Ross ER. Electroencephalographic activity after brain death. *Archives of Neurology* 1987;44:948–54.

15. McMahan J. The metaphysics of brain death. *Bioethics* 1995;9:91–126.

16. Bartlett ET, Youngner SJ. Human death and the destruction of the neocortex. In: Zaner RM, ed. *Death: beyond whole-brain criteria.* Dordrecht, Holland: Reidel Publishing Company, 1988:199–215.

17. Veatch RM. The impending collapse of the whole-brain definition of death. *Hastings Center Report* 1993;23:18–24.

18. Hauerwas S. Religious concepts of brain death and associated problems. *Annals of the New York Academy of Sciences* 1978;315:329–38.

19. Lamb D. *Death, brain death and ethics.* London: Croom Helm, 1985.

20. Gertler GB. Brain birth: a proposal for defining when a fetus is entitled to human life status. *Southern California Law Review* 1986;59:1061–78.

21. Shea MC. Embryonic life and human life. *Journal of Medical Ethics* 1985;11:205–9.

22. Tauer CA. Personhood and human embryos and fetuses. *Journal of Medicine and Philosophy* 1985;10:253–66.

23. Beller FK, Zlatnik GP. The beginning of human life. *Journal of Assisted Reproduction and Genetics* 1995;12:477–83.

24. Board for Social Responsibility (Working Party on Human Fertilisation and Embryology). *Personal origins.* London: CIO Publishing, 1985.

25. Kushner T. Having life versus being alive. *Journal of Medical Ethics* 1984;10:5–8.

26. Grobstein C. *From chance to purpose: an appraisal of external human fertilization.* Reading, Mass.: Addison-Wesley Publishing, 1981.

27. Singer P, Wells D. *The reproductive revolution: new ways of making babies.* Oxford: Oxford University Press, 1984.

28. Kuhse H, Singer P. Abortion and contraception: the moral significance of fertilization. See reference 6: 145–61.

29. Bergström RM, Bergström L. Prenatal development of stretch reflex functions and brainstem activity in the human. *Annales Chirurgiae et Gynaecologiae Fennicae* 1963;52:1–21.

30. Anderson CM, Torres F, Faoro A. The EEG of the early premature. *Electroencephalography and Clinical Neurophysiology* 1985;60:95–105.

31. Tawia S. When is the capacity for sentience acquired during human fetal development? *The Journal of Maternal-Fetal Medicine* 1992;1:153–65.

32. Royal College of Obstetricians and Gynaecologists. *Fetal awareness: report of a working party.* London: RCOG Press, 1997.

33. Flower M. Neuromaturation and the moral status of human fetal life. In: Doerr E, Prescott J, eds. *Abortion rights and fetal "personhood."* Long Beach: Crestline Press, 1989:71–85.

34. Kuljis RO. Development of the human brain: the emergence of the neural substrate for pain perception and conscious experience. See reference 6:49–56.

35. Lloyd-Thomas AR, Fitzgerald M. Reflex responses do not necessarily signify pain. *British Medical Journal* 1996;313:797–8.

36. Szawarski Z. Probably no pain in the absence of "self". *British Medical Journal* 1996;313:796–7.

37. Maynard-Moody S. *The dilemma of the fetus: fetal research, medical progress and moral politics.* New York: St Martin's Press, 1995.

Further Readings

"A Definition of Irreversible Coma: Report of the Ad Hoc Committee of the Harvard Medical School to Examine the Definition of Death." *JAMA* 205 (1968): 337.

Bernat, J.L. "A Defense of the Whole-Brain Concept of Death." *Hastings Cent Rep* 28:2 (Mar.–Apr. 1998): 14–23.

Bernat, J.L. "The Biophilosophical Basis of Whole-Brain Death." *Soc Philos Policy* 19:2 (2002): 324–42.

Canadian Medical Association. "Guidelines for the Diagnosis of Brain Death. *CMAJ* 136 (Jan. 15, 1987): 220A–B.

Curran, W.J. "An Historical Perspective on the Law of Personality and Status with Special Regard to the Human Fetus and the Rights of Women." *Milbank Memorial Fund Quarterly* 61:1 (Winter 1983): 58–75.

Downie, J. "Brain Death and Brain Life: Rethinking the Connection." *Bioethics* 4:3 (1990): 216–226.

Gillon, R. "Pregnancy, Obstetrics and the Moral Status of the Fetus." *J of Med Ethics* 14:1 (Mar. 1988): 3–4.

Justin, R.G., and F. Rosner. "Maternal/Fetal Rights: Two Views." *JAM Women's Assoc* 44:3 (May–June 1989): 90–95.

Kluge, E.-H. W. "When Caesarean Section Operations Imposed by a Court Are Justified." *J of Med Ethics* 14:4 (Dec. 1988): 206–211.

Rich, B.A. "Postmodern Personhood: A Matter of Consciousness." *Bioethics* 11:3 (1997): 206–216.

Strong, C., and Anderson, G. "The Moral Status of the Near-term Fetus." *J of Med Ethics* 15:1 (Mar. 1989): 25–27.

Theoret Med 5 (1984): 16. Issue editor, D.A. Walton. The whole issue is devoted to the definition of death.

Tomlinson, Tom. "The Conservative Use of the Brain-Death Criterion: A Critique." *J Med Philos* 9:4 (1984): 377–393.

Zaner, Richard M., ed. *Death: Beyond Whole-Brain.* Dordrecht and Boston: Kluwer Academic, 1988.

CHAPTER 13
ABORTION

Introduction

Abortion is generally defined as the deliberate termination of a pregnancy prior to foetal viability.[1] While this definition makes no reference to killing or bringing about the death of the foetus, the usual reason for performing an abortion is not simply to terminate the pregnancy by removing the foetus from the uterus but also to kill the foetus. Since, biologically speaking, a human foetus is a human being, abortion is really the deliberate bringing about of the death of a human being.

Historically, abortions have been approached in a variety of ways. In Roman and Greek times, they were not considered either legally or ethically reprehensible because an unborn foetus was not considered a person.[2] Even early Christian writers such as St. Augustine and St. Thomas Aquinas[3] more or less shared this view. In more recent times, abortion became a criminal misdemeanour and ultimately was considered an act of murder. It was considered defensible only under exceptional circumstances: specifically, when the life of the pregnant woman was threatened and her life could only be saved through an abortion. This exception was enshrined in Section 251 of the *Criminal Code of Canada*, but it was struck down in1988 by the Supreme Court of Canada in the famous case of *R. v. Morgentaler*. (Excerpts from that case are reproduced on pp. 311–324.) Since 1988, Canada has not had any statute law specifically dealing with abortion.

Wayne Sumner presents a philosopher's perspective on abortion. In a classic Canadian discussion, he depicts the issue of abortion as involving a complex series of questions that deal with personhood, autonomy and a balance of social and individual rights. Susan Sherwin presents a feminist point of view. She argues that any discussion of abortion that does not centre on the position of the woman as someone who is socially embedded in a male-oriented and male-dominated culture falsifies the issue. Sherwin's reasoning constitutes one of the more dominant voices in Canadian feminist-oriented bioethics.

The preceding selections differ in many respects; however, they all agree that the human foetus is not a person from the "moment" of conception but acquires personhood at some time during its development. This viewpoint is not shared by everyone. Specifically, it is rejected by the modern Roman Catholic Church, which maintains that the foetus is a person from the very beginning. This position is clearly expressed in *Donum vitae*. Representative parts of *Donum vitae*, which deals mainly with the new reproductive technologies, are reproduced in Chapter 16. It may be instructive to compare the perspective on the status of the human foetus that is reflected in this document with the views that are expressed in the selections in this chapter.

Notes

1. See Canadian Medical Association, Policy Statement on Abortion.
2. Roman civil law recognized the fiction that an unborn child *en ventre sa mère* is a person in the sense that it will inherit property left to it while still unborn. However, that status did not carry over into the criminal sphere, which defined legal personhood. In Canada, the fiction was first introduced into civil proceedings in *Léveillé v. Montreal Tramway*.
3. St. Thomas Aquinas, *Commentarium in quatuor libros sententiarium Magistri Petri Lombardi* IVd31.

R. v. Morgentaler
Supreme Court of Canada

The Chief Justice — The principal issue raised by this appeal is whether the abortion provisions of the Criminal Code, R.S.C. 1970, c. C-34, infringe the "right to life, liberty and security of the person and the right not to be deprived thereof except in accordance with the principles of fundamental justice" as formulated in s. 7 of the Canadian Charter of Rights and Freedoms.

...

Relevant Statutory and Constitutional Provisions

Criminal Code

251. (1) Every one who, with intent to procure the miscarriage of a female person, whether or not she is pregnant, uses any means for the purpose of carrying out his intention is guilty of an indictable offence and is liable to imprisonment for life.

(2) Every female person who, being pregnant, with intent to procure her own miscarriage, uses any means or permits any means to be used for the purpose of carrying out her intention is guilty of an indictable offence and is liable to imprisonment for two years.

(3) In this section, "means" includes
(a) the administration of a drug or other noxious thing,
(b) the use of an instrument, and
(c) manipulation of any kind.

(4) Subsections (1) and (2) do not apply to

R. v. Morgentaler [1988] 1 S.C.R. 30, 63 O.R.(2d) 281, 26 O.A.C. 1, 44 D.L.R.(4th) 385, 82 N.R. 1, 3 C.C.C. (3d) 449, 62 C.R. (3d) 1, 31 C.R.R.

(a) a qualified medical practitioner, other than a member of a therapeutic abortion committee for any hospital, who in good faith uses in an accredited or approved hospital any means for the purpose of carrying out his intention to procure the miscarriage of a female person, or

(b) a female person who, being pregnant, permits a qualified medical practitioner to use in an accredited or approved hospital any means described in paragraph (a) for the purpose of carrying out her intention to procure her own miscarriage, if, before the use of those means, the therapeutic abortion committee for that accredited or approved hospital, by a majority of the members of the committee and at a meeting of the committee at which the case of such female person has been reviewed,

(c) has by certificate in writing stated that in its opinion the continuation of the pregnancy of such female person would or would be likely to endanger her life or health, and

(d) has caused a copy of such certificate to be given to the qualified medical practitioner.

(5) The Minister of Health of a province may by order

(a) require a therapeutic abortion committee for any hospital in that province, or any member thereof, to furnish to him a copy of any certificate described in paragraph (4) (c) issued, by that committee, together with such other information relating to the circumstances surrounding the issue of that certificate as he may require, or

(b) require a medical practitioner who, in that province, has procured the miscarriage of any female person named in a certificate described in paragraph (4) (c), to furnish to him a copy of that certificate, together with such other information relating to

the procuring of the miscarriage as he may require.

(6) For the purposes of subsections (4) and (5) and this subsection

"accredited hospital" means a hospital accredited by the Canadian Council on Hospital Accreditation in which diagnostic services and medical, surgical and obstetrical treatment are provided;

"approved hospital" means a hospital in a province approved for the purposes of this section by the Minister of Health of that province;

"board" means the board of governors, management or directors, or the trustees, commission or other person or group of persons having the control and management of an accredited or approved hospital;

"qualified medical practitioner" means a person entitled to engage in the practice of medicine under the laws of the province in which the hospital referred to in subsection (4) is situated;

"therapeutic abortion committee" for any hospital means a committee, comprised of not less than three members each of whom is a qualified medical practitioner, appointed by the board of that hospital for the purpose of considering and determining questions relating to terminations of pregnancy within that hospital.

(7) Nothing in subsection (4) shall be construed as making unnecessary the obtaining of any authorization or consent that is or may be required, otherwise than under this Act, before any means are used for the purpose of carrying out an intention to procure the miscarriage of a female person.

A. The Canadian Charter of Rights and Freedoms

1. The Canadian Charter of Rights and Freedoms guarantees the rights and free-

doms set out in it subject only to such reasonable limits prescribed by law as can be demonstrably justified in a free and democratic society.

7. Everyone has the right to life, liberty and security of the person and the right not to be deprived thereof except in accordance with the principles of fundamental justice.

...

III

...

B. Security of the Person

The law has long recognized that the human body ought to be protected from interference by others. At common law, for example, any medical procedure carried out on a person without that person's consent is an assault. Only in emergency circumstances does the law allow others to make decisions of this nature. Similarly, art. 19 of the Civil Code of Lower Canada provides that "The human person is inviolable" and that "No person may cause harm to the person of another without his consent or without being authorized by law to do so." "Security of the person," in other words, is not a value alien to our legal landscape. With the advent of the Charter, security of the person has been elevated to the status of a constitutional norm. This is not to say that the various forms of protection accorded to the human body by the common and civil law occupy a similar status. "Security of the person" must be given content in a manner sensitive to its constitutional position. The above examples are simply illustrative of our respect for individual physical integrity.

... Nor is it to say that the state can never impair personal securities interests. There may well be valid reasons for interfering with security of the person. It is to say, however, that if the state does interfere with security of the person, the Charter requires such interference to conform with the principles of fundamental justice.

... The case law leads me to the conclusion that state interference with bodily integrity and serious state-imposed psychological stress, at least in the criminal law context, constitute a breach of security of the person. It is not necessary in this case to determine whether the right extends further, to protect either interests central to personal autonomy, such as a right to privacy, or interests unrelated to criminal justice.

... Parliament could choose to infringe security of the person if it did so in a manner consistent with the principles of fundamental justice. The present discussion should therefore be seen as a threshold inquiry and the conclusions do not dispose definitively of all the issues relevant to s. 7. With that caution, I have no difficulty in concluding that the encyclopedic factual submissions addressed to us by counsel in the present application establish beyond any doubt that s. 251 of the Criminal Code is *prima facie* a violation of the security of the person of thousands of Canadian women who have made the difficult decision that they do not wish to continue with a pregnancy. At the most basic, physical and emotional level, every pregnant woman is told by the section that she cannot submit to a generally safe medical procedure that might be of clear benefit to her unless she meets criteria entirely unrelated to her own priorities and aspirations. Not only does the removal of decision-making power threaten women in a physical sense; the indecision of knowing whether an abortion will be granted inflicts emotional stress. Section 251 clearly interferes with a woman's bodily integrity in both a physical and emotional sense. Forcing a woman, by threat of criminal sanction, to carry a foetus to term unless she meets certain criteria unrelated to her own priorities and aspirations, is a profound interference with a woman's body and thus a violation of security of the person. Section 251, therefore, is required by the Charter to comport with the principles of fundamental justice.

... [T]he operation of the decision-making mechanism set out in s. 251 creates additional glaring breaches of security of the person. The evidence indicates that s. 251 causes a certain amount of delay for women who are successful in meeting its criteria. In the context of abortion, any unnecessary delay can have profound consequences on the woman's physical and emotional well-being.

More specifically, in 1977, the *Report of the Committee on the Operation of the Abortion Law* (the Badgley Report) revealed that the average delay between a pregnant woman's first contact with a physician and a subsequent therapeutic abortion was eight weeks (p. 146). Although the situation appears to have improved since 1977, the extent of the improvement is not clear. The intervener, the Attorney General of Canada, submitted that the average delay in Ontario between the first visit to a physician and a therapeutic abortion was now between one and three weeks. Yet the respondent Crown admitted in a supplementary factum filed on November 27, 1986, with the permission of the Court that (p. 3):

... the evidence discloses that some women may find it very difficult to obtain an abortion: by necessity, abortion services are limited, since hospitals have budgetary, time, space and staff constraints as well as many medical responsibilities. As a result of these problems a woman may have to apply to several hospitals.

If forced to apply to several different therapeutic abortion committees, there can be no doubt that a woman will experience serious delay in obtaining a therapeutic abortion ...

The entire process [of obtaining an abortion] was found to be protracted with

women requiring three to seven contacts with health professionals ... but in the case of abortion, the implications of any delay, according to the evidence, are potentially devastating. The first factor to consider is that different medical techniques are employed to perform abortions at different stages of pregnancy. The testimony of expert doctors at trial indicated that in the first twelve weeks of pregnancy, the relatively safe and simple suction dilation and curettage method of abortion is typically used in North America. From the thirteenth to the sixteenth week, the more dangerous dilation and evacuation procedure is performed, although much less often in Canada than in the United States. From the sixteenth week of pregnancy, the instillation method is commonly employed in Canada. This method requires the intra-amniotic introduction of prostaglandin, urea, or a saline solution, which causes a woman to go into labour, giving birth to a foetus which is usually dead, but not invariably so. The uncontroverted evidence showed that each method of abortion progressively increases risks to the woman.

... The second consideration is that even within the periods appropriate to each method of abortion, the evidence indicated that the earlier the abortion was performed, the fewer the complications and the lower the risk of mortality.

... It is no doubt true that the overall complication and mortality rates for women who undergo abortions are very low, but the increasing risks caused by delay are so clearly established that I have no difficulty in concluding that the delay in obtaining therapeutic abortions caused by the mandatory procedures of s. 251 is an infringement of the purely physical aspect of the individual's right to security of the person.

... The above physical interference caused by the delays created by s. 251, involving a clear risk of damage to the physical well-being of a woman, is sufficient, in my view, to warrant inquiring whether s. 251 comports with the principles of fundamental justice.

However, there is yet another infringement of security of the person. It is clear from the evidence that s. 251 harms the psychological integrity of women seeking abortions. A 1985 report of the Canadian Medical Association, discussed in the [*Report on Therapeutic Abortion Services in Ontario*] Powell Report, at p. 15, emphasized that the procedure involved in s. 251, with the concomitant delays, greatly increases the stress levels of patients and that this can lead to more physical complications associated with abortion.

... I have already noted that the instillation procedure requires a woman actually to experience labour and to suffer through the birth of a foetus that is usually but not always dead. ... The psychological injury caused by delay in obtaining abortions, much of which must be attributed to the procedures set out in s. 251, constitutes an additional infringement of the right to security of the person.

... [T]he evidence demonstrates that the system established by the section for obtaining a therapeutic abortion certificate inevitably does create significant delays. It is not possible to say that delay results only from administrative constraints, such as limited budgets or a lack of qualified persons to sit on therapeutic abortion committees. Delay results from the cumbersome operating requirements of s. 251 itself. ... Although the mandate given to the courts under the Charter does not, generally speaking, enable the judiciary to provide remedies for administrative inefficiencies, when denial of a right as basic as security of the person is infringed by the procedure and administrative structures created by the law itself, the courts are empowered to act.

... In summary, s. 251 is a law which forces women to carry a foetus to term contrary to their own priorities and aspirations and which imposes serious delay causing increased physical and psychological trauma to those women who meet its criteria. It must, therefore, be determined whether that infringement is accomplished in accordance with the principles of fundamental justice, thereby saving s. 251 under the second part of s. 7.

C. *The Principles of Fundamental Justice*

... A pregnant woman who desires to have an abortion must apply to the "therapeutic abortion committee" of an "accredited or approved hospital." Such a committee is empowered to issue a certificate in writing stating that in the opinion of a majority of the committee, the continuation of the pregnancy would be likely to endanger the pregnant woman's life or health. Once a copy of the certificate is given to a qualified medical practitioner who is not a member of the therapeutic abortion committee, he or she is permitted to perform an abortion on the pregnant woman and both the doctor and the woman are freed from any criminal liability.

... As is so often the case in matters of interpretation, however, the straightforward reading of this statutory scheme is not fully revealing. In order to understand the true nature and scope of s. 251, it is necessary to investigate the practical operation of the provisions.

... [T]he seemingly neutral requirement of s. 251(4) that at least four physicians be available to authorize and to perform an abortion meant in practice that abortions would be absolutely unavailable in almost one quarter of all hospitals in Canada.

Other administrative and procedural requirements of s. 251(4) reduce the availability of therapeutic abortions even further. For the purposes of s. 251, therapeutic abortions can only be performed in "accredited" or "approved" hospitals.

... [Furthermore t]he requirement that therapeutic abortions be performed only in "accredited" or "approved" hospitals effectively means that the practical availability of the exculpatory provisions of subs. (4) may be heavily restricted, even denied, through provincial regulation.

... A further flaw with the administrative system established in s. 251(4) is the failure to provide an adequate standard for therapeutic abortion committees which must determine when a therapeutic abortion should, as a matter of law, be granted. Subsection (4) states simply that a therapeutic abortion committee may grant a certificate when it determines that a continuation of a pregnancy would be likely to endanger the "life or health" of the pregnant woman. It was noted above that "health" is not defined for the purposes of the section.

... Various expert doctors testified at trial that therapeutic abortion committees apply widely differing definitions of health. For some committees, psychological health is a justification for therapeutic abortion; for others it is not. Some committees routinely refuse abortions to married women unless they are in physical danger, while for other committees it is possible for a married woman to show that she would suffer psychological harm if she continued with a pregnancy, thereby justifying an abortion. It is not typically possible for women to know in advance what standard of health will be applied by any given committee.

... It is no answer to say that "health" is a medical term and that doctors who sit on therapeutic abortion committees must simply exercise their professional judgment. A therapeutic abortion committee is a strange hybrid, part medical committee and part legal committee.

... The combined effect of all of these problems with the procedure stipulated in s. 251 for access to therapeutic abortions is a failure to comply with the principles of fundamental justice.

... The Crown argues in its supplementary factum that women who face difficulties in obtaining abortions at home can simply travel elsewhere in Canada to procure a therapeutic abortion. That submission would not be especially troubling if the difficulties facing women were not in large measure created by the procedural requirements of s. 251 itself. If women were seeking anonymity outside their home town or were simply confronting the reality that it is often difficult to obtain medical services in rural areas, it might be appropriate to say "let them travel." But the evidence establishes convincingly that it is the law itself which in many ways prevents access to local therapeutic abortion facilities. The enormous emotional and financial burden placed upon women who must travel long distances from home to obtain an abortion is a burden created in many instances by Parliament. Moreover, it is not accurate to say to women who would seem to qualify under s. 251(4) that they can get a therapeutic abortion as long as they are willing to travel.

... I conclude that the procedures created in s. 251 of the Criminal Code for obtaining a therapeutic abortion do not comport with the principles of fundamental justice.

...

V

... The appellants contended that the sole purpose of s. 251 of the Criminal Code is to protect the life and health of pregnant women. The respondent Crown submitted that s. 251 seeks to protect not only the life and health of pregnant women, but also the interests of the foetus. ... In my view, it is unnecessary for the purpose of deciding this appeal to evaluate or assess "foetal rights" as an independent constitutional value. Nor are we required to measure the full extent of the state's interest in establishing criteria unrelated to the pregnant woman's own priorities and aspirations.

What we must do is evaluate the particular balance struck by Parliament in s. 251, as it relates to the priorities and aspirations of pregnant women and the government's interests in the protection of the foetus.

Section 251 provides that foetal interests are not to be protected where the "life or health" of the woman is threatened. Thus, Parliament itself has expressly stated in s. 251 that the "life or health" of pregnant women is paramount. The procedures of s. 251(4) are clearly related to the pregnant woman's "life or health" for that is the very phrase used by the subsection.

... I think the protection of the interests of pregnant women is a valid governmental objective, where life and health can be jeopardized by criminal sanctions. ... I agree that protection of foetal interests by Parliament is also a valid governmental objective. It follows that balancing these interests, with the lives and health of women a major factor, is clearly an important governmental objective.

... I am equally convinced, however, that the means chosen to advance the legislative objectives of s. 251 do not satisfy any of the three elements of the proportionality component of *R. v. Oakes.* The evidence has led me to conclude that the infringement of the security of the person of pregnant women caused by s. 251 is not accomplished in accordance with the principles of fundamental justice.

... I conclude, therefore, that the cumbersome structure of subs. (4) not only unduly subordinates the s. 7 rights of pregnant women but may also defeat the value Parliament itself has established as paramount, namely, the life and health of the pregnant woman. ...

Conclusion

Section 251 of the Criminal Code infringes the right to security of the person of many pregnant women. The pro-cedures and administrative structures established in the section to provide for therapeutic abortions do not comply with the principles of fundamental justice. Section 7 of the Charter is infringed and that infringement cannot be saved under s. 1.

... Having found that this "comprehensive code" infringes the Charter, it is not the role of the Court to pick and choose among the various aspects of s. 251 so as effectively to re-draft the section. The appeal should therefore be allowed and s. 251 as a whole struck down under s. 52(1) of the Constitution Act, 1982. ...

Beetz J.:

... "Security of the person" must include a right of access to medical treatment for a condition representing a danger to life or health without fear of criminal sanction. If an act of Parliament forces a person whose life or health is in danger to choose between, on the one hand, the commission of a crime to obtain effective and timely medical treatment and, on the other hand, inadequate treatment or no treatment at all, the right to security of the person has been violated.

... With the greatest of respect, I cannot agree with the view that the therapeutic abortion committee is a "strange hybrid, part medical committee and part legal committee" as the Chief Justice characterizes it. ... The committee is not called upon to evaluate the sufficiency of the state interest in the foetus as against the woman's health. This evaluation of the state interest is a question of law already decided by Parliament in its formulation of s. 251(4).

... The wording of s. 251(4)(c) limits the authority of the committee. The word "health" is not vague but plainly refers to the physical or mental health of the pregnant woman. ... The standard is further circumscribed by the word "endanger." Not only must the continuation of the pregnancy affect the woman's life or health, it must endanger life or health, so that a committee that authorizes an abortion when this element is not present or fails to authorize it when it is present exceeds its authority. Finally, the expression "would or would be likely" eliminates any requirement that the danger to life or health be certain or immediate at the time the certificate is issued.

... Just as the expression of the standard in s. 251(4)(c) does not offend the principles of fundamental justice, the requirement that an independent medical opinion be obtained for a therapeutic abortion to be lawful also cannot be said to constitute a violation of these principles when considered in the context of pregnant women's right to security of the person. ... [B]y requiring that a committee state that the medical standard has been met for the criminal sanction to be lifted, Parliament seeks to assure that there is a reliable, independent and medically sound opinion that the continuation of the pregnancy would or would be likely to endanger the woman's life or health. ...

... [Although] the current mechanism in the Criminal Code does not accord with the principles of fundamental justice, [this] does not preclude, in my view, Parliament from adopting another system, free of the failings of s. 251(4), in order to ascertain that the life or health of the pregnant woman is in danger, by way of a reliable, independent and medically sound opinion.

Parliament is justified in requiring a reliable, independent and medically sound opinion in order to protect the state interest in the foetus. This is undoubtedly the objective of a rule which requires an independent verification of the practising physician's opinion that the life or health of the pregnant woman is in danger. It cannot be said to be simply a mechanism designed to protect the health of the pregnant woman ... Parliament requires this independent opinion because it is not only the woman's interest that is at stake in a decision to authorize an abortion.

The Ontario Court of Appeal alluded to this ... when it stated that "One cannot overlook the fact that the situation respecting a woman's right to control her own person becomes more complex when she becomes pregnant, and that some statutory control may be appropriate." The presence of the foetus accounts for this complexity. By requiring an independent medical opinion that the pregnant woman's life or health is in fact endangered, Parliament seeks to ensure that, in any given case, only therapeutic reasons will justify the decision to abort. The amendments to the Criminal Code in 1969 amounted to a recognition by Parliament, as I have said, that the interest in the life or health of the pregnant woman takes precedence over the interest of the state in the protection of the foetus when the continuation of the pregnancy would or would be likely to endanger the pregnant woman's life or health.

... I do not believe it to be unreasonable to seek independent medical confirmation of the threat to the woman's life or health when such an important and distinct interest hangs in the balance.

... I am of the view that there would still be circumstances in which the state interest in the protection of the foetus would require an independent medical opinion as to the danger to the life or health of the pregnant woman. Assuming without deciding that a right of access to abortion can be founded upon the right to "liberty," there would be a point in time at which the state interest in the foetus would become compelling. From this point in time, Parliament would be entitled to limit abortions to those required for therapeutic reasons and therefore require an independent opinion as to the health exception.

... Some delay is inevitable in connection with any system which purports to limit to therapeutic reasons the grounds upon which an abortion can be performed lawfully. ... Furthermore, rules promoting the safety of abortions designed to protect the interest of the pregnant woman will also cause some unavoidable delay. It is only insofar as the administrative structure creates delays which are unnecessary that the structure can be considered to violate the principles of fundamental justice. ... A fair structure, put in place to decide between those women who qualify for a therapeutic abortion and those who do not, should be designed with a view to efficiently meeting the demands which it must necessarily serve.

... Does the objective of protecting the foetus in s. 251 relate to concerns which are pressing and substantial in a free and democratic society? ... I am of the view that the protection of the foetus is and, as the Court of Appeal observed, always has been, a valid objective in Canadian criminal law. ... I think s. 1 of the Charter authorizes reasonable limits to be put on a woman's right having regard to the state interest in the protection of the foetus.

... The Crown must show that the means chosen in s. 251 are reasonable and demonstrably justified. ... [N]ot only are some of the rules in s. 251 unnecessary to the primary objective of the protection of the foetus and the ancillary objective of the protection of the pregnant woman's life or health, but their practical effect is to undermine the health of the woman which Parliament purports to consider so important. Consequently, s. 251 does not meet the proportionality test. ...

... The gist of s. 251(4) is, as I have said, that the objective of protecting the foetus is not of sufficient importance to defeat the interest in protecting pregnant women from pregnancies which represent a danger to life or health. I take this parliamentary enactment in 1969 as an indication that, in a free and democratic society, it would be unreasonable to limit the pregnant woman's right to security of the person by a rule prohibiting abor-

tions in all circumstances when her life or health would or would likely be in danger. This decision of the Canadian Parliament to the effect that the life or health of the pregnant woman takes precedence over the state interest in the foetus is also reflected in legislation in other free and democratic societies.

... Finally, I wish to stress that we have not been asked to decide nor is it necessary ... to decide whether a foetus is included in the word "everyone" in s. 7 so as to have a right to "life, liberty and security of the person" under the Charter.

The reasons of McIntyre and La Forest J.J. were delivered by *McIntyre J.* (dissenting):

pro-life ↓

... The charge here is one of conspiracy to breach the provisions of s. 251 of the Criminal Code. There is no doubt, and it has never been questioned, that the appellants adopted a course which was clearly in defiance of the provisions of the Code and it is difficult to see where any infringement of their rights, under s. 7 of the Charter, could have occurred. There is no female person involved in the case who has been denied a therapeutic abortion and, as a result, the whole argument on the right to security of the person, under s. 7 of the Charter, has been on a hypothetical basis. The case, however, was addressed by all the parties on that basis and the Court has accepted that position.

... In considering the constitutionality of s. 251 of the Criminal Code, it is first necessary to understand the background of this litigation and some of the problems which it raises. Section 251 of the Code has been denounced as ill-conceived and inadequate by those at one extreme of the abortion debate and as immoral and unacceptable by those at the opposite extreme. There are those, like the appellants, who assert that on moral and ethical grounds there is a simple solution to the problem: the inherent "right of women to control their own bodies" requires the repeal of s. 251 in favour of the principle of "abortion on demand." Opposing this view are those who contend with equal vigour, and also on moral and ethical grounds, for a clear and simple solution: the inherent "right to life of the unborn child" requires the repeal of s. 251(4), (5), (6) and (7) in order to leave an absolute ban on abortions. The battle lines so drawn are firmly held and the attitudes of the opposing parties admit of no compromise.

... [Parliament has made an] attempt ... to balance the competing interests of the unborn child and the pregnant woman. Where the provisions of s. 251(4) are met, the abortion may be performed without legal sanction. Where they are not, abortion is deemed to be socially undesirable and is punished as a crime.

... The values we must accept for the purposes of this appeal are those expressed by Parliament which holds the view that the desire of a woman to be relieved of her pregnancy is not, of itself, justification for performing an abortion.

... It is not for the Court to substitute its own views on the merits of a given question for those of Parliament. ... [I]ts role is confined to deciding whether the solution enacted by Parliament offends the Charter. If it does, the provision must be struck down or declared inoperative, and Parliament may then enact such different provisions as it may decide.

... The Court must not resolve an issue such as that of abortion on the basis of how many judges may favour "prochoice" or "pro-life." To do so would be contrary to sound principle and the rule of law affirmed in the preamble to the Charter which must mean that no discretion, including a judicial discretion, can be unlimited.

... It is said that a law which forces a woman to carry a foetus to term unless she meets certain criteria unrelated to her own priorities and aspirations interferes with security of her person. ... All laws, it must be noted, have the potential for interference with individual priorities and aspirations. In fact, the very purpose of most legislation is to cause such interference. It is only when such legislation goes beyond interfering with priorities and aspirations, and abridges rights, that courts may intervene.

... In my view, it is clear that before it could be concluded that any enactment infringed the concept of security of the person, it would have to infringe some underlying right included in or protected by the concept. For the appellants to succeed here, then, they must show more than an interference with priorities and aspirations; they must show the infringement of a right which is included in the concept of security of the person. The proposition that women enjoy a constitutional right to have an abortion is devoid of support in the language of s. 7 of the Charter or any other section. While some human rights documents, such as the American Convention on Human Rights, 1969 (Article 4(1)), expressly address the question of abortion, the Charter is entirely silent on the point. It may be of some significance that the Charter uses specific language in dealing with other topics, such as voting rights, religion, expression and such controversial matters as mobility rights, language rights and minority rights, but remains silent on the question of abortion which, at the time the Charter was under consideration, was as much a subject of public controversy as it is today.

... Governmental action for the due governance and administration of society can rarely please everyone. It is hard to imagine a governmental policy or initiative which will not create significant stress or anxiety for some and, frequently, for many members of the community.

... To invade the s. 7 right of security of the person, there would have to be more than state-imposed stress or strain. ... The mere fact of pregnancy, let alone an unwanted pregnancy, gives rise to stress. The evidence reveals that much of the anguish associated with abortion is inherent and unavoidable and that there is really no psychologically painless way to cope with an unwanted pregnancy.

It is for these reasons I would conclude that, save for the provisions of the Criminal Code, which permit abortion where the life or health of the woman is at risk, no right of abortion can be found in Canadian law, custom or tradition, and that the Charter, including s. 7, creates no further right. Accordingly, it is my view that s. 251 of the Code does not in its terms violate s. 7 of the Charter.

... The solution to the abortion question in this country must be left to Parliament. It is for Parliament to pronounce on and to direct social policy. This is not because Parliament can claim all wisdom and knowledge but simply because Parliament is elected for that purpose in a free democracy and, in addition, has the facilities — the exposure to public opinion and information — as well as the political power to make effective its decisions. ...

I would dismiss the appeal.

...   *pro-choice*
                ↓

Minority Reasons of *Wilson J.:*

At the heart of this appeal is the question whether a pregnant woman can, as a constitutional matter, be compelled by law to carry the foetus to term. The legislature has proceeded on the basis that she can be so compelled.

... A consideration as to whether or not the procedural requirements for obtaining or performing an abortion comport with fundamental justice is purely academic if such requirements cannot as a constitutional matter be imposed at all. If a pregnant woman cannot, as a constitutional matter, be compelled by law to carry the foetus to term against her will, a review of the procedural requirements by which she may be compelled to do so seems pointless. Moreover, it would, in my opinion, be an exercise in futility for

the legislature to expend its time and energy in attempting to remedy the defects in the procedural requirements unless it has some assurance that this process will, at the end of the day, result in the creation of a valid criminal offence. I turn, therefore, to what I believe is the central issue that must be addressed.

... I agree with the Chief Justice that we are not called upon in this case to delineate the full content of the right to life, liberty and security of the person. ... What we are asked to do ... is define the content of the right in the context of the legislation under attack. Does section 251 of the Criminal Code ... violate her right to life, liberty and security of the person within the meaning of s. 7?

Leaving aside for the moment the implications of the section for the foetus and addressing only the s. 7 right of the pregnant woman, it seems to me that we can say with a fair degree of confidence that a legislative scheme for the obtaining of an abortion which exposes the pregnant woman to a threat to her security of the person would violate her right under s. 7.

... The Charter is predicated on a particular conception of the place of the individual in society. An individual is not a totally independent entity disconnected from the society in which he or she lives. Neither, however, is the individual a mere cog in an impersonal machine in which his or her values, goals and aspirations are subordinated to those of the collectivity. The individual is a bit of both. The Charter reflects this reality by leaving a wide range of activities and decisions open to legitimate government control while at the same time placing limits on the proper scope of that control. Thus, the rights guaranteed in the Charter erect around each individual, metaphorically speaking, an invisible fence over which the state will not be allowed to trespass. The role of the courts is to map out, piece by piece, the parameters of the defence.

The Charter and the right to individual liberty guaranteed under it are inextricably tied to the concept of human dignity. ... The idea of human dignity finds expression in almost every right and freedom guaranteed in the Charter. ... Thus, an aspect of the respect for human dignity on which the Charter is founded is the right to make fundamental personal decisions without interference from the state. This right is a critical component of the right to liberty. ... Liberty in a free and democratic society does not require the state to approve the personal decisions made by its citizens; it does, however, require the state to respect them.

... The question then becomes whether the decision of a woman to terminate her pregnancy falls within this class of protected decisions. I have no doubt that it does. This decision is one that will have profound psychological, economic and social consequences for the pregnant woman. The circumstances giving rise to it can be complex and varied and there may be, and usually are, powerful considerations militating in opposite directions. It is a decision that deeply reflects the way the woman thinks about herself and her relationship to others and to society at large. It is not just a medical decision; it is a profound social and ethical one as well. Her response to it will be the response of the whole person.

It is probably impossible for a man to respond, even imaginatively, to such a dilemma not just because it is outside the realm of his personal experience (although this is, of course, the case) but because he can relate to it only by objectifying it, thereby eliminating the subjective elements of the female psyche which are at the heart of the dilemma.

... Given then that the right to liberty guaranteed by s. 7 of the Charter gives a woman the right to decide for herself whether or not to terminate her pregnancy, does s. 251 of the Criminal Code violate this right? Clearly it does. The purpose of the section is to take the decision away from the woman and give it to a committee. ... The fact that the decision whether a woman will be allowed to terminate her pregnancy is in the hands of a committee is just as great a violation of the woman's right to personal autonomy in decisions of an intimate and private nature as it would be if a committee were established to decide whether a woman should be allowed to continue her pregnancy. Both these arrangements violate the woman's right to liberty by deciding for her something that she has the right to decide for herself.

... I agree with my colleague ... the present legislative scheme for the obtaining of an abortion clearly subjects pregnant women to considerable emotional stress as well as to unnecessary physical risk. I believe, however, that the flaw in the present legislative scheme goes much deeper than that. In essence, what it does is assert that the woman's capacity to reproduce is not to be subject to her own control. It is to be subject to the control of the state. She may not choose whether to exercise her existing capacity or not to exercise it. This is not, in my view, just a matter of interfering with her right to liberty in the sense (already discussed) of her right to personal autonomy in decision making, it is a direct interference with her physical "person" as well. She is truly being treated as a means — a means to an end which she does not desire but over which she has no control. She is the passive recipient of a decision made by others as to whether her body is to be used to nurture a new life. Can there be anything that comports less with human dignity and self-respect? How can a woman in this position have any sense of security with respect to her person? I believe that s. 251 of the Criminal Code deprives the pregnant woman of her right to security of the person as well as her right to liberty.

... I believe, therefore, that a deprivation of the s. 7 right which has the effect of infringing a right guaranteed elsewhere in the Charter cannot be in accordance with the principles of fundamental justice.

In my view, the deprivation of the s. 7 right with which we are concerned in this case offends s. 2(a) of the Charter. I say this because I believe that the decision whether or not to terminate a pregnancy is essentially a moral decision, a matter of conscience. I do not think there is or can be any dispute about that. The question is: whose conscience? Is the conscience of the woman to be paramount or the conscience of the state? I believe, for the reasons I gave in discussing the right to liberty, that in a free and democratic society it must be the conscience of the individual. Indeed, s. 2(a) makes it clear that this freedom belongs to "everyone," i.e., to each of us individually.

... The Chief Justice sees religious belief and practice as the paradigmatic example of conscientiously held beliefs and manifestations and as such protected by the Charter. But I do not think he is saying that a personal morality which is not founded in religion is outside the protection of s. 2(a). Certainly, it would be my view that conscientious beliefs which are not religiously motivated are equally protected by freedom of conscience in s. 2(a). In so saying I am not unmindful of the fact that the Charter opens with an affirmation that "Canada is founded upon principles that recognize the supremacy of God. ..." But I am also mindful that the values entrenched in the Charter are those which characterize a free and democratic society.

... It seems to me ... that in a free and democratic society "freedom of conscience and religion" should be broadly construed to extend to conscientiously held beliefs, whether grounded in religion or in a secular morality. Indeed, as a matter of statutory interpretation, "conscience" and "religion" should not be treated as tautologous if capable of independent, although related, meaning. Accordingly, for the

state to take sides on the issue of abortion, as it does in the impugned legislation by making it a criminal offence for the pregnant woman to exercise one of her options, is not only to endorse but also to enforce, on pain of a further loss of liberty through actual imprisonment, one conscientiously held view at the expense of another. It is to deny freedom of conscience to some, to treat them as means to an end, to deprive them ... of their "essential humanity." Can this comport with fundamental justice?

... In my view, the primary objective of the impugned legislation must be seen as the protection of the foetus. It undoubtedly has other ancillary objectives, such as the protection of the life and health of pregnant women, but I believe that the main objective advanced to justify a restriction on the pregnant woman's s. 7 right is the protection of the foetus. I think this is a perfectly valid legislative objective. ... I think s. 1 of the Charter authorizes reasonable limits to be put upon the woman's right having regard to the fact of the developing foetus within her body. The question is: at what point in the pregnancy does the protection of the foetus become such a pressing and substantial concern as to outweigh the fundamental right of the woman to decide whether or not to carry the foetus to term? At what point does the state's interest in the protection of the foetus become "compelling" and justify state intervention in what is otherwise a matter of purely personal and private concern?

... It would be my view ... that the value to be placed on the foetus as potential life is directly related to the stage of its development during gestation. The undeveloped foetus starts out as a newly fertilized ovum; the fully developed foetus emerges ultimately as an infant. A developmental progression takes place in between these two extremes and, in my opinion, this progression has a direct bearing on the value of the foetus as potential life. It is a fact of human experience that a miscarriage or spontaneous abortion of the foetus at six months is attended by far greater sorrow and sense of loss than a miscarriage or spontaneous abortion at six days or even six weeks. This is not, of course, to deny that the foetus is potential life from the moment of conception. ... It is simply to say that in balancing the state's interest in the protection of the foetus as potential life under s. 1 of the Charter against the right of the pregnant woman under s. 7, greater weight should be given to the state's interest in the later stages of pregnancy than in the earlier. The foetus should accordingly, for purposes of s. 1, be viewed in differential and developmental terms. ... A developmental view of the foetus ... supports a permissive approach to abortion in the early stages of pregnancy and a restrictive approach in the later stages. In the early stages the woman's autonomy would be absolute; her decision, reached in consultation with her physician, not to carry the foetus to term would be conclusive. The state would have no business inquiring into her reasons. Her reasons for having an abortion would, however, be the proper subject of inquiry at the later stages of her preg-nancy when the state's compelling inter-est in the protection of the foetus would justify it in prescribing conditions. The precise point in the development of the foetus at which the state's interest in its protection becomes "compelling" I leave to the informed judgment of the legisla-ture which is in a position to receive guidance on the subject from all the rele-vant disciplines. It seems to me, however, that it might fall somewhere in the sec-ond trimester.

... One final word. I wish to empha-size that in these reasons I have dealt with the existence of the developing foe-tus merely as a factor to be considered in assessing the importance of the legisla-tive objective under s. 1 of the Charter. I have not dealt with the entirely separate question whether a foetus is covered by the word "everyone" in s. 7 so as to have an independent right to life under that section. The Crown did not argue it and it is not necessary to decide it in order to dispose of the issues on this appeal.

I would allow the appeal.

...

Appeal allowed, McIntyre and La Forest J.J. dissenting.

Toward a Credible View of Abortion

L. W. Sumner

As little as a decade ago most moral philosophers still believed that the exer-cise of their craft did not include defend-ing positions on actual moral problems. More recently they have come to their senses, one happy result being a spate of articles in the last few years on the sub-ject of abortion.[1] These discussions have contributed much toward an understand-ing of the abortion issue, but for the most part they have not attempted a full analysis of the morality of abortion.[2] Such an analysis is too large a task for a single paper, but a sketch of it will be

"Toward a credible view of abortion" by L. W. Sumner (*Canadian Journal of Philosophy* 4, September 1974, pp. 163–181) published by the University of Calgary Press.

undertaken here, the details to be filled in elsewhere.[3]

The moral problem which abortion poses results from some familiar biological and social contingencies. Because *homo sapiens* is a mammal the young of the species are carried by the female during the period of initial development. The weight of reproduction itself is therefore divided unequally between the sexes. Social practice ordinarily enhances this unequal division of labour by arranging that the woman will rear the children as well as bearing them. Her fertility is therefore no small matter for a woman, affecting as it does her opportunity to plan the course of her own life. Thus in the first instance she seeks to control whether (or when) she will conceive. But once conception has occurred its normal outcome is avoidable only by terminating the pregnancy, that is to say by killing the developing fetus. Such an intentional interruption of the gestation process is an abortion. And so the issues are drawn. Were one or another of these contingencies otherwise abortion might create no moral problem. But as matters now stand the liberty of the woman may conflict directly with the life of the fetus. Such is the stuff of the abortion issue.

The temporal boundaries of abortion are conception and birth: abortion is necessarily post-conceptive and pre-natal. Therein lies its ambiguous moral status. Contraception functions by preventing pregnancy rather than interrupting it. For this reason it does not destroy life and only a small minority persists in objecting to it (or to some particular contraceptive method) on moral grounds. At the other extreme, infanticide involves killing the newborn child. Only an even smaller minority is able to accept infanticide on moral grounds, except perhaps in some extreme cases. Contraception and infanticide are relatively clear moral cases precisely because they are located on either side of pregnancy. Abortion is a difficult case precisely because it occu-

pies this uncertain middle ground. Pro-abortionists tend to assimilate it to contraception while anti-abortionists tend to assimilate it to infanticide. An analysis of the morality of abortion must properly locate it on this continuum between the clear cases.

To speak of the morality of abortion may obscure the fact that there are at least two distinct moral problems concerning abortion. The first requires developing and defending a moral evaluation of abortion itself. We may assume that it will answer the question: When is an abortion morally permissible and when is it not? The second problem requires developing and defending a state policy on abortion. We may assume that it will answer the question: When should an abortion be legally permissible and when should it not? These questions are both moral ones, since they both ask for evaluations from the moral point of view, but they are different moral questions, since evaluating abortion is not the same as evaluating abortion policies. Once we have decided on the moral status of abortion, it is a further issue how it should be treated by the law.[4]

To be complete, positions on the morality of abortion must speak to both problems and most have done so. Two such positions are worth outlining as material for discussion. The first, which may be called the liberal position, is a defense of abortion and of a woman's right to have an abortion if she so chooses. It has at its heart the contention that abortion is a matter private to the woman because it does not substantially affect the welfare of any other person. As such, it raises no moral issues whatsoever, although it may, because of its potential hazards, raise prudential ones. As in the case of other medical procedures, we need to ensure only that the operation is carried out safely, efficiently, and with consent. Any further legal regulation of abortion is incompatible with the principle that the state has no right to interfere in the private activities of the individual. Laws which prohibit or restrict abortion constitute an illegitimate tampering with individual liberties. A woman has the right to decide for herself whether to bear children, a right which is already recognized when the state refrains from regulating contraception. The availability of abortion is simply a further guarantee of this right for cases in which an unwanted pregnancy has already occurred. Furthermore, prohibitive or restrictive abortion policies have the defect of enforcing the moral views of some (anti-abortionists) against the rest. Indeed, in the light of the traditional Catholic position on abortion, such policies establish the moral beliefs of a particular religious sect, thus undermining the separation of church and state. A permissive policy, or no policy at all, leaves each woman free to decide the matter for herself.

What may by contrast be called the conservative position rests upon the view that abortion is not a private matter because it involves the killing of the fetus. It is generally agreed that the taking of human life is in most circumstances wrong. But the fetus is a human life and so abortion is always homicide. As such, it is morally justifiable only in very special circumstances, such as when the continuation of pregnancy would endanger the life of the woman. The welfare or liberty of one person is not in general sufficient to justify the killing of another. It is also usually agreed that protection of human life is one of the legitimate functions of the law. Prohibitive or restrictive laws are therefore not to be seen as the enforcement of private morals or as the establishment of a church but rather as a proper extension of laws forbidding homicide. While it may be true that more permissive laws would produce benefits for women, and perhaps for others as well, these bene-

fits must always be balanced against the toll in human life which abortion necessarily exacts.

These two positions are the ones most commonly heard in discussions of the morality of abortion. Each is internally coherent, each has a venerable tradition behind it, and each is now promoted by vocal and organized pressure groups. The two positions are also diametrically opposed and between them they define the opposite poles in the abortion debate. Nevertheless, it is likely that each position commands the allegiance only of a minority among persons aware of the abortion problem. Many, perhaps most, find themselves somewhere in the middle ground between the two sides. To such persons neither position as it stands seems very credible, because each represents an extreme among available possibilities. The one focuses entirely on the rights of the woman and ignores the fate of the fetus; the other just as resolutely fastens on the welfare of the fetus and subordinates the problem of the woman. The one entirely assimilates abortion to contraception, while the other simply identifies it with infanticide. Each position attaches itself too thoroughly to one of the two ingredients whose conjunction creates the moral issue in the first place. Surely abortion is not just a private matter but is also not always a fullblown case of homicide. Surely there are less crude and less simplistic alternatives available than either of these.

So goes the view from the middle. This paper is an attempt to vindicate this view. It will argue that neither of the standard positions is acceptable because each is too extreme. It will also outline a more credible, because more moderate, alternative. The first step involves a closer look at the two given positions. Out of each can be distilled the basic argument around which the position as a whole is built.

Privacy Argument

P1 Actions which cause no harm are never morally wrong.

P2 The law may not legitimately prohibit actions which cause no harm.

P3 The fetus is not a human individual.

P4 Abortion is never morally wrong.

P5 The law may not legitimately prohibit abortion.

Homicide Argument

H1 It is always morally wrong to kill a human individual.

H2 The law may legitimately prohibit the killing of human individuals.

H3 The fetus is a human individual.

H4 Abortion is always morally wrong.

H5 The law may legitimately prohibit abortion.

Neither of these arguments is here formulated so as to be logically tight, although the missing steps could be easily supplied, and each argument is presented in a particularly strong and unqualified form. The arguments are therefore more extreme even than the positions from which they were extracted, and it may be that few would defend them in their present form. As stated, however, they will serve as excellent reference points for discussion. Ultimately it will be clearer to what extent, and in what manner, they must be weakened in order to be acceptable.

The arguments plainly have a common structure. Each contains two conclusions which speak to the two moral questions about abortion. Analogous conclusions in the two arguments (P4 and H4, P5 and H5) are mutually incompatible. Each argument derives its conclusions from three premises, of which the first two

(P1 and P2, H1 and H2) are moral principles. The third premise in each case (P3 and H3) seems to be a statement of fact about the fetus which serves as the hinge between principles and conclusions. Further, the real differences between the arguments, in virtue of which they yield incompatible conclusions, do not seem to lie in the moral principles to which they appeal. These principles form a mutually compatible set and when put in a somewhat more qualified manner might all have considerable appeal. The point of departure would appear to lie in the third premise. There the homicide argument seems to flatly affirm what the privacy argument just as flatly denies, namely that the fetus is human.

This question about "the status of the fetus" is obviously in one way or another at the heart of the abortion debate.[5] It cannot be true that abortion is homicide unless the fetus is to be accounted a human person, and it cannot be true that abortion is a private matter unless the fetus is not to be so accounted. Doubts about abortion are above all doubts about how to classify, and therefore treat, the fetus. Sooner or later this question must be confronted. The larger part of this paper will be spent confronting it.

It will be convenient to organize the discussion as a commentary on the privacy and homicide arguments, but particularly on the latter. It is natural to begin by examining the contention that the fetus is human. The structure of the argument suggests that this is the crucial fact about the fetus whose acceptance will pave the way to acceptance of the argument's conservative conclusions. If this is so then one implication follows immediately. It cannot be that the humanity of the fetus is a matter of theological tenet or religious dogma. It is sometimes argued that an individual is human in virtue of possession of a soul, or perhaps a distinctively human soul, and thus that the fetus is human from

328 Part V: Decisions About Life and Death

the moment that it acquires such a soul. The history of controversy about abortion within the Catholic Church consists largely of disagreement over when to locate this moment of 'ensoulment'.[6] Whereas Aquinas seems to have believed that the event occurred sometime during the gestation period, the weight of official opinion now is that it accompanies conception. The role of this opinion within the homicide argument will be obvious.

Whatever the merits of contrary positions within this theological debate, its outcome cannot affect our evaluation of the homicide argument or of abortion. The one characteristic of the event of ensoulment which seems to be universally accepted is that, whenever it occurs, it is not observable or open to any sort of empirical test. There exists no empirical method of confirming that, or when, an individual is ensouled. But if the premise concerning the fetus is to play its role within the homicide argument it must be open to confirmation or disconfirmation. Otherwise the argument as a whole is undecidable and will carry no weight whatever for anyone who rejects the theology on which it rests. Sectarian dogmas based upon faith, revelation, or scriptural authority can have no place in public moral discussion of abortion. They may of course be used to reinforce the consciences of the faithful, but the homicide argument, if it is to carry any weight whatever for the unfaithful, must be able to stand free of theological props.

However, once we have agreed that whether an individual is human is an empirical fact about that individual, we encounter an intractable problem. The argument cannot just stipulate what it will mean by this word 'human' for that again would be to abandon its aim of widespread acceptance. It must show that in some common and ordinary sense of the word the fetus is clearly human. But therein lies the problem: there are too many such common and ordinary senses. Like all predicates the word

'human' is a tool of classification; when we use it we distinguish the category of things human from things not human. But different categories suit different purposes and different contexts, and so the word comes to be used in different senses. For example, in saying that a person is human we may mean that he is particularly warm, or gentle, or loving (as opposed to inhuman, i.e. cold, callous, unfeeling), or we may mean that he is fallible or imperfect (as opposed to superhuman or divine). As a classificatory term 'human' in this respect somewhat resembles the word 'real', which can be opposed to any of 'artificial', 'counterfeit', 'fake', 'forged', 'synthetic', 'imitation', 'illusory', and so on, depending on the sort of object being described and on the context. Like 'real', 'human' admits of a variety of meanings. No doubt there are some common threads running through these meanings, but the fact remains that deciding whether the fetus is human is rather like deciding whether the wax apple is real. It may or may not be, depending on the categories one has in mind.

The nature of the term 'human' makes things at once easy and difficult for the proponent of the homicide argument. It is easy to show that in some ordinary sense the fetus is human, but it is difficult to show either that it is human in all such senses or that one particular sense is privileged. The nature of the problem will be clearer if we restrict our attention, as proponents of the homicide argument tend to do, to senses of 'human' which are biological in nature. It is sometimes claimed that advances in biology (and especially in genetics and embryology) in the past two centuries or so have shown beyond any doubt that the fetus is human from conception.[7] Biologists and other professionals have agreed that the fetus is human, and there's an end to it. We must be wary of arguments of the form "the professionals all agree ..." For one thing the professionals seldom do all agree, and the existence of many prominent pro-abortionist biologists and obstetricians would seem to indicate that they do not all agree in this instance. But even if they did, it is surely not a matter for them to decide. They will of course be expert in a number of facts which are relevant to deciding whether a fetus is human, but these may not be the only relevant facts and anyway scientific professionals have no license to tell us how to construct our categories. It will be apparent presently how deciding that a fetus is human is not making a simple statement of fact about it but rather drawing a particular conclusion from accepted facts or organizing these facts in a certain manner. Professionals are not notably better qualified than the rest of us to draw such conclusions or to decide how the facts are best organized.

If we explore what biology can tell us that is relevant to classifying individuals as human we find again more possible categories than we want. There are at least three distinct senses of the word 'human', each of which is derived from and therefore consonant with the biological facts. The first and simplest of these may be called the *specific* sense, because it pertains to the distinction of animal species. Certainly one thing we can mean by saying that an individual is human is that it is not a baboon or a tuna or a woodpecker. The category of human individuals which is generated by this sense of the word has the undoubted virtue of being quite sharp at the edges: it includes all and only members of the species *homo sapiens*. We would be uncertain only of hybrids or mutations, and these are rare.

This specific sense of 'human' can be used as the basis of two other, still biological, senses of the term. Each of these further senses generates a narrower category of human individuals, since it includes only a subset of the members of the species. When biologists do animal classification (taxonomy) they tend to describe the characteristics of a given species in terms of a model individual of the species which satisfies two conditions: it is structurally and functionally normal and it is mature. This procedure is a simplifying device which involves describing the model individual first and then allowing for variations displayed by members of the species which are either abnormal (runts and albinos, for example) or immature and not fully developed. Species are compared primarily in terms of the properties of their standard or model members. Thus *homo sapiens* is identified, and differentiated from other primate species, in terms of the height range, weight range, posture, skeletal and muscular structure, brain size, and so on, of the normal and mature individual.[8] What is interesting for our purpose is that normality and maturity can themselves serve as criteria which generate quite different, though overlapping, categories of human individuals.

Consider first normality. If a member of our species is abnormal enough in physiology then he is liable to be described as a freak, or a monster, or a vegetable, or an animal. Even staid medical science continues to use the term 'monster' to describe a specified set of gross abnormalities or anomalies[9] Since fetal growth proceeds so rapidly from such a small beginning, even minor deviations from normal development early in pregnancy can produce gross malformations in the later fetus. No part of the human physiology is immune. The most extreme fetal malformations affect the central nervous system: total absence or extreme underdevelopment of the brain, nonclosure of the spinal column, and so on. Other major organ systems are however also susceptible to gross malformations. When we refer to such malformed individuals as monsters it certainly seems that we are denying that they are completely or fully human, despite the fact that they may be genetically quite normal and that they are unquestionably members of our species. They fail of being fully human because they are so abnormal, because they fall so far short of the paradigm or model member of the species. It is only at the margin, only in the extreme cases, that we are likely to describe members of the species, on physiological grounds, as monsters or to say that they are less than human. But to the extent that we do so we are employing a sense of the word 'human' other than the specific one. It is appropriate to call it the *normic* sense.

Finally, a member of the species can fail to exhibit the characteristics of the model individual not because it is abnormal but because it is immature. Thus if we follow the adult backward through the developmental process we sooner or later reach a stage when the individual is so undeveloped or immature that we begin to speak of its potential, or what it will become, rather than what it is. Thus the chicken is at the earliest stage an egg, the oak an acorn, the plant a seed. It is proper to say that the egg, acorn, or seed will grow into, develop into, or become the chicken, oak, or plant and also that they are not yet these things. Likewise, in our species, at the earliest stage of development the individual is a single cell (zygote), the result of the union of sperm and ovum. It is common and natural to say that this cell is a potential human individual, or that it will grow into, develop into, or become a human individual but that it is not yet a human individual. Again we tend to use this classification only at the margin; the child or infant is a human individual, but the zygote will become one. And again the operative consideration seems to be the degree to which the individual fails to exhibit the properties of the model member of the species. The zygote is microscopic in size, spherical in shape, and contains no organ systems whatsoever. When we react to this difference in degree by saying that the zygote is not yet a human individual we are once more employing a sense of the term other than

the specific sense. Since level of development is now central it seems suitable to call this third sense of the word 'human' the *developmental* sense.

There may well be other ways in which categories of human individuals are constructed out of raw biological data, but these three will suffice for the present discussion. It seems that even the hard facts of biology generate no unique and privileged category of human individuals. In the specific sense all members of the species are human, however abnormal or undeveloped. In the normic sense only those members of the species are human who display, or will come to display, to a sufficient degree the physiological characteristics of the normal individual. In the developmental sense only those members of the species are human who have reached some minimal stage of development. It should be stressed that each of these senses of the word is quite legitimate. Each is grounded in the biological data, though each organizes these data differently. Each picks out one of the strands of meaning in the ordinary word 'human', and each of the resulting categories appears in common speech. Each is internally coherent and each enables us to distinguish tolerably well between what is human and what is not. Finally, each corresponds to analogous distinctions for other animal species.

If we bring these categories to bear on the fetus we derive divergent answers to the question whether the fetus is human. We must remember that 'the fetus' is a developmental stage in the history of the individual. Technically, the fetal stage does not occupy even all of the individual's pre-natal history, since it is preceded by the zygotal stage (first five weeks) and embryonic stage (next four weeks). If we use the term 'fetus' loosely to cover all developmental stages prior to birth, then it is clear that the class of fetuses contains individuals very different in many important ways. A newly fertilized ovum or zygote is a tiny dot barely visible to the naked eye, while the full-term fetus is usually 18–22 inches long and 5–10 pounds in weight, with almost all major bodily systems in working order. Given the sheer quantity of development in the first nine months of life, the fetal category *must* contain very different sorts of individuals. We should of course be wary of attributing to all fetuses characteristics pertaining only to a particular stage of development.

In the specific sense of the word all fetuses conceived of human parents are human, regardless of normality or developmental stage. In the normic sense most fetuses are human, gross abnormalities being rare. In the developmental sense the zygote is clearly not yet human and the full-term fetus is just as clearly human, while the fetus at some stages in between will not be easily classifiable. We will return later, from a slightly different perspective, to both the extreme and the middle cases. For the present we need only note that in the developmental sense of the word some fetuses are human while others are not and that the difference between them lies only in their level of development.

We are now back where we started. The deceptively simple question 'Is the fetus a human individual?' has no unique answer, even when only biological data are admitted. We can perhaps now see why many biologists shy away from this category of humanity. It is not itself a ground-floor biological category, but rather a way of organizing ground-floor data. Unfortunately, there are a number of alternative ways of organizing and presenting these data, none of which is privileged *so long as we consider only the facts themselves*. Even though our question certainly looks like a factual one, there seems no way to answer it satisfactorily by appeal even to a limited range of facts. The substance of premise H3 of the homicide argument is that all fetuses conceived of human parents are human.

This contention is true of the specific sense of the term 'human' and only of that sense. Thus the homicide argument requires this sense of the word, but there is so far no way of showing that this sense is privileged or that it should be preferred. The status of the homicide argument is thus far undecidable. The privacy argument, however, fares less well. The substance of its premise P3 is that no fetus, regardless of stage of development, is human. We have located no common biological sense of the word 'human' in which this claim is true. Unless some viable candidate has been overlooked, which is certainly possible, we are entitled to suspect that the privacy argument rests its conclusions on a highly implausible premise.

It is an attractive strategy to consider the homicide argument piecemeal, and to begin with that premise which looks like a straightforwardly empirical one. It can now be seen why the strategy must fail. In the absence of a specific context the question of the humanity of the fetus is undecidable. But the homicide argument itself, through its first two premises, provides just such a context. Once these premises are given (and it should be remembered that each of them appears a familiar and attractive moral principle) then only one step remains to generate the argument's conclusions. In this context, to concede that the fetus is human is to concede that it is to be included within the scope of the two moral principles and therefore to concede the conclusions. Conversely, if the conclusions are to be avoided, given the principles, then the humanity of the fetus must be denied. This surely is why debates about whether the fetus is human are so heated: each side knows the moral issue at stake, namely when it is morally permissible for the fetus to be killed. The assumption common to both sides is that if the fetus is human it is wrong to kill it. Against this assumption the question of the humanity of the fetus is no longer a neutral and empirical one, which is how it has so far been treated in this discussion. Now the fate of the fetus turns on the answer to this question alone. Suddenly all of the moral passion which is part of the abortion debate is infused into this supposed question of fact, and a decision on it, one way or the other, becomes itself a moral decision. It ought to be obvious that some basic and hard moral decisions must somewhere be involved in either accepting or rejecting the homicide argument. This fact is concealed when we are first asked to accept some moral principles which appear quite reasonable and then, because of the 'facts' of the matter, shown that we are thereby committed to some strong conclusions about abortion. The facts will simply not bear this weight and the underlying moral disagreement will show itself as a preference for one or another interpretation of the word 'human'. Our assessment of the homicide argument will be much more clearheaded if the moral decisions involved are clearly located and carefully identified.

The homicide argument must be evaluated as a whole and not piecemeal. It is a requirement of logic that in order for the argument to be sound it must not equivocate on this word 'human': the sense of the term which is employed in one part of the argument must be employed throughout. We have seen already that H3 requires the specific sense of the term; this sense must therefore be employed as well in the two moral principles H1 and H2. When interpreted in this manner the principles include in their scope all members of the species, including the fetus. To assent to the principles is to agree that the fetus, regardless of its level of development, is to be treated from the moral point of view in just the same manner as the child or the adult. It is now obvious just how much is being conceded in making even the first two moves in the argument, and how short the distance is from there to its conclu-

sions. If H3 is rendered uncontroversially true by use of the specific sense of 'human' the moral issue simply shifts to the two principles. In no way can this issue be evaded: Does the fetus belong within the scope of H1 and H2? Can we devise moral principles concerning homicide which are plausible for both the fetus and the adult? Should the fetus be accorded the same treatment, and therefore the same protection of life, as the adult? This surely is the moral crux in the abortion debate: not whether the fetus is human but how it is to be treated.

The homicide argument makes the moral claim that the fetus is to be treated in the same way as the adult and it does this by including the fetus within the scope of its principles concerning homicide. These principles state that it is wrong to take human life and that human life should have legal protection. In this somewhat stark form they are probably too strong for most moral tastes; surely killing is sometimes morally justifiable and should be sometimes legally justifiable. Still, if the argument is to yield suitably conservative conclusions about abortion, such as that abortion is justifiable only to save the life of the mother, the principles must be given a strong formulation. Proponents of the homicide argument speak sometimes of human life as possessing a uniquely high or absolute value, where this seems to mean that nothing but the preservation of life can compensate the loss of life. If we incorporate this valuation into the two principles we derive the result that it is wrong to kill except to preserve life and that in all cases, save this one, killing must be prohibited by law. Even in this somewhat weakened form, these principles are not easy to live by. They suffice to condemn killing in almost every instance, since it is only rarely that killing is necessary to preserve life. Virtually all warfare and political terrorism, along with such practices of the state as the death penalty and firing upon criminal suspects would be unjustifiable. We would also need to question such technological advances as the automobile where we trade annually many thousands of lives for an increase in convenience. It is a fairly safe guess that few among us are really willing to carry such principles to their inevitable conclusions. But if not, then we cannot pretend to accept the principles. This burden weighs heavy upon proponents of the homicide argument. It is generally their purpose to show that abortion is permissible only to save the life of the mother and that in all other circumstances it should be proscribed by law. In order to generate these conclusions they require principles of the sort now under consideration. Once adopted, these principles must be applied to all cases and not just to that of abortion. The view that life can be sacrificed only for life is perhaps an admirable one, but it is a high ideal with radical implications. The acceptance of these implications, all of them, is the test of the anti-abortionist's sincerity.

Let us suppose, as the argument requires, that these are acceptable moral principles concerning human life. They are formulated for, and commonly applied to, post-natal life — infants, children, and adults. The question remains: Is the fetus to be included within their scope? In asking this question we place a severe strain on our moral principles. How far back in the life-history of the individual are we to take them to apply? To birth only? To conception? How different from the child or adult must the individual be before we will place him in a separate moral category? The point of the homicide argument is to extend these principles back to conception. To decide whether this extension is plausible we should look at the extreme case: the zygote, the individual at the point of conception, at the earliest stage in his life-history. If it is plausible to extend the principles to the zygote then it is plausible to extend them to all fetal stages; if it

is not then the homicide argument must be rejected.

We must remember that at conception the zygote is a single cell, a tiny and barely visible entity. Consider now the following situation. Some experimental work has been done on a so-called 'morning-after' pill which is sometimes loosely referred to as a contraceptive but is in fact an abortifacient, since it causes the expulsion of the zygote should the woman conceive. What are we to think of a woman who regularly uses such a pill? She does so not knowing whether she will conceive, but knowing that if she does then the pill will cause the death of the zygote. Is she committing homicide? Her behaviour is structurally similar to that of someone who regularly leaves time bombs in randomly selected locations, set to explode at randomly selected times, not knowing whether anyone will be in the proximity when the bomb explodes, but knowing that if someone is then he will die. Is our moral attitude toward the two cases the same? Are we likely to condemn the woman, on moral grounds, as a probable killer? Would we consider her using the morning-after pill to fall into a different category from using an oral contraceptive? Would we insist that the pill be taken off the market, that all testing of it be curtailed? Would we support a law which made the use of the pill punishable with the severity usual to homicide statutes? The homicide argument requires affirmative answers to all of these questions.

There is as yet no morning-after pill in general use. But many women do now use the intrauterine device (IUD) which probably also works to expel the fertilized ovum by preventing its implantation in the wall of the uterus.[10] If so, it too is an abortifacient and all of the foregoing questions can be raised concerning it. Again the homicide argument requires that we regard women on the IUD as presumptively guilty of multiple homicide. Are we really ready to do so? Should we pass a law forbidding use of the IUD and begin arresting women who are using it? Is every such woman a public menace comparable to the setter of time bombs? If the homicide argument is correct then human life on a grand scale is at stake and innocent victims are dying every hour. But can we really accept this view of the matter?

Some laboratory experiments have united sperm and ovum in an artificial extrauterine environment. The resulting zygote does not long survive because of the absence of the sustaining uterine wall. Are experimenters who permit such conceptions murderers? Are their experiments comparable, morally speaking, to those Nazi medical experiments which cost the lives of their victims? Or consider the matter this way. Suppose that one experiment involves killing the sperm and ovum just before union while a second kills the resulting zygote immediately after union. Should we regard the two as radically different in their moral implications because conception occurred in the second but not in the first? The homicide argument requires that we do so. Finally, a large number of pregnancies end in spontaneous abortions. If the homicide argument is correct every such case costs a human life. Should we not take care that the abortion, while certainly accidental and unintended, was not in any way the result of negligence on the part of the woman? After all, we do take just such care to ensure that accidental death resulting from a highway accident was not the result of negligence on the part of the driver. A genuine desire to protect human life in the womb, however early its development, would surely require such steps. But are we really prepared to accept them?

The argument so far is simply an attempt to identify commonly shared moral intuitions. The homicide argument has certain unavoidable implications for the case of the zygote. If these implications are unacceptable then the argument

must be rejected. I believe that most persons who reflect carefully on the situations described will be unable to accept these implications. I know that I cannot. Most persons, I suspect, regard the developmental stage of the individual as relevant to the morality of killing that individual. Killing the zygote does not strike us as homicide because developmentally the zygote is too primitive, too unlike the adult, child, or even the fetus in its later stages. It is precisely level of development which the homicide argument rules out as relevant. It tries to draw a firm and inflexible line at conception. Before that point no questions about homicide occur, while immediately after it the individual is to be regarded morally as the equal of a child or adult. Few will accept this hard and fast division of cases. The zygote for most will not seem to fall in a different moral category from the sperm or ovum, despite the fact that the zygote is, and the sperm and ovum are not, a genetically complete member of the species. Abortion at the earliest stage, through the agency of the morning-after pill or IUD, will be regarded by most as morally identical to contraception. At this extreme, abortion is indeed assimilable to contraception for the purposes of morality.

Consider now the opposite extreme case, the full-term fetus. At term, the fetus differs from the newborn (neonate) principally in its occupation of a quite different environment. Because this environment is both confined and fluid, the fetus is unable to breathe or to ingest food. Both oxygen and nourishment are received from the maternal blood supply through the medium of the placenta. All other organ systems which will be functioning just after birth are functioning just before it. The birth process transfers the individual to a new environment and severs the direct physical link between mother and child: the neonate must breathe and eat. In no other important respect does birth alter the individual. The process occupies only a few minutes and the individual is the same size, weight, and shape directly after it as before. Most of his bodily systems are unaffected by the process. In the light of these facts it seems difficult to accept the view that birth is of crucial importance from the point of view of the morality of killing. Assuming that it is wrong to kill the infant directly after birth, it would seem equally wrong, and for the same reasons, to kill it directly before birth. The differences between full-term fetus and neonate do not seem morally relevant, especially when we consider that the temporal point at which birth occurs varies widely and therefore that many full-term fetuses are older and more developed than many newborn infants. It would seem natural then to extend our moral principles concerning killing beyond the neonate to embrace the full-term fetus. At this extreme, abortion is morally assimilable to infanticide. If this view of the matter is taken, then the privacy argument as well cannot be accepted, since it implies that abortion at no stage of pregnancy, however late, is to be considered as an instance of homicide.

If I am right, then upon reflection most persons would be willing to include the full-term fetus, but not the zygote, within the scope of moral principles concerning homicide. They will therefore reject both the homicide argument and the privacy argument. Since attention has here been focused especially on the homicide argument, its fate should be described in detail. Its three premises must all employ the same sense of the word 'human'. The appeal to moral intuition implies that if the specific sense is chosen, so as to render H3 true, then H1 and H2 are both false. Conversely, if the developmental sense is chosen so as to render H1 and H2 true, H3 is false. There is no possible formulation of the homicide argument which preserves the truth of all three premises. In order to be acceptable, the homicide argument must be amended. There are two alternatives open:

Amended Homicide Argument (1)

H1 It is always morally wrong to kill a human individual.

H2 The law may legitimately prohibit the killing of human individuals.

H3* Some fetuses are human individuals and some are not.

H4* Some instances of abortion are morally wrong and some are not.

H5* The law may sometimes legitimately prohibit abortion and sometimes not.

Amended Homicide Argument (2)

H1* It is sometimes morally wrong to kill a human individual and sometimes not.

H2* The law may sometimes legitimately prohibit the killing of human individuals and sometimes not.

H3 The fetus is a human individual.

H4* Some instances of abortion are morally wrong and some are not.

H5* The law may sometimes legitimately prohibit abortion and sometimes not.

Formulation (1) employs the developmental sense of 'human' and therefore preserves H1 and H2 from the homicide argument, but not H3. Formulation (2) employs the specific sense of 'human' and so preserves H3 from the homicide argument, but not H1 and H2. It is now clear that the question of whether the fetus is human is not in itself crucial to the argument, since the same conclusions are derivable in either case. The considerations which would lead us to classify the fetus at different stages as human or not, in the developmental sense, are of course relevant since the developmental level of the fetus plays a large part in our moral decisions concerning abortion. But the ultimate questions at stake are moral ones.

The liberal and conservative positions, and the arguments on which they rest, are unacceptable because they entail conclusions which are too extreme. The case against these positions has been made entirely by appeal to commonly shared moral intuitions. It would be strengthened if these intuitions could be shown to cohere well with our considered views on moral issues other than, but related to, abortion.

It does not seem wrong to kill a zygote, even if the reason for doing so is simply that the woman does not wish to be pregnant, while it does seem wrong to kill a full-term fetus for this reason. The difference between the two cases seems to lie principally in the level of development of the fetus. This suggests a developmental approach to abortion in which the justifying conditions for an abortion will contract as the fetus develops. On this conception, the fetus comes gradually to be treated as a moral person in the full sense.[11]

The question is why fetal development should be considered morally relevant in this way. As the fetus grows, it changes in two main respects: globally (increase in size, alteration of shape) and systematically (acquisition of major body systems). Of these, the latter seems the more important from the moral point of view. We should probably treat as moral persons individuals who were systematically identical to us, especially in the functioning of their central nervous systems, but who differed, even radically, in size, shape, or both. Even among organ systems many seem only marginally relevant. There is nothing distinctive about much of our bodies: other animals are swifter, stronger, better shielded, and keener of sense than we. In one respect alone are we pre-eminent, our brains having evolved to a point where we have

the capacity for thought and the expression of thought (language). Emphasis on the development of the central nervous system is the physiological correlate of the ancient view that man is distinguished from other creatures by his rationality.

It seems plausible to suppose that we are willing to treat a fetus as a moral person only when it has come to possess a central nervous system developed at least to some minimal extent. Once this developmental view of abortion is taken, it can be connected to views on cognate moral issues. A zygote and an embryo are distinguished by their relative lack of a central nervous system. A similar lack is rare, though possible, among other members of the species. An anencephalic is an individual in which the higher levels of the brain remain underdeveloped or totally absent. Such individuals rarely survive until birth and never long thereafter. In such cases, abortion, or for that matter infanticide, does not seem morally objectionable. The condition is also approximated in those victims of disease or accident who have permanently lost the functioning of the higher levels of the brain but continue to live. In such cases, euthanasia does not seem morally objectionable. An early abortion is therefore similar, from the moral point of view, to some cases of eugenic abortion (early or late) and to some cases of euthanasia, in that the individual who is killed lacks at the time a central nervous system functioning in more than a rudimentary manner. The cases are of course distinguished by the fact that the early fetus has not yet developed such a system while the anencephalic will never develop one and the accident victim has lost the functioning of a developed system. Thus in the former case but in neither of the latter one is preventing the evolution of an individual who otherwise would come to possess not only a highly developed central nervous system but also all of the characteristics typical of adult members of the species. But there seems nothing wrong with preventing the development of a human person (thus the moral innocuousness of contraception) while there seems much wrong with terminating the life of one which has already developed to a considerable degree. This single difference in the case of early abortion does not appear therefore to be morally relevant.

Somewhat further afield, we encounter the treatment of other species. This issue is too complex to be discussed thoroughly but some broad features should be noted. Our attitudes toward other species are complicated by our need for a reliable food supply, by our love of killing for its own sake, and by our habit of keeping certain species of animals as pets. In general the protection of life we offer to other species is largely determined by our own needs: thus we may hunt mountain lions to extinction while supporting a burgeoning population of household cats and we may eliminate wolves while protecting poodles. But we do make a pervasive distinction between the value of human life and the value of the life of all other animal species, once again on the basis of what is considered distinctive in us. Thus through all the complicating factors we display a marked preference for the more intelligent and highly evolved species. The differences are, as always, most apparent at the extremes. We destroy insects when they are merely inconvenient for us while feeling a much closer kinship to those species of great apes who are our nearest living relatives. Here too we construct our moral categories in part around this most crucial of all human characteristics.

To mould these still scattered attitudes and practices into a single coherent system would require a thoroughgoing analysis of life and death and above all an account of when and why killing is wrong. This undertaking is too ambitious for the present but until it has been completed no view of abortion can be taken

as firmly established. Once such an analysis is available, however, it is very likely that only a developmental view of abortion will be compatible with it.

It has thus far been left unspecified how abortion should be regarded between the extreme cases of the zygote and the full-term fetus. I will simply state my view of the matter with little supporting argument.[12] The major factors relevant to evaluating abortion are the situation and needs of the mother and the level of development of the fetus. The gradual and continuous nature of the latter renders the drawing of sharp lines out of the question. The attempt to draw such a line (whether at conception or birth) is precisely the mistake common to the liberal and conservative positions. Any such line must make an arbitrary distinction between adjacent and similar cases. The developmental view must allow for the gradual acquisition by the fetus of the status of a moral person and the accompanying right to protection of life. It is customary to divide pregnancy (calculated at 40 weeks) into trimesters of approximately 13 weeks. Even by the end of the first trimester the fetus is well advanced in the development of its central nervous system, as well as other bodily systems. It has entered a transitional or threshold stage between its early undeveloped state and its later developed state. Likewise, the end of that trimester is the latest point at which the safest abortion procedures (dilatation and curettage, vacuum aspiration) can be employed, and by that time every woman has had an adequate opportunity to decide whether she wishes to continue her pregnancy. For all these reasons, during the early weeks of pregnancy an abortion is morally permissible whatever the woman's reason for wishing it, while during the final four or five months it is permissible only in very special circumstances analogous to those which justify killing in the case of post-natal persons.

Between these relatively clear cases lies the borderline threshold period occupying a few weeks around the end of the first trimester. During this stage, the morality of abortion is simply unclear.

This is so far only a sketch of a position, but when it is fully elaborated and properly defended we have a developmental view of abortion which is far more plausible than either the liberal or conservative position. While it lacks the elegant simplicity of the extreme views, it makes up this lack by taking into account factors which they simply ignore. The morality of abortion is a difficult question in part because the fetus itself is so different at various stages of pregnancy. Only the developmental view allows us to attend to these differences in adopting a moral stance on abortion. It is for this reason that it both matches more closely our intuitions about abortion and coheres better with our views on related moral issues than does either of the more prominent positions.

The abortion policy appropriate to this view would permit abortion at the request of the woman before some fixed time limit, and would carefully screen abortions after that limit. Since the law must operate a workable policy, it cannot tolerate borderline cases and therefore must establish a clear and definite time limit. It is reasonable to set this limit around the end of the third month of pregnancy. Such a limit lies within the threshold period, coincides with the latest stage at which the safest abortion methods can be used, allows every woman sufficient time to discover that she is pregnant and decide whether to terminate the pregnancy, and captures the majority of abortions actually performed even where there is no time limit. After the third month the law will consider abortion as homicide and will specify the grounds on which it will be permitted. We may assume that these grounds will be narrow and strictly medical in nature and that some screening apparatus will be established. Again, the details of the policy and of its justification cannot be considered here.

Notes

1. R. B. Brandt, "The Morality of Abortion," *The Monist*, LVI, No. 4 (October 1972); B. A. Brody, "Abortion and the Law," *Journal of Philosophy*, LXVIII, No. 12 (June 17, 1971), and "Thomson on Abortion," *Philosophy and Public Affairs*, I, No. 3 (Spring 1972); R. J. Gerber, "Abortion: Parameters for Decision," *Ethics*, LXXXII, No. 2 (January 1972); Judith Jarvis Thomson, "A Defense of Abortion," *Philosophy and Public Affairs*, I, No. 1 (Fall 1971); Michael Tooley, "Abortion and Infanticide," *Philosophy and Public Affairs*, II, No. 1 (Fall 1972); Mary Anne Warren, "On the Moral and Legal Status of Abortion," *The Monist*, LVII, No. 1 (January 1973); Roger Wertheimer, "Understanding the Abortion Argument," *Philosophy and Public Affairs*, I, No. 1 (Fall 1971); B. A. Brody, "Abortion and the Sanctity of Human Life," *American Philosophical Quarterly*, X, No. 2 (April 1973).

2. The exceptions are the articles by Tooley and Warren (see note 1), each of which attempts to justify what I have classified as a liberal position on abortion. The present paper was completed before I encountered these articles and thus I have not commented on their arguments. Two of my purposes, however, are to discard this liberal view and to argue for an alternative to it.

3. A more thorough treatment of the matters discussed in this paper, and others pertinent to the abortion issue, is included in a book now in progress.

4. An answer to the first question is, however, an important step toward answering the second. The close connection between a particular view of the morality of abortion and a particular sort of abortion law is stressed by Brody, *op. cit.*

5. The unavoidability of this issue is the main point of the discussion by Brody.

6. For an account of this history see John T. Noonan, Jr., "An Almost Absolute Value in History," in *The Morality of Abortion: Legal and Historical Perspectives*, ed. John T. Noonan, Jr. (Cambridge: Harvard University Press, 1970).

7. Catholic law professor Sergio Cotta, speaking for the Vatican against the 1973 U.S. Supreme Court decision on abortion: "By investigating the basic genetic structure of life, science has determined with unquestionable certainty that since the moment of conception the embryo is a living human being, entirely distinct from the parents." Reported in the *Toronto Star*, January 24, 1973.

8. For a typical taxonomical profile of our species see E. L. Cockrum et al., *Biology* (Philadelphia: W. B. Saunders Company, 1966).

9. For a standard classification and description of fetal abnormalities see Edith L. Potter, *Pathology of the Fetus and Infant*, 2nd ed. (Chicago: Year Book Medical Publishers, 1961).

10. See the discussion of the intrauterine device in Germain Grisez, *Abortion: The Myths, the Realities, and the Arguments* (New York and Cleveland: Corpus Books, 1970), 106–109.

11. For the purpose of this discussion an individual is being treated as a full moral person when the conditions generally accepted as justifying the killing of that individual are those and only those which are generally accepted as justifying killing members of the species in general. In the language of the earlier discussion, he must be included within the scope of general moral principles concerning homicide.

12. A full defense of this view is made in the book referred to in footnote 3.

Abortion Through a Feminist Ethics Lens

Susan Sherwin

Abortion has long been a central issue in the arena of applied ethics, but the distinctive analysis of feminist ethics is generally overlooked in most philosophic discussions. Authors and readers commonly presume a familiarity with the feminist position and equate it with liberal defences of women's right to choose abortion, but, in fact, feminist ethics yields a different analysis of the moral questions

Earlier versions of this paper were read to the Department of Philosophy, Dalhousie University, and to the Canadian Society for Women in Philosophy in Kingston. I am very grateful for the comments received from colleagues in both forums; particular thanks go to Lorraine Code, David Braybrooke, Richmond Campbell, Sandra Taylor, Terry Tomkow and Kadri Vihvelin for their patience and advice.

surrounding abortion than that usually offered by the more familiar liberal defenders of abortion rights. Most feminists can agree with some of the conclusions that arise from certain non-feminist arguments on abortion, but they often disagree about the way the issues are formulated and the sorts of reasons that are invoked in the mainstream literature.

Among the many differences found between feminist and non-feminist arguments about abortion is the fact that most non-feminist discussions of abortion consider the questions of the moral or legal permissibility of abortion in isolation from other questions, ignoring (and thereby obscuring) relevant connections to other social practices that oppress women. They are generally grounded in masculinist conceptions of freedom (e.g., privacy, individual choice, individuals' property rights in their own bodies) that do not meet the needs, interests, and intuitions of many of the women concerned. In contrast, feminists seek to couch their arguments in moral concepts that support their general campaign of overcoming injustice in all its dimensions, including those inherent in moral theory itself.[1] There is even disagreement about how best to understand the moral question at issue: non-feminist arguments focus exclusively on the morality and/or legality of performing abortions, whereas feminists insist that other questions, including ones about accessibility and delivery of abortion services must also be addressed.

Although feminists welcome the support of non-feminists in pursuing policies that will grant women control over abortion decisions, they generally envision very different sorts of policies for this purpose than those considered by non-feminist sympathizers. For example, Kathleen McDonnell (1984) urges feminists to develop an explicitly "'feminist morality' of abortion. ... At its root it would be characterized by the deep appreciations of the complexities of life, the refusal to polarize and adopt simplistic formulas" (p. 52). Here, I propose one conception of the shape such an analysis should take.

Women and Abortion

The most obvious difference between feminist and non-feminist approaches to abortion can be seen in the relative attention each gives to the interests and experiences of women in its analysis. Feminists consider it self-evident that the pregnant woman is a subject of principal concern in abortion decisions. In most non-feminist accounts, however, not only is she not perceived as central, she is rendered virtually invisible. Non-feminist theorists, whether they support or oppose women's right to choose abortion, focus almost all their attention on the moral status of the developing embryo or the fetus.

In pursuing a distinctively feminist ethics, it is appropriate to begin with a look at the role of abortion in women's lives. Clearly, the need for abortion can be very intense; women have pursued abortions under appalling and dangerous conditions, across widely diverse cultures and historical periods. No one denies that if abortion is not made legal, safe, and accessible, women will seek out illegal and life-threatening abortions to terminate pregnancies they cannot accept. Anti-abortion activists seem willing to accept this price, but feminists judge the inevitable loss of women's lives associated with restrictive abortion policies to be a matter of fundamental concern.

Although anti-abortion campaigners imagine that women often make frivolous and irresponsible decisions about abortion, feminists recognize that women have abortions for a wide variety of reasons. Some women, for instance, find themselves seriously ill and incapacitated throughout pregnancy; they cannot continue in their jobs and may face enormous difficulties in fulfilling their responsibilities at home. Many employers and schools will not tolerate pregnancy in their employees or students, and not every woman is able to put her job, career, or studies on hold. Women of limited means may be unable to take adequate care of children they have already home and they may know that another mouth to feed will reduce their ability to provide for their existing children. Women who suffer from chronic disease, or who feel too young, or too old, or who are unable to maintain lasting relationships may recognize that they will not be able to care properly for a child at this time. Some who are homeless, or addicted to drugs, or who are diagnosed as carrying the AIDS virus may be unwilling to allow a child to enter the world under such circumstances. If the pregnancy is a result of rape or incest, the psychological pain of carrying it to term may be unbearable, and the woman may recognize that her attitude to the child after birth will always be tinged with bitterness. Some women have learned that the fetuses they carry have serious chromosomal anomalies and consider it best to prevent them from being born with a condition bound to cause suffering. Others, knowing the fathers to be brutal and violent, may be unwilling to subject a child to the beatings or incestuous attacks they anticipate; some may have no other realistic way to remove the child (or themselves) from the relationship.

Or a woman may simply believe that bearing a child is incompatible with her life plans at this time, since continuing a pregnancy is likely to have profound repercussions throughout a woman's entire life. If the woman is young, a pregnancy will very likely reduce her chances of education and hence limit her career and life opportunities: "The earlier a woman has a baby, it seems, the more likely she is to drop out of school; the less education she gets, the more likely she is to remain poorly paid, peripheral to the labour market, or unemployed, and the more children she will have between one and three more than her working childless counterpart" (Petchesky 1984, p. 150). In many circumstances, having a child will exacerbate the social and economic forces already stacked against her by virtue of her sex (and her race, class, age, sexual orientation, or the effects of some disability, etc.). Access to abortion is a necessary option for many women if they are to escape the oppressive conditions of poverty.

Whatever the reason, most feminists believe that a pregnant woman is in the best position to judge whether abortion is the appropriate response to her circumstances. Since she is usually the only one able to weigh all the relevant factors, most feminists reject attempts to offer any general abstract rules for determining when abortion is morally justified. Women's personal deliberations about abortion include contextually defined considerations reflecting her commitment to the needs and interests of everyone concerned including herself, the fetus she carries, other members of her household, etc. Because there is no single formula available for balancing these complex factors through all possible cases, it is vital that feminists insist on protecting each woman's right to come to her own conclusions. Abortion decisions are, by their very nature, dependent on specific features of each woman's experience; theoretically dispassionate philosophers and other moralists should not expect to set the agenda for these considerations in any universal way. Women must be acknowledged as full moral agents with the responsibility for making moral decisions about their own pregnancies.[2] Although I think that it is possible for a woman to make a mistake in her moral judgment on this matter (i.e., it is possible that a woman may come to believe that she was wrong about her decision to continue or terminate a pregnancy), the intimate nature of this sort of decision makes it unlikely that anyone else is in a position to arrive at a more reliable conclusion; it is, therefore, improper to grant others the authority to interfere in women's decisions to seek abortions.

Feminist analysis regards the effects of unwanted pregnancies on the lives of women individually and collectively as a central element in the moral evaluation of abortion. Even without patriarchy, bearing a child would be a very important event in a woman's life. It involves significant physical, emotional, social, and (usually) economic changes for her. The ability to exert control over the incidence, timing, and frequency of childbearing is often tied to her ability to control most other things she values. Since we live in a patriarchal society, it is especially important to ensure that women have the authority to control their own reproduction.[3] Despite the diversity of opinion among feminists on most other matters, virtually all feminists seem to agree that women must gain full control over their own reproductive lives if they are to free themselves from male dominance.[4] Many perceive the commitment of the political right wing to opposing abortion as part of a general strategy to reassert patriarchal control over women in the face of significant feminist influence (Petchesky 1980, p. 112).

Women's freedom to choose abortion is also linked with their ability to control their own sexuality. Women's subordinate status often prevents them from refusing men sexual access to their bodies. If women cannot end the unwanted pregnancies that result from male sexual dominance, their sexual vulnerability to particular men can increase, because caring for an(other) infant involves greater financial needs and reduced economic opportunities for women.[5] As a result, pregnancy often forces women to become dependent on men. Since a woman's dependence on a man is assumed to entail that she will remain sexually loyal

to him, restriction of abortion serves to channel women's sexuality and further perpetuates the cycle of oppression.

In contrast to most non-feminist accounts, feminist analyses of abortion direct attention to the question of how women get pregnant. Those who reject abortion seem to believe that women can avoid unwanted pregnancies by avoiding sexual intercourse. Such views show little appreciation for the power of sexual politics in a culture that oppresses women. Existing patterns of sexual dominance mean that women often have little control over their sexual lives. They may be subject to rape by strangers, or by their husbands, boyfriends, colleagues, employers, customers, fathers, brothers, uncles, and dates. Often, the sexual coercion is not even recognized as such by the participants, but is the price of continued "good will" — popularity, economic survival, peace, or simple acceptance. Few women have not found themselves in circumstances where they do not feel free to refuse a man's demands for intercourse, either because he is holding a gun to her head or because he threatens to be emotionally hurt if she refuses (or both). Women are socialized to be compliant and accommodating, sensitive to the feelings of others, and frightened of physical power; men are socialized to take advantage of every opportunity to engage in sexual intercourse and to use sex to express dominance and power. Under such circumstances, it is difficult to argue that women could simply "choose" to avoid heterosexual activity if they wish to avoid pregnancy. Catherine MacKinnon neatly sums it up: "the logic by which women are supposed to consent to sex [is]: preclude the alternatives, then call the remaining option 'her choice,'" (MacKinnon 1989, p. 192).

Nor can women rely on birth control alone to avoid pregnancy. There simply is no form of reversible contraception available that is fully safe and reliable. The pill and the IUD are the most effective means offered, but both involve significant health hazards to women and are quite dangerous for some. No woman should spend the 30 to 40 years of her reproductive life on either form of birth control. Further, both have been associated with subsequent problems of involuntary infertility, so they are far from optimum for women who seek to control the timing of their pregnancies.

The safest form of birth control involves the use of barrier methods (condoms or diaphragms) in combination with spermicidal foams or jelly. But these methods also pose difficulties for women. They may be socially awkward to use: young women are discouraged from preparing for sexual activity that might never happen and are offered instead romantic models of spontaneous passion. (Few films or novels interrupt scenes of seduction for the fetching of contraceptives.) Many women find their male partners unwilling to use barrier methods of contraception and they do not have the power to insist. Further, cost is a limiting factor for many women. Condoms and spermicides are expensive and are not covered under most health care plans. There is only one contraceptive option which offers women safe and fully effective birth control: barrier methods with the back-up option of abortion.[6]

From a feminist perspective, a central moral feature of pregnancy is that it takes place in women's bodies and has profound effects on women's lives. Gender-neutral accounts of pregnancy are not available; pregnancy is explicitly a condition associated with the female body.[7] Because the need for abortion is experienced only by women, policies about abortion affect women uniquely. Thus, it is important to consider how proposed policies on abortion fit into general patterns of oppression for women. Unlike non-feminist accounts, feminist ethics demands that the effects on the oppression of women be a principal consideration when evaluating abortion policies.

The Fetus

In contrast, most non-feminist analysts believe that the moral acceptability of abortion turns on the question of the moral status of the fetus. Even those who support women's right to choose abortion tend to accept the central premise of the anti-abortion proponents that abortion can only be tolerated if it can be proved that the fetus is lacking some criterion of full personhood.[8] Opponents of abortion have structured the debate so that it is necessary to define the status of the fetus as either valued the same as other humans (and hence entitled not to be killed) or as lacking in all value. Rather than challenging the logic of this formulation, many defenders of abortion have concentrated on showing that the fetus is indeed without significant value (Tooley 1972, Warren 1973); others, such as Wayne Sumner (1981), offer a more subtle account that reflects the gradual development of fetuses whereby there is some specific criterion that determines the degree of protection to be afforded them which is lacking in the early stages of pregnancy but present in the later stages. Thus, the debate often rages between abortion opponents who describe the fetus as an "innocent," vulnerable, morally important, separate being whose life is threatened and who must be protected at all costs, and abortion supporters who try to establish some sort of deficiency inherent to fetuses which removes them from the scope of the moral community.

The woman on whom the fetus depends for survival is considered as secondary (if she is considered at all) in these debates. The actual experiences and responsibilities of real women are not perceived as morally relevant (unless they, too, can be proved innocent by establishing that their pregnancies are a result of rape or incest). It is a common assumption of both defenders and opponents of women's right to choose abortion that many women will be irresponsible in their choices. The important question, though, is whether fetuses have the sort of status that justifies interfering in women's choices at all. In some contexts, women's role in gestation is literally reduced to that of "fetal containers"; the individual women disappear or are perceived simply as mechanical life-support systems.[9]

The current rhetoric against abortion stresses the fact that the genetic make-up of the fetus is determined at conception and the genetic code is incontestably human. Lest there be any doubt about the humanity of the fetus, we are assailed with photographs of fetuses at various stages of development demonstrating the early appearance of recognizably human characteristics, e.g., eyes, fingers, and toes. The fact that the fetus in its early stages is microscopic, virtually indistinguishable from other primate fetuses to the untrained eye, and lacking in the capacities that make human life meaningful and valuable is not deemed relevant by the self-appointed defenders of fetuses. The anti-abortion campaign is directed at evoking sympathetic attitudes towards this tiny, helpless being whose life is threatened by its own mother; it urges us to see the fetus as entangled in an adversarial relationship with the (presumably irresponsible) woman who carries it. We are encouraged to identify with the "unborn child" and not with the (selfish) woman whose life is also at issue.

Within the non-feminist literature, both defenders and opponents of women's right to choose abortion agree that the difference between a late-term fetus and a newborn infant is "merely geographical" and cannot be considered morally significant. But a fetus inhabits a woman's body and is wholly dependent on her unique contribution to its maintenance while a newborn is physically separate though still in need of a lot of care. One can only view the distinction between being in or out of a woman's womb as morally irrelevant if one discounts the perspective of the pregnant woman; feminists seem to be alone in recognizing her perspective as morally important.[10]

Within anti-abortion arguments, fetuses are identified as individuals; in our culture which views the (abstract) individual as sacred, fetuses qua individuals should be honoured and preserved. Extraordinary claims are made to try to establish the individuality and moral agency of fetuses. At the same time, the women who carry these fetal individuals are viewed as passive hosts whose only significant role is to refrain from aborting or harming their fetuses. Since it is widely believed that the woman does not actually have to do anything to protect the life of the fetus, pregnancy is often considered (abstractly) to be a tolerable burden to protect the life of an individual so like us.[11]

Medicine has played its part in supporting these sorts of attitudes. Fetal medicine is a rapidly expanding specialty, and it is commonplace in professional medical journals to find references to pregnant women as "fetal environments." Fetal surgeons now have at their disposal a repertory of sophisticated technology that can save the lives of dangerously ill fetuses; in light of such heroic successes, it is perhaps understandable that women have disappeared from their view. These specialists see fetuses as their patients, not the women who nurture them. Doctors perceive themselves as the *active* agents in saving fetal lives and, hence, believe that they are the ones in direct relationship with the fetuses they treat.

Perhaps even more distressing than the tendency to ignore the woman's agency altogether and view her as a purely passive participant in the medically controlled events of pregnancy and childbirth is the growing practice of viewing women as genuine threats to the well-being of the fetus. Increasingly, women are viewed as irresponsible or hostile towards their fetuses, and the relationship between them is characterized as adversarial (Overall 1987, p. 60). Concern for the well-being of the fetus is taken as licence for doctors to intervene to ensure that women comply with medical "advice." Courts are called upon to enforce the doctors' orders when moral pressure alone proves inadequate, and women are being coerced into undergoing unwanted Caesarean deliveries and technologically monitored hospital births. Some states have begun to imprison women for endangering their fetuses through drug abuse and other socially unacceptable behaviours. An Australian state recently introduced a bill that makes women liable to criminal prosecution "if they are found to have smoked during pregnancy, eaten unhealthful foods, or taken any other action which can be shown to have adversely affected the development of the fetus" (Warren 1989, p. 60).

In other words, physicians have joined with anti-abortionist activists in fostering a cultural acceptance of the view that fetuses are distinct individuals, who are physically, ontologically, and socially separate from the women whose bodies they inhabit, and who have their own distinct interests. In this picture, pregnant women are either ignored altogether or are viewed as deficient in some crucial respect and hence subject to coercion for the sake of their fetuses. In the former case, the interests of the women concerned are assumed to be identical with those of the fetus; in the latter, the women's interests are irrelevant because they are perceived as immoral, unimportant, or unnatural. Focus on the fetus as an independent entity has led to presumptions which deny pregnant women their roles as active, independent, moral agents with a primary interest in what becomes of the fetuses they carry. Emphasis on the fetus's status has led to an assumed licence to interfere with women's reproductive freedom.

A Feminist View of the Fetus

Because the public debate has been set up as a competition between the rights of women and those of fetuses, feminists have often felt pushed to reject claims of fetal value in order to protect women's claims. Yet, as Addelson (1987) has argued, viewing abortion in this way "tears [it] out of the context of women's lives" (p. 107). There are other accounts of fetal value in the context of women's lives that are more plausible and less oppressive to women.

On a feminist account, fetal development is examined in the context in which it occurs, within women's bodies rather than in the imagined isolation implicit in many theoretical accounts. Fetuses develop in specific pregnancies which occur in the lives of particular women. They are not individuals housed in generic female wombs, nor are they full persons at risk only because they are small and subject to the whims of women. Their very existence is relational, developing as they do within particular women's bodies, and their principal relationship is to the women who carry them.

On this view, fetuses are morally significant, but their status is relational rather than absolute. Unlike other human beings, fetuses do not have any independent existence; their existence is uniquely tied to the support of a specific other. Most non-feminist commentators have ignored the relational dimension of fetal development and have presumed that the moral status of fetuses could be resolved solely in terms of abstract metaphysical criteria of personhood. They imagine that there is some set of properties (such as genetic heritage, moral agency, self-consciousness, language use, or self-determination) which will entitle all who possess them to be granted the moral status of persons (Warren 1973, Tooley 1972). They seek some particular feature by which we can neatly divide the world into the dichotomy of moral persons (who are to be valued and protected) and others (who are not entitled to the same group privileges); it follows that it is a merely empirical question whether or not fetuses possess the relevant properties.

But this vision misinterprets what is involved in personhood and what it is that is especially valued about persons. Personhood is a social category, not an isolated state. Persons are members of a community; they develop as concrete, discrete, and specific individuals. To be a morally significant category, personhood must involve personality as well as biological integrity.[12] It is not sufficient to consider persons simply as Kantian atoms of rationality; persons are all embodied, conscious beings with particular social histories. Annette Baier (1985) has developed a concept of persons as "second persons" which helps explain the sort of social dimension that seems fundamental to any moral notion of personhood:

> A person, perhaps, is best seen as one who was long enough dependent upon other persons to acquire the essential arts of personhood. Persons essentially are *second* persons, who grow up with other persons. ... The fact that a person has a life *history*, and that a people collectively have a history depends upon the humbler fact that each person has a childhood in which a cultural heritage is transmitted, ready for adolescent rejection and adult discriminating selection and contribution. Persons come after and before other persons [pp. 84–85; her emphasis].

Persons, in other words, are members of a social community which shapes and values them, and personhood is a relational concept that must be defined in terms of interactions and relationships with others.

A fetus is a unique sort of being in that it cannot form relationships freely with others, nor can others readily form relationships with it. A fetus has a primary and particularly intimate relationship with the woman in whose womb it develops; any other relationship it may have is indirect, and must be mediated through the pregnant woman. The relationship that exists between a woman and her fetus is clearly asymmetrical, since she is the only party to the relationship who is capable of making a decision about whether the interaction should continue and since the fetus is wholly dependent on the woman who sustains it while she is quite capable of surviving without it.

However much some might prefer it to be otherwise, no one else can do anything to support or harm a fetus without doing something to the woman who nurtures it. Because of this inexorable biological reality, she bears a unique responsibility and privilege in determining her fetus's place in the social scheme of things. Clearly, many pregnancies occur to women who place very high value on the lives of the particular fetuses they carry, and choose to see their pregnancies through to term despite the possible risks and costs involved; hence, it would be wrong of anyone to force such a woman to terminate her pregnancy under these circumstances. Other women, or some of these same women at other times, value other things more highly (e.g., their freedom, their health, or previous responsibilities which conflict with those generated by the pregnancies), and choose not to continue their pregnancies. The value that women ascribe to individual fetuses varies dramatically from case to case. There is no absolute value that attaches to fetuses apart from their relational status determined by the context of their particular development.

Since human beings are fundamentally relational beings, it is important to remember that fetuses are characteristically limited in the relationships in which they can participate; within those relationships, they can make only the most restricted "contributions."[13] After birth, human beings are capable of a much wider range of roles in relationships with an infinite variety of partners; it is that very diversity of possibility and experience that leads us to focus on the abstraction of the individual as a constant through all her/his relationships. But until birth, no such variety is possible, and the fetus is defined as an entity within a woman who will almost certainly be principally responsible for it for many years to come.

No human, and especially no fetus, can exist apart from relationships; feminist views of what is valuable about persons must reflect the social nature of their existence. Fetal lives can neither be sustained nor destroyed without affecting the women who support them. Because of a fetus's unique physical status — *within* and dependent on a particular woman — the responsibility and privilege of determining its specific social status and value must rest with the woman carrying it. Fetuses are not persons because they have not developed sufficiently in social relationships to be persons in any morally significant sense (i.e., they are not yet second persons). Newborns, although just beginning their development into persons, are immediately subject to social relationships, for they are capable of communication and response in interaction with a variety of other persons. Thus, feminist accounts of abortion stress the importance of protecting women's right to continue as well as to terminate pregnancies as each sees fit.

Feminist Politics and Abortion

Feminist ethics directs us to look at abortion in the context of other issues of power and not to limit discussion to the standard questions about its moral and legal acceptability. Because coerced pregnancy has repercussions for women's oppressed status generally, it is important to ensure that abortion not only be made legal but that adequate services be made accessible to all women who seek them. This means that within Canada, where medically approved abortion is technically recognized as legal (at least for the moment), we must protest the fact that it is not made available to many of the women who have the greatest need for abortions: vast geographical areas offer no abortion services at all, but unless the women of those regions can afford to travel to urban clinics, they have no meaningful right to abortion. Because women depend on access to abortion in their pursuit of social equality, it is a matter of moral as well as political responsibility that provincial health plans should cover the cost of transport and service in the abortion facilities women choose. Ethical study of abortion involves understanding and critiquing the economic, age, and social barriers that currently restrict access to medically acceptable abortion services.[14]

Moreover, it is also important that abortion services be provided in an atmosphere that fosters women's health and well-being; hence, the care offered should be in a context that is supportive of the choices women make. Abortions should be seen as part of women's overall reproductive health and could be included within centres that deal with all matters of reproductive health in an open, patient-centred manner where effective counselling is offered for a wide range of reproductive decisions.[15] Providers need to recognize that abortion is a legitimate option so that services will be delivered with respect and concern for the physical, psychological, and emotional effects on a patient. All too frequently, hospital-based abortions are provided by practitioners who are uneasy about their role and treat the women involved with hostility and resentment. Increasingly, many anti-abortion activists have personalized their attacks and focussed their attention on harassing the women who enter and leave abortion clinics. Surely requiring a woman to pass a gauntlet of hostile protesters on her way to and from an abortion is not conducive to effective health care. Ethical exploration of abortion raises questions about how women are treated when they seek abortions,[16] achieving legal permission for women to dispose of their fetuses if they are determined enough to manage the struggle should not be accepted as the sole moral consideration.

Nonetheless, feminists must formulate their distinctive response to legislative initiatives on abortion. The tendency of Canadian politicians confronted by vocal activists on both sides of the abortion issue has been to seek "compromises" that seem to give something to each (and, thereby, also deprives each of important features sought in policy formation). Thus, the House of Commons recently passed a law (Bill C-43) that allows a woman to have an abortion only if a doctor certifies that her physical, mental, or emotional health will be otherwise threatened. Many non-feminist supporters of women's right to choose consider this a victory and urge feminists to be satisfied with it, but feminists have good reason to object. Besides their obvious objection to having abortion returned to the Criminal Code, feminists also object that this policy considers doctors and not women the best judges of a woman's need for abortion; feminists have little reason to trust doctors to appreciate the political dimension of abortion or to respond adequately to women's needs. Abortion must be a woman's decision, and not one controlled by her doctor. Further, experience shows that doctors are already reluctant to provide abortions to women; the opportunity this law presents for criminal persecution of doctors by anti-abortion campaigners is a sufficient worry to inhibit their participation.[17] Feminists want

women's decision making to be recognized as legitimate, and cannot be satisfied with a law that makes abortion a medical choice.

Feminists support abortion on demand because they know that women must have control over their reproduction. For the same reason, they actively oppose forced abortion and coerced sterilization, practices that are sometimes inflicted on the most powerless women, especially those in the Third World. Feminist ethics demands that access to voluntary, safe, effective birth control be part of any abortion discussion, so that women have access to other means of avoiding pregnancy.[18]

Feminist analysis addresses the context as well as the practice of abortion decisions. Thus, feminists also object to the conditions which lead women to abort wanted fetuses because there are not adequate financial and social supports available to care for a child. Because feminist accounts value fetuses that are wanted by the women who carry them, they oppose practices which force women to abort because of poverty or intimidation. Yet, the sorts of social changes necessary if we are to free women from having abortions out of economic necessity are vast; they include changes not only in legal and health care policy, but also in housing, child care, employment, etc. (Petchesky 1980, p. 112). Nonetheless, feminist ethics defines reproductive freedom as the condition under which women are able to make truly voluntary choices about their reproductive lives, and these many dimensions are implicit in the ideal.

Clearly, feminists are not "pro-abortion," for they are concerned to ensure the safety of each pregnancy to the greatest degree possible; wanted fetuses should not be harmed or lost. Therefore, adequate pre- and post-natal care and nutrition are also important elements of any feminist position on reproductive freedom. Where anti-abortionists direct their energies to trying to prevent women from obtaining abortions, feminists seek to protect the health of wanted fetuses. They recognize that far more could be done to protect and care for fetuses if the state directed its resources at supporting women who continue their pregnancies, rather than draining away resources in order to police women who find that they must interrupt their pregnancies. Caring for the women who carry fetuses is not only a more legitimate policy than is regulating them; it is probably also more effective at ensuring the health and well-being of more fetuses.

Feminist ethics also explores how abortion policies fit within the politics of sexual domination. Most feminists are sensitive to the fact that many men support women's right to abortion out of the belief that women will be more willing sexual partners if they believe that they can readily terminate an unwanted pregnancy. Some men coerce their partners into obtaining abortions the women may not want.[19] Feminists understand that many women oppose abortion for this very reason, being unwilling to support a practice that increases women's sexual vulnerability (Luker 1984, (pp. 209–15). Thus, it is important that feminists develop a coherent analysis of reproductive freedom that includes sexual freedom (as women choose to define it). That requires an analysis of sexual freedom that includes women's right to refuse sex; such a right can only be assured if women have equal power to men and are not subject to domination by virtue of their sex.[20]

In sum, then, feminist ethics demands that moral discussions of abortion be more broadly defined than they have been in most philosophic discussions. Only by reflecting on the meaning of ethical pronouncements on actual women's lives and the connections between judgments on abortion and the conditions of domination and subordination can we come to an adequate understanding of the moral status of abortion in our society. As Rosalind Petchesky (1980) argues, feminist discussion of abortion "must be moved beyond the framework of a 'woman's right to choose' and connected to a much broader revolutionary movement that addresses all the conditions of women's liberation" (p. 113).

Notes

1. For some idea of the ways in which traditional moral theory oppresses women, see Morgan (1987) and Hoagland (1988).

2. Critics continue to want to structure the debate around the *possibility* of women making frivolous abortion decisions and hence want feminists to agree to setting boundaries on acceptable grounds for choosing abortion. Feminists ought to resist this injunction, though. There is no practical way of drawing a line fairly in the abstract; cases that may appear "frivolous" at a distance often turn out to be substantive when the details are revealed, i.e., frivolity is in the eyes of the beholder. There is no evidence to suggest that women actually make the sorts of choices worried critics hypothesize about: e.g., a woman eight months pregnant who chooses to abort because she wants to take a trip or gets in "a tiff" with her partner. These sorts of fantasies, on which demands to distinguish between legitimate and illegitimate personal reasons for choosing abortion chiefly rest, reflect an offensive conception of women as irresponsible; they ought not to be perpetuated. Women, seeking moral guidance in their own deliberations about choosing abortion, do not find such hypothetical discussions of much use.

3. In her monumental historical analysis of the early roots of Western patriarchy, Gerda Lerner (1986) determined that patriarchy began in the period from 3100 to 600 B.C. when men appropriated women's sexual and reproductive capacity; the earliest states entrenched patriarchy by institutionalizing the sexual and procreative subordination of women to men.

4. There are some women who claim to be feminists against choice in abortion. See, for instance, Callahan (1987), though few spell out their full feminist program. For reasons I develop in this paper, I do not think this is a consistent position.

5. There is a lot the state could do to ameliorate this condition. If it provided women with adequate financial support, removed the inequities in the labour market, and provided affordable and reliable child care, pregnancy need not so often lead to a woman's dependence on a particular man. The fact that it does not do so is evidence of the state's complicity in maintaining women's subordinate position with respect to men.

6. See Petchesky (1984), especially Chapter 5, "Considering the Alternatives: The Problems of Contraception," where she documents the risks and discomforts associated with pill use and IUDs and the increasing rate at which women are choosing the option of diaphragm or condom with the option of early legal abortions as back-up.

7. See Zillah Eisenstein (1988) for a comprehensive theory of the role of the pregnant body as the central element in the cultural subordination of women.

8. Thomson (1971) is a notable exception to this trend.

9. This seems reminiscent of Aristotle's view of women as "flower pots" where men implant the seed with all the important genetic information and the movement necessary for development and women's job is that of passive gestation, like the flower pot. For exploration of the flower pot picture of pregnancy, see Whitbeck (1973) and Lange (1983).

10. Contrast Warren (1989) with Tooley (1972).

11. The definition of pregnancy as a purely passive activity reaches its ghoulish conclusion in the increasing acceptability of sustaining brain-dead women on life support systems to continue their functions as incubators until the fetus can be safely delivered. For a discussion of this new trend, see Murphy (1989).

12. This apt phrasing is taken from Petchesky (1986), p. 342.

13. Fetuses are almost wholly individuated by the women who bear them. The fetal "contributions" to the relationship are defined by the projections and interpretations of the pregnant woman in the latter stages of pregnancy if she chooses to perceive fetal movements in purposeful ways (e.g., "it likes classical music, wine, exercise").

14. Some feminists suggest we seek recognition of the legitimacy of non-medical abortion services. This would reduce costs and increase access dramatically, with no apparent increase in risk, provided that services were offered by trained, responsible practitioners concerned with the well-being of their clients. It would also allow the possibility of increasing women's control over abortion. See, for example, McDonnell (1984), chap. 8.

15. For a useful model of such a centre, see Wagner and Lee (1989).

16. See CARAL/Halifax (1990) for women's stories about their experiences with hospitals and free-standing abortion clinics.

17. The Canadian Medical Association has confirmed those fears. In testimony before the House of Commons committee reviewing the bill, the CMA reported that over half the doctors surveyed who now perform abortions expect to stop offering them if the legislation goes through. Since the Commons passed the bill, the threats of withdrawal of service have increased. Many doctors plan to abandon their abortion service once the law is introduced, because they are unwilling to accept the harassment they anticipate from anti-abortion zealots. Even those who believe that they will eventually win any court case that arises fear the expense and anxiety involved as the case plays itself out.

18. Therefore, the Soviet model, where women have access to multiple abortions but where there is no other birth control available, must also be opposed.

19. See CARAL/Halifax (1990), pp. 20–21, for examples of this sort of abuse.

20. It also requires that discussions of reproductive and sexual freedom not be confined to "the language of control and sexuality characteristic of a technology of sex" (Diamond and Quinby 1988, p. 197), for such language is alienating and constrains women's experiences of their own sexuality.

References

Addelson, Kathryn Pyne. "Moral Passages." In *Women and Moral Theory*. Edited by Eva-Feder Kittay and Diana T. Meyers. Totowa, NJ: Rowman & Littlefield, 1987.

Baier, Annette. *Postures of the Mind: Essays on Minds and Morals*. Minneapolis: University of Minnesota Press, 1985.

Callahan, Sidney. "A Pro-Life Feminist Makes Her Case." *Utne Reader* (March/April 1987): 104–14.

Daly, Mary. *Beyond God the Father: Toward a Philosophy of Women's Liberation*. Boston: Beacon Press, 1973.

Diamond, Irene, and Lee Quinby. "American Feminism and the Language of Control." In *Feminism & Foucault: Reflections on Resistance*. Edited by Irene Diamond and Lee Quinby. Boston: Northeastern University Press, 1988.

Eisenstein, Zillah R. *The Female Body and the Law*. Berkeley: University of California Press, 1988.

Hoagland, Sara Lucia. *Lesbian Ethics: Toward New Values*. Palo Alto, CA: Institute of Lesbian Studies, 1988.

Lange, Lynda. "Woman Is Not a Rational Animal: On Aristotle's Biology of Reproduction." In *Discovering Reality: Feminist Perspectives on Epistemology, Metaphysic, Methodology, and Philosophy of Science*. Edited by Sandra Harding and Merrill B. Hintikka. Dordrecht, Holland: D. Reidel, 1983.

Lerner, Gerda. *The Creation of Paradise*. New York: Oxford University Press, 1986.

Luker, Kristin. *Abortion and the Politics of Motherhood*. Berkeley: University of California Press, 1984.

MacKinnon, Catherine. *Toward a Feminist Theory of the State*. Cambridge, MA: Harvard University Press, 1989.

McDonnell, Kathleen. *Not an Easy Choice: A Feminist Re-examines Abortion*. Toronto: The Women's Press, 1986.

McLaren, Angus, and Arlene Tigar McLaren. *The Bedroom and the State: The Changing Practices and Politics of Contraception and Abortion in Canada, 1880–1980*. Toronto: McClelland and Stewart, 1986.

Morgan, Kathryn Pauly. "Women and Moral Madmen." In *Science, Morality and Feminist Theory*. Edited by Marsha Hanen and Kai Nielsen. *Canadian Journal of Philosophy*, Supplementary Volume 13:201–26.

Murphy, Julien S. "Should Pregnancies Be Sustained in Brain-dead Women? A Philosophical Discussion of Postmortem Pregnancy." In *Healing Technology: Feminist Perspectives*. Edited by Kathryn Srother Ratcliff et al. Ann Arbor: The University of Michigan Press, 1987.

Overall, Christine. *Ethics and Human Reproduction: A Feminist Analysis*. Winchester, MA: Allen and Unwin, 1987.

Petchesky, Rosalind Pollack. "Reproductive Freedom: Beyond 'Woman's Right to Choose.'" In *Women: Sex and Sexuality*. Edited by Catharine R. Simpson and Ethel Spector Person. Chicago: University of Chicago Press, 1980.

———. *Abortion and Woman's Choice: The State, Sexuality, and Reproductive Freedom*. Boston: Northeastern University Press, 1984.

Sumner, L. W. *Abortion and Moral Theory*. Princeton: Princeton University Press, 1981.

Thomson, Judith Jarvis. "A Defense of Abortion." *Philosophy and Public Affairs* 1 (1971): 47–66.

Tooley, Michael. "Abortion and Infanticide." *Philosophy and Public Affairs* 2:1 (Fall 1972): 37–65.

Van Wagner, Vicki, and Bob Lee. "Principles into Practice: An Activist Vision of Feminist Reproductive Health Care." In *The Future of Human Reproduction*. Edited by Christine Overall. Toronto: The Women's Press, 1989.

Warren, Mary Anne. "On the Moral and Legal Status of Abortion." *The Monist* 4:57(1973): 43–61.

———. "On the Moral Significance of Birth." *Hypatia* 4:2 (Summer 1989): 46–65.

Whitbeck, Carolyn. "Theories of Sex Difference." *The Philosophical Forum* 5: 1–2 (Fall/Winter 1973–74): 54–80.

Further Readings

Borowski v. Canada (Attorney General) [1989] 1 S.C.R. 342, affirming on other grounds (1987) 33 C.C.C. (3d) 402.

Congregation for the Doctrine of the Faith. *Donum Vitae*: Instruction on Respect for Human Life in Its Origin and on the Dignity of Procreation, Feb. 22, 1987. Vatican.

Engelhardt, Jr., Tristam. *The Foundations of Bioethics*. Oxford: Oxford Univ. Press, 1986, pp. 301–317.

Feinberg, Joel, ed. *The Problem of Abortion*. Belmont, Calif.: Wadsworth, 1973.

Foot, Philippa. "The Problem of Abortion and the Principle of Double Effect." *Oxford Review* 5.

Kluge, E.-H.W. "Abortion," in E.-H. Kluge, *The Practice of Death*. New Haven and London: Yale Univ. Press, 1975, pp. 1–100.

Makdur, I. "Sterilization and Abortion from the Point of View of Islam." In *Islam and Family Planning*, vol. 2 (271).

Murphy v. Dodd et al., 70 O.R. (2d) 681.

Murray, T.H. "Moral Obligation to the Not-Yet Born: The Fetus as Patient," *Clin Perinatol* 14 (June 1987): pp. 329–343.

Ney, P.G., and A.R. Wickett. "Mental Health and Abortion: Review and Analysis." *Psych J of Univ Ottawa* 14:4 (Nov. 1989).

Noonan, J.T. ed. *The Morality of Abortion: Legal and Historical Perspectives.* Cambridge, MA: Harvard Univ. Press, 1970.

Overall, Christine. *Ethics and Human Reproduction: A Feminist Analysis.* Bristol: Allen and Unwin, 1987.

————. "Selective Termination of Pregnancy and Women's Reproductive Autonomy." *Hastings Center Rep* 20:3 (1990): 6–11.

Sacred Congregation for the Doctrine of the Faith. *Declaration on Procured Abortion.* Rome: Vatican, 1985.

Shaw, M., and A. Doudera, eds. *Defining Human Life: Medical, Legal and Ethical Implications.* Ann Arbor, Mich.: AUPHA Press, 1983.

Thompson, J.J. "A Defense of Abortion," *Philos and Pub Affairs* 1:1 (1971): 47–66.

Tooley, Michael. *Analysis of Abortion and Infanticide.* Oxford: Clarendon Press, 1983.

Tremblay v. Daigle, 62 D.L.R. (4th) 634.

Wertheimer, Roger. "Understanding the Abortion Argument," *Philos and Pub Affairs*, 1:1 (Fall 1971): 67–95.

CHAPTER 14
ASSISTED SUICIDE, EUTHANASIA AND CESSATION OF TREATMENT

Introduction

Historically, people used to die by accident, through a disease, or simply as a result of gradual physical deterioration and old age. Most of the time, the way death occurred had nothing formalized about it. It just happened — expectedly or otherwise — and there was little anyone could do. Most of the time, too — accidents excepted — it occurred at home. Modern scientific medicine and modern health care have changed all that. Death and dying have moved into the institutionalized setting of the hospital or health care facility. Consequently, death and dying have become increasingly medicalized, not only in terms of the criteria that are used to determine death, but also in the sense that dying itself has become imbued with the nimbus of medical practice, and the ethos of the medical profession has tended to determine the shape a particular dying will take.

This has raised several problems. One centres on the fact that the traditional ethos of the health care professions in general, and of medicine in particular, has been to save and/or sustain life. That makes it psychologically very difficult for some of these professionals to allow death to occur. More often than not, death is seen as a professional failure. However, sometimes, when continued life only promises a meaningless prolongation of indignity and suffering, patients see death as a release and want to hasten the dying process — or at least not oppose it. Patients who see it that way do not perceive death as something that health care professionals should try to prevent at all costs.

In fact, public opinion polls have consistently shown that the majority of Canadians feel that when death is inevitable and the future holds only irremediable suffering, it is ethically acceptable for physicians to deliberately assist in the deaths of their patients. In 1984, the proportion who believed this stood at 66%; by 1989 it had risen to 77% and in 1999 — the latest year for which figures are available — the percentage still stood around 75%.[1] This appears to put the traditional ethos of the health care professions squarely in conflict with the preferences of Canadian society.

Providing patients only with comfort measures and allowing death to occur is usually called *passive euthanasia*; bringing about the death of a patient deliberately by active means is called *active euthanasia*. Therefore, Canadian public opinion has consistently accepted not only passive euthanasia but active euthanasia as well — or at least physician-assisted suicide.

Of course, there have always been some physicians who believed that while the Hippocratic Oath required them to refrain from deliberately bringing about death, it did not prohibit them from letting nature take its course when death was inevitable and the prolongation of life meant only a prolongation of suffering.[2] In other words, there have always been some physicians who maintained that passive euthanasia was ethically acceptable. On the other hand, Canadian statute law has always taken a much firmer stance. Not only does it prohibit taking active steps to bring about the death of a patient, characterizing it as murder,[3] it also goes on to say that once medical treatment has been initiated, the professional has a duty to continue if stopping the treatment is likely to imperil the patient's life or health. In other words, Canadian statute law not only rejects active euthanasia but passive euthanasia as well.[4]

This disparity of these positions raises several important questions: Are medical tradition and the law in touch with current ethical perceptions or do they merely reflect the privately held morality of physicians and politicians? Are active and passive euthanasia really different, as some members of the medical profession claim? Is statute law correct in condemning both? Is public opinion correct in accepting both? And if public opinion should be respected, how should this respect be translated into medical practice and social policy?

Several recent Canadian cases deal with euthanasia and assisted suicide. One of the more notable is the *Latimer* case (referenced at the end of this introduction). It concerns a father who killed his daughter, Tracy, by carbon monoxide poisoning. Tracy was tragically disfigured, incurably disabled by cerebral palsy and apparently in constant pain. According to court testimony, Tracy had been born "clinically dead" and had had to be resuscitated. As a result, she suffered serious brain damage due to lack of oxygen. Shortly after her birth she developed muscle spasms — seizures — and for a while had a seizure every minute. Drug treatment reduced the frequency of her seizures: initially to one every twenty minutes and later to five or six seizures each day. It was expected that this would continue the rest of her life. Some seizures were light; others were severe to the point where her whole body shook. She had no use of her arms and legs and would never have been able to sit up on her own, though she could be propped up in a wheelchair. During the last five years of her life, she could not even roll over like any two- or three-month-old baby. Her brain simply could not control the muscles of her body. Her muscles tightened when they should not. As a result, her body became "twisted up." To relieve the tension of certain muscles and the associated pain, Tracy underwent a number of operations to have certain muscles cut: the muscles at the top of her legs (so her hips would not dislocate), her toes, her heel cords, knee muscles and so on. During one surgery, stainless steel rods were put on either side of her spine to straighten her body sufficiently to relieve the cramping of her stomach and her lungs. Tracy had great difficulty swallowing her food and it took a long time —

and considerable skill — to feed her. Often she could not keep her food down and would vomit. The family kept a bucket near her for this purpose whenever they fed her. Tracy had to be kept in diapers at all times because she had no control over her excretory functions. She could not focus her eyes and was always cross-eyed. Her mother assessed her physical and mental development as that of a two- or three-month-old baby. Although she recognized her mother, father and her siblings, she could not understand her own name. She did not know the difference between "yes" and "no." Her only forms of communication were laughing, smiling and crying. At trial, Mr. Latimer claimed that he had killed Tracy to end her suffering. Nevertheless, he was found guilty of murder. This judgment was upheld on appeal. However, the Supreme Court ordered a new trial when it was found that prospective jurors in the first trial had been asked whether they would be likely to convict Mr. Latimer — apparently with the aim of selecting only jurors who would bring in a "guilty" verdict.[5] A new trial was held, and Mr. Latimer was again found guilty. The Supreme Court refused to change the original verdict. The case of Tracy Latimer is one of *non-voluntary active euthanasia*.

The case of *Rodriguez v. British Columbia (Attorney General)*, the first selection in this chapter, is fundamentally different. It involved a woman who suffered from amyotrophic lateral sclerosis (Lou Gehrig's disease) who wished to have assistance in dying if and when, in her estimation, she could live no longer. However, section 241(b) of the *Criminal Code* prohibits people from assisting anyone in committing suicide. Ms. Rodriguez decided to challenge the constitutionality of this provision. She argued that since suicide is not illegal in Canada, all persons have a freedom-right to take their own lives. However — so she argued — persons like her, with severe disabilities, cannot take their own lives. Consequently, so she maintained, section 241(b) of the Code discriminates against persons who suffer from a physical disability. It therefore violates the principle of equality and justice, which is enshrined in section 15 of the Charter of Rights and Freedoms. The Supreme Court unanimously agreed that this was indeed the case. However, it found on a bare majority (5 to 4) that this sort of discrimination was justified because it was demonstrably necessary in a free and democratic society (section 1 of the Charter).

There is a follow-up to the Rodriguez story in the recent case of *R. v. Genereux*.[6] It involves a physician with two patients who were HIV sero-positive but who did not yet have full-blown AIDS. They asked for, and received from Dr. Genereux, prescriptions for a sufficient amount of opioids to allow them to commit suicide. Dr. Genereux knew that they intended to kill themselves when he wrote the prescriptions. One patient attempted suicide and failed; the other succeeded. Dr. Genereux was found guilty of assisting suicide. He was sentenced to two years less-a-day imprisonment and three years probation. The Ontario Court of Appeal unanimously upheld the verdict. However, it refused to increase the sentence for fear of sending the wrong message to physicians who wished to alleviate the suffering of terminal patients but might become afraid to use sufficiently large doses of painkillers, seeing that this would hasten the patients' death. (It might be an interesting question to ask whether the Ontario Court of Appeal thereby endorsed the doctrine of double effect.)

Latimer differs from *Rodriguez* and *Genereux* in that the former involves the actions of a proxy or substitute decision-maker for an incompetent person, who decides that the incompetent person is better off dead. The courts rejected this choice — even though competent persons have the right to choose death for themselves. This raises the difficult question of whether the range of choices open to people who make decisions for the incompetent should be more limited than those open to everyone else. In this context, the articles on consent and proxy decision-making in previous chapters might usefully be reconsidered.

In the next selection, James Rachels, in a classic article, takes a look at the supposed distinction between active and passive euthanasia. He argues that while the distinction may be of psychological benefit, logically and ethically it carries very little weight.

The article by Richard Doerflinger focuses on assisted suicide and raises a warning: Doerflinger argues that allowing assisted suicide — or, for that matter, any form of deliberate and actively imposed death — even in special cases, constitutes the beginning of a slippery slope whose horrible consequences were only too obvious in Nazi Germany. The notion of a slippery slope, which is emotionally appealing but conceptually difficult, deserves close examination. Some of the suggested readings at the end of this chapter present a different perspective.

The article by Quill, Dresser and Brock deals with an issue that is touched on by Doerflinger and the others which is central to contemporary palliative care: Sometimes, to achieve a proper analgesic effect, physicians have to prescribe such large doses of painkillers that they hasten the death of the patient. Strictly speaking, this is tantamount to killing the patient for her or his own good. Physicians sometimes defend this sort of action by appealing to the so-called *doctrine or rule of double effect*. This is a doctrine that was developed by Catholic theologians in the Middle Ages. It says that as long as an act is not inherently bad, as long as the intent in performing the act is only to achieve the good outcome, as long as the negative side effect that accompanies the act is not a necessary means of achieving the good outcome, and as long there is a proportionality between the good outcome and the negative side effect, then the act is ethically acceptable. The doctrine was originally developed to help physicians who were faced with a difficult pregnancy and had to decide whether to kill the foetus in order to save the life of the mother, or save the life of the mother and kill the foetus. The doctrine of double effect was subsequently adapted to the palliative context. Quill *et al.* deal with it in this context.

The final reading, the *Joint Statement on Resuscitative Interventions*, presents the current position of Canadian health care professionals and health care providers. You will note that it seems to represent a fundamental departure from the traditional professional ethos in its permissive stance towards passive euthanasia. It might be interesting to investigate whether this is something relatively new, or whether it merely constitutes an endorsement of something that, deep down, the health care professions had accepted all along.

Notes

1. Gallup Canada Inc., July 24, 1989. The regional distribution was as follows: 81% in Quebec, 77% in Ontario and B.C., 72% in Atlantic Canada, and 71% in the Prairie Provinces. The results were considered accurate within four percentage points, nineteen times out of twenty. The more recent Gallup poll (Fall of 1991) showed only a 2% variation in these figures. The 1999 poll, which was the latest one on this subject, indicated that support had remained steady around 75%.

2. Similar prohibitions were traditional for other health care professionals.

3. See the various provisions in the Revised Statutes of Canada 1985, c.C-46; especially Part VIII, "Offences Against the Person."

4. See above, ss. 216, 217, 219, 220 *et passim.*

5. *R. v. Latimer* [1997] 1 S.C.R. 217.

6. *R. v. Genereux* [1999] Ont. C.A. 136 C.C.C. (3d) 338.

Rodriguez v. British Columbia (Attorney General)

Lamer C.J. (dissenting):

Ms. Rodriguez suffers from amyotrophic lateral sclerosis (ALS), which is widely known as Lou Gehrig's disease; her life expectancy is between 2 and 14 months but her condition is rapidly deteriorating. Very soon she will lose the ability to swallow, speak, walk and move her body without assistance. Thereafter she will lose the capacity to breathe without a respirator, to eat without a gastrotomy and will eventually become confined to a bed. ... She does not wish to die so long as she still has the capacity to enjoy life. However, by the time she no longer is able to enjoy life, she will be physically unable to terminate her life without assistance. Ms. Rodriguez seeks an order which will allow a qualified medical practitioner to set up technological means by which she might, by her own hand, at the time of her choosing, end her life.

...

The relevant provision of the Criminal Code is as follows:

241. Every one who

(a) counsels a person to commit suicide, or

(b) aids or abets a person to commit suicide, whether suicide ensues or not, is guilty of an indictable offence and liable to imprisonment for a term not exceeding fourteen years.

The relevant sections of the Charter are as follows:

1. The Canadian Charter of Rights and Freedoms guarantees the rights and freedoms set out in it subject only to such reasonable limits prescribed by law as can be demonstrably justified in a free and democratic society.

7. Everyone has the right to life, liberty and security of the person and the right not to be deprived thereof except in accordance with the principles of fundamental justice.

[1993] 3 S.C.R. 519.

12. Everyone has the right not to be subjected to any cruel and unusual treatment or punishment.

15. (1) Every individual is equal before and under the law and has the right to the equal protection and equal benefit of the law without discrimination and, in particular, without discrimination based on race, national or ethnic origin, colour, religion, sex, age or mental or physical disability.

... In medical matters, the common law recognizes to a very large degree the right of each individual to make decisions regarding his or her own person, despite the sometimes serious consequences of such choices. ... That does not mean that these values are absolute. However, in my opinion s. 15(1) requires that limitations on these fundamental values should be distributed with a measure of equality.

In this connection, and without expressing any opinion on the moral value of suicide, I am forced to conclude that the fact that persons unable to end their own lives cannot choose suicide because they do not legally have access to assistance is — in legal terms — a disadvantage giving rise to the application of s. 15(1) of the Charter. ... I conclude that s. 241(*b*) of the Criminal Code infringes the right to equality guaranteed in s. 15(1) of the Charter. This provision has a discriminatory effect on persons who are or will become incapable of committing suicide themselves, even assuming that all the usual means are available to them, because due to an irrelevant personal characteristic such persons are subject to limitations on their ability to take fundamental decisions regarding their lives and persons that are not imposed on other members of Canadian society.

... An individual's right to control his or her own body does not cease to obtain merely because that individual has become dependent on others for the physical maintenance of that body; indeed, in such circumstances, this type of autonomy is often most critical to an individual's feeling of self-worth and dignity. ... I ... wish to stress, however, that the scope of self-determination with respect to bodily integrity in our society is never absolute. While there may be no limitations on the treatments to which a patient may refuse or discontinue, there are always limits on the treatment which a patient may demand, and to which the patient will be legally permitted to consent. ... Most important of these limits is s. 14 of the Criminal Code, which stipulates that an individual may not validly consent to have death inflicted on him or her. ...

With these limitations in mind, I conclude that the objective of s. 241(*b*) of the Code may properly be characterized as the protection of vulnerable people, whether they are consenting or not, from the intervention of others in decisions respecting the planning and commission of the act of suicide. Underlying this legislative purpose is the principle of preservation of life. ... However, I hasten to add that the repeal of the offence of attempted suicide demonstrates that Parliament will no longer preserve human life at the cost of depriving physically able individuals of their right to self-determination. ...

... There is no way, under the present legislation, to distinguish between those people whose freely chosen will it is to terminate their life, and those people who are potentially being pressured or coerced by others. Vulnerability, in a sense, is simply imposed on all people who happen to be physically unable to commit suicide independently and the right to choose suicide is therefore removed from this entire class of persons. ... The vulnerable are effectively protected under s. 241(*b*), but so... are those who are not vulnerable, who do not wish the state's protection, but who are brought within the operation of s. 241(*b*) solely as a result of a physical disability. ...

... The principal fear is that the decriminalization of assisted suicide will increase the risk of persons with physical disabilities being manipulated by others. This "slippery slope" argument appeared to be the central justification behind the Law Reform Commission of Canada's recommendation not to repeal this provision.

... While I share a deep concern over the subtle and overt pressures that may be brought to bear on such persons if assisted suicide is decriminalized, even in limited circumstances, I do not think legislation that deprives a disadvantaged group of the right to equality can be justified solely on such speculative grounds, no matter how well intentioned. Similar dangers to the ones outlined above have surrounded the decriminalization of attempted suicide as well. It is impossible to know the degree of pressure or intimidation a physically able person may have been under when deciding to commit suicide. The truth is that we simply do not and cannot know the range of implications that allowing some form of assisted suicide will have for persons with physical disabilities. What we do know and cannot ignore is the anguish of those in the position of Ms. Rodriguez. Respecting the consent of those in her position may necessarily imply running the risk that the consent will have been obtained improperly. The proper role of the legal system in these circumstances is to provide safeguards to ensure that the consent in question is as independent and informed as is reasonably possible.

... I agree with the importance of distinguishing between the situation where a person who is aided in his or her decision to commit suicide and the situation where the decision itself is a product of someone else's influence. However, I fail to see how preventing against abuse in one context must result in denying self-determination in another. I remain unpersuaded by the government's apparent contention that it is not possible to design legislation that is somewhere in between complete decriminalization and absolute prohibition.

In my view, there is a range of options from which Parliament may choose in seeking to safeguard the interests of the vulnerable and still ensure the equal right to self-determination of persons with physical disabilities. ... Regardless of the safeguards Parliament may wish to adopt, however, I find that an absolute prohibition that is indifferent to the individual or the circumstances in question cannot satisfy the constitutional duty on the government to impair the rights of persons with physical disabilities as little as reasonably possible. ... I find the infringement of s. 15 by this provision cannot be saved under s. 1. ...

I have held that s. 241(b) violates the equality rights of *all* persons who desire to commit suicide but are or will become physically unable to do so unassisted. Restricting the remedy to those who are terminally ill, and suffering from incurable diseases or conditions, ... does not follow from the principles underlying my holding, and might well itself give rise to a violation of the equality rights of those who do not fit that description but wish to commit suicide and need assistance. ... To summarize, then, I would make a constitutional exemption available to Ms. Rodriguez, and others, on the following conditions:

1. the constitutional exemption may only be sought by way of application to a superior court;

2. the applicant must be certified by a treating physician and independent psychiatrist ... to be competent to make the decision to end her own life, and the physicians must certify that the applicant's decision has been made freely and voluntarily, and at least one of the physicians must be present with the applicant at the time the applicant commits assisted suicide;

3. the physicians must also certify:
   (i) that the applicant is or will become physically incapable of committing suicide unassisted, and (ii) that they have informed him or her, and that he or she understands, that he or she has a continuing right to change his or her mind about terminating his or her life;

4. notice and access must be given to the Regional Coroner ...;

5. the applicant must be examined daily by one of the certifying physicians;

6. the constitutional exemption will expire [after a set period of time]; and

7. the act causing the death of the applicant must be that of the applicant him- or herself, and not of anyone else. ...

...

Sopinka J. (for the majority of the Supreme Court):

In my view, [the position outlined by Chief Justice Lamer fails on the following grounds:]

1. It recognizes a constitutional right to legally assisted suicide beyond that of any country in the western world, beyond any serious proposal for reform in the western world and beyond the claim made in this very case. The apparent reason for the expansion beyond the claim in this case is that restriction of the right to the terminally ill could not be justified under s. 15.

2. It fails to provide ... safeguards. ...

3. The conditions imposed are vague and in some respects unenforceable. ...

4. ... The conditions ... are to serve merely as guidelines, leaving it to individual judges to decide upon application whether to grant or withhold the right to commit suicide. ...

I have concluded that the conclusion of my colleagues cannot be supported under the provisions of the Charter.

... The appellant seeks a remedy which would assure her some control over the time and manner of her death. ... She fears that she will be required to live until the deterioration from her disease is such that she will die as a result of choking, suffocation or pneumonia caused by aspiration of food or secretions. She will be totally dependent upon machines to perform her bodily functions and completely dependent upon others. Throughout this time, she will remain mentally competent and able to appreciate all that is happening to her. Although palliative care may be available to ease the pain and other physical discomfort which she will experience, the appellant fears the sedating effects of such drugs and argues, in any event, that they will not prevent the psychological and emotional distress which will result from being in a situation of utter dependence and loss of dignity. That there is a right to choose how one's body will be dealt with, even in the context of beneficial medical treatment, has long been recognized by the common law. To impose medical treatment on one who refuses it constitutes battery, and our common law has recognized the right to demand that medical treatment which would extend life be withheld or withdrawn. In my view, these considerations lead to the conclusion that the prohibition in s. 241(*b*) deprives the appellant of autonomy over her person and causes her physical pain and psychological stress in a manner which impinges on the security of her person. The appellant's security interest (considered in the context of the life and liberty interest) is therefore engaged, and it is necessary to determine whether there has been any deprivation thereof that is not in accordance with the principles of fundamental justice. ...

That respect for human dignity is one of the underlying principles upon which our society is based is unquestioned. I have difficulty, however, in characterizing this in itself as a principle of fundamental justice within the meaning of s. 7. While respect for human dignity is the genesis for many principles of fundamental justice, not every law that fails to accord such respect runs afoul of these principles. To state that "respect for human dignity and autonomy" is a principle of fundamental justice, then, is essentially to state that the deprivation of the appellant's security of the person is contrary to principles of fundamental justice because it deprives her of security of the person. This interpretation would equate security of the person with a principle of fundamental justice and render the latter redundant. ...

Section 241(*b*) has as its purpose the protection of the vulnerable who might be induced in moments of weakness to commit suicide. This purpose is grounded in the state interest in protecting life and reflects the policy of the state that human life should not be depreciated by allowing life to be taken. This policy finds expression not only in the provisions of our Criminal Code which prohibit murder and other violent acts against others notwithstanding the consent of the victim, but also in the policy against capital punishment and, until its repeal, attempted suicide. This is not only a policy of the state, however, but is part of our fundamental conception of the sanctity of human life. ...

[T]he principle of sanctity of life is no longer seen to require that all human life be preserved at all costs. Rather, it has come to be understood, at least by some, as encompassing quality of life considerations, and to be subject to certain limitations and qualifications reflective of personal autonomy and dignity. An analysis of our legislative and social policy in this area is necessary in order to determine whether fundamental principles have evolved such that they conflict with the validity of the balancing of interests undertaken by Parliament.

Mr. Justice Sopinka now discusses withdrawing treatment:

The distinction between withdrawing treatment upon a patient's request ... and assisted suicide on the other has been criticized as resting on a legal fiction — that is, the distinction between active and passive forms of treatment. The criticism is based on the fact that the withdrawal of life supportive measures is done with the knowledge that death will ensue, just as is assisting suicide, and that death does in fact ensue as a result of the action taken. ... Whether or not one agrees that the active vs. passive distinction is maintainable, however, the fact remains that under our common law, the physician has no choice but to accept the patient's instructions to discontinue treatment. ...

The fact that doctors may deliver palliative care to terminally ill patients without fear of sanction, it is argued, attenuates to an even greater degree any legitimate distinction which can be drawn between assisted suicide and what are currently acceptable forms of medical treatment. The administration of drugs designed for pain control in dosages which the physician knows will hasten death constitutes active contribution to death by any standard. However, the distinction drawn here is one based upon intention — in the case of palliative care the intention is to ease pain, which has the effect of hastening death, while in the case of assisted suicide, the intention is undeniably to cause death. ... In my view, distinctions based upon intent are important, and in fact form the basis of our criminal law. While factually the distinction may, at times, be difficult to draw, legally it is clear. The fact that in some cases, the third party will, under the guise of palliative care, commit euthanasia or assist in suicide and go unsanctioned due to the difficulty of proof cannot be said to render the existence of the prohibition fundamentally unjust. ...

I also place some significance in the fact that the official position of various medical associations is against decriminalizing assisted suicide (Canadian Medical Association, British Medical Association, Council of Ethical and Judicial Affairs of the American Medical Association, World Medical Association and the American Nurses Association). Given the concerns about abuse that have been expressed and the great difficulty in creating appropriate safeguards to prevent these, it cannot be said that the blanket prohibition on assisted suicide is arbitrary or unfair, or that it is not reflective of fundamental values at play in our society. I am thus unable to find that any principle of fundamental justice is violated by s. 241(*b*). ...

In order to come within the protection of s. 12, the appellant must demonstrate ... that she is subjected to treatment or punishment at the hands of the state, and second, that such treatment or punishment is cruel and unusual. ... In my opinion, it cannot be said that the appellant is subjected by the state to any form of punishment within the meaning of s. 12. ...

Two difficult and important issues arise with respect to this application of s. 15:

1. whether a claim by the terminally ill who cannot commit suicide without assistance can be supported on the ground that s. 241*(b)* discriminates against all disabled persons who are unable to commit suicide without assistance;

2. whether deprivation of the ability to choose suicide is a benefit or burden within the meaning of s. 15 of the Charter. ...

I will assume that s. 15 of the Charter is infringed and consider the application of s. 1. ...

Section 241(*b*) protects all individuals against the control of others over their lives. To introduce an exception to this blanket protection for certain groups would create an inequality. ... [T]his protection is grounded on a substantial consensus among western countries, medical organizations and our own Law Reform Commission that in order to effectively protect life and those who are vulnerable in society, a prohibition without exception on the giving of assistance to commit suicide is the best approach. ... There is no halfway measure that could be relied upon with assurance to fully achieve the legislation's purpose; first, because the purpose extends to the protection of the life of the terminally ill. Part of this purpose, as I have explained above, is to discourage the terminally ill from choosing death over life. Secondly, even if the latter consideration can be stripped from the legislative purpose, we have no assurance that the exception can be made to limit the taking of life to those who are terminally ill and genuinely desire death. ...

I conclude, therefore, that any infringement of s. 15 is clearly justified under s. 1 of the Charter ...

Active and Passive Euthanasia

James Rachels

The distinction between active and passive euthanasia is thought to be crucial for medical ethics. The idea is that it is permissible, at least in some cases, to withhold treatment and allow a patient to die, but it is never permissible to take any direct action designed to kill the patient. This doctrine seems to be accepted by most doctors, and it is endorsed in a statement adopted by the House of Delegates of the American Medical Association on December 4, 1973:

> The intentional termination of the life of one human being by another — mercy killing — is contrary to that for which the medical profession stands and is contrary to the policy of the American Medical Association.

> The cessation of the employment of extraordinary means to prolong the life of the body when there is irrefutable evidence that biological death is imminent is the decision of the patient and/or his immediate family. The advice and judgment of the physician should be freely available to the patient and/or his immediate family.

However, a strong case can be made against this doctrine. In what follows I will set out some of the relevant arguments, and urge doctors to reconsider their views on this matter.

To begin with a familiar type of situation, a patient who is dying of incurable cancer of the throat is in terrible pain, which can no longer be satisfactorily alle-viated. He is certain to die within a few days, even if present treatment is continued, but he does not want to go on living for those days since the pain is unbearable. So he asks the doctor for an end to it, and his family joins in the request.

Suppose the doctor agrees to withhold treatment, as the conventional doctrine says he may. The justification for his doing so is that the patient is in terrible agony, and since he is going to die anyway, it would be wrong to prolong his suffering needlessly. But now notice this. If one simply withholds treatment, it may take the patient longer to die, and so he may suffer more than he would if more direct action were taken and a lethal injection given. This fact provides strong reason for thinking that, once the initial decision not to prolong his agony has been made, active euthanasia is actually preferable to passive euthanasia, rather than the reverse. To say otherwise is to endorse the option that leads to more suffering rather than less, and is contrary to the humanitarian impulse that prompts the decision not to prolong his life in the first place.

Part of my point is that the process of being "allowed to die" can be relatively slow and painful, whereas being given a lethal injection is relatively quick and painless. Let me give a different sort of example. In the United States about one in 600 babies is born with Down's syndrome. Most of these babies are otherwise healthy — that is, with only the usual pediatric care, they will proceed to an otherwise normal infancy. Some, how-

---

ever, are born with congenital defects such as intestinal obstructions that require operations if they are to live. Sometimes, the parents and the doctor will decide not to operate, and let the infant die. Anthony Shaw describes what happens then:

> ... When surgery is denied [the doctor] must try to keep the infant from suffering while natural forces sap the baby's life away. As a surgeon whose natural inclination is to use the scalpel to fight off death, standing by and watching a salvageable baby die is the most emotionally exhausting experience I know. It is easy at a conference, in a theoretical discussion, to decide that such infants should be allowed to die. It is altogether different to stand by in the nursery and watch as dehydration and infection wither a tiny being over hours and days. This is a terrible ordeal for me and the hospital staff — much more so than for the parents who never set foot in the nursery.

I can understand why some people are opposed to all euthanasia, and insist that such infants must be allowed to live. I think I can also understand why other people favor destroying these babies quickly and painlessly. But why should anyone favor letting "dehydration and infection wither a tiny being over hours and days"? The doctrine that says that a baby may be allowed to dehydrate and wither, but may not be given an injection that would end its life without suffering, seems so patently cruel as to require no further refutation. The strong language is not intended to offend, but only to put the point in the clearest possible way.

My second argument is that the conventional doctrine leads to decisions concerning life and death made on irrelevant grounds.

Consider again the case of the infants with Down's syndrome who need operations for congenital defects unrelated to the syndrome to live. Sometimes, there is no operation and the baby dies, but when there is no such defect, the baby lives on. Now, an operation such as that to remove an intestinal obstruction is not prohibitively difficult. The reason why such operations are not performed in these cases is, clearly, that the child has Down's syndrome and the parents and doctor judge that because of that fact it is better for the child to die.

But notice that this situation is absurd, no matter what view one takes of the lives and potentials of such babies. If the life of such an infant is worth preserving, what does it matter if it needs a simple operation? Or, if one thinks it better that such a baby should not live on, what difference does it make that it happens to have an unobstructed intestinal tract? In either case, the matter of life and death is being decided on irrelevant grounds. It is the Down's syndrome, and not the intestines, that is the issue. The matter should be decided, if at all, on that basis, and not be allowed to depend on the essentially irrelevant question of whether the intestinal tract is blocked.

What makes this situation possible, of course, is the idea that when there is an intestinal blockage, one can "let the baby die," but when there is no such defect there is nothing that can be done, for one must not "kill" it. The fact that this idea leads to such results as deciding life or death on irrelevant grounds is another good reason why the doctrine should be rejected.

One reason why so many people think that there is an important moral difference between active and passive euthanasia is that they think killing someone is morally worse than letting someone die. But is it? Is killing, in itself, worse than letting die? To investigate this issue, two cases may be considered that are exactly alike except that one involves killing whereas the other involves letting someone die. Then, it can be asked whether this difference makes any difference to the moral assessments. It is important that the cases be exactly alike, except for this one difference, since otherwise one cannot be confident that it is this difference and not some other that accounts for any variation in the assessments of the two cases. So, let us consider this pair of cases:

In the first, Smith stands to gain a large inheritance if anything should happen to his six-year-old cousin. One evening while the child is taking his bath, Smith sneaks into the bathroom and drowns the child, and then arranges things so that it will look like an accident.

In the second, Jones also stands to gain if anything should happen to his six-year-old cousin. Like Smith, Jones sneaks in planning to drown the child in his bath. However, just as he enters the bathroom Jones sees the child slip and hit his head, and fall face down in the water. Jones is delighted; he stands by, ready to push the child's head back under if it is necessary, but it is not necessary. With only a little thrashing about, the child drowns all by himself, "accidentally," as Jones watches and does nothing.

Now Smith killed the child, whereas Jones "merely" let the child die. That is the only difference between them. Did either man behave better, from a moral point of view? If the difference between killing and letting die were in itself a morally important matter, one should say that Jones's behavior was less reprehensible than Smith's. But does one really want to say that? I think not. In the first place, both men acted from the same motive, personal gain, and both had exactly the same end in view when they acted. It may be inferred from Smith's conduct that he is a bad man, although that judgment may be withdrawn or modified if certain further facts are learned about him — for example, that he is mentally deranged. But would not the very same thing be inferred about Jones from his conduct? And would not

the same further considerations also be relevant to any modification of this judgment? Moreover, suppose Jones pleaded, in his own defense, "After all, I didn't do anything except just stand there and watch the child drown. I didn't kill him; I only let him die." Again, if letting die were in itself less bad than killing, this defense should have at least some weight. But it does not. Such a "defense" can only be regarded as a grotesque perversion of moral reasoning. Morally speaking, it is no defense at all.

Now, it may be pointed out, quite properly, that the cases of euthanasia with which doctors are concerned are not like this at all. They do not involve personal gain or the destruction of normal healthy children. Doctors are concerned only with cases in which the patient's life is of no further use to him, or in which the patient's life has become or will soon become a terrible burden. However, the point is the same in these cases: the bare difference between killing and letting die does not, in itself, make a moral difference. If a doctor lets a patient die, for humane reasons, he is in the same moral position as if he had given the patient a lethal injection for humane reasons. If his decision was wrong — if, for example, the patient's illness was in fact curable — the decision would be equally regrettable no matter which method was used to carry it out. And if the doctor's decision was the right one, the method used is not in itself important.

The AMA policy statement isolates the crucial issue very well; the crucial issue is "the intentional termination of the life of one human being by another." But after identifying this issue, and forbidding "mercy killing," the statement goes on to deny that the cessation of treatment is the intentional termination of a life. This is where the mistake comes in, for what is the cessation of treatment, in these circumstances, if it is not "the intentional termination of the life of one human being by another"? Of course it is exactly that, and if it were not, there would be no point to it.

Many people will find this judgment hard to accept. One reason, I think, is that it is very easy to conflate the question of whether killing is, in itself, worse than letting die, with the very different question of whether most actual cases of killing are more reprehensible than most actual cases of letting die. Most actual cases of killing are clearly terrible (think, for example, of all the murders reported in the newspapers), and one hears of such cases every day. On the other hand, one hardly ever hears of a case of letting die, except for the actions of doctors who are motivated by humanitarian reasons. So one learns to think of killing in a much worse light than of letting die. But this does not mean that there is something about killing that makes it in itself worse than letting die, for it is not the bare difference between killing and letting die that makes the difference in these cases. Rather, the other factors — the murderer's motive of personal gain, for example, contrasted with the doctor's humanitarian motivation — account for different reactions to the different cases.

I have argued that killing is not in itself any worse than letting die; if my contention is right, it follows that active euthanasia is not any worse than passive euthanasia. What arguments can be given on the other side? The most common, I believe, is the following:

> The important difference between active and passive euthanasia is that, in passive euthanasia, the doctor does not do anything to bring about the patient's death. The doctor does nothing, and the patient dies of whatever ills already afflict him. In active euthanasia, however, the doctor does something to bring about the patient's death: he kills him. The doctor who gives the patient with cancer a lethal injection has himself caused his patient's death; whereas if he merely ceases treatment, the cancer is the cause of the death.

A number of points need to be made here. The first is that it is not exactly correct to say that in passive euthanasia the doctor does nothing, for he does do one thing that is very important: he lets the patient die. "Letting someone die" is certainly different, in some respects, from other types of action — mainly in that it is a kind of action that one may perform by way of not performing certain other actions. For example, one may let a patient die by way of not giving medication, just as one may insult someone by way of not shaking his hand. But for any purpose of moral assessment, it is a type of action nonetheless. The decision to let a patient die is subject to moral appraisal in the same way that a decision to kill him would be subject to moral appraisal: it may be assessed as wise or unwise, compassionate or sadistic, right or wrong. If a doctor deliberately let a patient die who was suffering from routinely curable illness, the doctor would certainly be to blame for what he had done, just as he would be to blame had he needlessly killed the patient. Charges against him would then be appropriate. If so, it would be no defense at all for him to insist that he didn't "do anything." He would have done something very serious indeed, for he let his patient die.

Fixing the cause of death may be very important from a legal point of view, for it may determine whether criminal charges are brought against the doctor. But I do not think that this notion can be used to show a moral difference between active and passive euthanasia. The reason why it is considered bad to be the cause of someone's death is that death is regarded as a great evil — and so it is. However, if it has been decided that euthanasia — even passive euthanasia — is desirable in a given case, it has also been decided that in this instance death is no greater an evil than the patient's continued existence. And if this is true the usual reason for not wanting to be the cause of someone's death simply does not apply.

Finally, doctors may think that all of this is only of academic interest — the sort of thing that philosophers may worry about but that has no practical bearing on their own work. After all, doctors must be concerned about the legal consequences of what they do, and active euthanasia is clearly forbidden by the law. But even so, doctors should also be concerned with the fact that the law is forcing upon them a moral doctrine that may well be indefensible, and has a considerable effect on their practices. Of course, most doctors are not now in the position of being coerced in this matter, for they do not regard themselves as merely going along with what the law requires. Rather, in statements such as the AMA policy state-

ment that I have quoted, they are endorsing this doctrine as a central point of medical ethics. In that statement, active euthanasia is condemned not merely as illegal but as "contrary to that for which the medical profession stands," whereas passive euthanasia is approved. However, the preceding considerations suggest that there is really no moral difference between the two, considered in themselves (there may be important moral differences in some cases in their *consequences*, but, as I pointed out, these differences may make active euthanasia, and not passive euthanasia, the morally preferable option). So, whereas doctors may have to discriminate between active and passive euthanasia to satisfy the law, they should not do any more than that. In particular, they should not give the distinction any added authority and weight by writing it into official statements of medical ethics.

Assisted Suicide: Pro-Choice or Anti-Life?

Richard Doerflinger

The intrinsic wrongness of directly killing the innocent, even with the victim's consent, is all but axiomatic in the Jewish and Christian worldviews that have shaped the laws and mores of Western civilization and the self-concept of its medical practitioners. This norm grew out of the conviction that human life is sacred because it is created in the image and likeness of God, and called to fulfillment in love of God and neighbor.

With the pervasive secularization of Western culture, norms against euthana-

sia and suicide have to a great extent been cut loose from their religious roots to fend for themselves. Because these norms seem abstract and unconvincing to many, debate tends to dwell not on the wrongness of the act as such but on what may follow from its acceptance. Such arguments are often described as claims about a "slippery slope," and debate shifts to the validity of slippery slope arguments in general.

Since it is sometimes argued that acceptance of assisted suicide is an out-

Richard Doerflinger, "Assisted Suicide: Pro-Choice or Anti-Life?" *Hastings Center Report* 19:1 (Jan./Feb. 1989) suppl. 16–19.

growth of respect for personal autonomy, and not lack of respect for the inherent worth of human life, I will outline how autonomy-based arguments in favor of assisting suicide do entail a statement about the value of life. I will also distinguish two kinds of slippery slope argument often confused with each other, and argue that those who favor social and legal acceptance of assisted suicide have not adequately responded to the slippery slope claims of their opponents.

Assisted Suicide versus Respect for Life

Some advocates of socially sanctioned assisted suicide admit (and a few boast) that their proposal is incompatible with the conviction that human life is of intrinsic worth. Attorney Robert Risley has said that he and his allies in the Hemlock Society are "so bold" as to seek to "overturn the sanctity of life principle" in American society. A life of suffering, "racked with pain," is "not the kind of life we cherish."[1]

Others eschew Risley's approach, perhaps recognizing that it creates a slippery slope toward practices almost universally condemned. If society is to help terminally ill patients to commit suicide because it agrees that death is objectively preferable to a life of hardship, it will be difficult to draw the line at the seriously ill or even at circumstances where the victim requests death.

Some advocates of assisted suicide therefore take a different course, arguing that it is precisely respect for the dignity of the human person that demands respect for individual freedom as the noblest feature of that person. On this rationale a decision as to when and how to die deserves the respect and even the assistance of others because it is the ultimate exercise of self-determination — "ultimate" both in the sense that it is the last decision one will ever make and in

the sense that through it one takes control of one's entire self. What makes such decisions worthy of respect is not the fact that death is chosen over life but that it is the individual's own free decision about his or her future.

Thus Derek Humphry, director of the Hemlock Society, describes his organization as "pro-choice" on this issue. Such groups favor establishment of a constitutional "right to die" modeled on the right to abortion delineated by the U.S. Supreme Court in 1973. This would be a right to choose *whether or not* to end one's own life, free of outside government interference. In theory, recognition of such a right would betray no bias toward choosing death.

Life versus Freedom

This autonomy-based approach is more appealing than the straightforward claim that some lives are not worth living, especially to Americans accustomed to valuing individual liberty above virtually all else. But the argument departs from American traditions on liberty in one fundamental respect.

When the Declaration of Independence proclaimed the inalienable human rights to be "life, liberty, and the pursuit of happiness," this ordering reflected a long-standing judgment about their relative priorities. Life, a human being's very earthly existence, is the most fundamental right because it is the necessary condition for all other worldly goods including freedom; freedom in turn makes it possible to pursue (without guaranteeing that one will attain) happiness. Safeguards against the deliberate destruction of life are thus seen as necessary to protect freedom and all other human goods. This line of thought is not explicitly religious but is endorsed by some modern religious groups:

> The first right of the human person is his life. He has other goods and some are more precious, but

this one is fundamental — the condition of all the others. Hence it must be protected above all others.[2]

On this view suicide is not the ultimate exercise of freedom but its ultimate self-contradiction: A free act that by destroying life destroys all the individual's future earthly freedom. If life is more basic than freedom, society best serves freedom by discouraging rather than assisting self-destruction. Sometimes one must limit particular choices to safeguard freedom itself, as when American society chose over a century ago to prevent people from selling themselves into slavery even of their own volition.

It may be argued in objection that the person who ends his life has not truly suffered loss of freedom, because unlike the slave he need not continue to exist under the constraints of a loss of freedom. But the slave does have some freedom, including the freedom to seek various means of liberation or at least the freedom to choose what attitude to take regarding his plight. To claim that a slave is worse off than a corpse is to value a situation of limited freedom less than one of no freedom whatsoever, which seems inconsistent with the premise of the "pro-choice" position. Such a claim also seems tantamount to saying that some lives (such as those with less than absolute freedom) are objectively not worth living, a position that "pro-choice" advocates claim not to hold.

It may further be argued in objection that assistance in suicide is only being offered to those who can no longer meaningfully exercise other freedoms due to increased suffering and reduced capabilities and lifespan. To be sure, the suffering of terminally ill patients who can no longer pursue the simplest everyday tasks should call for sympathy and support from everyone in contact with them. But even these hardships do not constitute total loss of freedom of choice. If they did, one could hardly claim that the patient is in a position to make the ultimate free choice about suicide. A dying person capable of making a choice of that kind is also capable of making less monumental free choices about coping with his or her condition. This person generally faces a bewildering array of choices regarding the assessment of his or her past life and the resolution of relationships with family and friends. He or she must finally choose at this time what stance to take regarding the eternal questions about God, personal responsibility, and the prospects of a destiny after death.

In short, those who seek to maximize free choice may with consistency reject the idea of assisted suicide, instead facilitating all choices *except* that one which cuts short all choices.

In fact proponents of assisted suicide do *not* consistently place freedom of choice as their highest priority. They often defend the moderate nature of their project by stating, with Derek Humphry, that "we do not encourage suicide for any reason except to relieve unremitting suffering." It seems their highest priority is the "pursuit of happiness" (or avoidance of suffering) and not "liberty" as such. Liberty or freedom of choice loses its value if one's choices cannot relieve suffering and lead to happiness; life is of instrumental value insofar as it makes possible choices that can bring happiness.

In this value system, choice as such does not warrant unqualified respect. In difficult circumstances, as when care of a suffering and dying patient is a great burden on family and society, the individual who chooses life despite suffering will not easily be seen as rational, thus will not easily receive understanding and assistance for this choice.

In short, an unqualified "pro-choice" defense of assisted suicide lacks coherence because corpses have no choices. A particular choice, that of death, is given priority over all the other choices it makes impossible, so the value of choice as such is not central to the argument.

A restriction of this rationale to cases of terminal illness also lacks logical force. For if ending a brief life of suffering can be good, it would seem that ending a long life of suffering may be better. Surely the approach of the California "Humane and Dignified Death Act" — where consensual killing of a patient expected to die in six months is presumably good medical practice, but killing the same patient a month or two earlier is still punishable as homicide — is completely arbitrary.

Slippery Slopes, Loose Cannons

Many arguments against sanctioning assisted suicide concern a different kind of "slippery slope": Contingent factors in the contemporary situation may make it virtually inevitable in practice, if not compelling at the level of abstract theory, that removal of the taboo against assisted suicide will lead to destructive expansions of the right to kill the innocent. Such factors may not be part of euthanasia advocates' own agenda; but if they exist and are beyond the control of these advocates, they must be taken into account in judging the moral and social wisdom of opening what may be a Pandora's box of social evils.

To distinguish this sociological argument from our dissection of the conceptual *logic* of the rationale for assisted suicide, we might call it a "loose cannon" argument. The basic claim is that socially accepted killing of innocent persons will interact with other social factors to threaten lives that advocates of assisted suicide would agree should be protected. These factors at present include the following:

The psychological vulnerability of elderly and dying patients. Theorists may present voluntary and involuntary euthanasia as polar opposites; in practice there are many steps on the road from dispassionate, autonomous choice to subtle

coercion. Elderly and disabled patients are often invited by our achievement-oriented society to see themselves as useless burdens on younger, more vital generations. In this climate, simply offering the *option* of "self-deliverance" shifts a burden of proof, so that helpless patients must ask themselves why they are *not* availing themselves of it. Society's offer of death communicates the message to certain patients that they *may* continue to live if they wish but the rest of us have no strong interest in their survival. Indeed, once the choice of a quick and painless death is officially accepted as rational, resistance to this choice may be seen as eccentric or even selfish.[3]

The crisis in health care costs. The growing incentives for physicians, hospitals, families, and insurance companies to control the cost of health care will bring additional pressures to bear on patients. Curt Garbesi, the Hemlock Society's legal consultant, argues that autonomy-based groups like Hemlock must "control the public debate" so assisted suicide will not be seized upon by public officials as a cost-cutting device. But simply basing one's own defense of assisted suicide on individual autonomy does not solve the problem. For in the economic sphere also, offering the option of suicide would subtly shift burdens of proof.

Adequate health care is now seen by at least some policymakers as a human right, as something a society owes to all its members. Acceptance of assisted suicide as an option for those requiring expensive care would not only offer health care providers an incentive to make that option seem attractive — it would also demote all other options to the status of strictly private choices by the individual. As such they may lose their moral and legal claim to public support — in much the same way that the U.S. Supreme Court, having protected abortion under a constitutional "right of privacy," has quite logically denied any government obligation to provide public funds for this strictly private choice. As life-extending care of the terminally ill is increasingly seen as strictly elective, society may become less willing to appropriate funds for such care, and economic pressures to choose death will grow accordingly.

Legal doctrines on "substituted judgment." American courts recognizing a fundamental right to refuse life-sustaining treatment have concluded that it is unjust to deny this right to the mentally incompetent. In such cases the right is exercised on the patient's behalf by others, who seek either to interpret what the patient's own wishes might have been or to serve his or her best interests. Once assisted suicide is established as a fundamental right, courts will almost certainly find that it is unjust not to extend this right to those unable to express their wishes. Hemlock's political arm, Americans Against Human Suffering, has underscored continuity between "passive" and "active" euthanasia by offering the Humane and Dignified Death Act as an amendment to California's "living will" law, and by including a provision for appointment of a proxy to choose the time and manner of the patient's death. By such extensions our legal system would accommodate nonvoluntary, if not involuntary, active euthanasia.

Expanded definitions of terminal illness. The Hemlock Society wishes to offer assisted suicide only to those suffering from terminal illnesses. But some Hemlock officials have in mind a rather broad definition of "terminal illness." Derek Humphry says "two and a half million people alone are dying of Alzheimer's disease."[4] At Hemlock's 1986 convention, Dutch physician Pieter Admiraal boasted that he had recently broadened the meaning of terminal illness in his country by giving a lethal injection to a young quadriplegic woman — a Dutch court found that he acted within judicial guidelines allowing euthanasia for the termi-

nally ill, because paralyzed patients have difficulty swallowing and could die from aspirating their food at any time.

The medical and legal meaning of terminal illness has already been expanded in the United States by professional societies, legislatures, and courts in the context of so-called passive euthanasia. A Uniform Rights of the Terminally Ill Act proposed by the National Conference of Commissioners on Uniform State Laws in 1986 defines a terminal illness as one that would cause the patient's death in a relatively short time if life-preserving treatment is *not* provided — prompting critics to ask if all diabetics, for example, are "terminal" by definition. Some courts already see comatose and vegetative states as "terminal" because they involve an inability to swallow that will lead to death unless artificial feeding is instituted. In the *Hilda Peter* case, the New Jersey Supreme Court declared that the traditional state interest in "preserving life" referred only to "cognitive and sapient life" and not to mere "biological" existence, implying that unconscious patients are terminal, or perhaps as good as dead, so far as state interests are concerned. Is there any reason to think that American law would suddenly resurrect the older, narrower meaning of "terminal illness" in the context of *active* euthanasia?

Prejudice against citizens with disabilities. If definitions of terminal illness expand to encompass states of severe physical or mental disability, another social reality will increase the pressure on patients to choose death: long-standing prejudice, sometimes bordering on revulsion, against people with disabilities. While it is seldom baldly claimed that disabled people have "lives not worth living," able-bodied people often say they could not live in a severely disabled state or would prefer death. In granting Elizabeth Bouvia a right to refuse a feeding tube that preserved her life, the California Appeals Court bluntly stated that her physical handicaps led her to "consider her existence meaningless" and that "she cannot be faulted for so concluding." According to disability rights expert Paul Longmore, in a society with such attitudes toward the disabled, "talk of their 'rational' or 'voluntary' suicide is simply Orwellian newspeak."[5]

Character of the medical profession. Advocates of assisted suicide realize that most physicians will resist giving lethal injections because they are trained, in Garbesi's words, to be "enemies of death." The California Medical Association firmly opposed the Humane and Dignified Death Act, seeing it as an attack on the ethical foundation of the medical profession.

Yet California appeals judge Lynn Compton was surely correct in his concurring opinion in the *Bouvia* case, when he said that a sufficient number of willing physicians can be found once legal sanctions against assisted suicide are dropped. Judge Compton said this had clearly been the case with abortion, despite the fact that the Hippocratic Oath condemns abortion as strongly as it condemns euthanasia. Opinion polls of physicians bear out the judgment that a significant number would perform lethal injections if they were legal.

Some might think this division or ambivalence about assisted suicide in the medical profession will restrain broad expansions of the practice. But if anything, Judge Compton's analogy to our experience with abortion suggests the opposite. Most physicians still have qualms about abortion, and those who perform abortions on a full-time basis are not readily accepted by their colleagues as paragons of the healing art. Consequently they tend to form their own professional societies, bolstering each other's positive self-image and developing euphemisms to blunt the moral edge of their work.

Once physicians abandon the traditional medical self-image, which rejects direct killing of patients in all circumstances, their new substitute self-image may require ever more aggressive efforts to make this killing more widely practiced and favorably received. To allow killing by physicians in certain circumstances may create a new lobby of physicians in favor of expanding medical killing.

The human will to power. The most deeply buried yet most powerful driving force toward widespread medical killing is a fact of human nature: Human beings are tempted to enjoy exercising power over others; ending another person's life is the ultimate exercise of that power. Once the taboo against killing has been set aside, it becomes progressively easier to channel one's aggressive instincts into the destruction of life in other contexts. Or as James Burtchaell has said: "There is a sort of virginity about murder; once one has violated it, it is awkward to refuse other invitations by saying, 'But that would be murder!'"[6]

Some will say assisted suicide for the terminally ill is morally distinguishable from murder and does not logically require termination of life in other circumstances. But my point is that the skill and the instinct to kill are more easily turned to other lethal tasks once they have an opportunity to exercise themselves. Thus Robert Jay Lifton has perceived differences between the German "mercy killings" of the 1930s and the later campaign to annihilate the Jews of Europe, yet still says that "at the heart of the Nazi enterprise ... is the destruction of the boundary between healing and killing."[7] No other boundary separating these two situations was as fundamental as this one, and thus none was effective once it was crossed. As a matter of historical fact, personnel who had conducted the "mercy killing" program were quickly and readily recruited to operate the killing chambers of the death camps.[8] While the contemporary United States fortunately lacks the anti-Semitic and totalitarian attitudes that made the Holocaust possible, it has its own trends and pressures that may combine with acceptance of medical killing to produce a distinctively American catastrophe in the name of individual freedom.

These "loose cannon" arguments are not conclusive. All such arguments by their nature rest upon a reading and extrapolation of certain contingent factors in society. But their combined force provides a serious case against taking

the irreversible step of sanctioning assisted suicide for any class of persons, so long as those who advocate this step fail to demonstrate why these predictions are wrong. If the strict philosophical case on behalf of "rational suicide" lacks coherence, the pragmatic claim that its acceptance would be a social benefit lacks grounding in history or common sense.

Notes

1. Presentation at the Hemlock Society's Third National Voluntary Euthanasia Conference, "A Humane and Dignified Death," September 25–27, 1986, Washington, D.C. All quotations from Hemlock Society officials are from the proceedings of this conference unless otherwise noted.

2. Vatican Congregation for the Doctrine of the Faith, *Declaration on Procured Abortion* (1974), para. 11.

3. I am indebted for this line of argument to Dr. Eric Chevlen.

4. Denis Herbstein, "Campaigning for the Right to Die," *International Herald Tribune,* 11 September 1986.

5. Paul K. Longmore, "Elizabeth Bouvia, Assisted Suicide, and Social Prejudice," *Issues in Law & Medicine* 3:2 (1987), 168.

6. James T. Burtchaell, *Rachel Weeping and Other Essays on Abortion* (Kansas City: Andrews & McMeel, 1982), 188.

7. Robert Jay Lifton, *The Nazi Doctors: Medical Killing and the Psychology of Genocide* (New York: Basic Books, 1986), 14.

8. Yitzhak Rad, *Belzec, Sobibor, Treblinka* (Bloomington, IN: Indiana University Press, 1987), 11, 16–17.

The Rule of Double Effect: A Critique of Its Role in End-of-Life Decision Making

Timothy E. Quill, Rebecca Dresser and Dan W. Brock

According to the ethical principle known as the "rule of double effect," effects that would be morally wrong if caused intentionally are permissible if foreseen but

unintended. This principle is often cited to explain why certain forms of care at the end of life that result in death are morally permissible and others are

---

"The Rule of Double Effect: A Critique of Its Role in End-of-Life Decision Making," by Timothy E. Quill, Rebecca Dresser, and Dan W. Brock. *New England Journal of Medicine*, Vol 337:4, 1768–1771.

not.[1-9]According to the rule, administering high-dose opioids to treat a terminally ill patient's pain may be acceptable even if the medication causes the patient's death. In contrast, the rule does not authorize practices such as physician-assisted suicide, voluntary euthanasia, and certain instances of forgoing life-sustaining treatment.

The rule of double effect is a conceptually and psychologically complex doctrine that distinguishes between permissible and prohibited actions by relying heavily on the clinician's intent. The doctrine's complexities and ambiguities have limited its value as a guide to clinical practice.[10] In this article, we examine the rule's religious and philosophical origins, its inconsistencies with current law, and its shortcomings as a practical clinical guide. We also propose alternative principles to govern care at the end of life.

Background

The rule of double effect, which was developed by Roman Catholic moral theologians in the Middle Ages,[11,12] is applied to situations in which it is impossible for a person to avoid all harmful actions.[11-15] In such situations, a person must decide whether one potentially harmful action is preferable to another.

Suppose a terminally ill man experiencing unrelenting pain and suffering asks his physician for help in ending his misery. If the physician kills the patient to end his suffering, the patient's death is intended. According to the rule of double effect, the goal of relieving the patient's pain and suffering is good, but the means chosen to achieve the goal is wrong within the moral system that prohibits the intentional killing of innocent persons.[11,12]

The word "intentional" suggests, however, that the deaths of innocent persons may be permissible if brought about

unintentionally. With the same goal of relieving the patient's unbearable pain and suffering, the physician might provide large doses of analgesic medication even though the patient could die sooner as a result. If the physician refrains from providing such medication because of the lethal risk it poses, the failure to intervene harms the patient by allowing the potentially treatable pain to continue. But if the physician provides the medication, the action may hasten the patient's death and thus inflict a different harm. The rule of double effect construes the physician's provision of medication in the second scenario as an intentional action to relieve pain and suffering with the foreseen but unintended risk of causing an earlier death. The physician's action thus does not violate the prohibition against intentionally killing innocent persons.

Classic formulations of the rule of double effect emphasize four key conditions.[15-17] The first concerns the nature of the act, which must be good, such as the relief of pain, or at least morally neutral and not in a category that is absolutely prohibited, such as the killing of innocent persons. The second concerns the agent's intention. The "good effect and not the evil effect must be intended." The bad effect, such as respiratory depression after the administration of opioids, may be "foreseen, but not intended." The third condition is the distinction between means and effects. The bad effect, such as death, must not be a means to the good effect, such as the relief of suffering. The fourth condition is the proportionality between the good effect and the bad effect. The good effect must outweigh the bad effect. The bad effect can be permitted only when there is "proportionally grave reason" for it.

The first condition determines whether an act is ever potentially permissible, and the second and third conditions are used to determine whether the potentially inflicted harm is intentional or unintentional, as either a means or an end. The fourth condition requires the agent to compare the net good and bad effects of potentially acceptable actions to determine which course would produce an effect of proportionately greater value. Thus, the agent should choose the action with the most favorable balance of good and bad effects, within the limits set by the first three conditions of the rule of double effect.

Clinical Applications of the Rule of Double Effect to End-of-Life Decisions

Many medical ethicists cite the rule of double effect to explain why a clinician is permitted to administer high doses of opioid analgesics to relieve severe pain in a terminally ill patient toward the end of life, even in amounts that could cause the patient to die sooner than he or she would otherwise.[1-9] The physician's goal in these circumstances is to relieve the patient's suffering, and the means is the use of opioid analgesics in doses that might contribute to an earlier death. Neither the patient nor the physician intends for the patient to die, either as a mean or as an end. If death occurs, it is an unintended (though possibly foreseen) side effect. The more severe and intractable the patient's pain, the greater the justification for risking an earlier death. Thus, the amount of opioid pain reliever that is given and the rapidity with which it is increased must be in proportion to the amount of pain and suffering.

Some physicians have been reluctant to use sufficient doses of opioid pain relievers, even when their patients are dying, in part because of fears (both ethical and legal) about contributing to an earlier death.[18] The rule of double effect has helped some physicians to overcome this hesitation. Yet other clinicians remain unwilling to prescribe sufficient doses in part because they do not distinguish morally or psychologically between actions performed with the intent to cause death and those performed with the foreseen possibility of causing death.[7,19,20]

Voluntary euthanasia, in which the physician administers a lethal injection at the request of a suffering patient, clearly violates the rule's requirement that death not be intentionally caused as a means or an end.[21] However, problems arise when the rule is used to argue against physician-assisted suicide. The goal of physician-assisted suicide is to relieve intolerable suffering, but the means to this end is to provide the patient with a death-producing agent.[21] Providing a patient with a means to end life could be held to violate the prohibition against intentionally causing death (or contributing to the patient's intentional act of ending his or her own life), even if the physician's overarching purpose is to relieve intolerable suffering. Yet the physician may have many purposes in providing such prescriptions.[10,22] to offer a sleeping aid, to reassure the patient by providing a potential escape from suffering that the physician hopes or expects will not be used, or to relieve suffering, with death as an inevitable but unintended side effect. The simple classifications of intent provided by the rule of double effect are not easily applied to the physician's intentions in this clinical setting. Moreover, it is the patient's action, not the physician's, that directly causes death in the case of physician-assisted suicide.

The rule of double effect is also of limited assistance in evaluating the practice known as terminal sedation.[21,23-25] In this situation, the consenting patient is sedated to the point of unconsciousness in order to relieve otherwise untreatable pain and suffering and is then allowed to die of dehydration or other intervening complications. The goal of administering the sedative, to relieve otherwise unrelievable suffering, is good. Whether death is intended or merely foreseen is less clear. Unlike the use of high-dose opioids to relieve pain, with death as a possible but undesired side effect, terminal sedation inevitably causes death, which in many cases is what the patient desires. Although the overall goal of terminal sedation is to relieve otherwise uncontrollable suffering, life-prolonging therapies are withdrawn with the intent of hastening death. Terminal sedation would thus not be permitted under the rule of double effect, even though it is usually considered acceptable according to current legal and medical ethical standards.[25-27]

Finally, although there is a clinical, ethical, and legal consensus that patients have the right to refuse life-sustaining treatment, such decisions are sometimes problematic when analyzed according to the rule of double effect. Some patients with conditions such as advanced emphysema may decide to discontinue mechanical ventilation knowing they may die but hoping they will be able to live unencumbered by medical technology.[28] In such cases, the clinician is permitted to remove the ventilator under the rule of double effect. Other patients, however, may make the same decision with the explicit intention of escaping severe suffering by hastening death.[28,29] In these cases, the rule of double effect does not permit the clinician to remove the ventilator, because of the intention to cause death. The rule may cause confusion about physicians' responsibilities with regard to stopping life support and may account for the reluctance of some physicians to carry out patients' wishes to forgo treatment.[18,30] In one large series, 39 percent of physicians who had sedated patients while stopping life support reported that they had done so with the intention of hastening death, in clear violation of the rule of double effect.[31]

The Rule of Double Effect and U.S. Criminal Law

The recent Supreme Court rulings on physician-assisted suicide illustrate the similarities and differences in how current law and the rule of double effect evaluate the clinician's conduct in various end-of-life practices.[26,27] The law incorporates similar considerations in evaluating the administration of pain-relieving opioids. Although criminal law does not exempt from liability all persons who unintentionally cause another person's death, conduct posing a risk to life is permissible if it is justified by the expected benefits. An example is risky surgery performed to correct a serious medical condition.[32] Because the law includes a principle resembling the proportionality provision in the rule of double effect, clinicians may administer potentially lethal medications when they are necessary to relieve a terminally ill patient's suffering.[33]

On the other hand, the rule of double effect and the criminal law have different views on forgoing life-sustaining treatment. In contrast to the rule of double effect, the law permits, indeed requires, clinicians to forgo treatment at the request of a competent patient, even when the expressed purpose is to cause the patient's death. Similarly, terminal sedation with the patient's informed consent is legally permissible. These practices are lawful because death results from omitting medical interventions refused by patients who are exercising their rights to self-determination and protection of their physical integrity.

Current law joins the rule of double effect in prohibiting clinicians from providing or administering lethal medications with the explicit purpose of causing a patient's death. Here one could argue that the law shares some of the rule's weaknesses and uncertainties. As noted above, physicians may have various aims when they provide terminally ill patients with prescriptions for potentially lethal medications. In the case of a patient who ingests a lethal overdose of a drug prescribed by a physician, prosecutors ordinarily would have great difficulty establishing beyond a reasonable doubt that the physician acted intentionally or knowingly to help the patient die, which would be necessary to support a conviction for assisting in suicide. Moreover, the general refusal of jurors to convict physicians charged with assisted suicide or homicide for contributing to the consensual deaths of their suffering, terminally ill patients indicates that many ordinary persons disagree with the prohibition against *all* intentional direct killing, incorporated in both the rule of double effect and current criminal law.

Ethical and Policy Issues

The rule of double effect has many shortcomings as an ethical guide for either clinical practice or public policy. First, the rule originated in the context of a particular religious tradition.[12,13] American society incorporates multiple religious, ethical, and professional traditions, so medicine must accommodate various approaches to assessing the morality of end-of-life practices. Many persons and groups reject the position that death should never be intentionally hastened when unrelievable suffering is extreme and death is desired by the patient.[34–36] Yet the rule's absolute prohibition against deliberately taking human life seems to apply even to a competent, terminally ill patient who seeks to end suffering through the cessation of life-sustaining therapy.

Second, the analysis of intention used in the rule of double effect is problematic, difficult to validate externally, and inconsistent with other analyses of human intention. Even philosophers and theologians sympathetic to the distinction between intended and foreseen consequences have failed to find an unambiguous way to draw the distinction in many difficult cases.[37–39] Moreover, according to modern psychology, human intention is multilayered, ambiguous, subjective, and often contradictory.[10,40] The rule of double effect does not acknowledge this complexity; instead, intention is judged according to the presence or absence of a clear purpose. Clinicians familiar with the requirements of the rule may learn to express their intentions in performing ambiguous acts such as providing terminal sedation or withdrawing life support in terms of foreseen but unintended consequences; at the same time, other clinicians may reasonably interpret these acts as clear violations of the rule.

Third, in most moral, social, and legal realms, people are held responsible for all reasonably foreseeable consequences of their actions, not just the intended consequences. Physicians are not exempt from this expectation. This understanding of moral responsibility encourages people to exercise due care in their actions and holds them responsible for that which is under their control.[40] The important moral question is whether the risk of foreseeable harm is justified by an action's good effects. It is the principle of proportionality that determines when the risk of undesirable consequences is justified.

Fourth, autonomy is a central tenet of Western medical ethics and law.[41,42] Those who give considerable weight to patients' rights to determine their own care believe that the patient's informed consent to an action that may cause death is more fundamental than whether the physician intends to hasten death. From this perspective, the crucial moral considerations in evaluating any act that could cause death are the patient's right to self-determination and bodily integrity, the provision of informed consent, the absence of less harmful alternatives, and the severity of the patient's suffering.

Finally, the rule of double effect has had both desirable and undesirable effects on clinical conduct. The rule has reassured clinicians that prescribing high-dose opioids for pain in terminally ill patients is morally permissible, and that is all to the good.[7] More controversially, the rule has reinforced absolute societal and professional prohibitions against directly and intentionally causing death.[8,9] Unfortunately, the rule of double effect has also had negative effects on clinical practice, particularly when patients are making decisions that include death as a likely consequence. Concern about violating the rule's absolute prohibition against intentionally causing death may account for the reluctance of some physicians to honor their patients' requests to withdraw life-sustaining therapy.[18,30] Furthermore, the unwillingness of some physicians to provide adequate medication for pain relief, particularly if the medication could contribute to an earlier death, may reflect their failure to accept the rule's simplistic account of intention in such situations.

Conclusions

For clinicians and others who believe in an absolute prohibition against actions that intentionally cause death, the rule of double effect may be useful as a way of justifying adequate pain relief and other palliative measures for dying patients. But the rule is not a necessary means to that important end. Furthermore, the rule's absolute prohibitions, unrealistic characterization of physicians' intentions, and failure to account for patients' wishes make it problematic in many circumstances. In keeping with the traditions of medicine and broader society, we believe that physicians' care of their dying patients is properly guided and justified by patients' informed consent, the degree of suffering, and the absence of less harmful alternatives to the treatment contemplated.

We are indebted to James Childress, Ph.D., for his contribution to early drafts of the manuscript.

References

1. Council on Ethical and Judicial Affairs, American Medical Association. Decisions near the end of life. *JAMA* 1992;276:2229–33.

2. ABIM End-of-Life Patient Care Project Committee. Caring for the dying: Identification and promotion of physician competence. Educational resource document. Philadelphia: American Board of Internal Medicine, 1996.

3. American College of Physicians. ACP ethics manual. 3rd ed. *Ann Intern Med* 1992;117:947–60.

4. Council on Scientific Affairs, American Medical Association. Good care of the dying patient. *JAMA* 1996;275:474–8.

5. President's Commission for the Study of Ethical Problems in Medicine and Biomedical and Behavioral Research.. Deciding to forego life-sustaining treatment: a report on the ethical, medical, and legal issues in treatment decisions. Washington, D.C.; Government Printing Office, 1983.

6. *Guidelines on the termination of life-sustaining treatment and the care of the dying: a report.* Briarcliff Manor, N.Y.: Hastings Center, 1987.

7. Foley KM. Competent care for the dying instead of physician-assisted suicide. *N Engl J Med* 1997;336:54–8.

8. Pellegrino ED. Doctors must not kill. *J Clin Ethics* 1992;3:95–102.

9. Kass LR. Is there a right to die? *Hastings Cent Rep* 1993;23(1):34–43.

10. Quill TE. The ambiguity of clinical intentions. *N Engl J Med* 1993;329:1039–40.

11. The history of intention in ethics. In: Kenny AJP. *Anatomy of the soul.* Oxford, England. Basil Blackwell, 1973: appendix.

12. Mangan JT. An historical analysis of the principle of double effect. *Theol Studies* 1949;10:41–61.

13. Pope John Paul II. *Evangelium vitae.* Washington, D.C.: U.S. Catholic Conference, March 30, 1995:189.

14. Granfield D. *The abortion decision.* Garden City, N.Y.: Image Books, 1971:126–36.

15. Garcia JLA. Double effect. In: Reich WT, ed. *Encyclopedia of bioethics.* Vol. 2. New York: Simon and Schuster, 1995:636–41.

16. Marquis DB. Four versions of double effect. *J Med Philos* 1991;16:515–44.

17. Kuhse H. *The sanctity-of-life doctrine in medicine: a critique.* Oxford, England: Clarendon Press, 1987.

18. Solomon MZ, O'Donnell L, Jennings B, et al. Decisions near the end of life: professional views on life-sustaining treatments. *Am J Public Health* 1993;83:14–23.

19. Foley KM. Pain, physician-assisted suicide and euthanasia. *Pain Forum* 1995;4:163–78.

20. Hill CS Jr. When will adequate pain treatment be the norm? *JAMA* 1995;274:1881–2.

21. Quill TE, Lo B, Brock D. Palliative options of last resort: a comparison of voluntarily stopping eating and drinking, terminal sedation, physician assisted suicide and voluntary active euthanasia. *JAMA* [1997;278(23):2099–104].

22. Annas GJ. The promised end — constitutional aspects of physician assisted suicide. *N Engl J Med* 1996;335:683–7.

23. Trout RD, Berde DB, Mitchell C, Grier HE. Barbiturates in the care of the terminally ill. *N Engl J Med* 1991;327:1678–81.

24. Ventafridda V, Riparnonti C, DeConno F, Tamburini M, Cassileth BR. Symptom prevalence and control during cancer patients' last days of life. *J Palliat Care* 1990;6(3):7–11.

25. Cherny NI, Portenoy RK. Sedation in the management of refractory symptoms: guidelines for evaluation and treatment. *J Palliat Care* 1994;10(2):31–8.

26. Vacco v. Quill. No. 117 S.Ct. 2293 (1997).

27. Washington v. Glucksberg. No. 117 S.Ct. 2258 (1997).

28. Alpers A, Lo B. Does it make clinical sense to equate terminally ill patients who require life-sustaining interventions with those who do not? *JAMA* 1997;277:1705–8.

29. Orentlicher D. The legalization of physician-assisted suicide. *N Engl J Med* 1996;335:663–7.

30. The SUPPORT Principal Investigators. A controlled trial to improve care for seriously ill hospitalized patients: the Study to Understand Prognoses and Preferences for Outcomes and Risks of Treatments (SUPPORT). *JAMA* 1999;274:1591–8. [Erratum, *JAMA* 1996;275:1232.]

31. Wilson WC, Smedira NG, Fink C, McDowell JA, Luce JM. Ordering and administration of sedatives and analgesics during the withholding and withdrawal of life support from critically ill patients. *JAMA* 1992;267:949–53.

32. American Law Institute. *Model penal code and commentaries*. Philadelphia: American Law Institute, 1985:229–41. (Section 2.02.)

33. Cantor NL, Thomas GC. Pain relief, acceleration of death, and criminal law. *Kennedy Inst Ethics J* 1996;6:107–27.

34. Blendon RJ, Szalay US, Knox RA. Should physicians aid their patients in dying? The public perspective. *JAMA* 1992;267:2658–62.

35. Graber MA, Levy BI, Weir RF, Oppliger RA. Patients' views about physician participation in assisted suicide and euthanasia. *J Gen Intern Med* 1996;11:71–6.

36. Bachman JG, Aleser KH, Doukas DJ, Lichtenstein RL, Corning AD, Brody H. Attitudes of Michigan physicians and the public toward legalizing physician-assisted suicide and voluntary euthanasia. *N Engl J Med* 1996;3344:303–9.

37. Fried C. *Right and wrong*. Cambridge, Mass.: Harvard University Press, 1978.

38. Nagel T. *The view from nowhere*. Oxford, England: Oxford University Press, 1986.

39. Donagan A. *The theory of morality*. Chicago: University of Chicago Press, 1977.

40. Brody H. Causing, intending, and assisting death. *J Clin Ethics* 1993;4:112–8.

41. Meisel A. *The right to die*. 2nd ed. New York: Wiley, 1995.

42. Brock D. Death and dying. In: Veatch RM, ed. *Medical ethics*. 2nd ed. Sudbury, Mass.: Jones and Bartlett, 1997;363–94.

Joint Statement on Resuscitative Interventions

Canadian Medical Association

This joint statement ... is intended to provide guidance for the development of policies on the appropriate use of cardiopulmonary resuscitation (CPR). ... The sponsors of this statement encourage health care facilities to develop policies for their institutions.

CPR was developed as a treatment intervention for cases of sudden unexpected cardiac or respiratory arrest. CPR is understood to include mouth-to-mouth resuscitation, chest compression, bag-and-mask positive-pressure ventilation, intubation and defibrillation. However, unless a specific order to the contrary (do-not-resuscitate [DNR]) has been recorded on the person's health record by the responsible physician, it has come to be used as a standard intervention in virtually all cases of sudden cardiac or respiratory arrest, whether unexpected or not. (Throughout this document "arrest" is taken to include severe bradycardia in children.)

After several decades of experience and review, it appears that there are people who benefit from this treatment, and others for whom there is no benefit and potential significant harm. In these latter situations, CPR is not only generally unsuccessful but also inappropriate, as it may serve only to increase pain and suffering and prolong dying. Withholding resuscitation does not imply the withholding of treatment and supportive care, including palliative care.

"Joint statement on resuscitation interventions" — Reprinted from *CMAJ* 1 Dec 1995; 153(11) pages 1652A–C by permission of the publisher. © 1995 Canadian Medical Association.

It is timely to reconsider the use of resuscitative interventions in the context of a changing societal environment that recognizes the autonomy of the individual, encourages increased public discussion of bioethical issues and stresses the need for empirical evidence of positive patient outcomes following treatment.

Policy Development

General

Health care facilities are encouraged to use an interdisciplinary committee to develop a policy, a program for policy implementation and a conflict-resolution mechanism. This committee should include lay people and representatives of medicine, nursing, social work, pastoral care and other disciplines as required. The committee should also have access to legal and ethical consultation.

The policy should identify which resuscitative interventions are available in the facility; with the conflict-resolution mechanism, it should ensure sensitivity to cultural and religious differences. The implementation program should include education of everyone who will be affected by the policy, including caregivers. The policy must be in accordance with relevant federal and provincial or territorial law. It should be reviewed regularly and revised when necessary in light of developments in clinical, ethical and legal aspects of the topic.

Since policies and guidelines cannot cover all possible situations, appropriate consultation mechanisms should be available to address specific issues in a timely manner.

Guiding Principles

The following principles are integral to the development of CPR policy:

1. Good health care requires open communication, discussion, and sensitivity to cultural and religious differences among caregivers, potential recipients of care, their family members and significant others.

2. A person must be given sufficient information about the benefits, risks and likely outcomes of all treatment options to enable him or her to make informed decisions.

3. A competent person has the right to refuse, or withdraw consent to any clinically indicated treatment, including life-saving or life-sustaining treatment. Competence can be difficult to assess because it is not always a constant state. A person may be competent to make decisions regarding some aspects of life but not others; as well, competence can be intermittent — a person may be lucid and oriented at certain times of the day, and not at others. The legal definition and assessment of competence are governed by the provinces or territories. Facilities should be aware of the laws (e.g., capacity to consent and age of consent) regarding the assessment and documentation of incompetence.

4. When a person is incompetent, treatment decisions must be based on his or her wishes, if these are known. The person's decision may be found in an advance directive or may have been communicated to the physician, other members of the health care team or other relevant people. In some jurisdictions, legislation specifically addresses the issue of decision-making about medical treatment for incompetent people; the legislative requirements should be followed.

5. When an incompetent person's wishes are not known, treatment decisions must be based on the person's best interests, taking into account:

    1. the person's known values and preferences;
    2. information received from those who are significant in the person's

life and who could help in determining his or her best interests;

3. aspects of the person's culture
   and religion that would influence
   a treatment decision; and,

4. the person's diagnosis and
   prognosis.

In some jurisdictions legislation
specifies who should be recognized
as designated decision-makers (proxies) for incompetent people; this legislation should be followed. The term
"proxy" is used broadly to identify:
people who make a treatment decision based on the decision a person
would have made for himself or herself (substitute decision-maker);
people who help in determining what
decision would be in the person's
best interest; and people who, under
provincial legislation, are deemed an
appropriate choice for making treatment decisions.

6. There is no obligation to offer a person futile or non-beneficial treatment. Futile and non-beneficial
   treatments are controversial concepts when applied to CPR. Policymakers should determine how these
   concepts should be interpreted in the
   policy on resuscitation, in light of the
   facility's mission, the values of the
   community it serves, and ethical and
   legal developments. For the purposes.
   of this document and in the context
   of resuscitation, "futile" and "non-
   beneficial" are understood as follows.
   In some situations a physician can
   determine that a treatment is "medically" futile or non-beneficial
   because it offers no reasonable hope
   of recovery or improvement, or
   because the person is permanently
   unable to experience any benefit. In
   other cases the utility and benefit of
   a treatment can only be determined
   with reference to the person's subjective judgement about his or her overall well-being. As a general rule a
   person should be involved in deter-

mining futility in his or her case. In
exceptional circumstances such discussions may not be in the person's
best interests. If the person is incompetent the principles for decision
making for incompetent people
should be applied.

CPR as a Treatment Option

The efficacy of CPR in restoring cardiac
and respiratory functioning varies from
nil to very high, depending on a number
of factors. On the basis of research studies of such outcomes four general categories can be distinguished:

a. people who are likely to benefit
   from CPR;

b. people for whom benefit is
   uncertain;

c. people for whom benefit is
   unlikely; and,

d. people who almost certainly will
   not benefit.

These categories can be adapted to the
particular circumstances of the care setting and are compatible with policies that
establish levels of care or intervention.

Competence

Determination of competence is made by
the attending physician in consultation
with other caregivers. If the person for
whom resuscitation is being considered is
incompetent, decisions should be made
on his or her behalf as indicated earlier
(guiding principles 4 and 5). If the person's incompetence is uncertain or intermittent, efforts should be made to
facilitate the regaining of competence.

Treatment Decisions

Treatment decisions about potential
resuscitative interventions should be
made within the context of discussions
concerning the plan of treatment, and on
the basis of the person's medical condition and his or her expressed wishes.

These decisions should be considered before the need for intervention arises or a crisis occurs. They should be made in the context of the person's autonomy and with full disclosure of options in a supportive environment.

1. **People who are likely to benefit from CPR**
   There is a good chance that CPR will restore cardiac and respiratory function and that the restored function will be maintained. The likelihood of the person's returning to his or her pre-arrest condition is high.

2. **People for whom benefit is uncertain**
   The person's condition or prognosis, or both, may not have been assessed before the loss of cardiac and respiratory function. It is unknown or uncertain whether CPR will restore functioning. The subsequent prognosis or the likelihood of adverse consequences is also unknown or uncertain.

3. **People for whom benefit is unlikely**
   There is little chance that CPR will restore cardiac and respiratory function; even if the function is restored, it is unlikely to be maintained. The likelihood of the patient returning to his or her pre-arrest condition is low.

4. **People who almost certainly will not benefit**
   There is almost certainly no chance that the person will benefit from CPR, either because the underlying illness or disease makes recovery from arrest virtually unprecedented or because the person will be permanently unable to experience any benefit.

Communication

1. **Health care recipients** Informed consent to any treatment implies that the individual has a clear understanding of the treatment options and the possible outcomes. Information must be provided in a language that the person can understand. The implications of the person's choices should be explored in the context of life goals, values and preferences.

   Communication about CPR should take into account the clinical condition of the person:

   1. People who are likely to benefit from CPR and people for whom benefit is uncertain will normally be made aware that emergency, life-saving measures will be instituted if the need arises. This information should be presented during discussion about the plan of treatment so as not to alarm the person.

   2. People for whom benefit from CPR is unlikely should be made fully aware of the limitations of CPR. Their life goals, values and preferences should be discussed before or shortly after admission to a health care facility, before the need for resuscitative intervention arises.

   3. People who almost certainly will not benefit from CPR are not candidates for CPR, and it should not be presented as a treatment option. Whether this is discussed with the person is a matter of judgement based on the circumstances of the case and the principles specified earlier.

2. **Family members and significant others** Members of the health care team should encourage a person to advise family members, significant others and potential proxy decision-makers of his or her decision about CPR. Such communication should be documented on the person's health record.

3. **Health care providers** Decisions about whether CPR is an appropriate treatment option should be clearly noted on the person's health record along with the outcome of any discussions so that all health care providers involved in his or her care are aware of these decisions. Communication and discussion among those involved in providing care to the person are vital in ensuring that the individual's decisions are respected.

   Because nurses, social workers and pastoral care workers have a unique opportunity to explore end-of-life issues in detail, they should be kept fully informed about the treatment plan of each person under their care, including decisions regarding CPR.

Implementation of Decisions

1. **Situations in which CPR should be performed**
   People likely to benefit from CPR should be given this treatment if the need arises, unless they have specifically rejected it. People for whom the benefit of CPR is uncertain or unlikely should be given this treatment if the need arises, unless they have specifically rejected it. CPR should be initiated until the person's condition has been assessed.

2. **Situations in which CPR should not be performed**
   People who have rejected CPR and those who almost certainly will not benefit from it should not be given this treatment if an arrest occurs.

Review of Decisions

Appropriate intervals for review of decisions concerning CPR should be determined. The review should follow the same guidelines as the original decision regarding resuscitation.

In the following circumstances a review of decisions should be undertaken immediately:

1. if a competent person (or proxy) changes his or her decision about resuscitation; or,

2. if there is a significant, unexpected change in a person's condition.

Palliative Care and Other Treatments

A decision not to initiate CPR does not imply the withholding or withdrawing of any other treatment or intervention.

A person who will not receive CPR should receive all other appropriate treatments, including palliative care, for his or her physical, mental and spiritual comfort.

This joint statement was approved by the Canadian Healthcare Association, the CMA, the Canadian Nurses Association and the Catholic Health Association of Canada and was developed in cooperation with the Canadian Bar Association.

Further Readings

Beauchamp, T.L. "A Reply to Rachels on Active and Passive Euthanasia." In Beauchamp and Perlin, *Ethical Issues in Death and Dying*. Englewood Cliffs, N.J.: Prentice Hall, 1978.

Beauchamp, T.L. *Intending Death*. Upper Saddle River, N.J.: Prentice Hall, 1996.

Brody, B.A., and A. Halevy. "Is Futility a Futile Concept?" *J Med Philos* 20 (1995): 123–144.

Engelhardt, Jr., H.T. "Euthanasia and Children: The Injury of Continued Existence." *J Paed* 83:170 (1973).

de Haan, J. "The Ethics of Euthanasia: Advocates' Perspectives. *Bioethics* 16:2 (Apr. 2002): 154–172.

Foot, P. "Euthanasia." *Philos Pub Affairs* 6:2 (Winter 1977).

Kamisar, Yale. "Some Non-Religious Objections Against Proposed Mercy-Killing Legislation." *Minnesota Law Review* 42 (May 1958): 969–1042.

Kamm, F. "Physician-Assisted Suicide, the Doctrine of Double Effect, and the Ground of Value," *Ethics* 109 (1999): 586–605.

Kluge, E.-H.W. *The Practice of Death.* New Haven: Yale Univ. Press, 1975.

Law Reform Commission of Canada. Report 20, *Euthanasia, Aiding Suicide and Cessation of Treatment* (1983).

Macklin, R. *Mortal Choices.* New York: Pantheon Books, 1987.

Magnet, J.E., and E.-H.W. Kluge. *Withholding Treatment from Defective Newborn Children.* Cowansville, PQ: Brown Legal Publications, 1985.

Ogden, R. "The Right to Die: A Policy Proposal for Euthanasia and Aid in Dying." *Can Pub Policy* 20:1 (Mar. 1994): 1–25.

Perrett, R.W. "Killing, Letting Die and the Bare Difference Argument," *Bioethics* 10 (1996): 131–139.

Pope Pius XII. "Prolongation of Life: Allocution to an International Congress of Anesthesiologists" (Nov. 24, 1957). *Osservatore Romano* 4 (1957).

Rachels, James. *The End of Life: Euthanasia and Morality.* Oxford: Oxford Univ. Press, 1986.

Ramsey, P. "On (Only) Caring for the Dying." In *The Patient as Person.* New Haven and London: Yale Univ. Press, 1970. pp. 120–123.

R. v. Genereux, [1999] Ont. C.C.A. 136 C.C.C. (3d) 338.

Rodriguez, E. "The Arguments for Euthanasia and Physician-Assisted Suicide: Ethical Reflection." *Linacre Q* 68:3 (Aug. 2001): 251–261.

Wray, E. "Assisted Suicide and Human Rights." *Bull of Med Ethics* 172 (Oct. 2001): 18–21.

Useful Web Sites

http://www.priestsforlife.org/magisterium/iuraetbona.htm   A Catholic Web page on euthanasia

http://www.silk.net/RelEd/suicide.htm   A Catholic Web page on assisted suicide

http://ncf.davintech.ca/freeport/social.services/rt-die/menu   Right to Die Society of Canada

http://www.finalexit.org/backiss-frame.html   The World Federation of Right to Die Societies

CHAPTER 15
THE RIGHT TO HAVE CHILDREN

Introduction

The selections in this chapter deal with the question, Is there a right to have children? The issue is important because if there is such a right, and if people availed themselves of it without limitation, this would lead to a logarithmic increase in population. Given that both national and global resources are finite, the result would be catastrophic — as Malthus pointed out in 1798 in his *An Essay on the Principles of Population*.

At the same time, the Universal Declaration of Human Rights states that "men and women of full age, without any limitation to race, nationality or religion, have the right to marry and found a family."[1] This is often interpreted as meaning that there is a right to have biological offspring of one's own, that this is a fundamental human right, and that how this right is exercised is up to the individual person: To paraphrase a remark by Pierre Elliott Trudeau — "The state has no business in the bedrooms of the nation!"

One can argue over whether the framers of the Universal Declaration of Human Rights actually meant to convey that there is a fundamental right to have biological offspring of one's own, and one can question whether they considered this right to have no conditions or limits. The fact is that the Universal Declaration of Human Rights was in part a politically motivated statement, and the Declaration was modified in 1968 in the Proclamation of Teheran to read, "Parents have the basic right to determine freely *and responsibly* the number and spacing of their children" (emphasis added) — which suggests that the right is not as absolute as it might appear at first glance. Moreover, the "World Population Plan of Action," which was passed by the International Population Conference in Bucharest in 1974, said that "individual reproductive behaviour and the needs and aspirations of society should be reconciled. ... All couples and individuals have the basic right to decide freely and responsibly the number and spacing of their children and to have the information, education and means to do so; the responsibility of couples and individuals in the exercise of this right takes into account the needs of their living and future children, and their responsibilities towards the community." In a similar vein, the "Recommendations on Further Implementing the World Population Plan of Action," which was approved by the 1984 International Population Conference in Mexico City, emphasized that "any recognition of rights also implies responsibilities," and stated that when people make reproductive choices they should "take into consideration their own situation, as well as the implications of their decisions on the balanced development of their children and on the community and society in which they live." These sentiments were reaffirmed in the "Programme of Action" that was adopted by the International Conference on Population and Development, held in Cairo in 1994. These are not merely political sentiments. Most ethical theorists agree that no rights are absolute. Minimally, their exercise is conditioned by the situations in which they are claimed, and by the equal and competing rights of others.

The excerpt from the *White Paper on Family Planning* of the People's Republic of China is very much in line with this last consideration. It argues that all rights are conditioned by the social contexts in which they arise, and that the right to have children is no exception: It is conditioned by the need for social survival and by the equal and competing rights of others. Therefore, society may condition and limit the right to have children for the sake of all concerned. The selection from the Canadian Medical Association's brief to the Royal Commission on New Reproductive Technologies distinguishes between different senses in which the right to have children may be understood, and discusses the matter in the context of the new reproductive technologies. Being representative of the official view of almost 60,000 Canadian physicians, it provides an interesting companion piece to the *White Paper on Family Planning*.

Both the *White Paper* and the CMA's brief present what are essentially philosophical and pragmatic arguments. The case of *Eve* moves the discussion to the juridical plane and centres in the legal rights of the individual person. It involves a mentally severely disabled young woman whose mother wanted to have her sterilized. The mother felt that since Eve could never take care of a child and she herself was simply too old to take care of any children, and moreover, since for various reasons birth control was unworkable, sterilization was the appropriate method of choice — especially since it is the favourite method of birth control for middle-aged women. The Supreme Court examined the matter in terms of the Canadian Charter of Rights and Freedoms. In the process, it dealt both with the issue of what standards substitute decision-makers should use when making decisions on behalf of incompetent persons, as well as with the central question of the right to have children. The Court did not find that there was a legal right to have children. However, it did find that (for a woman at least) there is a "fundamental privilege" to have children and that sterilization may not be undertaken except for clearly therapeutic reasons that are rooted in the health-needs of the incompetent person.[2] Kluge examines the logical and ethical tenability of the Supreme Court's judgement and points to some interesting implications. Specifically, he considers what it means to say that there is a "fundamental privilege" to have children. He argues that in refusing to allow proxy decision-makers to opt for non-therapeutic sterilization, the Court seriously undermined the ethics of proxy or substitute decision-making. Purdy restates the question of the right to have children in light of recent advances in genetic screening: If one has good grounds to suppose that one's children will suffer from a severe genetic disease, is it ethical to try and have children anyway? Can having children ever be immoral?

Notes

1. United Nations General Assembly, *Universal Declaration of Human Rights.* New York, N.Y., 1948. Resolution 217.A(iii).

2. It may be of interest to note that the House of Lords, in its decision in *re B (a minor)*, [1987] All ER 206, 219, reversed its previous rejection of non-consensual and non-therapeutic sterilization and criticized the Supreme Court of Canada's decision *in re Eve.* See *in re Eve (infra).*

"Responsible Family Planning"

Excerpt from the White Paper on Family Planning, *People's Republic of China*

VII. The Correct Choice for Human Rights Protection

In the practice of carrying out [the] family planning programme, whilst persistently proceeding from its reality and taking into full account and observing principles and regulations concerning population and family planning formulated by international institutions and organizations, the Chinese government has gradually set up guiding principles, policies, measures and methods that reflect the basic interests and various rights and interests of the people, and has continuously improved these as the actual situations change, so as to better safeguard the right to subsistence and development of the Chinese nation.

It has been China's consistent stand and principle in international exchange and cooperation to fully respect the sovereignty of all nations, and not to interfere with the internal affairs of other nations. The "Programme of Action" adopted by the International Conference on Population and Development by that conference in Cairo, 1994, pointed out: "The formulation and implementation of population-related policies is the responsibility of each country and should take into account the economic, social and environmental diversity of conditions in each country, with full respect for the various religious and ethical values, cultural backgrounds and philosophical convictions of its people, as well as the shared but differentiated responsibilities of all the world's people for

By permission of Education Office, The Consulate General of the People's Republic of China in Vancouver.

a common future." Only by proceeding from the reality of the country, independently setting up its population policy and target, as well as plans and measures to realize this target, can the population problem of each country be effectively solved. Positive results of solving [the] population problem through international cooperation can only be achieved under the premise of respecting the sovereignty of each country, and by adopting the attitude of mutual understanding and the seeking of common ground while preserving differences. As the national situation, the degree and pattern of social and economic development, cultural habits and values, and the specific characteristics of the population problem in each country differ, there will be differences in the plan and dynamics of problem solving in each country, which is a normal phenomenon.

Not only has China never imposed its ways and ideas of solving its own population problem on anyone else, but it has, instead, always understood and welcomed all good-intentioned criticism and useful suggestions from outside. However, some people, distorting or disregarding the basic facts, have made improper comments on China's family planning programme, criticizing it as a "violation of human rights," and denouncing it as "inhumane." They have even tried to impose their values and ideas on China, using the excuse of "protecting human rights" to put pressure on China and to interfere in China's internal affairs. This is totally unacceptable. Any such practice of interfering in China's internal affairs has not only deviated from the basic principle set up in the field of population by the international community, but it has also violated the established principles of international law, which will neither help promote a healthy development of China's family planning programme nor the stability of the world's population.

China has always held that concepts of human rights are a product of historical development, closely related to social, political and economic conditions, as well as the individual nation's particular history, culture and concepts. The realization and optimization of human rights is a historical process. A citizen's right of choice in reproduction is also part of this process.

The great changes in the world population situation in the mid-twentieth century, the rapid world population growth and the severe consequence[s] ensuing have aroused increasing attention from the international community and various countries. The contradiction between population on one hand and survival and development on the other is especially sharp in developing countries with a fast population growth. Irrational international economic order, stagnant economic and social development, and the pressure of a large population have continually widened the gap between developed and developing countries in terms of welfare and living conditions, increasing rather than decreasing the number of those living below the poverty line. With recognition of the seriousness of the population problem and the urgent need to control population growth, people's understanding and attitudes towards reproduction and other associated rights have changed, responding to new historical conditions, becoming more comprehensive.

The "World Population Plan of Action," approved at the International Population Conference held in Bucharest in 1974, states: "Individual reproductive behaviour and the needs and aspirations of society should be reconciled. ... All couples and individuals have the basic right to decide freely and responsibly the number and spacing of their children and to have the information, education and means to do so; the responsibility of couples and individuals in the exercise of this right takes into account the needs of their living and future children, and their responsibilities towards the community."

The "Recommendations on Further Implementing the World Population Plan of Action," approved at the 1984 International Population Conference held in Mexico City, again emphasized that "Any recognition of rights also implies responsibilities." Accordingly, when couples and individuals exercise their right to the choice of reproduction, they should "take into consideration their own situation, as well as the implications of their decisions on the balanced development of their children and on the community and society in which they live." The "Recommendations" point out that "governments can do more to assist people in making their reproductive decisions in a responsible way."

The "Programme of Action" adopted at the International Conference on Population and Development held in Cairo in 1994 once again points out that "these [reproductive] rights rest on the recognition of the basic right of all couples and individuals to decide freely and responsibly the number, spacing and timing of their children and to have the information and means to do so, and the right to attain the highest standard of sexual and reproductive health. ... In the exercise of this right, they should take into account the needs of their living and future children and their responsibilities towards the community. The promotion of the responsible exercise of these rights for all people should be the fundamental basis for government- and community-supported policies and programmes in the area of reproductive health, including family planning."

Family planning in China is pursued in complete accordance with the relevant principles and human rights requirements designated by the international community. China's family planning policies and programmes combine citizens' rights and duties, joining the interests of the individual with those of society. These conform to the basic principles outlined at the various international population conferences and have been established on the basis of the relationship of interpersonal interests under socialism.

Never in any country are rights and duties absolute, but rather, they are relative. There are no duties apart from rights, or rights apart from duties. When there is conflict between social needs and individual interests, a means has to be sought to mediate it. This is something that the government of every sovereign country is doing. As China has a large population, the Chinese government has to limit the number of births of its citizens. This is a duty incumbent on each citizen as it serves the purpose of making the whole society and whole nation prosperous, and it is not proceeding from the private interest of some individuals. This is wholly justifiable and entirely consistent with the moral concepts of Chinese society. To talk about citizens' rights and duties out of reality in an abstract and absolute way does not hold water either in China or in any other country. In a heavily populated developing country like China, if the reproductive freedom of couples and individuals is unduly emphasized at the expense of their responsibilities to their families, children and societal interests in matters of child bearing, indiscriminate reproduction and unlimited population growth will inevitably ensue. The interests of the majority of the people, including those of new-born infants, will be seriously harmed.

We should see that in China, especially in rural, backward and remote areas, there is a gap between the desire for childbirth of some couples of childbearing age and the demand of the present family planning policy, and shortcomings of one kind or another are unavoidable in family planning work. However, as the family planning policy fundamentally conforms to the interests of the majority of the Chinese people and, during its actual implementation, the actual difficulties and reasonable demands of some people have been taken into consideration and the legal rights and interests of the citizens are strongly protected, the family planning policy has won understanding and recognition from the broad masses of the people. Through [a] long period of practice, the Chinese people have realized more and more deeply from their practical interests that family planning is a cause that benefits the nation and the people, and they have increasingly come to understand and support this cause. After unremitting efforts, including drawing useful experience from other countries, the management level and service quality of China's family planning programme has continually been improved and the shortcomings and problems in its actual work have been remarkably reduced. We believe that all those who do not seek to hold prejudice will respect this basic fact.

Concluding Remarks

China is home to more than one-fifth of the world's population. It thoroughly understands the responsibility it bears in stabilizing world population growth and the essential role it should play. Family planning as an effective solution to China's population problems is more than just responsibility towards the well-being of the Chinese people and future generations; it is a duty owed to maintaining the stability of the world population. Working for the common interests of all of humanity, at the same time working for individual interests of each nation, the international community and each nation should work together to solve the population problems facing individual nations and the entire world. This will promote development and progress in every country and throughout human society.

Twenty-one years have passed since the First International Population Conference was held in Bucharest in 1974. The government of each nation and the international community as a whole have made new progress in implementing the "World Population Plan of Action" and the "Mexico City Declaration." The rate of increase in world population has been further slowed. Still, world population continues to increase by 90 million per annum, and it will reach 6.25 billion by the end of the century and 8.4 billion by 2025. Control of world population remains an urgent and difficult task. China, as always, will continue to work in concert with all the nations of the world to carry out the "Programme of Action of the International Conference on Population and Development" and make positive contributions to stabilizing world population and ensuring a happier future for mankind.

The Right to Have Children

Canadian Medical Association

The Meaning of the Phrase

Once these questions are asked, they entrain a series of still more fundamental questions: What does the notion of a right to have children amount to? Does it mean that everyone has the right to biological offspring of their own? That everyone has

"The right to have children" — Reprinted from Canadian Medical Association 1991, pages 40–52, by permission of the publisher. © 1991 Canadian Medical Association.

the right to be a parent? A combination of these? Or is there something else entirely that is here at stake? These are not questions of mere lexicography. Depending how the notion of a right to have children is understood, different consequences follow.

The Right to Parent

If it is understood as the right to be a parent, then nothing in principle would bar society from interfering in the reproductive capabilities of its citizens. So long as people were provided with children to parent, their right would be fulfilled. Involuntary sterilization for reasons unrelated to the health of the individual person would, therefore, not be ruled out. The capacity to parent would not thereby be affected. Furthermore, as long as society provided anyone who wanted it with the opportunity to parent, society would not have an obligation to investigate and correct the causes of infertility.

For medicine, this would mean that investigations into infertility would not have to rank high on any list of research priorities. Although infertility might well be a health issue and might be of interest to physicians from a scientific perspective, this would not necessarily be the case. Nor would physicians' obligation to their patient, whether that be understood in an individual or in a global sense, include the duty to assist in the fulfilment of parental aspirations.

The Right to Have Biological Offspring of One's Own

On the other hand, if the right to have children were to be understood as the right to have biological offspring of one's own, the situation would be entirely different. Then society would have an obligation to try to prevent or, failing prevention, to cure infertility. It would also have a *prima facie* obligation to fund those areas of research that are directed toward improving the chances of biological parenthood.

However, by the same token, it would not follow that society had an obligation to assist or even encourage biological parents to keep their offspring. In other words, it would be gratuitous to assume that biological progenitors had an automatic right to parent the children that carried their genetic heritage. This would become particularly important in the contemporary context, where surrogate motherhood has become a reality.

For medicine, this interpretation would entail an obligation to assist those who are unable to have biological offspring of their own. That obligation, in turn, would affect the orientation that the profession would have to adopt in this matter. Among other things, it would mean that investigations into the causes of infertility from a preventive perspective would become as much a priority item for the profession as would investigations into other preventable health problems, and research projects aimed at ways of curing infertility and infertility-associated problems would be mandated. The profession might even be faced with an obligation to develop new techniques of reproduction for those who are inherently incapable of having children. Furthermore, because equity and justice would demand that the right to have children could not be confined only to women, research into such things as artificial placentas, male pregnancies, etc., would become entirely appropriate.

The Right to Reproduce and to Parent

Finally, if the right to have children is understood to include both the right to have biological offspring of one's own and the right to be a parent to them, the picture would shift once again. Not only would society have an obligation to fund research aimed at eradicating or curing infertility, it would also have an obligation to help everyone in their efforts to function as parents — even if they have difficulties doing so.

This would assume considerable significance in the case of mentally or otherwise handicapped people. A whole domain of social support services would be implicated. It should also be clear that the orientation of these services could not be directed solely toward the prospective parents. It would be coloured by an admixture of the obligation that the state has toward children independent of any other duty.[1] The difficulties inherent in reconciling the two duties might well create a difficult situation.

Not only would the medical profession have an obligation to assist patients in their efforts to have biological offspring of their own, it would also have an obligation to delve into the psychology of parenting, to provide psychiatric assistance to those who need it to realize their right to parent. In other words, the profession would have to address and deal with medically based social implications of and requirements for parenting.

A Modified Social Notion

The Association suggests that there is a fourth way to understand the notion: a way that combines some of the features of the interpretations just canvassed. The right to have children should be seen as the right to take advantage of the opportunity to function in parental capacity, where it is an underlying assumption of this notion that in the normal course of events, this opportunity will arise because of the exercise of normal biological functions.

The Argument The Association favours this interpretation for several reasons. First, it places the right firmly where it belongs: into the overall social context. It thereby recognizes that this right is not absolute. It is subject to those concerns and considerations that motivate society when dealing with any other right. It may be overruled when it conflicts with a more fundamental right or with a deeper social obligation. Furthermore, it means that like any right, the right to have children has certain preconditions. In the present case, these preconditions would centre in the capability of individuals to make reasoned choices and to function in a parental role.[2]

Second, it means that considerations of equity can be grounded in an appeal to equal opportunity. It therefore requires society to act whenever there is an inequity of opportunity, whether that be for people in general or for specific groups. This is particularly important for handicapped people who have the capacity to parent, but who may exercise that capacity only with societal assistance.

Third, it recognizes that society has a *prima facie* obligation to try to alleviate any impediments to the exercise of the reproductive biological functions that are normally found in human beings. Therefore, society would have a *prima facie* obligation to fund research into the causes of and cures for non-voluntary infertility and to make the results of that research available on an equitable basis.

Fourth, it would cast the medical and associated health care professions in an appropriate role in this matter: as providing assistance with the fulfilment of this right to have children, but not as judges of who should and who should not have that right. In other words, it would deny control in this matter to all but the individuals themselves.

Supporting Arguments This interpretation finds support in arguments that are intended to show that there is a right to have children. The Association hastens to add that it does not support all such arguments.

The Association does not support the argument that is based on the biological nature of the human species. This argument begins with the observation that unless human beings reproduce, the species will disappear. From this it deduces that the right to reproduce —

that is, the right to have children — is grounded in the biological nature of humanity itself.[3]

Although the Association is conscious that the biological facts referred to are beyond doubt, it contends that they do not support the conclusion. The fact that a species will disappear unless its members reproduce entails neither a right nor a duty to reproduce. Any such inference would require the premise that the species should continue to exist in the first place. However, the very biological facts that form the underpinning of this reasoning cast doubt on the tenability of such a premise.

More important, the Association wishes to dissociate itself from this sort of approach for another reason: it would have pernicious consequences. It would mean that not every person has the right to reproduce. It would follow that all and only those people who could reasonably be expected to contribute to the survival of the species would have that right. That, however, would exclude all who carry identifiable dominant lethal genes or who carry genes that would not be advantageous in a changing global environment. In fact, it would deny the right to everyone whose reproduction would in any way compromise the survival of the species as a whole. Instead of grounding a universal right to have children, the argument would entail a right governed by the most rigorous eugenic and evolutionary standards. The Association cannot support such a position.

Another argument for the right to have children that the Association cannot accept derives from the contention that most people want to have children. Using this as a premise, the argument then concludes that people do have a *prima facie* right. Although the argument admits that this right may be overruled on certain occasions, it contends that it could never be overruled as a matter of social whim.[4]

Although the Association applauds some aspects of this argument — in particular the thesis that the right to have children should not be overruled as a matter of societal whim — it cannot attach itself to the reasoning as a whole. The Association believes that the premise on which the argument is based is ethically unacceptable. More specifically, the Association rejects the premise that the desire to have children creates a *prima facie* right. The Association contends that, to accept that premise, it would have to accept the more general thesis that the existence of a desire in itself creates a right. In the eyes of the Association, a desire does not secure a right — not even a *prima facie* right. If it were otherwise, pathological murderers would have a *prima facie* right to their victims simply because they desire to kill them, kleptomaniacs would have a *prima facie* right to the goods of others, and so on.

The Association also notes with alarm that acceptance of the underlying premise would spell disaster for health care funding. It would mean that as soon as any member of society desired to be treated in a certain fashion, or to have access to a certain treatment modality, society had a *prima facie* obligation to provide it.

The entire practice of medicine would also be hamstrung by such an assumption. It would put the practising physician into the position of having to justify the refusal of a medically inappropriate treatment against the *prima facie* right of the patient. Although the wishes and desires of members of society are relevant when considering the extent of health care services, and although they are of central importance in the physician–patient relationship, they cannot be seen as determining.

A third argument is based on the fact that human beings have the potential to grow as persons in the context of a family. It is this context that provides an opportunity to develop qualities like empathy and compassion. It is here, also, that they can develop as nurturers, providers of security and so on. Without children, however, these potentials will never be fulfilled.[5]

The Association is sympathetic toward the sentiment expressed in this argument. It accepts the thesis that the realization of human potential may be a good in itself, and that its development might appropriately be encouraged. However, the Association cannot accept in its unconditioned form the premise that is associated with this sentiment. On a pragmatic level, in some instances the insistence on the realization of such a potential may predictably lead to dysfunctional families. Furthermore, the realization of a potential is ethically acceptable only for those potentials whose realization should be encouraged. Not all potentials fall into this category. The potential for psychotic dysfunctions falls under this rubric. Finally, and in any case, the Association would argue that the right to realize a potential is a *prima facie* right at best. The considerations that were alluded to in the previous discussion of the argument from desire are here apropos as well.

Another argument centres in the thesis that society offers its members the opportunity to have biological offspring as a matter of general and socially sanctioned expectation through an expression of their sexuality in a socially acceptable fashion. This expectation is so fundamental and so universal that it amounts to a right.

It strikes the Association that this line of reasoning is persuasive. At the same time, the Association is conscious that this line of reasoning does not stand alone. If it is accepted, its consequences would be as immediate as they would be powerful. They would include the conclusion that the right to have children is fundamental to membership in society itself, and that it may be limited or conditioned only by the circumstances in which a society may find itself and by the competing rights of others.

This would have important consequences for how the right to have children would manifest itself in practice, as well as for the obligations that it would impose on society in general and the profession of medicine in particular.

Societal implications would include society's perception of normalcy with respect to the exercise of a given right. For example, it is a normal expectation of society that people will not unnecessarily and irresponsibly expose others to harm. Therefore, the right to freedom of reproduction would be limited by this expectation.

This in turn would mean that society would have the right, and indeed the duty, to interfere with those expressions of sexuality that put other members of society at risk. The duty to control the spread of sexually transmitted diseases would here be implicated.

It would also mean that society would not be derelict in its duty if it did not develop and provide techniques of reproductive technology that went beyond ameliorating inequities of opportunity in this regard. In other words, this perspective would allow society to exercise its discretion in funding those techniques of reproductive technology whose primary function is personal convenience.

For the profession of medicine, it would mean that the refusal of individual physicians to provide what thus could be called elective reproductive services would not stand in contravention of their ethical mandate.

These implications notwithstanding, the Canadian Medical Association is inclined to accept this perspective. The Association is of the opinion that the right to have children is indeed a socially guaranteed right that finds its basis in the fact of social membership itself. However, the Association also believes that for that very reason, this right is not absolute. It is subject to the limiting conditions that affect all other socially grounded rights. The conditions that normally attend the expectation of opportunity for sexual expression and the opportunity for having children are here crucial. They may shift as the resources and abilities of society change. However, the fact remains that the right is conditioned.

Some Consequences

As has already been indicated, the perception of the right to have children, and the reasoning in support of it, have certain important consequences. One of these consequences centres in the expectation of normalcy referred to above. The predominant expectation of people who want children is that the children they have will meet the social norm in terms of natures and abilities. People may be aware that there is a statistical possibility that this expectation may not be met, that is, their biological offspring may suffer from some congenital disease or condition.[6] This awareness is sometimes expressed in terms of the fears that they might not have children that will be normal and healthy. Nevertheless, because people's expectations tend to be shaped by the norm of experience, their usual expectations are that their children will be normal.

The expectation in Canadian society, therefore, as a matter of perceived right, is not simply for a child as such. It also contains as a strong undercurrent the expectation that the child will be normal and healthy. This undercurrent forms part of the overall framework in which the notion of the right to have a child is at home. That in turn leads to the expectation — again as a matter of right — that if either the expectation of having a child in the first instance, or of having a normal child in the second, is unlikely to be met, then society has an obligation to assist those who cannot share in these expectations.

If this inference is granted, then the assistance that society may legitimately be expected to provide may take various forms, depending on the reason why the

initial expectation is unlikely to be met. If the reason lies in infertility, then society may be seen to have an obligation to try to overcome it. The various medical techniques of assisted reproduction would then be implicated.

If the reason lies in a defect in the genetic endowment of the parents, society may be expected to try to remedy the relevant defects, or at least to ameliorate their impact. Techniques of genetic screening for carrier status and the development of techniques of germ line therapy would here have their place. So would programs designed to assist the parents of children suffering from congenital anomalies, and to assist the children themselves.

Finally, if the reason lies in the conditions that contribute to the offspring's development *in utero*, then it would seem appropriate to say that society should address the situation. The development and funding of intra-uterine screening technology, methods of intra-uterine therapy, gene therapy, etc., would here become relevant. So would efforts to provide a salubrious environment for the possibility of conception and for the gestational development of a fetus.[7]

There are only two conditions under which society would be freed from an obligation in these matters: when the reason for action is the convenience of members of society; and when it would be impossible to provide a remedy. In the former case, social actions would be at the discretion of the general will and would be subject to the availability of resources. In the second case, society would have a *prima facie* obligation to attempt to provide a remedy in some other fashion, for instance, by developing appropriately structured adoption laws, or by exploring other approaches to child bearing. Surrogate motherhood would provide a recent, albeit controversial, example.

However, the Association wishes to emphasize that in its opinion, if the reason why certain people cannot have children is by its nature irremediable, then society cannot be expected to attempt to provide a remedy. The law has an expression that applies in this context: "Equity does not require the impossible." Ethics accepts a similar principle.

A second consequence that would seem to follow is: if, under the circumstances, and despite society's best efforts, prospective parents carry such a severe and irremediable genetic load that the quality of life of any children they might have would be irremediably impaired, then these prospective parents should be counselled to exercise responsibility and not to have children. The reason lies not so much in the burden that such children would impose on society, but in the fact that the children themselves would be the recipients of harm.[8]

To reiterate, if there is a right to have children, and if that right is derivable from the fact of social existence and the expectations that normally are legitimated by such existence, then such a right is neither absolute nor unconditioned. It is conditioned by the competing rights of others. If others have rights that are more basic or more fundamental, then these rights will overrule the right to have children.

On this assumption, the right to have children is conditioned and not absolute. It presupposes that certain requirements are met. For example, it presupposes that society is materially capable of providing the opportunity for sexual expression and for supporting the children that foreseeably will result from it. It also presupposes that the other members of society are willing to subordinate their relevant and competing rights if and when the need arises. Finally, it presupposes that those who claim the right are themselves able to treat as persons the children that might result from their sexual activities.

The last point is crucial: the right to have children is not like the right to have an object or an animal. Children are persons and must be treated as persons. The right to have children is, therefore, better understood as the right to take advantage of opportunities that are open to everyone as a matter of course. When those opportunities are not present, then society has an obligation to assist those who lack the opportunities. When such a lack can be remedied by the development or application of reproductive technologies, then society has a *prima facie* obligation to develop and apply them. However, any societal action in this regard must always be with an eye to the fact that children are persons.

Notes*

1. For a fuller discussion of this from a legal perspective, see the discussion of parens patriae powers of the courts by Supreme Court Justice La Forest in *Eve*.

2. Compare *Re B (a minor),* [1987] All ER 206, 219, at 213; Lord Halsham:

   ... whilst I find La Forest J.'s history of the *parens patriae* jurisdiction of the Crown ... extremely helpful, I find, with great respect, his conclusion ... that the procedure of sterilization "should *never* [sic] be authorised for non-therapeutic purposes" totally unconvincing and in startling contradiction to the welfare principle. ... To talk of the "basic right" to reproduce of an individual who is not capable of knowing the causal connection between intercourse and childbirth, the nature of pregnancy, what is involved in delivery, unable to form maternal instincts or to care for a child appears to me wholly to part company with reality.

---

* These notes have been renumbered to aid the reader.

Lord Oliver's position, although focused on the ability to make a choice, was essentially similar:

> [In the case of D], Heilbron J. declined to sanction an operation which involved depriving [D] of the right to reproduce. That, if I may say so respectfully, was plainly a right decision. But the right to reproduce is of value only if accompanied by the ability to make a choice.

For a similar position, see Alberta Institute of Law Research and Reform: *Competence and Human Reproduction*, Report no. 52, Edmonton, Alberta, 1989: 13:

> 6(1) In addition to the matters referred to in section 5, before determining whether an order authorizing the performance of an elective sterilization would be in the best interests of the person in respect of whom the order is sought, the judge shall consider (j) the ability of the person to care for a child at the time of application and any likely changes in that ability.

3. For a discussion of this, see Vaux K: *Birth Ethics: Religious and Cultural Values in the Genesis of Life* (Crossroads, New York, N.Y., 1989), Chapter 3, "Biologic ethics of attraction and affection."

4. This current is reflected in *re Eve* as well as most other Canadian and U.K. cases dealing with non-consensual sterilization of incompetents.

5. See *re Eve* for judicial recognition of this strand.

6. The awareness of such a possibility may be the result of a family history, genetic screening, etc. Huntington's chorea, thalassaemia, Tay-Sachs, etc., are here implicated. At present, the list of diseases or conditions extends to well over 200.

7. For discussion of research funding, see also Québec, Ministère de la Santé et des Services sociaux: *Rapport du Comité de Travail sur les Nouvelles Technologies de Reproduction Humaine*, Quebec, 1988: 92.

8. For a discussion of this position, see Purdy L.M.: Genetic diseases: can having children be immoral? In Buckley J.J. ed., *Genetics Now: Ethical Issues in Genetic Research*, Univ Press of America, Washington, D.C., 1978. [Included below.]

Eve v. Mrs. E.

Lamer, Wilson, Le Dain and La Forest J.J.

LA FOREST J. — These proceedings began with an application by a mother for permission to consent to the sterilization of her mentally retarded daughter who also suffered from a condition that makes it extremely difficult for her to communicate with others. The application was heard by McQuaid J. of the Supreme Court of Prince Edward Island — Family Division. In the interests of privacy, he called the daughter "Eve," and her mother "Mrs. E."

[1987], 3 D.L.R. (4th) S.C.C., [1987] 2 S.C.R. 388 (S.C.C.).

Background

... [Mr. Justice McQuaid, the trial judge, on the basis of the evidence before him, found that the following description summed up Eve's situation:]

The evidence established that Eve is 24 years of age, and suffers what is described as extreme expressive aphasia. She is unquestionably at least mildly to moderately retarded. She has some learning skills, but only to a limited level. She is described as being a pleasant and affectionate person who, physically, is an adult person, quite capable of being attracted to, as well as attractive to, the opposite sex. While she might be able to carry out the mechanical duties of a mother, under supervision, she is incapable of being a mother in any other sense. Apart from being able to recognize the fact of a family unit, as consisting of a father, a mother, and children residing in the same home, she would have no concept of the idea of marriage, or indeed, the consequential relationship between intercourse, pregnancy and birth. Expressive aphasia was described as a condition in which the patient is unable to communicate outwardly thoughts or concepts which she might have perceived. Particularly in the case of a person suffering from any degree of retardation, the result is that even an expert such as a psychiatrist is unable to determine with any degree of certainty if, in fact, those thoughts or concepts have actually been perceived, or whether understanding of them does exist. Little appears to be known of the cause of this condition, and even less of its remedy. In the case of Eve, this condition has been diagnosed as extreme.

From the evidence, he [Mr. Justice McQuaid] further concluded:

[t]hat Eve is not capable of informed consent, that her moderate retardation is generally stable, that her condition is probably non-inheritable, that she is incapable of effective alternative means of contraception, that the psychological or emotional effect of the proposed operation would probably be minimal, and that the probable incidence of pregnancy is impossible to predict.

Mrs. E. wanted to be sure she had a right to consent to the sterilization of Eve, so she applied ... for the following remedies:

(a) that Eve be declared a mentally incompetent pursuant to the provisions of the Mental Health Act;

(b) that Mrs. E. be appointed the committee of the person of Eve;

(c) that Mrs. E. be authorized to consent to a tubal ligation operation being performed on Eve.

... Having reviewed the Canadian and English case law and found no governing authorities, McQuaid J. considered whether the court should, in the exercise of its *parens patriae* jurisdiction, intervene on behalf of Eve. He had no doubt that the court could authorize a surgical procedure necessary to health even though a side-effect might be sterilization, and he postulated that it could also do so where the public interest clearly required it, though he found it difficult to come up with an example. However, McQuaid J. was of the view that Eve, like other individuals, was entitled to the inviolability of her person, a right that superseded her right to be protected from pregnancy. That this might result in inconvenience and even hardship to others was irrelevant. The law must protect those who are unable to protect themselves; it must ensure the protection of the higher right. He, therefore, concluded that the court had no authority or jurisdiction to authorize a surgical procedure on a mentally retarded person, the intent and purpose of which was solely contraceptive. It followed that, except for clinically therapeutic reasons, parents or others similarly situated could not give a valid consent to such a surgical procedure either, at least in the absence of clear and unequivocal statutory authority. He, therefore, denied the application.

An appeal to the Supreme Court of Prince Edward Island, *in banco*, was launched, and an order was then made appointing the Official Trustee as Guardian ad litem for Eve. The appeal was allowed. The general view of the court is set forth in an addendum to its notes of judgment as follows:

> In rendering judgment in this matter, we are unanimously of the opinion that the Court has, in proper circumstances, the authority and jurisdiction to authorize the sterilization of a mentally incompetent person for non-therapeutic reasons. The jurisdiction of the Court originates from its parens patriae powers towards individuals who are unable to look after themselves and gives the Court authority to make the individual a ward of the Court.

The court, however, differed on the evidence. A majority (Large and Campbell J.J.) was of the view, MacDonald J. dissenting, that there was sufficient evidence to warrant the sterilization of Eve. The court therefore ordered that:

(a) "Eve" be appointed a ward of the Court pursuant to the *parens patriae* jurisdiction for the sole purpose of facilitating and authorizing her sterilization;

(b) the Court authorizes the sterilization of "Eve" by a competent medical practitioner;

(c) the Court reserves its approval of the method of sterilization to be followed pending further submissions of counsel as to the medically preferred surgical procedure.

... Leave to appeal to this Court was then granted to Eve's Guardian *ad litem* by the Prince Edward Island Supreme Court, Appeal Division. The major issues raised in this appeal are substantially as follows:

1. Is there relevant provincial legislation that gives a court jurisdiction to appoint a committee vested with the power to consent to or authorize surgical procedures for contraceptive purposes on an adult who is mentally incompetent?

2. In the absence of statutory authority, does the court's *parens patriae* jurisdiction allow the court to consent to the sterilization of an adult who is mentally incompetent?

3. What is the appropriate standard of proof to be applied in a case where an application is made to the court for its substituted consent to a nontherapeutic procedure on behalf of a mentally incompetent adult? Upon whom is the onus of proof?

4. If the court has jurisdiction to provide substituted consent for a nontherapeutic procedure on behalf of a mentally incompetent adult, did the Supreme Court of Prince Edward Island, in banco, properly exercise its jurisdiction in granting an order authorizing the sterilization of Eve?

5. Does the Canadian Charter of Rights and Freedoms protect an individual against sterilization without that individual's consent?

6. If the Charter provides such protection, when will it permit the nontherapeutic sterilization of a mentally incompetent who is incapable of giving consent?

7. Does the Charter give an individual the right to choose not to procreate, and if so does the court have jurisdiction to make that choice on behalf of an individual who is unable to do so?

General Considerations

Before entering into a consideration of the specific issues before this Court, it may be useful to restate the general issue briefly. The Court is asked to consent, on behalf of Eve, to sterilization since she, though an adult, is unable to do so herself. Sterilization by means of a tubal ligation is usually irreversible. And hysterectomy, the operation authorized by the Appeal Division, is not only irreversible; it is major surgery. Eve's sterilization is not being sought to treat any medical condition. Its purposes are admittedly non-therapeutic. One such purpose is to deprive Eve of the capacity to become pregnant so as to save her from the possible trauma of giving birth and from the resultant obligations of a parent, a task the evidence indicates she is not capable of fulfilling. As to this, it should be noted that there is no evidence that giving birth would be more difficult for Eve than for any other woman.

A second purpose of the sterilization is to relieve Mrs. E. of anxiety about the possibility of Eve's becoming pregnant and of having to care for any child Eve might bear.

... *[Mr. Justice La Forest then discusses the history and rationale of proxy decision making in the U.K. and the role of the courts. He then turns to the U.S. and discusses two approaches to proxy decision making that have been used there.]*

... While many state courts have, in recent cases, been prepared to recognize an inherent power in courts of general jurisdiction to authorize sterilization of mentally incompetent persons, they differ on the standard of review. Two dis-

tinct approaches have emerged: the "best interests" approach and the "substituted judgment" approach. In five of the nine states in which equitable jurisdiction to authorize the non-consensual sterilization of a mentally incompetent person is recognized, that jurisdiction is based on the inherent equitable power of the courts to act in the best interests of the mentally incompetent person. ... The test necessarily leads to uncertainties ... and in an effort to minimize abuses, American courts have developed guidelines to assist in determining whether the best interests of the affected person would be furthered through sterilization. ...

... As noted, these facts indicate that the courts of the United States in acting under the best interests test have a very wide discretion.

The second approach, the substituted judgment test, raises Charter implications.

... The primary purpose of the substituted judgment test is to attempt to determine what decision the mental incompetent would make, if she were reviewing her situation as a competent person, but taking account of her mental incapacity as one factor in her decision. It allows the court to consider a number of factors bearing directly upon the condition of the mental incompetent. Thus the court may consider such issues as the values of the incompetent, any religious beliefs held by her, and her societal views as expressed by her family. In essence, an attempt is made to determine the actual interests and preferences of the mental incompetent. This, it is thought, recognizes her moral dignity and right to free choice. Since the incompetent cannot exercise that choice herself, the court does so on her behalf. The fact that a mental incompetent is, either because of age or mental disability, unable to provide any aid to the court in its decision does not preclude the use of the substituted judgment test.

The respondent submitted that this test should be adopted in this country. As in the case of the best interests test, various guidelines have been developed by the courts in the United States to ensure the proper use of this test.

... [I]t is easy to understand the natural feelings of a parent's heart. ... [However,] a court ... must exercise great caution to avoid being misled by this all too human mixture of emotions and motives. So we are left to consider whether the purposes underlying the operation are necessarily for Eve's benefit and protection.

The justifications advanced are the ones commonly proposed in support of non-therapeutic sterilization. ... Many are demonstrably weak. The [Law Reform] Commission dismisses the argument about the trauma of birth by observing at p. 60:

> For this argument to be held valid would require that it could be demonstrated that the stress of delivery was greater in the case of mentally handicapped persons than it is for others. Considering the generally known wide range of post-partum response would likely render this a difficult case to prove.

The argument relating to fitness as a parent involves many value-loaded questions. Studies conclude that mentally incompetent parents show as much fondness and concern for their children as other people; see *Sterilization*, supra, p. 33 et seq., 63–64. Many, it is true, may have difficulty in coping, particularly with the financial burdens involved. But this issue does not relate to the benefit of the incompetent; it is a social problem, and one, moreover, that is not limited to incompetents. Above all it is not an issue that comes within the limited powers of the courts, under the *parens patriae* jurisdiction, to do what is necessary for the benefit of persons who are unable to care for themselves. Indeed, there are human rights considerations that should

make a court extremely hesitant about attempting to solve a social problem like this by this means. It is worth noting that in dealing with such issues, provincial sterilization boards have revealed serious differences in their attitudes as between men and women, the poor and the rich, and people of different ethnic backgrounds.

As far as the hygienic problems are concerned, the following view of the Law Reform Commission ([*Sterilization*] at p. 34) is obviously sound:

> ... if a person requires a great deal of assistance in managing their own menstruation, they are also likely to require assistance with urinary and fecal control, problems which are much more troublesome in terms of personal hygiene.

Apart from this, the drastic measure of subjecting a person to a hysterectomy for this purpose is clearly excessive.

The grave intrusion on a person's rights and the certain physical damage that ensues from non-therapeutic sterilization without consent, when compared to the highly questionable advantages that can result from it, have persuaded me that it can never safely be determined that such a procedure is for the benefit of that person. Accordingly, the procedure should never be authorized for non-therapeutic purposes under the *parens patriae* jurisdiction.

To begin with, it is difficult to imagine a case in which non-therapeutic sterilization could possibly be of benefit to the person on behalf of whom a court purports to act, let alone one in which that procedure is necessary in his or her best interest. And how are we to weigh the best interests of a person in this troublesome area, keeping in mind that an error is irreversible? Unlike other cases involving the use of the *parens patriae* jurisdiction, an error cannot be corrected by the subsequent exercise of judicial discretion. That being so, one need only recall Lord

Eldon's remark, supra, that "it has always been the principle of this Court, not to risk damage to children which it cannot repair" to conclude that non-therapeutic sterilization may not be authorized in the exercise of the *parens patriae* jurisdiction. McQuaid J. was, therefore, right in concluding that he had no authority or jurisdiction to grant the application.

Nature or the advances of science may, at least in a measure, free Eve of the incapacity from which she suffers. Such a possibility should give the courts pause in extending their power to care for individuals to such irreversible action as we are called upon to take here. The irreversible and serious intrusion on the basic rights of the individual is simply too great to allow a court to act on the basis of possible advantages which, from the standpoint of the individual, are highly debatable. Judges are generally ill-informed about many of the factors relevant to a wise decision in this difficult area. They generally know little of mental illness, of techniques of contraception or their efficacy. And, however well presented a case may be, it can only partially inform. If sterilization of the mentally incompetent is to be adopted as desirable for general social purposes, the legislature is the appropriate body to do so. It is in a position to inform itself and it is attuned to the feelings of the public in making policy in this sensitive area. The actions of the legislature will then, of course, be subject to the scrutiny of the courts under the Canadian Charter of Rights and Freedoms and otherwise.

... The foregoing, of course, leaves out of consideration therapeutic sterilization and where the line is to be drawn between therapeutic and non-therapeutic sterilization. On this issue, I simply repeat that the utmost caution must be exercised commensurate with the seriousness of the procedure. Marginal justifications must be weighed against what is in every case a grave intrusion on the physical and mental integrity of the person.

... I cannot agree that a court can deprive a woman of that privilege for purely social or other non-therapeutic purposes without her consent. The fact that others may suffer inconvenience or hardship from failure to do so cannot be taken into account. The Crown's parens patriae jurisdiction exists for the benefit of those who cannot help themselves, not to relieve those who may have the burden of caring for them.

I should perhaps add ... that sterilization may, on occasion, be necessary as an adjunct to treatment of a serious malady, but I would underline that this, of course, does not allow for subterfuge or for treatment of some marginal medical problem.

The foregoing remarks dispose of the arguments based on the traditional view of the parens patriae jurisdiction as exercised in this country. Counsel for the respondent strongly contended, however, that the Court should adopt the substituted judgment test recently developed by a number of state courts in the United States. That test, he submitted, is to be preferred to the best interests test because it places a higher value on the individuality of the mentally incompetent person. It affords that person the same right, he contended, as a competent person to choose whether to procreate or not.

There is an obvious logical lapse in this argument. I do not doubt that a person has a right to decide to be sterilized. That is his or her free choice. But choice presupposes that a person has the mental competence to make it. It may be a matter of debate whether a court should have the power to make the decision if that person lacks the mental capacity to do so. But it is obviously fiction to suggest that a decision so made is that of the mental incompetent, however much the court may try to put itself in her place. What the incompetent would do if she or he could make the choice is simply a matter of speculation. The sophistry embodied in the argument favouring substituted judgment has been fully revealed in *Eberhardy* ... where ... the court stated:

> The fault we find in the New Jersey case is the *ratio decidendi* of first concluding, correctly we believe, that the right to sterilization is a personal choice, but then equating a decision made by others with the choice of the person to be sterilized. It clearly is not a personal choice, and no amount of legal legerdemain can make it so.

> ...

> We conclude that the question is not choice because it is sophistry to refer to it as such, but rather the question is whether there is a method by which others, acting in behalf of the person's best interests and in the interests, such as they may be, of the state, can exercise the decision. Any governmentally sanctioned (or ordered) procedure to sterilize a person who is incapable of giving consent must be denominated for what it is, that is, the state's intrusion into the determination of whether or not a person who makes no choice shall be allowed to procreate.

Counsel for the respondent ... argued that there is what he called a fundamental right to free procreative choice. Not only, he asserted, is there a fundamental right to bear children; there is as well a fundamental right to choose not to have children and to implement that choice by means of contraception. ... [H]e appears to base this argument on s. 7 of the Charter. But assuming for the moment that liberty as used in s. 7 protects rights of this kind (a matter I refrain from entering into), counsel's contention seems to me to go beyond the kind of protection s. 7 was intended to afford. All s. 7 does is to give a remedy to protect individuals against laws or other state action that deprive them of liberty. It has no application here.

Another Charter related argument must be considered. In response to the appellant's argument that a court-ordered sterilization of a mentally incompetent person, by depriving that person of the right to procreate, would constitute an infringement of that person's rights to liberty and security of the person under s. 7 of the Canadian Charter of Rights and Freedoms, counsel for the respondent countered by relying on that person's right to equality under s. 15(1) of the Charter, saying "that the most appropriate method of ensuring the mentally incompetent their right to equal protection under s. 15(1) is to provide the mentally incompetent with a means to obtain non-therapeutic sterilizations, which adequately protects their interests through appropriate judicial safeguards." A somewhat more explicit argument along the same lines was made by counsel for the Public Trustee of Manitoba. His position was stated as follows:

> It is submitted that in the case of a mentally incompetent adult, denial of the right to have his or her case presented by a guardian *ad litem* to a Court possessing jurisdiction to give or refuse substituted consent to a non-therapeutic procedure such as sterilization, would be tantamount to a denial to that person of equal protection and equal benefit of the law. Such a denial would constitute discrimination on the basis of mental disability, which discrimination is prohibited by Section 15 of The Canadian Charter of Rights and Freedoms.

Section 15 of the Charter was not in force when these proceedings commenced but, this aside, these arguments appear flawed. They raise in different form an issue already dealt with, i.e., that the decision made by a court on an application to consent to the sterilization of an incompetent is somehow that of the incompetent. More troubling is that the issue is, of course, not raised by the incompetent, but by a third party. The court undoubtedly has the right and duty to protect those who are unable to take care of themselves, and in doing so it has a wide discretion to do what it considers to be in their best interests. But this function must not, in my view, be transformed so as to create a duty obliging the court, at the behest of a third party, to make a choice between the two alleged constitutional rights — the right to procreate or not to procreate — simply because the individual is unable to make that choice. All the more so since, in the case of non-therapeutic sterilization as we saw, the choice is one the courts cannot safely exercise.

... Since, barring emergency situations, a surgical procedure without consent ordinarily constitutes battery, it will be obvious that the onus of proving the need for the procedure is on those who seek to have it performed. And that burden, though a civil one, must be commensurate with the seriousness of the measure proposed. In conducting these procedures, it is obvious that a court must proceed with extreme caution; otherwise ... it would open the way for abuse of the mentally incompetent. ... I would allow the appeal and restore the decision of the judge who heard the application.

Sterilisation of the Mentally Severely Handicapped: A Violation of the Right to Have Children?

Eike-Henner W. Kluge

Introduction

The Universal Declaration of Human Rights (1948) stated, and the Declaration of Teheran (1968) reiterated, that every person 'of full age' has the right to have children and 'found a family'. The right thus enunciated is usually interpreted as being universal, inalienable and indefeasible: and it is at least in part on this basis that many jurisdictions have rejected the non-consensual sterilisation of the mentally severely handicapped as being both discriminatory and unethical when performed for reasons other than to safeguard the health and welfare of the

handicapped person. It is on this basis also that most commentators have rejected such sterilisation.

However, both the general thesis, as well as its application to the mentally severely handicapped, may be challenged. The general claim may be challenged on three grounds: the nature of the right claimed, as well as its legitimacy, is extremely dubious; the grounding of the alleged right presents severe ontological problems; and the claim that such a right is indefeasible ignores the contextual nature of all rights. As to the particular claim as advanced for the mentally severely handicapped, three further argu-

E.-H. W. Kluge, "Sterilisation of the Mentally Severely Handicapped: A Violation of the Right to Have Children?" *Ethical Problems in Reproductive Medicine* 1989; 1:1, 12–15.

ments may be raised against it: the mentally severely handicapped cannot meet the basic precondition for such a right; insistence on such a right would violate the rights of children; and, finally, it would also violate the rights of other people.

While none of these considerations, even if successful, entail that the mentally severely handicapped should be sterilised as a matter of course, they do entail that under circumstances where conception and procreation of the mentally severely handicapped can reasonably be prevented only in this fashion, sterilisation is ethically permissible.

The Nature of the Claim

To begin with the nature of the claim itself: what precisely does the alleged right to have children amount to? Several possibilities come to mind, but one is generally taken to be central: the right to have biological progeny of one's own. In the interest of clarity, however, it should be noted that such an interpretation is rather simplistic. In the first place, one cannot have a right to what it is impossible to provide. Many persons are irremediably sterile and cannot have biological progeny. In their case, therefore, the alleged right would fail for want of its logical precondition. Whence it would follow that, contrary to the initial claim, the alleged right would not be universal (unless, of course, it were to be argued that the right is universal after all, and that in cases such as these, society has an obligation to develop and employ techniques of artificial reproduction that would overcome this problem. We shall not pursue the issue here.)

Second, the right, no matter how construed, centrally involves children. Children, however, are not objects. They are persons. Therefore it follows that if there is a right to have progeny at all, it could not ethically be interpreted in a proprietary or dispositionary fashion. It

would have to be understood in some other way. But how?

Finally, the right to have biological progeny of one's own would not ordinarily be considered to be satisfied by the mere existence of such progeny without any contact and association on part of the progenitor. A direct and personal interaction of an ongoing and formative sort is also taken to be implicated. An acceptable interpretation of the right claim, therefore, must include this associative parameter.

How to combine all this into a reasonable whole? The Universal Declaration of Human Rights, in its insistence on the right to 'found a family', points the way. Whatever its cultural idiosyncrasies of constitution, the family context is one of nurturing, of education, and of raising children. In short, insofar as the person context is concerned, it is one of parenting. Therefore in keeping with the preceding considerations we suggest that the claim of a universal right to have children amounts to this: everyone has the right to (attempt to) have biological progeny and parent without undue state interference.

Grounding the Right

If we assume that this is an appropriate interpretation, the next question is, 'How could such a right be grounded?' The literature, and indeed pure reasoning itself, suggest several possibilities: in the biological survival needs of the human species, the fact of individual desire, the requirements for the realisation of a truly human potential, and the fact of social policy. We shall not here examine these possibilities in detail but merely sketch some consideration.

No purely material fact, and *a fortiori* no fact of biology, can establish an ethical right. That requires an ethical premise, which is here not given. Less abstractly, it is one thing to say that the human species will not survive unless its members reproduce; but is another to say that it ought to reproduce, or that it has the right to do so. Furthermore, even if the right were granted, it would not follow that every member of the species therefore had a right to progeny. Logically, such an inference would commit the fallacy of division because materially, the facts of biology would deny it. At best, what would follow from this basis would be that all and only those whose progeny could reasonably be expected to advance species survival would have such a right. The biological argument, therefore, would only allow for a limited right conditioned by evolutionary considerations.

The argument from individual desire fares no better. To put it bluntly, the connection between desire and right must be shown. It cannot merely be assumed. Otherwise it begs the question. As to the argument from the realisation of personal potential, it faces the same problem. The existence of a fact, in this case, personal potential, does not establish a right. As it stands, the argument assumes that the connection between the fact (desire) and the right is established independently, in some other fashion; but that is not the case. The argument requires that children be considered as objects, as entities whose function it is to assist in the development of others. That, however, is ethically anathema. What one can argue is that *if* there is a particular potential and *if* there is a child, then *ceteris paribus* whoever has that potential has a *prima facie* right to use the child's existence to realise the potential. But *only if* the child will not be treated as an object. That, however, is quite different from the right claimed in the first instance. It is not the right to bring about a child for that purpose.

The argument from social existence has two versions, one legally oriented, the other ethical. The former focuses in the law extant in a given society. We shall

not deal with it here. The latter is based on the thesis that society, whether it recognises this explicitly in its laws or not, *de facto* guarantees each of its members certain fundamental rights as a condition of membership, and that the right to procreation and to parenting is one of these. However, while we may grant that society does indeed guarantee certain fundamental rights to its members, this does not establish that the right in question is one of them.

Furthermore, even if we did allow that there was such a right and that it was grounded in the fact of social existence, this would not show that it was absolute and unconditioned. The very fact that it was grounded in the social context would entail that like all other rights thus grounded, it would be subject to conditioning constraints. For one thing, it would be conditioned by the competing rights of others. Therefore if the exercise of this right interfered with the exercise of another person's more fundamental right, e.g., the right to life, then the right would become ineffective. For another, it would be conditioned from the perspective of society as a whole. That is to say children, both as persons and as biological organisms, have needs. Providing for these, however, is not simply a parental function. No matter how wealthy, well-endowed or positioned, no set of parents can meet these conditions alone. Directly or indirectly, meeting them involves whole social institutions such as health, education and welfare which no one is wholly able to defray. The coming-into-being of a child, therefore, is a social affair; and society, by allowing someone to claim the right to have a child, acquires the obligation to provide for its needs if, when and as it becomes necessary. Justice, however, entails that no one can have an obligation unilaterally thrust upon him or her. There must be some ethically acceptable way for the individual to escape the obligation. This means that it must be possible for society to avoid being locked into the relevant obligations vis-à-vis the new child. This would be possible only by preventing the child from coming into existence in the first place. It therefore follows that although there may be a socially guaranteed right to have children, that right is not absolute but defeasible from the side of society itself.

Finally, the right also is defeasible from the side of the child. That is to say, there are situations in which the conditions governing the genesis of a child are the beginning of a causal chain which predictably will eventuate in such a qualitative state for the child that, were it imposed *de novo* upon a person who is already present, it would constitute the infliction of harm. To procreate under such circumstances would be tantamount to a temporally protracted infliction of harm. Therefore while the act of procreation *per se* may be morally blameless, the act *under such circumstances* would be blameworthy and constitute an injury. Under such circumstances, therefore, the right to have a child fails.

The Mentally Severely Handicapped

The right to have a child, therefore, even if it is granted, is neither universal, absolute nor unconditioned. So far, we have only argued this for persons in general. How does it apply to the mentally severely handicapped?

To avoid confusion, we shall define a mentally severely handicapped person as someone who is congenitally so severely impaired that he or she cannot look after his or her needs as an independent and autonomous being but requires continuous supervision and assistance in order to allow him or her to survive and function; and furthermore as someone who cannot grasp the nature of a child as a person, and who fails to comprehend the requirements inherent in providing for a

child. Does such an individual have a right to have a child, in the sense discussed above? And is there a right on the part of society to sterilise such an individual in order to prevent him or her from having children?

If our preceding analysis is correct, then the answer to the first question is negative. There are two reasons for this: one logical, the other ethical. *Ex hypothesi*, the mentally severely handicapped cannot perceive, relate to or otherwise treat children as persons. Consequently, they cannot fulfil the requirements of a parenting role. Since the ability to fulfil such a role is a precondition of the right to have children, it follows that the right itself fails from a purely logical perspective. As to the ethical reason for its failure, the very nature of the handicap entails that a child born into such a situation would play the role of an object of personal development and self-gratification for the severely handicapped. However, as we said before, no right can involve the use of persons purely as objects in an instrumental fashion. The right, therefore, fails once again.

It might be argued that while the inabilities of the handicapped to parent and to see children as persons may be admitted, this does not entail that they do not have a right to have children. Instead, it entails that society has an obligation to provide for the services of someone who will take over those areas of parenting which the severely handicapped are constitutionally unable to provide: to act, as it were, *in loco parentis* towards the children. The inability of the handicapped thus being made up, their right is preserved and they will be able to benefit from and enjoy the remainder of the parenting experience.

But such an argument would fail. The central precondition ineluctably associated with the right to have a child is that the individual who claims the right must be able to experience, relate to and otherwise interact with the child as a person. The proposal at hand would not allow the mentally severely handicapped to meet this precondition. It would be the parent-proxy, the individual who is provided by society to act *in loco parentis*, who would relate to the children in the requisite manner. Short of changing his or her nature, nothing can be done for or to the mentally severely handicapped that would allow him or her to meet this condition. For him or her, the children will still remain objects. In more formal terms, if a's having quality ϕ is a necessary precondition of having right $R,$ then the fact that b has quality ϕ does not establish that therefore a has R after all. The only way in which a can acquire R is for a to acquire ϕ. In this case it would mean that the mentally severely handicapped would have to cease being mentally severely handicapped. If that were possible, there would be no ethical problem. As it stands, however, it is not the case.

Sterilisation

If the foregoing is correct, then the mentally severely handicapped do not have a right to have children in the sense we have developed. Society has both a right and a duty to step in. But in what fashion? Surely sterilisation is too restrictive? Surely contraception and even abortion are less permanent, less irreversible and less intrusive alternatives?

As to abortion, it is almost as intrusive as tubal ligation and since it does not prevent future conceptions, it is a potentially repetitive procedure. Given that it does have an intrusive nature, it follows on the last count that any advantage it might have over sterilisation would have to be sought in the fact that it did not bring about an irreversible condition. That, however, prompts the following question: Under what circumstances would reversibility be a relevant consideration? The answer is only in those cases where the factor that mandated interference in the first place, the severe mental handicap, was not a permanent characteristic of the individual in question. However, instead of telling against sterilisation *per se*, this surely means that sterilisation is unacceptable *in those cases*. It does not mean that in cases where the severe mental handicap is permanent, sterilisation should also be withheld, in the expectation of a miracle, as it were.

Turning to contraception, since it is the least permanent and least intrusive alternative, it appears to be the method of choice. However, those methods of contraception which under the circumstances would be the most appropriate, subcutaneous implants, IUDs, etc., while they are indeed least intrusive in a mechano/physiological sense, emerge as quite intrusive when it is considered that they are biochemically active on the person as a whole. In any case they do have quantifiable risks of morbidity and mortality that exceed those of sterilisation. Their attractiveness on this count, therefore, wanes. As to their lack of permanence and irreversibility, not only do they also have long-term effects in that direction, but relevance of the criterion of reversibility should also be re-examined.

We suggest, therefore, that there are cases in which sterilisation is appropriate. All and only those, namely, where according to all appropriate standards of medical certitude the severe mental handicap is a permanent feature of the individual.

However, a fundamental question remains: Does the state have the right to breach the principle of inviolability and commit trespass to the person in the pursuit of its right and in order to prevent perceived harm to future persons?

There must be a proportion between a right/duty that is claimed and the method used to pursue it. And here the following consideration seems germane. Sterilisation by vasectomy or tubal ligation is currently being used by competent people on a voluntary basis to control their own fertility. Nor is sterilisation deemed ethically inappropriate or indefensible in this context. The method itself, therefore, is ethically acceptable *per se.* The only reason an objection might arise is that in the case of the mentally severely handicapped it would be imposed in a nonconsensual manner. Here, however, we should like to suggest the following as a particularisation of the principle of equality. If a particular method or procedure is unobjectionable when employed by a competent individual on a voluntary basis in order to con-trol a particular activity or bodily function, then the fact that it is employed by a proxy decision-maker for an incompetent individual for reasons that are ethically defensible in their own right does not render it ethically objectionable. If this principle is false, then nothing that a proxy decision-maker decides on the basis of comparison with normal situations will ever be ethically defensible. On the other hand, if, as we have suggested, it is correct, then in many cases sterilisation will be an ethically appropriate way to proceed.

Genetic Diseases: Can Having Children Be Immoral?

L. M. Purdy

I. Introduction

Suppose you know that there is a fifty percent chance you have Huntington's chorea, even though you are still free of symptoms, and that if you do have it, each of your children has a fifty percent chance of having it also. Should you now have children?

There is always some possibility that a pregnancy will result in a diseased or handicapped child. But certain persons run a higher than average risk of producing such a child. Genetic counselors are increasingly able to calculate the probability that certain problems will occur; this means that more people can find out whether they are in danger of creating unhealthy offspring *before* the birth of a child.

Since this kind of knowledge is available, we ought to use it wisely. I want in this paper to defend the thesis that it is wrong to reproduce when we know there is a high risk of transmitting a serious disease or defect. My argument for this claim is in three parts. The first is that we should try to provide every child with a normal opportunity for health; the second is that in the course of doing this it is not wrong to prevent possible children from existing. The third is that this duty may require us to refrain from childbearing.[1]

One methodological point must be made. I am investigating a problem in biomedical ethics: this is a philosophical enterprise. But the conclusion has practical importance since individuals do face the choice I examine. This raises a question: what relation ought the outcome of this inquiry bear to social policy?[2] It may be held that a person's reproductive life should not be interfered with. Perhaps

---

L. M. Purdy, "Genetic Diseases: Can Having Children Be Immoral?" in *Genetics Now: Ethical Issues in Genetic Research,* ed. J. J. Buckley, Jr. (Washington, D.C.: University Press of America, 1978). Reprinted by permission.

this is a reasonable position, but it does not follow from it that it is never wrong for an individual to have children or that we should not try to determine when this is the case. All that does follow is that we may not coerce persons with regard to childbearing. Evaluation of this last claim is a separate issue which cannot be handled here.

I want to deal with this issue concretely. The reason for this is that, otherwise, discussion is apt to be vague and inconclusive. An additional reason is that it will serve to make us appreciate the magnitude of the difficulties faced by diseased or handicapped individuals. Thus it will be helpful to consider a specific disease. For this purpose I have chosen Huntington's chorea.[3]

II. Huntington's Chorea: Course and Risk

Let us now look at Huntington's chorea. First we will consider the course of the disease, then its inheritance pattern.

The symptoms of Huntington's chorea usually begin between the ages of thirty and fifty, but young children can also be affected. It happens this way:

> Onset is insidious. Personality changes (obstinacy, moodiness, lack of initiative) frequently antedate or accompany the involuntary choreic movements. These usually appear first in the face, neck, and arms, and are jerky, irregular, and stretching in character. Contractions of the facial muscles result in grimaces; those of the respiratory muscles, lips, and tongue lead to hesitating, explosive speech. Irregular movements of the trunk are present; the gait is shuffling and dancing. Tendon reflexes are increased. … Some patients display a fatuous euphoria; others are spiteful, irascible, destructive, and violent. Paranoid reactions are common. Poverty of thought and impair-

ment of attention, memory, and judgment occur. As the disease progresses, walking becomes impossible, swallowing difficult, and dementia profound. Suicide is not uncommon.[4]

The illness lasts about fifteen years, terminating in death.

Who gets Huntington's chorea? It is an autosomal dominant disease; this means it is caused by a single mutant gene located on a non-sex chromosome. It is passed from one generation to the next via affected individuals. When one has the disease, whether one has symptoms and thus knows one has it or not, there is a 50% chance that each child will have it also. If one has escaped it then there is no risk to one's children.[5]

How serious is this risk? For geneticists, a ten percent risk is high.[6] But not every high risk is unacceptable: this depends on what is at stake.

There are two separate evaluations in any judgment about a given risk. The first measures the gravity of the worst possible result; the second perceives a given risk as great or small. As for the first, in medicine as elsewhere, people may regard the same result quite differently:

> … The subjective attitude to the disease or lesion itself may be quite at variance with what informed medical opinion may regard as a realistic appraisal. Relatively minor limb defects with cosmetic overtones are examples here. On the other hand, some patients regard with equanimity genetic lesions which are of major medical importance.[7]

For devastating diseases like Huntington's chorea, this part of the judgment should be unproblematic: no one could want a loved one to suffer so.

There may be considerable disagreement, however, about whether a given probability is big or little. Individuals vary a good deal in their attitude toward this aspect of risk.[8] This suggests that it would be difficult to define the "right" attitude to a particular risk in many circumstances. Nevertheless, there are good grounds for arguing in favor of a conservative approach here. For it is reasonable to take special precautions to avoid very bad consequences, even if the risk is small. But the possible consequences here *are* very bad: a child who may inherit Huntington's chorea is a child with a much larger than average chance of being subjected to severe and prolonged suffering. Even if the child does not have the disease, it may anticipate and fear it, and anticipating an evil, as we all know, may be worse than experiencing it. In addition, if a parent loses the gamble, his child will suffer the consequences. But it is one thing to take a high risk for oneself; to submit someone else to it without his consent is another.

I think that these points indicate that the morality of procreation in situations like this demands further study. I propose to do this by looking first at the position of the possible child, then at that of the potential parent.[9]

III. Reproduction: The Possible Child's Position

The first task in treating the problem from the child's point of view is to find a way of referring to possible future offspring without seeming to confer some sort of morally significant existence upon them. I will call children who might be born in the future but who are not now conceived "possible" children, offspring, individuals, or persons. I stipulate that this term implies nothing about their moral standing.

The second task is to decide what claims about children or possible children are relevant to the morality of childbearing in the circumstances being considered. There are, I think, two such claims. One is that we ought to provide every child with at least a normal opportunity for a good life. The other is that we do not harm possible children if we pre-

vent them from existing. Let us consider both these matters in turn.

A. *Opportunity for a Good Life*

Accepting the claim that we ought to try to provide for every child a normal opportunity for a good life involves two basic problems: justification and practical application.

Justification of the claim could be derived fairly straightforwardly from either utilitarian or contractarian theories of justice, I think, although a proper discussion would be too lengthy to include here. Of prime importance in any such discussion would be the judgment that to neglect this duty would be to create unnecessary unhappiness or unfair disadvantage for some persons.

The attempt to apply the claim that we should try to provide a normal opportunity for a good life leads to a couple of difficulties. One is knowing what it requires of us. Another is defining "normal opportunity." Let us tackle the latter problem first.

Conceptions of "normal opportunity" vary among societies and also within them: *de rigueur* in some circles are private music lessons and trips to Europe, while in others providing eight years of schooling is a major sacrifice. But there is no need to consider this complication since we are here concerned only with health as a prerequisite for normal opportunity. Thus we can retreat to the more limited claim that every parent should try to ensure normal health for his child. It might be thought that even this moderate claim is unsatisfactory since in some places debilitating conditions are the norm. One could circumvent this objection by saying that parents ought to try to provide for their children health normal for that culture, even though it may be inadequate if measured by some outside standard. This conservative position would still justify efforts to avoid the birth of children at risk for Huntington's chorea and other serious genetic diseases.

But then what does this stand require of us: is sacrifice entailed by the duty to try to provide normal health for our children? The most plausible answer seems to be that as the danger of serious disability increases, the greater the sacrifice demanded of the potential parent. This means it would be more justifiable to recommend that an individual refrain from childbearing if he risks passing on spina bifida than if he risks passing on webbed feet. Working out all the details of such a schema would clearly be a difficult matter; I do not think it would be impossible to set up workable guidelines, though.

Assuming a rough theoretical framework of this sort, the next question we must ask is whether Huntington's chorea substantially impairs an individual's opportunity for a good life.

People appear to have different opinions about the plight of such persons. Optimists argue that a child born into a family afflicted with Huntington's chorea has a reasonable chance of living a satisfactory life. After all, there is a fifty percent chance it will escape the disease even if a parent has already manifested it, and a still greater chance if this is not so. Even if it does have the illness, it will probably enjoy thirty years of healthy life before symptoms appear; and, perhaps, it may not find the disease destructive. Optimists can list diseased or handicapped persons who have lived fruitful lives. They can also find individuals who seem genuinely glad to be alive. One is Rick Donohue, a sufferer from the Joseph family disease: "You know, if my mom hadn't had me, I wouldn't be here for the life I have had. So there is a good possibility I will have children."[10] Optimists therefore conclude that it would be a shame if these persons had not lived.

Pessimists concede these truths, but they take a less sanguine view of them. They think a fifty percent risk of serious disease like Huntington's chorea appallingly high. They suspect that a child born into an afflicted family is liable to spend its youth in dreadful anticipation and fear of the disease. They expect that the disease, if it appears, will be perceived as a tragic and painful end to a blighted life. They point out that Rick Donohue is still young and has not yet experienced the full horror of his sickness.

Empirical research is clearly needed to resolve this dispute: we need much more information about the psychology and life history of sufferers and potential sufferers. Until we have it we cannot know whether the optimist or the pessimist has a better case; definitive judgment must therefore be suspended. In the meantime, however, common sense suggests that the pessimist has the edge.

If some diseased persons do turn out to have a worse than average life there appears to be a case against further childbearing in afflicted families. To support this claim two more judgments are necessary, however. The first is that it is not wrong to refrain from childbearing. The second is that asking individuals to so refrain is less of a sacrifice than might be thought.[11] I will examine each of these judgments.

B. The Morality of Preventing the Birth of Possible Persons

Before going on to look at reasons why it would not be wrong to prevent the birth of possible persons, let me try to clarify the picture a bit. To understand the claim it must be kept in mind that we are considering a prospective situation here, not a retrospective one: we are trying to rank the desirability of various alternative future states of affairs. One possible future state is this: a world where nobody is at risk for Huntington's chorea except as a result of random mutation. This state has been achieved by sons and daughters of persons afflicted with

1

Huntington's chorea ceasing to reproduce. This means that an indeterminate number of children who might have been born were not born. These possible children can be divided into two categories: those who would have been miserable and those who would have lived good lives. To prevent the existence of members of the first category it was necessary to prevent the existence of all. Whether or not this is a good state of affairs depends on the morality of the means and the end. The end, preventing the existence of miserable beings, is surely good; I will argue that preventing the birth of possible persons is not intrinsically wrong. Hence this state of affairs is a morally good one.

Why then is it not in itself wrong to prevent the birth of possible persons? It is not wrong because there seems to be no reason to believe that possible individuals are either deprived or injured if they do not exist. They are not deprived because to be deprived in a morally significant sense one must be able to have experiences. But possible persons do not exist. Since they do not exist, they cannot have experiences. Another way to make this point is to say that each of us might not have been born, although most of us are glad we were. But this does not mean that it makes sense to say that we would have been deprived of something had we not been born. For if we had not been born, we would not exist, and there would be nobody to be deprived of anything. To assert the contrary is to imagine that we are looking at a world in which we do not exist. But this is not the way it would be: there would be nobody to look.

The contention that it is wrong to prevent possible persons from existing because they have a right to exist appears to be equally baseless. The most fundamental objection to this view is that there is no reason to ascribe rights to entities which do not exist. It is one thing to say that as-yet-nonexistent persons will have certain rights if and when they

exist: this claim is plausible if made with an eye toward preserving social and environmental goods.[12] But what justification could there be for the claim that nonexistent beings have a right to exist?

Even if one conceded that there was a presumption in favor of letting some nonexistent beings exist, stronger claims could surely override it.[13] For one thing, it would be unfair not to recognize the prior claim of already existing children who are not being properly cared for. One might also argue that it is simply wrong to prevent persons who might have existed from doing so. But this implies that contraception and population control are also wrong.

It is therefore reasonable to maintain that because possible persons have no right to exist, they are not injured if not created. Even if they had that right, it could rather easily be overridden by counterclaims. Hence, since possible persons are neither deprived nor injured if not conceived, it is not wrong to prevent their existence.

C. Conclusion of Part III

At the beginning of Part III I said that two claims are relevant to the morality of childbearing in the circumstances being considered. The first is that we ought to provide every child with at least a normal opportunity for a good life. The second is that we do not deprive or injure possible persons if we prevent their existence.

I suggested that the first claim could be derived from currently accepted theories of justice: a healthy body is generally necessary for happiness and it is also a prerequisite for a fair chance at a good life in our competitive world. Thus it is right to try to ensure that each child is healthy.

I argued, with regard to the second claim, that we do not deprive or injure possible persons if we fail to create them. They cannot be deprived of anything because they do not exist and hence cannot have experiences. They cannot be injured because only an entity with a right to exist could be injured if prevented from existing; but there are no good grounds for believing that they are such entities.

From the conjunction of these two claims I conclude that it is right to try to ensure that a child is healthy even if by doing so we preclude the existence of certain possible persons. Thus it is right for individuals to prevent the birth of children at risk for Huntington's chorea by avoiding parenthood. The next question is whether it is seriously wrong *not* to avoid parenthood.

IV. Reproduction: The Potential Parent's Situation

I have so far argued that if choreics live substantially worse lives than average, then it is right for afflicted families to cease reproduction. But this conflicts with the generally recognized freedom to procreate and so it does not automatically follow that family members ought not to have children. How can we decide whether the duty to try to provide normal health for one's child should take precedence over the right to reproduce?

This is essentially the same question I asked earlier: how much must one sacrifice to try to ensure that one's offspring is healthy? In answer to this I suggested that the greater the danger of serious disability, the more justifiable considerable sacrifice is.

Now asking someone who wants a child to refrain from procreation seems to be asking for a large sacrifice. It may, in fact, appear to be too large to demand of anyone. Yet I think it can be shown that it is not as great as it initially seems.

Why do people want children? There are probably many reasons, but I suspect that the following include some of the most common. One set of reasons has to do

with the gratification to be derived from a happy family life — love, companionship, watching a child grow, helping mold it into a good person, sharing its pains and triumphs. Another set of reasons centers about the parents as individuals — validation of their place within a genetically continuous family line, the conception of children as a source of immortality, being surrounded by replicas of themselves.

Are there alternative ways of satisfying these desires? Adoption or technological means provide ways to satisfy most of the desires pertaining to family life without passing on specific genetic defects. Artificial insemination by donor is already available; implantation of donor ova is likely within a few years. Still another option will exist if cloning becomes a reality. In the meantime, we might permit women to conceive and bear babies for those who do not want to do so themselves.[14] But the desire to extend the genetic line, the desire for immortality, and the desire for children that physically resemble one cannot be met by these methods.

Many individuals probably feel these latter desires strongly. This creates a genuine conflict for persons at risk for transmitting serious genetic diseases like Huntington's chorea. The situation seems especially unfair because, unlike normal people, through no fault of their own, doing something they badly want to do may greatly harm others.

But if my common sense assumption that they are in grave danger of harming others is true, then it is imperative to scrutinize their options carefully. On the one hand, they can have children: they satisfy their desires but risk eventual crippling illness and death for their offspring. On the other, they can remain childless or seek nonstandard ways of creating a family: they have some unfulfilled desires, but they avoid risking harm to their children.

I think it is clear which of these two alternatives is best. For the desires which must remain unsatisfied if they forgo normal procreation are less than admirable. To see the genetic line continued entails a sinister legacy of illness and death; the desire for immortality cannot really be satisfied by reproduction anyway; and the desire for children that physically resemble one is narcissistic and its fulfillment cannot be guaranteed even by normal reproduction. Hence the only defence of these desires is that people do in fact feel them.

Now, I am inclined to accept William James' dictum regarding desires: "Take any demand, however slight, which any creature, however weak, may make. Ought it not, for its own sole sake be satisfied? If not, prove why not."[15] Thus I judge a world where more desires are satisfied to be better than one in which fewer are. But not all desires should be regarded as legitimate, since, as James suggests, there may be good reasons why these ought to be disregarded. The fact that their fulfillment will seriously harm others is surely such a reason. And I believe that the circumstances I have described are a clear example of the sort of case where a desire must be judged illegitimate, at least until it can be shown that sufferers from serious genetic diseases like Huntington's chorea do not live considerably worse than average lives. Therefore, I think it is wrong for individuals in this predicament to reproduce.

V. Conclusion

Let me recapitulate. At the beginning of this paper I asked whether it is wrong for those who risk transmitting severe genetic disease like Huntington's chorea to have "blood" children. Some despair of reaching an answer to this question.[16]

But I think such pessimism is not wholly warranted, and that if generally accepted would lead to much unnecessary harm. It is true that in many cases it is difficult to know what ought to be done. But this does not mean that we should throw up our hands and espouse a completely laissez-faire approach: philosophers can help by probing the central issues and trying to find guidelines for action.

Naturally there is no way to derive an answer to this kind of problem by deductive argument from self-evident premises, for it must depend on a complicated interplay of facts and moral judgments. My preliminary exploration of Huntington's chorea is of this nature. In the course of the discussion I suggested that, if it is true that sufferers live substantially worse lives than do normal persons, those who might transmit it should not have children. This conclusion is supported by the judgments that we ought to try to provide for every child a normal opportunity for a good life, that possible individuals are not harmed if not conceived, and that it is sometimes less justifiable for persons to exercise their right to procreate than one might think.

I want to stress, in conclusion, that my argument is incomplete. To investigate fully even a single disease, like Huntington's chorea, empirical research on the lives of members of afflicted families is necessary. Then, after developing further the themes touched upon here, evaluation of the probable consequences of different policies on society and on future generations is needed. Until the results of a complete study are available, my argument could serve best as a reason for persons at risk for transmitting Huntington's chorea and similar diseases to put off having children. Perhaps this paper will stimulate such inquiry.

Notes

1. There are a series of cases ranging from low risk of mild disease or handicap to high risk of serious disease or handicap. It would be difficult to decide where the

duty to refrain from procreation becomes compelling. My point here is that there are some clear cases.

I'd like to thank Lawrence Davis and Sidney Siskin for their helpful comments on an earlier version of this paper.

2. This issue is one which must be faced most urgently by genetic counselors. The proper role of the genetic counselor with regard to such decisions has been the subject of much debate. The dominant view seems to be that espoused by Lytt Gardner who maintains that it is unethical for a counselor to make ethical judgments about what his clients ought to do. ("Counseling in Genetics," *Early Diagnosis of Human Genetic Defects: Scientific & Ethical Considerations*, ed. Maureen Harris [H.E.W. Publication No. (NIH) 72–25; Fogarty Center Proceedings No. 6]; 192.) Typically this view is unsupported by an argument. For other views see Bentley Glass "Human Heredity and Ethical Problems," *Perspectives in Biology & Medicine*, Vol. 15 (winter '72) 237–53, esp. 242–52; Marc Lappé, "The Genetic Counselor Responsible to Whom?" *Hastings Center Report*, Vol. 1, No. 2 (Sept. '71) 6–8; E. C. Fraser, "Genetic Counseling" *Am. J. of Human Genetics* 26: 636–659, 1974.

3. I have chosen Huntington's chorea because it seems to me to be one of the clearest cases of high risk serious genetic disease known to the public, despite the fact that it does not usually manifest itself until the prime of life. The latter entails two further facts. First an individual of reproductive age may not know whether he has the disease; he therefore does not know the risk of passing on the disease. Secondly, an affected person may have a substantial number of years of healthy life before it shows itself. I do not think that this factor materially changes my case, however. Even if an individual does not in fact risk passing the disease to his children, *he cannot know that this is true*. And even thirty years of healthy life may well be seriously shadowed by anticipation and fear of the disease. Thus the fact that the disease develops late does not diminish its horror. If it could be shown that these factors could be adequately circumvented, my claim that there is a *class* of genetic disease of such severity that it would be wrong to risk passing them on would not be undermined.

It might also be thought that Huntington's chorea is insufficiently common to merit such attention. But, depending on reproductive patterns, the disease could become a good deal more widespread. Consider the fact that in 1916 nine hundred and sixty-two cases could be traced from six seventeenth-century arrivals in America. (Gordon Rattray Taylor, *The Biological Time Bomb* [New York, 1968], 176). But more importantly, even if the disease did not spread, it would still be seriously wrong, I think, to inflict it unnecessarily on *any* members of new generations. Finally, it should be kept in mind that I am using Huntington's chorea as an example of the sort of disease we should try to eradicate. Thus the arguments presented here would be relevant to a wide range of genetic diseases.

4. *The Merck Manual* (Rahway, N.J.: Merck, 1972), 1346.

5. Hymie Gordon, "Genetic Counseling," *JAMA*, Vol. 217, No. 9 (August 30, 1971), 1217.

6. Charles Smith, Susan Holloway, and Alan E. H. Emery, "Individuals at Risk in Families — Genetic Disease," *J. of Medical Genetics*, 8 (1971), 453. See also Townes in *Genetic Counseling*, ed. Daniel Bergsma, *Birth Defects Original Article Series*, Vol. VI, No. 1 (May 1970).

7. J. H. Pearn, "Patients' Subjective Interpretation of Risks Offered in Genetic Counseling," *Journal of Medical Genetics*, 10 (1973) 131.

8. Ibid., 132.

9. There are many important and interesting points that might be raised with respect to future generations and present society. There is no space to deal with them here, although I strongly suspect that conclusions regarding them would support my judgment that it is wrong for those who risk transmitting certain diseases to reproduce — for some discussion of future generations, see Gerald Leach, *The Biocrats* (Middlesex, England: Penguin Books, 1972), 150; M. P. Golding, "Obligations to Future Generations," *Monist* 56 (Jan. 1972) 84–99; Gordon Rattray Taylor, *The Biological Time Bomb* (New York, 1968), esp. 176. For some discussions of society, see Daniel Callahan, "The Meaning and Significance of Genetic Disease: Philosophical Perspectives," *Ethical Issues in Human Genetics,* ed. Bruce Hilton et al. (New York, 1973), 87 ff.; John Fletcher, "The Brink: The Parent–Child Bond in the Genetic Revolution," *Theological Studies* 33 (Sept. '72) 457–485; Glass (supra 2ᵃ); Marc Lappé, "Human Genetics," Annals of the *New York Academy of Sciences*, Vol. 26 (May 18, 1973), 152–59; Marc Lappé, "Moral Obligations and the Fallacies of 'Genetic Control,'" *Theological Studies* Vol. 33, No. 3 (Sept. '72) 411–427; Martin P. Golding, "Ethical Issues in Biological Engineering," *UCLA Law Review* Vol. 15: 267 (1968), 443–479; L. C. Dunn, *Heredity and Evolution in Human Populations* (Cambridge, Mass., 1959), 145; Robert S. Morison in *Ethical Issues in Human Genetics*, ed. Bruce Hilton et. al. (New York, 1973), 208.

10. *The New York Times,* September 30, 1975, p. 1, col. 6. The Joseph family disease is similar to Huntington's chorea except that symptoms start appearing in the twenties. Rick Donohue is in his early twenties.

11. There may be a price for the individuals who refrain from having children. We will be looking at the situation from their point of view shortly.

12. This is in fact the basis for certain parental duties. An example is the maternal duty to obtain proper nutrition before and during pregnancy, for this is necessary if the child is to have normal health when it is born.

13. One might argue that as many persons as possible should exist so that they may enjoy life.

14. Some thinkers have qualms about the use of some or all of these methods. They have so far failed to show why they are immoral, although, naturally, much careful study will be required before they could be unqualifiedly recommended. See, for example, Richard Hull, "Genetic Engineering: Comment on Headings," *The Humanist*, Vol. 32 (Sept./Oct. 1972), 13.

15. *Essays in Pragmatism,* ed. A. Castell (New York, 1948), 73.

16. For example, see Leach, 138. One of the ways the dilemma described by Leach could be lessened would be if society emphasized those aspects of family life not dependent on "blood" relationships and downplayed those that are.

Further Readings

Alberta Institute of Law Research and Reform. *Report for Discussion No. 6,* "Sterilization Decisions: Minors and Mentally Incompetent Adults." Edmonton, AB, 1988.

Alberta Institute of Law Research and Reform. *Report No. 52,* "Competence and Human Reproduction." Edmonton, AB, 1989.

Arras, J.D. "HIV and Childbearing," *Milbank Memorial Quarterly* 68:3 (1990): 353–382.

Bayles, Michael D. *Reproductive Ethics.* Englewood Cliffs, N.J.: Prentice Hall, 1984.

Chambers, D. "The Right to the Least Restrictive Alternative," in M. Kindred et al., eds. *The Mentally Retarded Citizen and the Law.* New York: Free Press, 1976.

Finch-Noyes, C.A.P. "Sterilization of the Mentally Retarded Minor: The Re K. Case." *Can J of Fam Law* 5:1 (1986): 277–99.

Great Britain, Department of Health and Social Services. *Report of the Committee of Enquiry into Human Sterilization and Embryology*, ed. by M. Warnock. London: HM Stationer's Office, 1984 (The Warnock Report).

Grubb, A., and D. Pearl. "Sterilization and the Courts." *Cambridge Law J* 46:3 (1987): 439–64.

Law Reform Commission of Canada. *Working Paper 24, Sterilization: Implications for Mentally Retarded and Mentally Ill Persons.* Ottawa: Minister of Supply and Services, 1978.

McLaren, Angus. "The Creation of a Haven for 'Human Thoroughbreds': Sterilization of the Feebleminded and the Mentally Ill in British Columbia." *Can Hist Review* 67:2 (1986): 127–50.

McLean, S. "The Right to Reproduce," in T. Campbell et al., eds., *Human Rights: From Rhetoric to Reality.* New York: Basil Blackwell, 1986.

Ryan, M.A. "The Argument for Unlimited Reproductive Liberty: A Feminist Critique." *Hastings Center Rep* 20:4 (1990): 6–12.

Stefan, S. "Whose Right Is It Anyway? Reproductive Rights of Incarcerated, Institutionalized and Incompetent Women." *Nova Law Review* 13:2 (1989): 405–456.

CHAPTER 16
THE NEW REPRODUCTIVE TECHNOLOGIES

Introduction

The last few decades have seen an exponential development in the new reproductive technologies. *In vitro* fertilization has moved from the field of animal husbandry into the medical clinic; genetic screening can determine the genetic makeup of a child still *in utero* and detect such deleterious traits as cystic fibrosis, the various trisomies, haemophilia and a whole host of other conditions; prenatal testing can detect the presence of spina bifida and other congenital defects; genetic engineering is starting to be used to modify the human genome for therapeutic purposes — even an artificial uterus is under development, and human cloning is just over the horizon. The list goes on. None of these developments is ethically neutral, and all of them have more or less important implications for the affected individuals as well as for society and humanity at large.

The selections in this chapter deal with the new reproductive technologies from the perspective of public policy and regulation. The chapter begins with an excerpt from Bill C-13, the *Assisted Human Reproduction Act* that was passed by the House of Commons in 2003.[1] It criminalizes some activities outright and controls certain others. It would therefore define the legal environment for any development and use of the new reproductive technologies.

The next selection, the CIHR Guidelines for Human Pluripotent Stem Cell Research, is included because the guidelines regulate the public funding of Canadian stem cell research — one of the "hottest" areas of research. This research uses cells that are derived from blastocysts (embryos at an early stage of development). Blastocysts contain pluripotent cells — so-called stem cells — that can develop into any kind of cell: liver cells, kidney cells, heart cells, etc., even neurons. These blastocysts are standardly derived in either of two ways: (1) They may be "left over" from IVF because it is standard practice to harvest and fertilize more ova than will be implanted. This is done because it is unclear how many will develop into implantable blastocysts (the attrition rate exceeds 50%) and it is also uncertain how many blastocysts will be healthy enough to warrant implantation. (2) The blastocysts may be specially produced by deliberately combining gametes that have been donated for research purposes. The stem cells that can be harvested from these blastocysts could be transplanted into people who suffer from degenerative diseases like diabetes, heart disease or Parkinson's disease, or they could be used to develop all sorts of other potentially life-saving therapies. The CIHR Guidelines regulate this research in the public sector from the perspective of research ethics, going beyond what is contained in the *Assisted Human Reproduction Act*. They are based in part on the Tri-Council guidelines for research on human subjects.[2] Since much of Canadian research is done through public–private partnerships in universities, the Guidelines effectively regulate private research as well — especially since no reputable academically based journal will publish research results that do not meet Tri-Council and CIHR ethics standards.

The following selection, *Donum vitae*, presents the Roman Catholic Church's official position on the development and use of the new reproductive technologies. *Donum vitae* is firmly rooted in religiously based ethical principles and the Catholic Church's perception of natural law. As such, it has no legal standing. However, more than a million Canadians and almost a billion people worldwide are guided by this declaration, and the view it presents exerts a tremendous influence on the attitudes and actions even of people who do not share that faith. It therefore functions as an important regulatory statement for a significant number of people, and for that reason alone deserves careful consideration.

The final selection in this chapter addresses a general policy issue that concerns all reproductive technologies. If the reproductive technologies can be characterized as a species of health care, and if everyone has the right to health care, is there a right to this technology? Christine Overall raises this question specifically in the context of IVF; however, with due alteration of detail, her remarks can be applied to all other reproductive modalities. It might be interesting to contrast Overall's views with those expressed by the Congregation for the Doctrine of the Faith.

Notes

1. The *Assisted Human Reproduction Act* has had several incarnations. Originally introduced in 1996 as Bill C-47 (*Human Reproductive and Genetic Technologies Act*), it was reintroduced in 2002 as Bill C-56 (*An Act Respecting Assisted Human Reproduction*) and was finally passed in the House of Commons in 2003 as Bill C-13 (*Assisted Human Reproduction Act*). At the time of publication, it was before the Senate as Bill C-6. It can be accessed at: **http://www.parl.gc.ca/PDF/37/3/ parlbus/chambus/house/bills/government/C-6_3.pdf**

2. The Tri-Council has representation from the Humanities Research Council of Canada, the Medical Research Council of Canada, and the National Sciences and Engineering Research Council of Canada. The Tri-Council's Policy Statement, *Ethical Conduct for Research Involving Humans,* may be accessed at **http://www.pre.ethics.gc.ca/english/policystatement/policystatement.cfm** See also pages 244–252 of this text (Chapter 10).

Excerpts from Bill C-13: An Act Respecting Assisted Human Reproduction

House of Commons, October 28, 2003

1. This Act may be cited as the *Assisted Human Reproduction Act.*

2. The Parliament of Canada recognizes and declares that

(*a*) the health and well-being of children born through the application of assisted human reproductive technologies must be given priority in all decisions respecting their use;

(*b*) the benefits of assisted human reproductive technologies and related research for individuals, for families and for society in general can be most effectively secured by taking appropriate measures for the protection and promotion of human health, safety, dignity and rights in the use of these technologies and in related research;

(*c*) while all persons are affected by these technologies, women more than men are directly and significantly affected by their application and the health and well-being of women must be protected in the application of these technologies;

(*d*) the principle of free and informed consent must be promoted and applied as a fundamental condition of the use of human reproductive technologies;

(*e*) persons who seek to undergo assisted reproduction procedures must not be discriminated against, including on the basis of their sexual orientation or marital status;

(*f*) trade in the reproductive capabilities of women and men and the exploitation of children, women and men for commercial ends raise health and ethical concerns that justify their prohibition; and

(*g*) human individuality and diversity, and the integrity of the human genome, must be preserved and protected.

3. The following definitions apply in this Act.

"Agency" means the Assisted Human Reproduction Agency of Canada established by subsection 21(1).

"assisted reproduction procedure" means any controlled activity referred to in section 10 that is performed for the purpose of creating a human being.

"chimera" means

(*a*) an embryo into which a cell of any non-human life form has been introduced; or

(*b*) an embryo that consists of cells of more than one embryo, foetus or human being.

"consent" means fully informed and freely given consent that is given in accordance with the applicable law governing consent and that conforms to the provisions of the *Human Pluripotent Stem Cell Research Guidelines* released by the Canadian Institutes of Health Research in March, 2002, as detailed in the Regulations.

"controlled activity" means an activity that may not be undertaken except in accordance with sections 10 to 12.

"donor" means

(*a*) in relation to human reproductive material, the individual from whose body it was obtained, whether for consideration or not; and

(*b*) in relation to an *in vitro* embryo, a donor as defined in the regulations.

"embryo" means a human organism during the first 56 days of its development following fertilization or creation, excluding any time during which its development has been suspended, and includes any cell derived from such an organism that is used for the purpose of creating a human being.

"foetus" means a human organism during the period of its development beginning on the fifty-seventh day following fertilization or creation, excluding any time during which its development has been suspended, and ending at birth.

"gene" includes a nucleotide sequence, and an artificially created gene or nucleotide sequence.

"genome" means the totality of the deoxyribonucleic acid sequence of a particular cell.

"health reporting information" means information provided under this Act respecting

(a) the identity, personal characteristics, genetic information and medical history of donors of human reproductive material and *in vitro* embryos, persons who have undergone assisted reproduction procedures and persons who were conceived by means of those procedures; and

(b) the custody of donated human reproductive materials and *in vitro* embryos and the uses that are made of them.

"human clone" means an embryo that, as a result of the manipulation of human reproductive material or an *in vitro* embryo, contains a diploid set of chromosomes obtained from a single — living or deceased — human being, foetus or embryo.

"human reproductive material" means a sperm, ovum or other human cell or a human gene, and includes a part of any of them.

"hybrid" means

(a) a human ovum that has been fertilized by a sperm of a non-human life form;

(b) an ovum of a non-human life form that has been fertilized by a human sperm;

(c) a human ovum into which the nucleus of a cell of a non-human life form has been introduced;

(d) an ovum of a non-human life form into which the nucleus of a human cell has been introduced; or

(e) a human ovum or an ovum of a non-human life form that otherwise contains haploid sets of chromosomes from both a human being and a non-human life form.

"*in vitro* embryo" means an embryo that exists outside the body of a human being.

"licence" means a licence issued in respect of a controlled activity or premises under section 40.

"Minister" means the Minister of Health.

"ovum" means a human ovum, whether mature or not.

"sperm" means a human sperm, whether mature or not.

"surrogate mother" means a female person who — with the intention of surrendering the child at birth to a donor or another person — carries an embryo or foetus that was conceived by means of an assisted reproduction procedure and derived from the genes of a donor or donors.

...

5. (1) No person shall knowingly,

(a) create a human clone by using any technique, or transplant a human clone into a human being or into any non-human life form or artificial device;

(b) create an *in vitro* embryo for any purpose other than creating a human being or improving or providing instruction in assisted reproduction procedures;

(c) for the purpose of creating a human being, create an embryo from a cell or part of a cell taken from an embryo or foetus or transplant an embryo so created into a human being;

(d) maintain an embryo outside the body of a female person after the fourteenth day of its development following fertilization or creation, excluding any time during which its development has been suspended;

(*e*) for the purpose of creating a human being, perform any procedure or provide, prescribe or administer any thing that would ensure or increase the probability that an embryo will be of a particular sex, or that would identify the sex of an *in vitro* embryo, except to prevent, diagnose or treat a sex-linked disorder or disease;

(*f*) alter the genome of a cell of a human being or *in vitro* embryo such that the alteration is capable of being transmitted to descendants;

(*g*) transplant a sperm, ovum, embryo or foetus of a non-human life form into a human being;

(*h*) for the purpose of creating a human being, make use of any human reproductive material or an *in vitro* embryo that is or was transplanted into a non-human life form;

(*i*) create a chimera, or transplant a chimera into either a human being or a non-human life form; or,

(*j*) create a hybrid for the purpose of reproduction, or transplant a hybrid into either a human being or a non-human life form.

(2) No person shall offer to do, or advertise the doing of, anything prohibited by this section.

(3) No person shall pay or offer to pay consideration to any person for doing anything prohibited by this section.

6. (1) No person shall pay consideration to a female person to be a surrogate mother, offer to pay such consideration or advertise that it will be paid.

(2) No person shall accept consideration for arranging for the services of a surrogate mother, offer to make such an arrangement for consideration or advertise the arranging of such services.

(3) No person shall pay consideration to another person to arrange for the services of a surrogate mother, offer to pay such consideration or advertise the payment of it.

(4) No person shall counsel or induce a female person to become a surrogate

mother, or perform any medical procedure to assist a female person to become a surrogate mother, knowing or having reason to believe that the female person is under 21 years of age.

(5) This section does not affect the validity under provincial law of any agreement under which a person agrees to be a surrogate mother.

7. (1) No person shall purchase, offer to purchase or advertise for the purchase of sperm or ova from a donor or a person acting on behalf of a donor.

(2) No person shall

(*a*) purchase, offer to purchase or advertise for the purchase of an *in vitro* embryo; or,

(*b*) sell, offer for sale or advertise for sale an *in vitro* embryo.

(3) No person shall purchase, offer to purchase or advertise for the purchase of a human cell or gene from a donor or a person acting on behalf of a donor, with the intention of using the gene or cell to create a human being or of making it available for that purpose.

(4) In this section, "purchase" or "sell" includes to acquire or dispose of in exchange for property or services.

8. (1) No person shall make use of human reproductive material for the purpose of creating an embryo unless the donor of the material has given written consent, in accordance with the regulations, to its use for that purpose.

(2) No person shall remove human reproductive material from a donor's body after the donor's death for the purpose of creating an embryo unless the donor of the material has given written consent, in accordance with the regulations, to its removal for that purpose.

(3) No person shall make use of an *in vitro* embryo for any purpose unless the donor has given written consent, in accordance with the regulations, to its use for that purpose.

9. No person shall obtain any sperm or ovum from a donor under 18 years of age, or use any sperm or ovum so obtained, except for the purpose of preserving the sperm or ovum or for the purpose of creating a human being that the person reasonably believes will be raised by the donor.

10. (1) No person shall, except in accordance with the regulations and a licence, alter, manipulate or treat any human reproductive material for the purpose of creating an embryo.

(2) No person shall, except in accordance with the regulations and a licence, alter, manipulate, treat or make any use of an *in vitro* embryo.

(3) No person shall, except in accordance with the regulations and a licence, obtain, store, transfer, destroy, import or export

(*a*) a sperm or ovum, or any part of one, for the purpose of creating an embryo; or

(*b*) an *in vitro* embryo, for any purpose.

11. (1) No person shall, except in accordance with the regulations and a licence, combine any part or any proportion of the human genome specified in the regulations with any part of the genome of a species specified in the regulations.

(2) The following definitions apply in this section.

"human genome" means the totality of the deoxyribonucleic acid sequence of the human species.

"species" means any taxonomic classification of non-human life.

12. (1) No person shall, except in accordance with the regulations and a licence,

(*a*) reimburse a donor for an expenditure incurred in the course of donating sperm or an ovum;

(*b*) reimburse any person for an expenditure incurred in the maintenance or transport of an *in vitro* embryo; or

(*c*) reimburse a surrogate mother for an expenditure incurred by her in relation to her surrogacy.

(2) No person shall reimburse an expenditure referred to in subsection (1) unless a receipt is provided to that person for the expenditure.

(3) No person shall reimburse a surrogate mother for a loss of work-related income incurred during her pregnancy, unless

(*a*) a qualified medical practitioner certifies, in writing, that continuing to work may pose a risk to her health or that of the embryo or foetus; and

(*b*) the reimbursement is made in accordance with the regulations and a licence.

13. No person who is licensed to undertake a controlled activity shall undertake it in any premises except in accordance with a licence permitting the use of the premises for that controlled activity.

Human Pluripotent Stem Cell Research: Guidelines for CIHR-Funded Research

The guidelines contained in this document set out the conditions under which the Canadian Institutes of Health Research (CIHR) will fund human pluripotent stem

Source: Human Pluripotent Stem Cell Research Guidelines for CIHR-Funded Research, clauses 3.0, 4, 5, 7-8. http://www.cihr-irsc.gc.ca/e/publications/1487.shtml, Canadian Institutes of Health Research, updated: 2003/04/09. Reproduced with the permission of the Minister of Public Works and Government Services Canada, 2004.

cell research, as well as those types of research that are not eligible for funding.

...

3.0 Guiding principles

The guidelines are based on the provisions of the *Tri-Council Policy Statement: Ethical Conduct for Research Involving Humans (TCPS)*. Therefore, the guidelines are based on several guiding principles, such as:

- Research undertaken should have potential health benefits for Canadians;
- Free and informed consent, provided voluntarily and with full disclosure of all information relevant to the consent;
- Respect for privacy and confidentiality; **and**
- No direct or indirect payment for tissues collected for stem cell research and no financial incentives.

4.0 Oversight of human pluripotent stem cell research

Because of the complex ethical issues and public concern in this area, a Stem Cell Oversight Committee will be created to conduct an ethical review of all human pluripotent stem cell research proposals approved by CIHR's scientific peer review panels. All research proposals will require approval from this Committee, as well as from the local Research Ethics Board (REB), and, where appropriate, the Animal Care Committee (ACC), before being funded. Its members will include experts in stem cell biology and therapeutics, medicine and health care, ethics, law, and social sciences, as well as representatives of the general public. ...

5.0 Creating a national registry

CIHR will establish an electronically accessible national registry of human embryonic stem cell lines generated in Canada. This registry will minimize the need to generate large numbers of cell lines, which should decrease the need for donation of large numbers of embryos.

All human embryonic stem cell lines generated using CIHR funds will be listed with the registry and made available by the researcher to other Canadian academic researchers, subject to reasonable cost-recovery charges. Participation in this registry will be a prerequisite for obtaining CIHR funding for human pluripotent stem cell research.

...

7.0 Guidelines for CIHR Funding of Human Pluripotent Stem Cell Research in Canada

7.1 Research eligible for CIHR funding

The following types of research are eligible for CIHR funding:

7.1.1
Research to derive and study human embryonic stem cell (ES) lines or other cell lines of a pluripotent nature from human embryos, provided that:

1. The embryos used were originally created for reproductive purposes and are no longer required for such purposes; **and**

2. There is free and informed consent from all the persons for whom the embryos were originally created for

reproductive purposes. Additionally, where "donor" gametes have been used to create the embryos, the gamete providers must have originally given free and informed consent to the unrestricted research use of any embryos created when these embryos were no longer required for reproductive purposes; **and**

3. Neither the ova nor the sperm from which the embryos were created, nor the embryos themselves, were obtained through commercial transactions, including exchange for service.

7.1.2

Research to derive and study human embryonic germ cell (EG) lines, or other cell lines of a pluripotent nature from human fetal tissue or amniotic fluid, provided that:

1. The proposed research does not compromise the pregnant woman's decision on whether to continue her pregnancy, **and**

2. There is free and informed consent from the pregnant woman.

7.1.3

Research to derive and study human stem cell lines of a pluripotent nature from the umbilical cord and placenta, provided that:

1. There is free and informed consent from the mother, or from both parents of the newborn if there are two people committed to parenting. If there is disagreement between the parents, the umbilical cord and placenta cannot be used for research.

7.1.4

Research to derive and study human stem cell lines of a pluripotent nature from human somatic tissues, provided that:

1. When the tissue is from a legally competent person, there is free and informed consent from the prospective research participant; **or**

2. When the tissue is from a legally incompetent person,

    1. the tissue has been obtained from a surgical, diagnostic or other legitimate practice not including research, **and**

    2. an appropriate legally competent third party has authorized its availability for research, **and**

    3. the donation is in accordance with applicable consent law in the province where the donation takes place; **or**

3. When the tissue is from a cadaver, there is a legally appropriate advance directive that appropriately specifies the use of tissue for stem cell research, or there is authorization from an appropriate legally competent third party.

7.1.5

Research on anonymized human embryonic stem cell lines, embryonic germ cell lines or other cell lines of a pluripotent nature that have been created in Canada, or created elsewhere and imported for research purposes, provided that:

1. They were created in accordance with CIHR's guidelines. It is incumbent on the recipient of the cell lines to ensure that they were derived in a manner consistent with the CIHR's guidelines. The recipient must provide satisfactory evidence to the local REB and the Stem Cell Oversight Committee that the cell lines fulfill the informed consent provisions before research can begin.

7.1.6

Research involving the grafting of human ES cells, EG cells or other human cells of a pluripotent nature into non-human adults, provided that:

1. The research is designed to reconstitute a specific tissue or organ to derive a pre-clinical model, **and**

2. There is evidence from prior studies in non-human species that the cells are not likely to contribute to gametes, **and**

3. These non-human animals grafted with human stem cells will not be used for reproductive purposes.

7.1.7

Research involving the grafting of human stem cells or other human cells of a pluripotent nature into legally competent humans, provided that:

1. There is overwhelming evidence from pre-clinical models for safety and efficacy, **and**

2. The research is carried out in well-designed clinical trials, **and**

3. There is free and informed consent from the prospective research participants.

7.2 Consent, privacy and confidentiality provisions

7.2.1

Embryos no longer wanted for reproductive purposes may be donated to another couple, used for research (including research to derive and study human ES cells), or discarded. These options should be discussed with the gamete providers (and the embryo providers if these are different individuals), and a decision regarding the eventual disposition of unwanted embryos should be made prior to the collection of gametes and the creation of embryos for reproductive purposes.

7.2.2

At the time when the embryos are to be used for research to derive and study ES cells (and other human cells or cell lines of a pluripotent nature), consent of the embryo providers must be reiterated. This requirement affirms the right to withdraw and is necessary because of the possible lengthy delay between the time at which the original consent is given and the time at which the embryos are utilized for research purposes. A renewal of the consent provided by the gamete providers (if the gamete providers are not the same individuals as the embryo providers), is not required provided that appropriate consent for the unrestricted research use of the embryos was given at the time of gamete donation.

7.2.3

For the purpose of obtaining free and informed consent to human stem cell research, at a minimum, researchers shall provide prospective research participants or legally competent third parties, in addition to the usual information given:

1. An explanation that the cell line(s) will be anonymized, except if the research involves autologous donation;

2. An assurance that prospective research participants are free not to participate and have the right to withdraw at any time before an anonymized cell line is created;

3. An explanation that the research could result in the production of a cell line that could be maintained for many years and used for different research purposes;

4. An explanation that the research participants will not benefit directly financially from any future commercialization of cell lines; nor will there be any personal benefit in terms of dispositional authority over any cell lines created (i.e., there will be no directed donation of the cells or cell lines to particular individuals), except if the research involves autologous donation.

7.2.4

Researchers must not pressure members of the fertility treatment team to generate more embryos than necessary for the optimum chance of reproductive success; this is tantamount to creating embryos for research.

7.2.5

All human stem cell lines, other human cells or cell lines of a pluripotent nature from human embryos, fetuses or adults, must be anonymized (i.e. no personal identifiers), except if the research involves autologous donation.

7.2.6

All researchers who make stem cell lines available to other academics will ensure that the cell lines are anonymized.

7.2.7

Physicians responsible for fertility treatment and physicians responsible for termination of pregnancy will not be part of a stem cell research team.

7.3 Commercial interest

7.3.1

Researchers or their institutions with financial interests in the outcome of the stem cell research must disclose this information to the Stem Cell Oversight Committee, the REB and the prospective research participants. In some instances, disclosure may not be a sufficient response to concerns about actual, perceived or potential conflicts of interest.

7.3.2

Copies of contracts between researchers, institutions and industry sponsors and any relevant budgetary information must be provided to the Stem Cell Oversight Committee and the local REB, to examine and evaluate any potential or actual conflict of interest and to ensure the right to publish freely after a modest interval.

7.4 Research ineligible for CIHR funding

The following types of research are not eligible for CIHR funding:

7.4.1

Research involving the creation of human embryos specifically to derive stem cell lines or other cell lines of a pluripotent nature.

7.4.2

Research involving somatic cell nuclear transfer into human oocytes for the purposes of developing human embryonic stem cell lines or other cell lines of a pluripotent nature (e.g., cloning).

7.4.3

Research involving the directed donation of stem cell lines, or other human cells or cell lines of a pluripotent nature to particular individuals, unless the research involves autologous donation.

7.4.4

Research in which human or non-human ES cells, EG cells or other cells of a pluripotent nature are combined with a human embryo.

7.4.5

Research in which human or non-human ES cells, EG cells or other cells of a pluripotent nature are grafted to a human fetus.

7.4.6

Research in which human ES cells, EG cells or other cells of a pluripotent nature are combined with a non-human embryo.

7.4.7

Research in which human ES cells, EG cells or other cells of a pluripotent nature are grafted to a non-human fetus.

8.0 Review

CIHR will review the field of human stem cell research on an ongoing basis to redraft the relevant guidelines as needed and, when appropriate, to broaden or narrow the scope of permitted research. This review process will also examine the need for national research ethics review and, when appropriate, amend it.

Respect for Human Life (*Donum Vitae*)

Congregation for the Doctrine of the Faith

Introduction

1. Biomedical Research and the Teaching of the Church

... Thanks to the progress of the biological and medical sciences, man has at his disposal ever more effective therapeutic resources; but he can also acquire new powers, with unforeseeable consequences, over human life at its very beginning and in its first stages. Various procedures now make it possible to intervene not only in order to assist but also to dominate the processes of procreation. These techniques can enable man to "take in hand his own destiny," but they also expose him "to the temptation to go beyond the limits of a reasonable dominion over nature."[1] They might constitute progress in the service of man, but they also involve serious risks. Many people are therefore expressing an urgent appeal that in interventions on procreation the values and rights of the human person be safeguarded. Requests for clarification and guidance are coming not only from the faithful but also from those who recognize the Church as "an expert in humanity"[2] with a mission to serve the "civilization of love"[3] and of life.

The Church's Magisterium does not intervene on the basis of a particular competence in the area of the experimental sciences; but having taken account of the data of research and technology, it intends to put forward, by virtue of its evangelical mission and apostolic duty, the moral teaching corresponding to the dignity of the person and to his or her integral vocation. It intends to do so by expounding the criteria of moral judgment as regards the applications of scientific research and technology, especially in relation to human life and its beginnings. These criteria are the respect, defence and promotion of man, his "primary and fundamental right" to life,[4] his dignity as a person who is endowed with a spiritual soul and with moral responsibility[5] and who is called to beatific communion with God. ...

2. Science and Technology at the Service of the Human Person

... It would on the one hand be illusory to claim that scientific research and its applications are morally neutral; on the other hand one cannot derive criteria for guidance from mere technical efficiency, from research's possible usefulness to some at the expense of others, or, worse still, from prevailing ideologies. Thus science and technology require, for their own intrinsic meaning, an unconditional respect for the fundamental criteria of the moral law: that is to say, they must be at the service of the human person, of his inalienable rights and his true and integral good according to the design and will of God.[6] ...

Instruction on Respect for Human Life in Its Origin and on the Dignity of Procreation Replies to Certain Questions of the Day, Congregation for the Doctrine of the Faith. February 22, 1987, Vatican.

3. Anthropology and Procedures in the Biomedical Field

Which moral criteria must be applied in order to clarify the problems posed today in the field of biomedicine? The answer to this question presupposes a proper idea of the nature of the human person in his bodily dimension.

For it is only in keeping with his true nature that the human person can achieve self-realization as a "unified totality":[7] and this nature is at the same time corporal and spiritual. By virtue of its substantial union with a spiritual soul, the human body cannot be considered as a mere complex of tissues, organs and functions, nor can it be evaluated in the same way as the body of animals; rather it is a constitutive part of the person who manifests and expresses himself through it. The natural moral law expresses and lays down the purposes, rights and duties which are based upon the bodily and spiritual nature of the human person. Therefore this law cannot be thought of as simply a set of norms on the biological level; rather it must be defined as the rational order whereby man is called by the Creator to direct and regulate his life and actions and in particular to make use of his own body.[8] A first consequence can be deduced from these principles: an intervention on the human body affects not only the tissues, the organs and their functions but also involves the person himself on different levels. It involves, therefore, perhaps in an implicit but nonetheless real way, a moral significance and responsibility. Pope John Paul II forcefully reaffirmed this to the World Medical Association when he said: "Each human person, in his absolutely unique singularity, is constituted not only by his spirit, but by his body as well. Thus, in the body and through the body, one touches the person himself in his con-crete reality. To respect the dignity of man consequently amounts to safe-guarding this identity of the man *'corpore et anima unus,'* as the Second Vatican Council says (*Gaudium et spes*, no. 14, par. 1). It is on the basis of this anthropological vision that one is to find the fundamental criteria for decision-making in the case of procedures which are not strictly therapeutic, as, for example, those aimed at the improvement of the human biological condition."[9]

Applied biology and medicine work together for the integral good of human life when they come to the aid of a person stricken by illness and infirmity and when they respect his or her dignity as a creature of God. No biologist or doctor can reasonably claim, by virtue of his scientific competence, to be able to decide about people's origin and destiny. This norm must be applied in a particular way in the field of sexuality and procreation, in which man and woman actualize the fundamental values of love and life. ...

4. Fundamental Criteria for a Moral Judgment

The fundamental values connected with the techniques of artificial human procreation are two: the life of the human being called into existence and the special nature of the transmission of human life in marriage. The moral judgment on such methods of artificial procreation must therefore be formulated in reference to these values.

Physical life, with which the course of human life in the world begins, certainly does not itself contain the whole of a person's value, nor does it represent the supreme good of man, who is called to eternal life. However, it does constitute in a certain way the "fundamental" value of life, precisely because upon this physical life all the other values of the person are based and developed.[10] The inviolability of the innocent human being's right to life "from the moment of conception until death"[11] is a sign and requirement of the very inviolability of the person to whom the Creator has given the gift of life. By comparison with the transmission of other forms of life in the universe, the transmission of human life has a special character of its own, which derives from the special nature of the human person. "The transmission of human life is entrusted by nature to a personal and conscious act and as such is subject to the all-holy laws of God: immutable and inviolable laws which must be recognized and observed. For this reason one cannot use means and follow methods which could be licit in the transmission of the life of plants and animals."[12]

Advances in technology have now made it possible to procreate apart from sexual relations through the meeting *in vitro* of the germ cells previously taken from the man and the woman. But what is technically possible is not for that very reason morally admissible. Rational reflection on the fundamental values of life and of human procreation is, therefore, indispensable for formulating a moral evaluation of such technological interventions on a human being from the first stages of his development.

Teachings of the Magisterium

... From the moment of conception, the life of every human being is to be respected in an absolute way because man is the only creature on earth that God has "wished for himself"[13] and the spiritual soul of each man is "immediately created" by God;[14] his whole being bears the image of the Creator. Human life is sacred because from its beginning it involves "the creative action of God"[15] and it remains forever in a special relationship with the Creator, who is its sole end.[16] God alone is the Lord of life from its beginning until its end: no one can, in

any circumstance, claim for himself the right directly to destroy an innocent human being.[17] Human procreation requires on the part of the spouses responsible collaboration with the fruitful love of God;[18] the gift of human life must be actualized in marriage through the specific and exclusive acts of husband and wife, in accordance with the laws inscribed in their persons and in their union.[19]

I. Respect for Human Embryos

...

1. What Respect is Due to the Human Embryo, Taking into Account His Nature and Identity?

The human being must be respected — as a person — from the very first instant of his existence. The implementation of procedures of artificial fertilization has made possible various interventions upon embryos and human fetuses. The aims pursued are of various kinds: diagnostic and therapeutic, scientific and commercial. From all of this, serious problems arise. Can one speak of a right to experimentation upon human embryos for the purpose of scientific research? What norms or laws should be worked out with regard to this matter? The response to these problems presupposes a detailed reflection on the nature and specific identity — the word "status" is used — of the human embryo itself.

At the Second Vatican Council, the Church for her part presented once again to modern man her constant and certain doctrine according to which: "Life, once conceived, must be protected with the utmost care; abortion and infanticide are abominable crimes."[20] More recently, the Charter of the Rights of the Family, published by the Holy See, confirmed that "Human life must be absolutely respected and protected from the moment of conception."[21]

This Congregation is aware of the current debates concerning the beginning of human life, concerning the individuality of the human being and concerning the identity of the human person. The Congregation recalls the teachings found in the *Declaration on Procured Abortion*: "From the time that the ovum is fertilized, a new life is begun which is neither that of the father nor of the mother; it is rather the life of a new human being with his own growth. It would never be made human if it were not human already. To this perpetual evidence ... modern genetic science brings valuable confirmation. It has demonstrated that, from the first instant, the programme is fixed as to what this living being will be: a man, this individual-man with his characteristic aspects already well determined. Right from fertilization is begun the adventure of a human life, and each of its great capacities requires time ... to find its place and to be in a position to act."[22] This teaching remains valid and is further confirmed, if confirmation were needed, by recent findings of human biological science which recognize that in the zygote (The zygote is the cell produced when the nuclei of the two gametes have fused.) resulting from fertilization the biological identity of a new human individual is already constituted. Certainly no experimental datum can be in itself sufficient to bring us to the recognition of a spiritual soul; nevertheless, the conclusions of science regarding the human embryo provide a valuable indication for discerning by the use of reason a personal presence at the moment of this first appearance of a human life: how could a human individual not be a human person? The Magisterium has not expressly committed itself to an affirmation of a philosophical nature, but it constantly

reaffirms the moral condemnation of any kind of procured abortion. This teaching has not been changed and is unchangeable.[23]

Thus the fruit of human generation, from the first moment of its existence, that is to say from the moment the zygote has formed, demands the unconditional respect that is morally due to the human being in his bodily and spiritual totality. The human being is to be respected and treated as a person from the moment of conception; and therefore from that same moment his rights as a person must be recognized, among which in the first place is the inviolable right of every innocent human being to life. ...

2. Is Prenatal Diagnosis Morally Licit?

If prenatal diagnosis respects the life and integrity of the embryo and the human foetus and is directed towards its safeguarding or healing as an individual, then the answer is affirmative.

For prenatal diagnosis makes it possible to know the condition of the embryo and of the foetus when still in the mother's womb. It permits, or makes it possible to anticipate earlier and more effectively, certain therapeutic, medical or surgical procedures. Such diagnosis is permissible, with the consent of the parents after they have been adequately informed, if the methods employed safeguard the life and integrity of the embryo and the mother, without subjecting them to disproportionate risks.[24]

But this diagnosis is gravely opposed to the moral law when it is done with the thought of possibly inducing an abortion depending upon the results: a diagnosis which shows the existence of a malformation or a hereditary illness must not be the equivalent of a death-sentence. Thus a woman would be committing a gravely illicit act if she were to request such a diagnosis with the deliberate intention of having an abortion should the results confirm the existence of a malformation or abnormality. The spouse or relatives or anyone else would similarly be acting in a manner contrary to the moral law if they were to counsel or impose such a diagnostic procedure on the expectant mother with the same intention of possibly proceeding to an abortion. So too the specialist would be guilty of illicit collaboration if, in conducting the diagnosis and in communicating its results, he were deliberately to contribute to establishing or favouring a link between prenatal diagnosis and abortion. ...

3. Are Therapeutic Procedures Carried Out on the Human Embryo Licit?

... Whatever the type of medical, surgical or other therapy, the free and informed consent of the parents is required, according to the deontological rules followed in the case of children. ... The legitimacy and criteria of such procedures have been clearly stated by Pope John Paul II: "A strictly therapeutic intervention whose explicit objective is the healing of various maladies such as those stemming from chromosomal defects will, in principle, be considered desirable, provided it is directed to the true promotion of the personal well-being of the individual without doing harm to his integrity or worsening his conditions of life. Such an intervention would indeed fall within the logic of the Christian moral tradition."[25]

4. How is One to Evaluate Morally Research and Experimentation on Human Embryos and Foetuses?

Medical research must refrain from operations on live embryos, unless there is a moral certainty of not causing harm to the life or integrity of the unborn child and the mother, and on condition that the parents have given their free and informed consent to the procedure. It follows that all research, even when limited to the simple observation of the embryo, would become illicit were it to involve risk to the embryo's physical integrity or life by reason of the methods used or the effects induced.

As regards experimentation, and presupposing the general distinction between experimentation for purposes which are not directly therapeutic and experimentation which is clearly therapeutic for the subject himself, in the case in point one must also distinguish between experimentation carried out on embryos which are still alive and experimentation carried out on embryos which are dead. *If the embryos are living, whether viable or not, they must be respected just like any other human person; experimentation on embryos which is not directly therapeutic is illicit.*[26]

No objective, even though noble in itself, such as a foreseeable advantage to science, to other human beings or to society, can in any way justify experimentation on living human embryos or foetuses, whether viable or not, either inside or outside the mother's womb. The informed consent ordinarily required for clinical experimentation on adults cannot be granted by the parents, who may not freely dispose of the physical integrity or life of the unborn child. Moreover, experimentation on embryos and foetuses always involves risk, and indeed in most cases it involves the certain expectation of harm to their physical integrity or even their death.

To use human embryos or foetuses as the object or instrument of experimentation constitutes a crime against their dignity as human beings having a right to the same respect that is due to the child already born and to every human person.

The *Charter of the Rights of the Family* published by the Holy See affirms: "Respect for the dignity of the human being excludes all experimental manipulation or exploitation of the human embryo."[27] The practice of keeping human embryos alive *in vivo* or *in vitro* for experimental or commercial purposes is totally opposed to human dignity.

In the case of experimentation that is clearly therapeutic, namely, when it is a matter of experimental forms of therapy used for the benefit of the embryo itself in a final attempt to save its life, and in the absence of other reliable forms of therapy, recourse to drugs or procedures not yet fully tested can be licit.[28]

The corpses of human embryos and foetuses, whether they have been deliberately aborted or not, must be respected just as the remains of other human beings. In particular, they cannot be subjected to mutilation or to autopsies if their death has not yet been verified and without the consent of the parents or of the mother. Furthermore, the moral requirements must be safeguarded that there be no complicity in deliberate abortion and that the risk of scandal be avoided. Also, in the case of dead foetuses, as for the corpses of adult persons, all commercial trafficking must be considered illicit and should be prohibited. ...

5. How Is One to Evaluate Morally the Use for Research Purposes of Embryos Obtained by Fertilization "in Vitro"?

... In the usual practice of *in vitro* fertilization, not all of the embryos are transferred to the woman's body; some are destroyed. Just as the Church condemns induced abortion, so she also forbids acts against the life of these human beings. *It is a duty to condemn the particular gravity of the voluntary destruction of human embryos obtained "in vitro" for the sole purpose of research, either by means of artificial insemination or by means of "twin fission."* By acting in this way the researcher usurps the place of God; and, even though he may be unaware of this,

he sets himself up as the master of the destiny of others inasmuch as he arbitrarily chooses whom he will allow to live and whom he will send to death, and kills defenseless human beings.

Methods of observation or experimentation which damage or impose grave and disproportionate risks upon embryos obtained *in vitro* are morally illicit for the same reasons. Every human being is to be respected for himself, and cannot be reduced in worth to a pure and simple instrument for the advantage of others. *It is therefore not in conformity with the moral law deliberately to expose to death human embryos obtained "in vitro."* In consequence of the fact that they have been produced *in vitro*, those embryos which are not transferred into the body of the mother and are called "spare" are exposed to an absurd fate, with no possibility of their being offered safe means of survival which can be licitly pursued.

6. What Judgment Should be Made on Other Procedures of Manipulating Embryos Connected with the "Techniques of Human Reproduction"?

Techniques of fertilization *in vitro* can open the way to other forms of biological and genetic manipulation of human embryos, such as attempts or plans for fertilization between human and animal gametes and the gestation of human embryos in the uterus of animals, or the hypothesis or project of constructing artificial uteruses for the human embryo. *These procedures are contrary to the human dignity proper to the embryo, and at the same time they are contrary to the right of every person to be conceived and to be born within marriage and from marriage.*[29] Also, attempts or hypotheses for obtaining a human being without any connection with sexuality through "twin *fission," cloning or parthenogenesis are to be considered contrary to the moral law, since they are in opposition to the dignity both of human procreation and of the conjugal union.*

The freezing of embryos, even when carried out in order to preserve the life of an embryo — cryopreservation — *constitutes an offence against the respect due to human beings* by exposing them to grave risks of death or harm to their physical integrity, and depriving them, at least temporarily, of maternal shelter and gestation, thus placing them in a situation in which further offences and manipulation are possible.

Certain attempts to influence chromosomic or genetic inheritance are not therapeutic but are aimed at producing human beings selected according to sex or other predetermined qualities. These manipulations are contrary to the personal dignity of the human being and his or her integrity and identity. Therefore in no way can they be justified on the grounds of possible beneficial consequences for future humanity.[30] Every person must be respected for himself: in this consists the dignity and right of every human being from his or her beginning.

II. Interventions Upon Human Procreation

By "artificial procreation" or "artificial fertilization" are understood here the different technical procedures directed towards obtaining a human conception in a manner other than the sexual union of man and woman. This instruction deals with fertilization of an ovum in a test-tube (*in vitro* fertilization) and artificial insemination through transfer into the woman's genital tracts of previously collected sperm.

... Even today, the usual practice [of *in vitro* fertilization] presupposes a hyperovulation on the part of the woman: a number of ova are withdrawn, fertilized and then cultivated *in vitro* for some days. Usually not all are transferred into the genital tracts of the woman; some embryos, generally called "spare," are destroyed or frozen. On occasion, some of the implanted embryos are sacrificed for various eugenic, economic or psychological reasons. Such deliberate destruction of human beings or their utilization for different purposes to the detriment of their integrity and life is contrary to the doctrine on procured abortion already recalled. The connection between *in vitro* fertilization and the voluntary destruction of human embryos occurs too often. This is significant: through these procedures, with apparently contrary purposes, life and death are subjected to the decision of man, who thus sets himself up as the giver of life and death by decree. ... The facts recorded and the cold logic which links them must be taken into consideration for a moral judgment on IVF and ET (*in vitro* fertilization and embryo transfer): the abortion-mentality which has made this procedure possible thus leads, whether one wants it or not, to man's domination over the life and death of his fellow human beings and can lead to a system of radical eugenics.

... Before formulating an ethical judgment on each of these procedures, the principles and values which determine the moral evaluation of each of them will be considered.

... By the term *heterologous artificial fertilization or procreation,* the Instruction means techniques used to obtain a human conception artificially by the use of gametes coming from at least one donor other than the spouses who are joined in marriage. Such techniques can be of two types

a) *Heterologous IVF and ET:* the technique used to obtain a human conception through the meeting *in vitro* of gametes taken from at least one donor other than the two spouses joined in marriage.

b)   *Heterologous artificial insemination:* the technique used to obtain a human conception through the transfer into the genital tracts of the woman of the sperm previously collected from a donor other than the husband.

... By *artificial homologous fertilization or procreation*, the Instruction means the technique used to obtain a human conception using the gametes of the two spouses joined in marriage. Homologous artificial fertilization can be carried out by two different methods:

a)   *Homologous IVF and ET:* the technique used to obtain a human conception through the meeting *in vitro* of the gametes of the spouses joined in marriage.

b)   *Homologous artificial insemination:* the technique used to obtain a human conception through the transfer into the genital tracts of a married woman of the sperm previously collected from her husband.

A. Heterologous Artificial Fertilization

1. Why Must Human Procreation Take Place in Marriage?

Every human being is always to be accepted as a gift and blessing of God. However, from the moral point of view a truly responsible procreation vis-à-vis the unborn child must be the fruit of marriage.

For human procreation has specific characteristics by virtue of the personal dignity of the parents and of the children: the procreation of a new person, whereby the man and the woman collaborate with the power of the Creator, must be the fruit and the sign of the mutual self-giving of the spouses, of their love and of

their fidelity.[31] The fidelity of the spouses in the unity of marriage involves reciprocal respect of their right to become a father and a mother only through each other. The child has the right to be conceived, carried in the womb, brought into the world and brought up within marriage: it is through the secure and recognized relationship to his own parents that the child can discover his own identity and achieve his own proper human development. The parents find in their child a confirmation and completion of their reciprocal self-giving: the child is the living image of their love, the permanent sign of their conjugal union, the living and indissoluble concrete expression of their paternity and maternity.[32] By reason of the vocation and social responsibilities of the person, the good of the children and of the parents contributes to the good of civil society; the vitality and stability of society require that children come into the world within a family and that the family be firmly based on marriage. The tradition of the Church and anthropological reflection recognize in marriage and in its indissoluble unity the only setting worthy of truly responsible procreation.

2. Does Heterologous Artificial Fertilization Conform to the Dignity of the Couple and to the Truth of Marriage?

Through IVF and ET and heterologous artificial insemination, human conception is achieved through the fusion of gametes of at least one donor other than the spouses who are united in marriage. *Heterologous artificial fertilization is contrary to the unity of marriage, to the dignity of the spouses, to the vocation proper to parents, and to the child's right to be conceived and brought into the world in marriage and from marriage.*[33]

Respect for the unity of marriage and for conjugal fidelity demands that the child be conceived in marriage; the bond existing between husband and wife accords the spouses, in an objective and inalienable manner, the exclusive right to become father and mother solely through each other.[34] Recourse to the gametes of a third person, in order to have sperm or ovum available, constitutes a violation of the reciprocal commitment of the spouses and a grave lack in regard to that essential property of marriage which is its unity.

Heterologous artificial fertilization violates the rights of the child; it deprives him of his filial relationship with his parental origins and can hinder the maturing of his personal identity. Furthermore, it offends the common vocation of the spouses who are called to fatherhood and motherhood: it objectively deprives conjugal fruitfulness of its unity and integrity; it brings about and manifests a rupture between genetic parenthood, gestational parenthood and responsibility for upbringing. Such damage to the personal relationships within the family has repercussions on civil society: what threatens the unity and stability of the family is a source of dissension, disorder and injustice in the whole of social life.

These reasons lead to a negative moral judgment concerning heterologous artificial fertilization: consequently fertilization of a married woman with the sperm of a donor different from her husband and fertilization with the husband's sperm of an ovum not coming from his wife are morally illicit. Furthermore, the artificial fertilization of a woman who is unmarried or a widow, whoever the donor may be, cannot be morally justified.

The desire to have a child and the love between spouses who long to obviate a sterility which cannot be overcome in any other way constitute understandable motivations; but subjectively good intentions do not render heterologous artificial fertilization conformable to the objective and inalienable properties of marriage or respectful of the rights of the child and of the spouses.

3. Is "Surrogate"* Motherhood Morally Licit?

No, for the same reasons which lead one to reject heterologous artificial fertilization: for it is contrary to the unity of marriage and to the dignity of the procreation of the human person.

Surrogate motherhood represents an objective failure to meet the obligations of maternal love, of conjugal fidelity and of responsible motherhood; it offends the dignity and the right of the child to be conceived, carried in the womb, brought into the world and brought up by his own parents; it sets up, to the detriment of families, a division between the physical, psychological and moral elements which constitute those families.

* By "surrogate mother" the Instruction means:

a) the woman who carries in pregnancy an embryo implanted in her uterus and who is genetically a stranger to the embryo because it has been obtained through the union of the gametes of "donors." She carries the pregnancy with a pledge to surrender the baby once it is born to the party who commissioned or made the agreement for the pregnancy.

b) the woman who carries in pregnancy an embryo to whose procreation she has contributed the donation of her own ovum, fertilized through insemination with the sperm of a man other than her husband. She carries the pregnancy with the pledge to surrender the child once it is born to the party who commissioned or made the agreement for the pregnancy.

B. Homologous Artificial Fertilization

Since heterologous artificial fertilization has been declared unacceptable, the question arises of how to evaluate morally the process of homologous artificial fertilization: IVF and ET and artificial insemination between husband and wife. First a question of principle must be clarified.

4. What Connection is Required from the Moral Point of View between Procreation and the Conjugal Act?

a) The Church's teaching on marriage and human procreation affirms the "inseparable connection, willed by God and unable to be broken by man on his own initiative, between the two meanings of the conjugal act: the unitive meaning and the procreative meaning. Indeed, by its intimate structure, the conjugal act, while most closely uniting husband and wife, capacitates them for the generation of new lives, according to laws inscribed in the very being of man and of woman."[35] This principle, which is based upon the nature of marriage and the intimate connection of the goods of marriage, has well-known consequences on the level of responsible fatherhood and motherhood. "By safeguarding both these essential aspects, the unitive and the procreative, the conjugal act preserves in its fullness the sense of true mutual love and its ordination towards man's exalted vocation to parenthood."[36] The same doctrine concerning the link between the meanings of the conjugal act and between the goods of marriage throws light on the moral problem of homologous artificial fertilization, since "it is never permitted to separate these different aspects to such a degree as positively to exclude either the procreative intention or the conjugal relation."[37]

Contraception deliberately deprives the conjugal act of its openness to procreation and in this way brings about a voluntary dissociation of the ends of marriage. Homologous artificial fertilization, in seeking a procreation which is not the fruit of a specific act of conjugal union, objectively effects an analogous separation between the goods and the meanings of marriage. Thus, *fertilization is licitly sought when it is the result of a "conjugal act which is per se suitable for the generation of children to which marriage is ordered by its nature and by which the spouses become one flesh."*[38] *But from the moral point of view procreation is deprived of its proper perfection when it is not desired as the fruit of the conjugal act, that is to say of the specific act of the spouses' union.*

b) The moral value of the intimate link between the goods of marriage and between the meanings of the conjugal act is based upon the unity of the human being, a unity involving body and spiritual soul.[39] Spouses mutually express their personal love in the "language of the body," which clearly involves both "spousal meanings" and parental ones.[40] The conjugal act by which the couple mutually express their self-gift at the same time expresses openness to the gift of life. It is an act that is inseparably corporal and spiritual. It is in their bodies and through their bodies that the spouses consummate their marriage and are able to become father and mother. In order to respect the language of their bodies and their natural generosity, the conjugal union must take place with respect for its openness to procreation; and the procreation of a person must be the fruit and the result of married love. The origin of the human being thus follows from a procreation that is "linked to the union, not only biological but also spiritual, of the parents, made one by the bond of marriage."[41] Fertilization achieved outside the bodies of the couple remains by this very fact deprived of the meanings and the values which are expressed in the language of the body and in the union of human persons.

c) Only respect for the link between the meanings of the conjugal act and respect for the unity of the human being make possible procreation in conformity with the dignity of the person. In his unique and unrepeatable origin, the child must be respected and recognized as equal in personal dignity to those who give him life. The human person must be accepted in his parents' act of union and love; the generation of a child must therefore be the fruit of that mutual giving[42] which is realized in the conjugal act wherein the spouses cooperate as servants and not as masters in the work of the Creator who is Love.[43]

In reality, the origin of a human person is the result of an act of giving. The one conceived must be the fruit of his parents' love. He cannot be desired or conceived as the product of an intervention of medical or biological techniques; that would be equivalent to reducing him to an object of scientific technology. No one may subject the coming of a child into the world to conditions of technical efficiency which are to be evaluated according to standards of control and dominion. *The moral relevance of the link between the meanings of the conjugal act and between the goods of marriage, as well as the unity of the human being and the dignity of his origin, demand that the procreation of a human person be brought about as the fruit of the conjugal act specific to the love between spouses.* The link between procreation and the conjugal act is thus shown to be of great importance on the anthropological and moral planes, and it throws light on the positions of the Magisterium with regard to homologous artificial fertilization.

5. Is Homologous "In Vitro" Fertilization Morally Licit?

The answer to this question is strictly dependent on the principles just mentioned. Certainly one cannot ignore the legitimate aspirations of sterile couples. For some, recourse to homologous IVF and ET appears to be the only way of fulfilling their sincere desire for a child. The question is asked whether the totality of conjugal life in such situations is not sufficient to ensure the dignity proper to human procreation. It is acknowledged that IVF and ET certainly cannot supply for the absence of sexual relations[44] and cannot be preferred to the specific acts of conjugal union, given the risks involved for the child and the difficulties of the procedure. But it is asked whether, when there is no other way of overcoming the sterility which is a source of suffering, homologous *in vitro* fertilization may not constitute an aid, if not a form of therapy, whereby its moral licitness could be admitted.

The desire for a child — or at the very least an openness to the transmission of life — is a necessary prerequisite from the moral point of view for responsible human procreation. But this good intention is not sufficient for making a positive moral evaluation of *in vitro* fertilization between spouses. The process of IVF and ET must be judged in itself and cannot borrow its definitive moral quality from the totality of conjugal life of which it becomes part nor from the conjugal acts which may precede or follow it.[45]

It has already been recalled that, in the circumstances in which it is regularly practiced, IVF and ET involves the destruction of human beings, which is something contrary to the doctrine on the illicitness of abortion previously mentioned.[46] But even in a situation in which every precaution were taken to avoid the death of human embryos, homologous IVF and ET dissociates from the conjugal act the actions which are directed to human fertilization. For this reason the very nature of homologous IVF and ET also must be taken into account, even abstracting from the link with procured abortion. Homologous IVF and ET is brought about outside the bodies of the couple through actions of third parties whose competence and technical activity determine the success of the procedure. Such fertilization entrusts the life and identity of the embryo into the power of doctors and biologists and establishes the domination of technology over the origin and destiny of the human person. Such a relationship of domination is in itself contrary to the dignity and equality that must be common to parents and children.

Conception *in vitro* is the result of the technical action which presides over fertilization. *Such fertilization is neither in fact achieved nor positively willed as the expression and fruit of a specific act of the conjugal union. In homologous IVF and ET, therefore, even if it is considered in the context of "de facto" existing sexual relations, the generation of the human person is objectively deprived of its proper perfection: namely, that of being the result and fruit of a conjugal act* in which the spouses can become "cooperators with God for giving life to a new person."[47] These reasons enable us to understand why the act of conjugal love is considered in the teaching of the Church as the only setting worthy of human procreation. For the same reasons the so-called "simple case," i.e., a homologous IVF and ET procedure that is free of any compromise with the abortive practice of destroying embryos and with masturbation, remains a technique which is morally illicit because it deprives human procreation of the dignity which is proper and connatural to it. Certainly, homologous IVF and ET fertilization is not marked by all that ethical negativity found in extra-conjugal procreation; the family

and marriage continue to constitute the setting for the birth and upbringing of the children. Nevertheless, in conformity with the traditional doctrine relating to the goods of marriage and the dignity of the person, *the Church remains opposed from the moral point of view to homologous "in vitro" fertilization. Such fertilization is in itself illicit and in opposition to the dignity of procreation and of the conjugal union, even when everything is done to avoid the death of the human embryo.*

Although the manner in which human conception is achieved with IVF and ET cannot be approved, every child which comes into the world must in any case be accepted as a living gift of the divine Goodness and must be brought up with love.

6. How Is Homologous Artificial Insemination to Be Evaluated from the Moral Point of View?

Homologous artificial insemination within marriage cannot be admitted except for those cases in which the technical means is not a substitute for the conjugal act but serves to facilitate and to help so that the act attains its natural purpose.

The teaching of the Magisterium on this point has already been stated.[48] This teaching is not just an expression of particular historical circumstances but is based on the Church's doctrine concerning the connection between the conjugal union and procreation and on a consideration of the personal nature of the conjugal act and of human procreation. "In its natural structure, the conjugal act is a personal action, a simultaneous and immediate cooperation on the part of the husband and wife, which by the very nature of the agents and the proper nature of the act is the expression of the mutual gift which, according to the words of Scripture, brings about union 'in one flesh.'"[49] Thus moral conscience "does not necessarily proscribe the use of certain artificial means destined solely either to the facilitating of the natural act or to ensuring that the natural act normally performed achieves its proper end."[50] If the technical means facilitates the conjugal act or helps it to reach its natural objectives, it can be morally acceptable. If, on the other hand, the procedure were to replace the conjugal act, it is morally illicit.

Artificial insemination as a substitute for the conjugal act is prohibited by reason of the voluntarily achieved dissociation of the two meanings of the conjugal act. Masturbation, through which the sperm is normally obtained, is another sign of this dissociation: even when it is done for the purpose of procreation, the act remains deprived of its unitive meaning: "It lacks the sexual relationship called for by the moral order, namely the relationship which realizes 'the full sense of mutual self-giving and human procreation in the context of true love'"[51]

7. What Moral Criterion Can Be Proposed with Regard to Medical Intervention in Human Procreation?

The medical act must be evaluated not only with reference to its technical dimension but also and above all in relation to its goal, which is the good of persons and their bodily and psychological health. The moral criteria for medical intervention in procreation are deduced from the dignity of human persons, of their sexuality and of their origin. *Medicine which seeks to be ordered to the integral good of the person must respect the specifically human values of sexuality.*[52] *The doctor is at the service of persons and of human procreation. He does not have the authority to dispose of them or to decide their fate.*

"A medical intervention respects the dignity of persons when it seeks to assist the conjugal act either in order to facilitate its performance or in order to enable it to achieve its objective once it has been normally performed."[53] On the other hand, it sometimes happens that a medical procedure technologically replaces the conjugal act in order to obtain a procreation which is neither its result nor its fruit. In this case the medical act is not, as it should be, at the service of conjugal union but rather appropriates to itself the procreative function and thus contradicts the dignity and the inalienable rights of the spouses and of the child to be born. The humanization of medicine, which is insisted upon today by everyone, requires respect for the integral dignity of the human person first of all in the act and at the moment in which the spouses transmit life to a new person. It is only logical therefore to address an urgent appeal to Catholic doctors and scientists that they bear exemplary witness to the respect due to the human embryo and to the dignity of procreation. The medical and nursing staff of Catholic hospitals and clinics are in a special way urged to do justice to the moral obligations which they have assumed, frequently also, as part of their contract. Those who are in charge of Catholic hospitals and clinics and who are often Religious will take special care to safeguard and promote a diligent observance of the moral norms recalled in the present Instruction.

8. The Suffering Caused by Infertility in Marriage

The suffering of spouses who cannot have children or who are afraid of bringing a handicapped child into the world is a suffering that everyone must understand and properly evaluate.

On the part of the spouses, the desire for a child is natural: it expresses the vocation to fatherhood and motherhood inscribed in conjugal love. This desire can be even stronger if the couple is affected by sterility which appears incurable. Nevertheless, marriage does not confer upon the spouses the right to have a child, but only the right to perform those natural acts which are *per se* ordered to procreation.[54] *A true and proper right to a child would be contrary to the child's dignity and nature. The child is not an object to which one has a right, nor can he be considered as an object of ownership: rather, a child is a gift, "the supreme gift"*[55] *and the most gratuitous gift of marriage, and is a living testimony of the mutual giving of his parents. For this reason, the child has the right, as already mentioned, to be the fruit of the specific act of the conjugal love of his parents; and he also has the right to be respected as a person from the moment of his conception.*

Nevertheless, whatever its cause or prognosis, sterility is certainly a difficult trial. The community of believers is called to shed light upon and support the suffering of those who are unable to fulfill their legitimate aspiration to motherhood and fatherhood. Spouses who find themselves in this sad situation are called to find in it an opportunity for sharing in a particular way in the Lord's cross, the source of spiritual fruitfulness. Sterile couples must not forget that "even when procreation is not possible, conjugal life does not for this reason lose its value. Physical sterility in fact can be for spouses the occasion for other important services in the life of the human person, for example, adoption, various forms of educational work, and assistance to other families and to poor or handicapped children."[56]

Many researchers are engaged in the fight against sterility. While fully safeguarding the dignity of human procreation some have achieved results which previously seemed unattainable. Scientists therefore are to be encouraged to continue their research with the aim of preventing the causes of sterility and of being able to remedy them so that sterile couples will be able to procreate in full respect for their own personal dignity and that of the child to be born.

...

Conclusion

The spread of technologies of intervention in the processes of human procreation raises very serious moral problems in relation to the respect due to the human being from the moment of conception, to the dignity of the person, of his or her sexuality, and of the transmission of life. With this Instruction the Congregation for the Doctrine of the Faith, in fulfilling its responsibility to promote and defend the Church's teaching in so serious a matter, addresses a new and heartfelt invitation to all those who, by reason of their role and their commitment, can exercise a positive influence and ensure that, in the family and in society, due respect is accorded to life and love. It addresses this invitation to those responsible for the formation of consciences and of public opinion, to scientists and medical professionals, to jurists and politicians. It hopes that all will understand the incompatibility between recognition of the dignity of the human person and contempt for life and love, between faith in the living God and the claim to decide arbitrarily the origin and fate of a human being. ...

During an audience granted to the undersigned Prefect after the plenary session of the Congregation for the Doctrine of the Faith, the Supreme Pontiff, John Paul II, approved this Instruction and ordered it to be published.

Given at Rome, from the Congregation for the Doctrine of the Faith, February 22, 1987. ...

Joseph Cardinal Ratzinger, *Prefect*

Alberto Bovone, *Titular Archbishop of Caesarea in Numidia, Secretary*

Notes*

1. Pope John Paul II, *Discourse to those taking part in the 81st Congress of the Italian Society of Internal Medicine and the 82nd Congress of the Italian Society of General Surgery*, October 27, 1980: AAS 72 (1980), 1126.

2. Pope Paul VI, *Discourse to the General Assembly of the United Nations Organization*, October 4, 1965: AAS 57 (1965), 878; Encyclical *Populorum progressio*, no. 13: AAS 59 (1967), 263.

3. Pope Paul VI, *Homily during the Mass closing the Holy Year*, December 25, 1975: AAS 68 (1976), 145; Pope John Paul II, Encyclical *Dives in misericordia*, no. 30: AAS 72 (1980), 1224.

4. Pope John Paul II, *Discourse to those taking part in the 35th General Assembly of the World Medical Association*, October 29, 1983: AAS 76 (1984), 390.

5. Cf. Declaration *Dignitatis humanae*, no. 2.

6. Cf. Pastoral Constitution *Gaudium et spes*, no. 35.

7. Pope John Paul II, Apostolic Exhortation *Familiaris consortio*, no. 11: AAS 74 (1982), 92.

8. Cf. Pope Paul VI, Encyclical *Humanae vitae*, no. 10: AAS 60 (1968), 487–488.

9. Pope John Paul II, *Discourse to the members of the 35th General Assembly of the World Medical Association*, October 29, 1983: AAS 76 (1984), 393.

10. Sacred Congregation for the Doctrine of the Faith, *Declaration on Procured Abortion*, no. 9: AAS 66 (1974), 736–737.

11. Pope John Paul II, *Discourse to those taking part in the 35th General Assembly of the World Medical Association*, October 29, 1983: AAS 76 (1984), 390.

12. Pope John XXIII, Encyclical *Mater et magistra*, III: AAS 53 (1961), 447.

13. Pastoral Constitution *Gaudium et spes*, no. 24.

14. Cf. Pope Pius XII, Encyclical *Humani generis*: AAS 42 (1950), 575; Pope Paul VI, *Professio fidei*: AAS 60 (1968), 436.

15. Pope John XXIII, Encyclical *Mater et magistra*, III: AAS 53 (1961), 447; cf. Pope John Paul II, *Discourse to priests participating in a seminar on "Responsible Procreation,"* September 17, 1983, *Insegnamenti di Giovanni Paolo II*, VI, 2 (1983), 562: "At the origin of each human person there is a creative act of God: no man comes into existence by chance; he is always the result of the creative love of God."

16. Cf. Pastoral Constitution *Gaudium et spes*, no. 24.

17. Cf. Pope Pius XII, *Discourse to the Saint Luke Medical-Biological Union*, November 12, 1944: *Discorsi e Radiomessaggi* VI (1944–1945), 191–192.

18. Cf. Pastoral Constitution *Gaudium et spes*, no. 50.

19. Cf. Pastoral Constitution *Gaudium et spes*, no. 51: "When it is a question of harmonizing married love with the responsible transmission of life, the moral character of one's behavior does not depend only on the good intention and the evaluation of the motives: the objective criteria must be used, criteria drawn from the nature of the human person and human acts, criteria which respect the total meaning of mutual self-giving and human procreation in the context of true love."

---

* These notes have been renumbered to aid the reader.

20. Pastoral Constitution *Gaudium et spes*, no. 51.

21. Holy See, *Charter of the Rights of the Family*, no. 4: *L'Osservatore Romano*, November 25, 1983.

22. Sacred Congregation for the Doctrine of the Faith, *Declaration on Procured Abortion*, nos. 12–13: AAS 66 (1974), 738.

23. Cf. Pope Paul VI, *Discourse to participants in the Twenty-third National Congress of Italian Catholic Jurists*, December 9, 1972: AAS 64 (1972), 777.

24. The obligation to avoid disproportionate risks involves an authentic respect for human beings and the uprightness of therapeutic intentions. It implies that the doctor "above all ... must carefully evaluate the possible negative consequences which the necessary use of a particular exploratory technique may have upon the unborn child and avoid recourse to diagnostic procedures which do not offer sufficient guarantees of their honest purpose and substantial harmlessness. And if, as often happens in human choices, a degree of risk must be undertaken, he will take care to assure that it is justified by a truly urgent need for the diagnosis and by the importance of the results that can be achieved by it for the benefit of the unborn child himself" (Pope John Paul II, *Discourse to Participants in the Pro-life Movement Congress*, December 3, 1982: *Insegnamenti di Giovanni Paolo II*, V, 3, [1982], 1512). This clarification concerning "proportionate risk" is also to be kept in mind in the following sections of the present Instruction, whenever this term appears.

25. Pope John Paul II, *Discourse to the participants in the 35th General Assembly of the World Medical Association*, October 29, 1983: AAS 76 (1984), 392.

26. Cf. Pope John Paul II, *Address to a Meeting of the Pontifical Academy of Sciences*, October 23, 1982: AAS 75 (1983), 37: "I condemn, in the most explicit and formal way, experimental manipulations of the human embryo, since the human being, from conception to death, cannot be exploited for any purpose whatsoever."

27. Holy See, *Charter of the Rights of the Family*, no. 4b: *L'Osservatore Romano*, November 25, 1983.

28. Cf. Pope John Paul II, *Address to the Participants in the Convention of the Pro-Life Movement*, December 3, 1982: *Insegnamenti di Giovanni Paolo II*, V, 3 (1982), 1511: "Any form of experimentation on the foetus that may damage its integrity or worsen its condition is unacceptable, except in the case of a final effort to save it from death." Sacred Congregation for the Doctrine of the Faith, *Declaration on Euthanasia*, no. 4: AAS 72 (1980), 550: "In the absence of other sufficient remedies, it is permitted, with the patient's consent, to have recourse to the means provided by the most advanced medical techniques, even if these means are still at the experimental stage and are not without a certain risk."

29. No one, before coming into existence, can claim a subjective right to begin to exist; nevertheless, it is legitimate to affirm the right of the child to have a fully human origin through conception in conformity with the personal nature of the human being. Life is a gift that must be bestowed in a manner worthy both of the subject receiving it and of the subjects transmitting it. This statement is to be borne in mind also for what will be explained concerning artificial human procreation.

30. Cf. Pope John Paul II, *Discourse to those taking part in the 35th General Assembly of the World Medical Association*, October 29, 1983: AAS 76 (1984), 391.

31. Cf. Pastoral Constitution on the Church in the Modern World, *Gaudium et spes*, no. 50.

32. Cf. Pope John Paul II, Apostolic Exhortation *Familiaris consortio*, no. 14: AAS 74 (1982), 96.

33. Cf. Pope Pius XII, *Discourse to those taking part in the 4th International Congress of Catholic Doctors*, September 29, 1949: AAS 41 (1949), 559. According to the plan of the Creator, "A man leaves his father and his mother and cleaves to his wife, and they become one flesh" (Gen. 2:24). The unity of marriage, bound to the order of creation, is a truth accessible to natural reason. The Church's Tradition and Magisterium frequently make reference to the Book of Genesis, both directly and through the passages of the New Testament that refer to it: *Mt* 19:4–6; *Mk* 10:5–8; *Eph* 5:31. Cf. Athenagoras, *Legatio por christianis*, 33: PG 6, 965–967; St. Chrysostom, In *Matthaeum homiliae*, LXII, 19, 1: PG 58, 597; St. Leo the Great, *Epist. ad Rusticum*, 4; PL 54, 1204; Innocent III, *Epist. Gaudemus in Domino*: DS 778; Council of Lyons II, IV *Session*: DS 860; Council of Trent, XXIV, *Session*: DS 1798. 1802; Pope Leo XIII, Encyclical *Arcanum Divinae Sapientiae*: AAS 12 (1879/80), 388–391; Pope Pius XI, Encyclical *Casti connubii*: AAS 22 (1930), 546–547; Second Vatican Council, *Gaudium et spes*, no. 48; Pope John Paul II, Apostolic Exhortation *Familiaris consortio*, no. 19: AAS 74 (1982), 101–102; *Code of Canon Law*, Can. 1056.

34. Cf. Pope Pius XII, *Discourse to those taking part in the 4th International Congress of Catholic Doctors*, September 29, 1949: AAS 41 (1949), 560; *Discourse to those taking part in the Congress of the Italian Catholic Union of Midwives*, October 29, 1951: AAS 43 (1951), 850; *Code of Canon Law*, Can. 1134.

35. Pope Paul VI, Encyclical Letter *Humanae vitae*, no. 12: AAS 60 (1968), 488–489.

36. *Loc. cit., ibid.*, no. 489.

37 Pope Pius XII, *Discourse to those taking part in the Second Naples World Congress on Fertility and Human Sterility*, May 19, 1956: AAS 48 (1956), 470.

38. *Code of Canon Law*, Can. 1061. According to this Canon, the conjugal act is that by which the marriage is consummated if the couple "have performed (it) between themselves in a human manner."

39. Cf. Pastoral Constitution *Gaudium et spes*, no. 14.

40. Cf. Pope John Paul II, *General Audience on January 16, 1980: Insegnamenti di Giovanni Paolo II*, III, 1 (1980), 148–152.

41. Pope John Paul II, *Discourse to those taking part in the 35th General Assembly of the World Medical Association*, October 29, 1983: AAS 76 (1984), 393.

42. Cf. Pastoral Constitution *Gaudium et spes*, no. 51.

43. Cf. Pastoral Constitution *Gaudium et spes*, no. 50.

44. Cf. Pope Pius XII, *Discourse to those taking part in the 4th International Congress of Catholic Doctors*, September 29, 1949: AAS 41 (1949), 560: "It would be erroneous ... to think that the possibility of resorting to this means (artificial fertilization) might render valid a marriage between persons unable to contract it because of the *impedimentum inpotentiae*."

45. A similar question was dealt with by Pope Paul VI, Encyclical *Humanae vitae*, no. 14: AAS 60 (1968), 490–491.

46. Cf. *supra*: I, 1 ff.

47. Pope John Paul II, Apostolic Exhortation *Familiaris consortio*, no. 14: AAS 74 (1982), 96.

48. Cf. *Response of the Holy Office*, March 17, 1897: DS 3323; Pope Pius XII, *Discourse to those taking part in the 4th International Congress of Catholic Doctors*, September 29, 1949: AAS 41 (1949), 560; *Discourse to the Italian Catholic Union of Midwives*, October 29, 1951: AAS 43 (1951), 850, *Discourse to those taking part in the Second Naples World Congress on Fertility and Human Sterility*, May 19, 1956: AAS 48 (1956), 471–473; *Discourse to those taking part in the 7th International Congress of the International Society of Haematology*, September 12, 1958: AAS 50 (1958), 733; Pope John XXIII, Encyclical *Mater et magistra*, III: AAS 53 (1961), 447.

49. Pope Pius XII, *Discourse to the Italian Catholic Union of Midwives*, October 29, 1951: AAS 43 (1951), 850.

50. Pope Pius XII, *Discourse to those taking part in the 4th International Congress of Catholic Doctors*, September 29, 1949: AAS 41 (1949), 560.

51. Sacred Congregation for the Doctrine of the Faith, *Declaration on Certain Questions Concerning Sexual Ethics*, no. 9: AAS 68 (1976), 86, which quotes the Pastoral Constitution *Gaudium et spes*, no. 51. Cf. *Decree of the Holy Office*, August 2, 1929: AAS 21 (1929), 490; Pope Pius XII, *Discourse to those taking part in the 26th Congress of the Italian Society of Urology*, October 8, 1953: AAS 45 (1953), 678.

52. Cf. Pope John XXIII, Encyclical *Mater et magistra*, III: AAS 53 (1961), 447.

53. Cf. Pope Pius XII, *Discourse to those taking part in the 4th International Congress of Catholic Doctors*, September 29, 1949: AAS 41 (1949), 560.

54. Cf. Pope Pius XII, *Discourse to those taking part in the Second Naples World Congress on Fertility and Human Sterility*, May 19, 1956: AAS 48 (1956), 471–473.

55. Pastoral Constitution *Gaudium et spes*, no. 50.

56. Pope John Paul II, Apostolic Exhortation *Familiaris consortio*, no. 14: AAS 74 (1982), 97.

Access to In Vitro Fertilization: Costs, Care and Consent

Christine Overall

Abstract

What would be a genuinely caring approach to the provision of procedures of so-called artificial reproduction such as in vitro fertilization (IVF)? What are appropriate and justified social policies with respect to attempting to enable infertile persons to have offspring? These urgent questions have provoked significant dis-

Christine Overall, "Access to In Vitro Fertilization: Costs, Care and Consent," *Dialogue* XXX (1991), 383–397.

agreements among theologians, sociologists, health care providers, philosophers and even — or especially — among feminists. In the existing literature and in developing social policy, three different kinds of answers can be discerned: (1) Some have suggested that access to IVF should be provided as a matter of right. (2) Some existing social policies and practices imply that access to IVF is a privilege. (3) Some theorists have argued that, because of its alleged violation of family values and marital security, or because of its risks, costs, and low success rate, IVF should not be available at all. After evaluating each of these views, I shall offer a feminist alternative, describing what I think would constitute the caring provision of in vitro fertilization.

1. The Right to Reproduce and the Right Not to Reproduce

Is there a moral *right* of access to in vitro fertilization? To answer that question requires consideration of the idea of a reproductive right. Some feminists are remarkably suspicious of any use of rights talk by a feminist, particularly in the context of reproductive technology.[1] While talk of rights does not exhaust feminist moral and political discourse about reproduction, and while appeals to rights can sometimes be used against women (for example, the appeal to the supposed "right" to be a "surrogate" or contract mother), surely the history of feminist activism with respect to abortion provides some indication that use of rights claims is not yet nugatory or outdated, and that claims about reproductive rights need clarification, not abandonment.

It is necessary, first, to distinguish between the right to reproduce and the right *not* to reproduce.[2] The two are sometimes unnecessarily conflated as, for example, when Justice Bertha Wilson referred in her Supreme Court decision on the Morgentaler case to "[t]he right to reproduce or not to reproduce which is in issue in this case."[3] The right not to reproduce means the entitlement not to be compelled to beget or bear children against one's will; the alternative to recognition of such a right is the acceptance of forced reproductive labour, or procreative slavery. To say that women have a right not to reproduce implies that there is no obligation of women to reproduce. The right not to reproduce is the entitlement not to be compelled to donate gametes or embryos against one's will, and the entitlement not to have to engage in forced reproductive labour. This right mandates access to contraception and abortion.

The right not to reproduce is distinct from the right to reproduce; that is, the right not to reproduce neither implies a right to reproduce nor follows from a right to reproduce. In my view, access to artificial reproduction cannot be defended by extension of the right not to reproduce.

The right to reproduce has two senses, the weak sense and the strong sense. The weak sense of the right to reproduce is a negative or liberty right: it is the entitlement not to be interfered with in reproduction, or prevented from reproducing. It would imply an obligation on the state not to inhibit or limit reproductive liberty, for example, through racist marriage laws, fornication laws,[4] forced sterilization, forced abortion, or coercive birth control programs. (In both the United States and Canada there is a sorry history of forced sterilization of people of colour and native people.)

In its strong sense, however, the right to reproduce as a positive or "welfare" right would be the right to receive all necessary assistance to reproduce. It would imply entitlement of access to any and all available forms of reproductive products, technologies and labour, including the gametes of other women and men, the gestational services of women and the full range of procreative techniques including in vitro fertilization, gamete intrafallopian transfer, uterine lavage, embryo freezing and sex preselection.

Liberal writers such as American legal theorist John A. Robertson defend the right to reproduce in the strong sense by claiming that it is just an extension of the right to reproduce in the weak sense. As he puts it, "the right of the married couple to reproduce noncoitally" and "the right to reproduce noncoitally with the assistance of donors and surrogates" both follow from "constitutional acceptance of a married couple's right to reproduce coitally."[5] Robertson believes that these rights entitle married couples certainly, and possibly single persons, to "create, store, transfer, donate and possibly even manipulate extra-corporeal embryos," and "to contract for eggs, sperm, embryos, or surrogates." They would also, he thinks, justify compelling a contract mother to hand over a child to its purchasers, even against her will.[6]

In addition, American attorney Lori B. Andrews argues that the right to reproduce in the strong sense is probably founded upon the right to marital privacy.[7]

Nevertheless, there is good reason to challenge the legitimacy and justification of this right to reproduce in the strong sense. Recognizing it would shift the burden of proof on to those who have moral doubts about the morality of technologies such as IVF and practices such as contract motherhood, for it suggests that a child is somehow owed to each of us, as individuals or as members of a couple, and that it is indefensible for society to fail to provide all possible means for obtaining one. Recognition of the right to reproduce in the strong sense would create an active right of access to women's bodies and in partic-

ular to their reproductive labour and products. Thus, it might be used, as Robertson advocates, to imply an entitlement to obtain other women's eggs, and to make use of donor insemination and uterine lavage of another woman, all in order to maximize the chances of reproducing.[8] It would guarantee the entitlement to hire a contract mother, and force contract mothers to surrender their infants after birth. This would constitute a type of slave trade in infants, and commit women to a modern form of indentured servitude. Finally, the right to reproduce in the strong sense might be used to found a claim to certain kinds of children — for example, children of a desired sex, appearance, or intelligence.

Exercise of the alleged right to reproduce in this strong sense could potentially require violation of some women's right not to reproduce. There is already good evidence, in both the United States and Great Britain, that eggs and ovarian tissue have been taken from some women without their knowledge, let alone their informed consent.[9] It is not difficult to imagine that recognizing a strong right to reproduce could require either a similar theft of eggs or embryos from some women, if none can be found to offer them willingly, or a commercial inducement to sell these products. It could be used as a basis for requiring fertile people to "donate" gametes and embryos. Even on a more ordinary level, recognition of a right to reproduce in the strong sense would seem to give men questionable rights over the reproductive products and labour of their female partners. Because of these implications — particularly the obligations that recognition of such a right would incur — I conclude that there is no right to reproduce in the strong sense. Even if some people willingly donate gametes, there is no *right* or entitlement on the part of the infertile that they should do so.

2. Access to Artificial Reproduction as a Privilege

Access to methods of artificial reproduction such as in vitro fertilization cannot be justified by reference to an alleged right to reproduce in the strong sense. But while I am arguing that there is no right in the strong sense to IVF, such a claim does not of course imply that all use of IVF is thereby unjustified.

However, if appeal to such a right is abandoned, then it may seem that we are committed to holding that having children by means of artificial reproduction is necessarily a *privilege* that must be earned through the possession of certain personal, social, sexual, and/or financial characteristics. The provision of reproductive technology then appears to become a luxury service, access to which can be controlled by means of criteria used to screen potential candidates.[10] Such limitations appear to be the price of sacrificing a right to reproduce in the strong sense.

And indeed, in actual practice, for processes such as IVF the criteria of eligibility have included such characteristics as sexual orientation — only heterosexuals need apply; marital status — single women are not usually eligible (unless they are part of an ongoing marriage-like relationship);[11] and consent of the spouse. Because IVF is costly, economic status and geographical location have also become, at least indirectly, criteria of eligibility. We can speculate that these are likely to lead to de facto discrimination against working-class women and women of colour.[12] Further criteria have also been used — for example, reproductive age, the absence of physical disabilities and characteristics such as "stability" and parenting capacities.[13] Some have also suggested or implied that infertility which is the result of the patient's own choices (for example, tubal ligation) should render the patient ineligible for IVF.

Should access to IVF be treated as a matter of privilege rather than right? Three arguments tell against this approach. First, persons who do not have fertility problems are not compelled to undergo any evaluation of their eligibility for parenthood. Moreover, some medical responses to infertility — for example, the surgical repair of damaged fallopian tubes — are undertaken without any inquiry into the patient's marital status, sexual orientation, or fitness for parenthood. If in vitro fertilization is classed as a medical procedure in the way that tubal repair is a medical procedure, then discrimination in access for the former and not for the latter is unjustified. The case of IVF seems to present an instance of discrimination on the basis of social criteria against people with infertility — and only certain kinds of infertility at that.

A second argument is the general difficulty of assessing the presence of some of the characteristics which have been assumed to be relevant for access to IVF. For example, for some women sexual orientation is a fluid and changing personal characteristic.[14] In addition, it is difficult to see how "stability" or aptitude for parenthood can be adequately measured, and there is likely to be a lot of disagreement about the appropriateness of criteria for evaluating these characteristics. One could also challenge the justification of allotting the assessment of these characteristics to IVF clinicians, who are not likely to have any better expertise than the rest of the population for making such evaluations.

Finally, it is essential to challenge the moral legitimacy of discrimination on the basis of characteristics such as sexual orientation and marital status.

Such discrimination is founded upon false assumptions about the nature and abilities of single and lesbian women, and about the kind of mothering they can provide. While promoting good parenting practices is indisputably a worthwhile social goal, there is no evidence to suggest either that marriage and heterosexuality necessarily make women better mothers, or that the presence of a father is indispensable to childhood developmental processes. Nor do any research findings suggest that the ability to pay the enormous financial costs of IVF increases one's capacity to be a good parent.

Thus, many purveyors of IVF (at least in Canada) seem to be guilty of an inconsistency. Medical practice is not usually premised on the assumption that only some patients deserve treatment, and IVF clinicians themselves see their role as relieving a disability or responding to an "illness" in infertile women.[15] Yet they are only willing to treat infertile women with social characteristics that they judge acceptable, and they disregard the experiences and needs of other infertile women who fail to conform to their criteria. There is no adequate justification for making access to procedures such as in vitro fertilization a privilege for which it is legitimate to erect social barriers that discriminate on arbitrary and unfair grounds — grounds such as marital status, sexual orientation, putative stability or parenting potential, or economic level. Moreover, given that IVF is, as I shall argue later, an experimental procedure rather than an established medical practice, it is particularly unjust to exact money from those women whose bodies function as experimental material.

Acceptance of these social barriers to accessibility is not the only alternative to claiming a right of access to IVF. Instead, it is important to critically evaluate screening processes for IVF, and to resist and reject practices of unjustified discrimination in access.

3. Calling a Halt to Artificial Reproduction: Religious Conservatives

Some critics of artificial reproduction regard access as neither a right nor a privilege; instead they condemn research in IVF and call for an end to IVF services. There are two very different reasons for this perspective.

On the one hand, it is claimed by some writers, particularly those influenced by the teachings of the Roman Catholic Church,[16] that in vitro fertilization threatens marital relationships, sexual interactions and the integrity of the nuclear family. One representative of this approach is Canadian philosopher Donald DeMarco, who states:

> IVF demands sundering flesh from spirit in an area where the integrity of parenthood demands they be one, and sundering [sic; probably "surrendering" is intended] that flesh to the manipulation of technicians. Inevitably, something important, though unseen, stands to be harmed in the process. And what stands to be harmed is human parenthood.[17]

As a mother myself, I have seldom found that human parenthood is "unseen." However, DeMarco explains further:

> By removing the child from the personal context of conjugal love, as IVF does, a decisive step is taken which necessarily depreciates that love. ... And to weaken this love which is the essential bonding act of the family ... is to weaken the family. And since the family is the basic unit of society, what weakens the family also weakens the society.[18]

But this set of claims is highly implausible. There is no evidence of an appreciable debilitation of the nuclear family attributable to the use of IVF. If anything, as many feminists have pointed out, the use of IVF strengthens the traditional nuclear family,[19] since it is usually provided only or primarily to persons who are part of heterosexual, married couples, and it does not challenge the traditional belief that a family is not a real family without one or more genetically related children. Moreover, the legitimacy and value of adoptive relationships is implicitly and unjustifiably called into question by DeMarco's argument, since adopted children are not linked to their social parents through "the personal context of conjugal love." Finally, there is in DeMarco's claims a peculiar reification of married heterosexual relationships, a reification which has an especially sinister aspect when DeMarco assures his readers elsewhere that "[h]usband and wife do have a *right to* engage in intercourse with each other."[20] DeMarco's belief that IVF "degrad[es] the two-in-one flesh unity of parents by deflating the importance of the flesh as a vehicle of love in the formation of new life"[21] suggests that heterosexual intercourse has an extraordinary vulnerability most of us would never have imagined. After all, nothing in the provision of IVF prevents heterosexual married couples from continuing to have sexual intercourse. DeMarco's claims also implicitly condemn any and all intercourse (such as that which involves contraception, or that between two persons one of whom is not fertile) that lacks the potential to result in conception. For all these reasons, DeMarco's reservations about IVF are not persuasive, and the call by religious conservatives for a ban on IVF lacks justification.

4. Calling a Halt to Artificial Reproduction: Feminists

At the other end of the spectrum of general opposition to IVF, however, are criticisms expressed by some feminist scholars, scientists, and activists, criticisms that carry considerable empirical weight. For example, Canadian journalist Ann Pappert has investigated the sorry success record — perhaps more appropriately called a failure record — of IVF in Canada and the United States. She states: "Of the more than 150 IVF clinics in the United States, half have never had a birth, and only a handful have recorded more than five. Fifty per cent of all U.S. IVF babies come from three clinics."[22] The success rate at the best IVF clinic in Canada is 13 percent; the majority of Canada's twelve IVF clinics have success rates of 8 percent or lower.[23]

The stressful and debilitating nature of the IVF experience for women has been powerfully documented by Canadian sociologist Linda Williams:[24] IVF's psychological costs include depression, anxiety and low self-esteem. But the physical suffering and health costs are even worse. They include the adverse effects of hormones such as Clomid, which are usually taken in large, concentrated doses to stimulate hyperovulation; repeated anaesthesia and surgery to extract eggs; the heightened risk of ectopic pregnancy; the development of ovarian cysts and of menstrual difficulties; and the early onset of menopause and an increased risk of some forms of cancer.

Moreover, while it is often said that the children "produced" through IVF are healthy, some recent studies in Australia dispute that claim. Rates of multiple pregnancy, spontaneous abortion, preterm delivery, perinatal death, birth defects and low birth weight are higher in IVF pregnancies than in other pregnancies.[25]

Because IVF represents an ongoing medical experiment on women and children, an experiment whose first success, Louise Joy Brown, is not yet fourteen years old, its long-term effects and risks are not known. Anita Direcks, a DES daughter from Holland, has written movingly about the parallels between the use of the synthetic hormone diethylstilbestrol (DES) allegedly to prevent miscarriage during the 1940s, 1950s and 1960s, and the use of in vitro fertilization, allegedly to alleviate infertility, during the 1970s and 1980s. Direcks writes:

> IVF is delivered by the same men who brought us DES, dangerous contraceptives, and other fertility-destroying technologies. One of the most important concerns I have in regard to IVF is the concern about the long-term effects of an IVF-treatment for mother and child: the consequences of the hormonal treatment, the medium, and so on. ... IVF is an experiment on healthy women.[26]

Indeed, the parallels between the development and use of DES and the development and use of IVF are alarming. DES was not adequately tested before being used on thousands of women; IVF was not adequately tested (not even on animals!) before being used on thousands of women. The long-term effects of DES were not widely known or were ignored when the drug was first being prescribed; the long-term effects of IVF are still not known. DES has intergenerational effects; there is a possibility that IVF may have intergenerational effects, especially in view of the extensive use of hormones in the generation of test-tube babies. DES was not effective in its alleged purpose, preventing miscarriages, but this was not made known to the public; IVF has a very low success rate, but this is almost systematically hidden from public awareness. Women using DES were not adequately informed about it; women undergoing IVF are not adequately informed about it. DES was recommended for routine use in all pregnancies, supposedly to produce "better babies"; similarly, some of the promoters and defenders of IVF have claimed that the process produces more intelligent infants. Thus, the potential uses for DES

were gradually and needlessly expanded, just as the potential uses for IVF are being gradually, and perhaps needlessly, expanded, including its use in cases of male infertility.

Second, there are significant similarities in the ideological underpinnings of DES development and the development of IVF. These include the idea of the inadequacy of women's bodies; the goal of improving women's reproductive functioning; the emphasis upon science and scientists as the white knights coming to rescue women from their underfunctioning reproductive systems; the emphasis upon doing everything possible in the attempt to produce a baby, genetically related to oneself, the eugenic emphasis on having the perfect baby; and the ongoing focus on fertility and reproduction as central to, and perhaps definitive of, women and womanhood.

As a result of considerations such as these, some feminists have called for a ban on further IVF research and practice. For example, Renate Klein and Robyn Rowland state, "IVF — in all its forms — must be ... abandoned. It is a failed and dangerous technology. And it produces a vulnerable population,[27] of women on which to continue experimentation." FINRRAGE, the Feminist International Network of Resistance to Reproductive and Genetic Engineering, calls for resistance to "the development and application of genetic and reproductive engineering" and to "the take-over of our bodies for male use, for profit making, population control, medical experimentation and misogynous science."[28]

Feminists who would ban IVF depict those women who use it in a way entirely opposite to the picture painted by liberals who identify IVF access as a right. Far from being free and equal contractors in the reproductive marketplace, women are depicted as victims who are the uncomprehending dupes of the scientific and medical systems. Whereas the rights advocates regard IVF as inevitably serving women's reproductive autonomy, advocates of a ban on IVF regard IVF as inevitably destroying it. Whereas the rights advocates claim, "Women want IVF," advocates of a ban on IVF claim, "Women do not (really) want IVF," or, "Women's want for IVF is artificial."

Does not this obsessive craving to have a child of one's own in many cases stem from an individual's sense of private property or the desire to have somebody around over whom one has substantial control for some years at least? Let us also face the questions that (a) is not this craving more created than natural and (b) does not the social pressure to fit to the image of "motherhood" put women in a more vulnerable position?[29]

But while many feminists have rightly stressed both the social construction of the desire for motherhood and the dangers and ineffectiveness of in vitro fertilization,[30] not all of them have been willing simply to attribute women's desire for IVF to false consciousness. Margarete Sandelowski suggests that:

> Feminists critical of the new conceptive technology and certain surrogacy and adoption arrangements suggest misguided volition on the part of infertile women, a failure of will associated not with causing infertility but with seeking solutions for it deemed hazardous to other women. ... Beyond being politically useful as evidence for women's oppressive socialization to become mothers and their continued subservience to institutionalized medicine, infertile women occupy no more empathic place in many current feminist discussions than in the medical and ethical debates on reproductive technology feminists criticize.[31]

Sandelowski argues that some feminist theorists "equate women's desire for children with their oppression as women, viewing this desire and the anguish women feel when it remains unfulfilled as socially constructed rather than authentically experienced."[32] Thus, women's desires are discounted and their autonomy denied through the designation of socialization as the shaper and molder of female selves. Similarly, Christine St. Peters argues,

> The appeal to resist [the social imperative that women achieve personhood only through motherhood], an appeal that is heavily pedagogic in tone, is a staple of virtually all the feminist discussions of female infertility, which generally argue that the desire for motherhood is socially constructed and therefore susceptible to revision. Of course this is demonstrably true, although to what extent we cannot prove, since we cannot definitively demonstrate where nature and culture are separable. But the limitations of the message are particularly obvious at a strategic level where we must respond to infertile women's suffering; here the often homiletic tone probably alienates many women, especially as we have not yet changed the social contexts in which the desire for children takes the shape of desiring genetically related offspring.[33]

In fact, women's motives for seeking IVF are complex,[34] and it is important not to deny or underestimate the needs and experiences of infertile women.[35] It is, surely, inappropriate for feminists to claim to understand better than infertile women themselves the origins and significance of their desire for children. Even if the longing felt by infertile women is socially produced, it is nevertheless real longing. Furthermore, that longing cannot be assumed to extinguish women's autonomy. Women who are "trying everything" in order to obtain a baby are not necessarily less autonomous, less free from social conditioning, than women who gestate and deliver without technological intervention, nor less free than the feminists who call into question infertile women's motivations.

Sociologist Judith Lorber claims that consent to IVF is not a freely chosen act unless the woman is "an equal or dominant in the situation."[36] But if that is the criterion for freedom of choice, then almost no women make free choices, ever. I find philosopher Mary Anne Warren more plausible when she claims, "Freedom is not an all or nothing affair. We can rarely be completely free of unjust or inappropriate social and economic pressures, but we can sometimes make sound and appropriate decisions, in the light of our own circumstances."[37]

Radical feminist Janice G. Raymond has poured scorn on the kind of approach I advocate here, which she dismissively labels the "nuanced" approach to evaluating reproductive technologies.[38] This approach, she says, seeks to "limit the abuse [of women by reproductive technologies] by gaining control of some of these technologies, and by ensuring equal access for all women who need/desire them." The error here, she suggests, is in conflating need with desire, and then claiming that to oppose such needs/desires is to "limit women's reproductive liberty, options, and choices." In fact, however, "women as a class have a stake in reclaiming the female body — not as female nature — and not just by taking the body seriously — but by refusing to yield control of it to men, to the fetus, to the State. ..."[39]

My view, however, is that as feminists we can be extremely critical of the easy equation of need and desire, and of the social processes that create women's alleged "need" for babies and that require that that "need" be fulfilled through a biologically related infant acquired in any way possible. We can also reject the facile claim that access to any and all reproductive services, products and labour, is indispensable to reproductive freedom. But it does not follow that feminists should protect women from these social processes and from acting on their own desires. We need not take women's desires as an unanalyzable and unrejectable given. But neither can we ignore or belittle what women say they feel. We can attack the manipulation of women's desires by current medical/scientific reproductive practices. But we can also resist the too-simple depiction of infertile women as nothing but dupes or victims.

Raymond claims that when radical feminists expose the victimization of women by men, they, the radical feminists, are then inappropriately "blamed for creating" that victimization.[40] Obviously, feminists did not create the harm of IVF to which they have called attention. What I am suggesting is that feminists can expose the harm of IVF to the women themselves most likely to be affected by it, and then let them make the decision about whether to seek access nevertheless.

The demand for an end to all use of IVF is an expression of a kind of feminist maternalism,[41] which seeks to protect the best interests of the women affected by IVF. I cannot agree with those who wish to ban IVF to protect women from the dangers of coercive IVF, any more than I can agree with so-called "pro-life feminists" who wish to ban abortion to protect women from the dangers of coercive abortions. It is not the role of feminist research and action to protect women from what is interpreted to be their own false consciousness. If, as Judith Lorber claims, women seeking IVF make "a patriarchal bargain" rather than a free choice,[42] then those women must be given the information and support they need in order to genuinely choose.

At this time, while women candidates are told something about the mechanical procedures for IVF, so far there is not much evidence that they are fully informed about the low success rates and the suffering and risks associated with IVF. The solution to the making of ideologically coerced choices is not always and necessarily the banning of the choices themselves, but education about that which is chosen.

Therefore, while I cannot support and endorse highly ineffective, costly and painful procedures such as IVF, until infertile women themselves, by the thousands, and especially those who seek and have sought IVF, call for the banning of artificial reproduction, I am uneasy about endorsing such a call by some feminists, any more than I would endorse a call for a ban on all interventionist hospital births in low-risk deliveries. I assume that when women are provided with complete information, real choices and full support with regard to artificial reproduction, they will be empowered to make reproductive decisions that will genuinely benefit themselves and their children. Based on my subjective impressions, from talking to women who have already rejected IVF, and to women who now have serious criticisms of IVF after trying it, it may well turn out that, when fully informed, women will reject in vitro fertilization at a much higher rate than they do now.

5. A Feminist Alternative

Or they may not. It is therefore necessary to consider what a caring, feminist approach to the provision of in vitro fertilization would look like — an approach which is founded upon women's experiences, values and beliefs, which acknowledges the political elements of reproductive choices and practices, which seeks to minimize harm to women and children, and which recognizes and fosters women's dignity and self-determination. The caring provision of artificial reproduction services requires (a) truly informed choice and consent; (b) equal and fair access, unbiased by geographic, economic, or social criteria; (c) adequate record keeping, follow-up and research;

and (d) appropriate support systems for all participants. All of these services could be provided in free-standing women's reproductive health clinics, run on feminist principles, where the health care providers are primarily both responsible and responsive to their women clients.[43]

First, then, it is necessary to ensure that women—as individuals, not as part of a couple — entering and participating in infertility treatment programs make a genuinely informed choice and consent. Counselling should not be provided by the clinic itself, but by third parties who have no personal investment in persuading clients to use the clinic's services.

The notion of informed choice involves not merely telling women of the possible risks of the procedure, but discussion of the alternatives to in vitro fertilization.[44] It would also require open acknowledgment of the experimental status of the procedure. This point has recently been emphasized by Marsden Wagner, Director of Maternal and Child Health, European Regional Office of the World Health Organization. Wagner says, "There has not been one single prospective, randomized controlled trial of the efficacy and safety of [IVF]. ... IVF is clearly an experimental procedure by all criteria. It should not be included in the health *care* budget, but in the health *research* budget."[45] Prospective patients must therefore be informed of IVF's unknowns, the short- and long-term risks, the possible benefits, the chances of success and failure, alternative approaches and treatments and pronatalist social pressures to procreate and other ways of responding to them. In particular, women who are offered in vitro fertilization for infertility in their male partners should clearly understand that they could become pregnant much more easily, safely and with lower risks if they made use of donor insemination.[46]

Second, it is essential to critically examine the artificial criteria, such as marital status, sexual orientation and ability to pay, that get in the way of women's fair access to reproductive technologies, with a view to dismantling those barriers that discriminate unjustifiably. If IVF is a valuable medical service (and, given its high risks and low success rate, that assumption is and will remain debatable) then it deserves to be made available, like other medical services, through medicare, as it is now in Ontario.

Third, an adequate system of record keeping should be established, to track the long-term effects of IVF on women and their offspring, and to ensure that any women who provide eggs for the program have genuinely chosen to do so, so that "egg-snatching" is eliminated. Moreover, donors should really be donors, not vendors; the commodification of reproductive products and services is morally unjustified. It is essential to resist the commercialization of reproduction and the spread of reproductive entrepreneurialism, the primary targets of which are likely to be poor women and women of colour. It would also be important to ensure thorough screening and long-term follow-up of donors of eggs and sperm, and to avoid too-frequent use of the same donors. The issue of control over and decision making about so-called "spare" embryos, including those that are subject to cryopreservation, must also be faced. In addition, offspring of artificial reproduction need certain protections, in particular, access to information about their origins and the health status of their biological parents (if they were conceived using donor gametes), and knowledge of the life-long questions about and implications of IVF for their own health prospects.

Finally, participants and potential participants in IVF programs should be provided with support systems to enable them to evaluate fully their own reasons and goals for being in the program, and to provide assistance throughout the emotionally and physically demanding

aspects of the treatment. It would be important that all counselling and group support not just function as a means of ensuring the patients' continued acquiescence, or eliminating those without the stamina to endure the ordeal,[47] but that it facilitate their active involvement and participation in their treatment.

I have tried to indicate what I think is a fair and caring approach to the justification of and access to in vitro fertilization. The approach that I have just sketched avoids, on the one hand, claiming access to artificial reproduction as a right in the strong sense, and on the other hand, making reproductive technology a privilege to be earned through the possession of certain personal, social, sexual and/or financial characteristics. Sweeping generalizations about the moral justification of all forms of artificial reproduction are on very uncertain ground: processes of artificial reproduction need to be evaluated individually, on their own merits, to determine which ones, if any, are genuinely valuable and worth supporting.

For the sake of brevity, this discussion has set aside some crucial macro-allocation questions about the relative importance of IVF in comparison to other health care services, particularly infertility prevention, prenatal care, research on acquired immunodeficiency syndrome (AIDS) and sex education. I do not assume that IVF inevitably ranks equal in importance with these other measures, or that IVF could not legitimately be limited perhaps by confining it to those who do not have any children already, or by eliminating IVF as a so-called "treatment" for male infertility for the sake of research in and access to other more pressing health services. Over the long term, certainly, the caring provision of artificial reproduction should also be coupled with research into the incidence and causes of and cures for infertility, and the elimination of iatrogenic and environmental sources of infertility, so that the apparent need for artificial reproduction is reduced. Ultimately, the genuinely caring provision of artificial reproduction will require a feminist reevaluation and reconstruction of all reproductive values, technologies and practices.

Notes

1. For example, see Janice G. Raymond, "Reproductive Technologies, Radical Feminism, and Socialist Liberalism," *Reproductive and Genetic Engineering: Journal of International Feminist Analysis*, 2, 2 (1989): 141.

2. Christine Overall, *Ethics and Human Reproduction: A Feminist Analysis* (Boston: Allen & Unwin, 1987), 166–96.

3. *Morgentaler, Smolling and Scott v. A. G. Canada,* Supreme Court of Canada, January 28, 1988. Judgment by Justice Wilson, 15.

4. Ethics Committee of the American Fertility Society, "The Constitutional Aspects of Procreative Liberty," in *Ethical Issues in the New Reproductive Technologies,* edited by Richard T. Hull (Belmont, CA: Wadsworth, 1990), 9.

5. John A. Robertson, "Procreative Liberty, Embryos, and Collaborative Reproduction: A Legal Perspective," in *Embryos, Ethics and Women's Rights: Exploring the New Reproductive Technologies,* edited by Elaine Hoffman Baruch, Amadeo F. D'Adamo, Jr., and Joni Seager (New York: Haworth Press, 1988), 180. Cf. Lori B. Andrews, "Alternative Modes of Reproduction," in *Reproductive Laws for the 1990s*, edited by Sherrill Cohen and Nadine Taub (Clifton, NJ: Humana Press, 1989), 364. Robertson's heterosexist bias is not much mitigated by his later concession that there is "a very strong argument for unmarried persons, either single or as couples, also having a positive right to reproduce" (Robertson, "Procreative Liberty," 181).

6. Robertson, "Procreative Liberty," 180, 186 and 190.

7. Uri B. Andrews, *New Conceptions: A Consumer's Guide to the Newest Infertility Treatments* (New York: Ballantyne Books, 1985), 138.

8. From this point of view, then, IVF with donor gametes could be more problematic than IVF in which a woman and a man make use of their own eggs and sperm.

9. Genoveffa Corea, "Egg Snatchers," in *Test-Tube Women: What Future for Motherhood?* edited by Rita Arditti, Renate Duelli Klein and Shelley Minden (London: Pandora Press, 1984), pp. 37–51.

10. Andrews, "Alternative Modes of Reproduction," 374–77.

11. Gena Corea and Susan Ince report that in the United States in 1985, 42 out of the 54 clinics accepted only married couples. See their "Report of a Survey of IVF Clinics in the U.S.," in *Made to Order: The Myth of Reproductive and Genetic Progress*, edited by Patricia Spallone and Deborah Lynn Steinberg (Oxford: Pergamon Press, 1987), 140.

12. Judith Lorber, "In Vitro Fertilization and Gender Politics," in Baruch et al., *Embryos, Ethics and Women's Rights,* 118–19.

13. There are comparable barriers to access to donor insemination. See, e.g., Deborah Lynn Steinberg, "Selective Breeding and Social Engineering: Discriminatory Policies of Access to Artificial Insemination by Donor in Great Britain," in Spallone et al., *Made to Order,* 184–89.

14. See Rebecca Shuster, "Sexuality as a Continuum: The Bisexual Identity," in *Lesbian Psychologies: Explorations and Challenges*, edited by the Boston Lesbian Psychologies Collective (Urbana, IL: University of Illinois Press, 1987), 56–71.

15. See Thomas A. Shannon, "In Vitro Fertilization: Ethical Issues," in Baruch et al., *Embryos, Ethics, and Women's Rights,* 156–57.

16. See Congregation for the Doctrine of the Faith, "Instruction on Respect for Human Life in Its Origin and on the Dignity of Procreation: Replies to Certain Questions of the Day" (Vatican City, 1987). This document, of course, also expresses many concerns about the treatment and destruction of embryos, arguments which are not evaluated here.

17. Donald DeMarco, *In My Mother's Womb: The Catholic Church's Defense of Natural Life* (Manassas, VA: Trinity Communications, 1987), 156–57.

18. Ibid., 157; cf. Ronald D. Lawler, "Moral Reflections on the New Technologies: A Catholic Analysis," in Baruch et al., *Embryos, Ethics, and Women's Rights,* 167–77.

19. Janice G. Raymond, "Fetalists and Feminists: They Are Not the Same," in Spallone et al., *Made to Order*, 63.

20. DeMarco, *In My Mother's Womb*, 147; my emphasis.

21. Ibid., 159.

22. Ann Pappert, "In Vitro in Trouble, Critics Warn," *Globe and Mail*, February 6, 1988, Al. For a comparable discussion of IVF success rates in France, see Françoise Laborie, "Looking for Mothers You Only Find Fetuses," in Spallone et al., *Made to Order*, 49–50.

23. Pappert, "In Vitro in Trouble," A14.

24. Linda S. Williams, "No Relief Until the End: The Physical and Emotional Costs of In Vitro Fertilization," in *The Future of Human Reproduction*, edited by Christine Overall (Toronto: Women's Press, 1989), 120–38.

25. "What You Should Know About In Vitro Fertilization," in *Our Bodies ... Our Babies? Women Look at the New Reproductive Technologies* (Ottawa: Canadian Research Institute for the Advancement of Women, 1989); "Current Developments and Issues: A Summary," *Reproductive and Genetic Engineering*, 2, 3 (1989): 253.

26. Anita Direcks, "Has the Lesson Been Learned? The DES Story and IVF," in Spallone et al., *Made to Order*, 163. For a discussion of the harmful effects of one hormone used in IVF, clomiphene citrate, see Renate Klein and Robyn Rowland, "Women as Test-Sites for Fertility Drugs: Clomiphene Citrate and Hormonal Cocktails," *Reproductive and Genetic Engineering: Journal of International Feminist Analysis*, 1, 3 (1988): 251–73.

27. Klein and Rowland, "Women as Test-Sites," 270.

28. "Resolution from the FINRRAGE Conference, July 3–8, 1985, Vallinge, Sweden," in Spallone et al., *Made to Order*, 211.

29. Sultana Kamal, "Seizure of Reproductive Rights? A Discussion on Population Control in the Third World and the Emergence of the New Reproductive Technologies in the West," in Spallone et al., *Made to Order*, 153.

30. See, e.g., Susan Sherwin, "Feminist Ethics and In Vitro Fertilization," in *Science Morality and Feminist Theory*, edited by Marsha Hanen and Kai Nielsen (Calgary: University of Calgary Press, 1987), 265–84.

31. Margarete Sandelowski, "Failures of Volition: An Historical Perspective on Female Agency and the Cause of Infertility," *Signs: Journal of Women in Culture and Society*, 15, 3 (Spring 1990): 498.

32. Ibid.

33. Christine St. Peters, "Feminist Discourse, Infertility and the New Reproductive Technologies," *National Women's Studies Association Journal*, 1, 3 (Spring 1989): 359.

34. Christine Crowe, "'Women Want It': In Vitro Fertilization and Women's Motivations for Participation," in Spallone et al., *Made to Order*, 84–93.

35. See Alison Solomon, "Integrating Infertility Crisis Counseling into Feminist Practice," *Reproductive and Genetic Engineering*, 1, 1 (1988): 41–49; and Naomi Pfeffer, "Artificial Insemination, In-Vitro Fertilization and the Stigma of Infertility," in *Reproductive Technologies: Gender, Motherhood and Medicine*, edited by Michelle Stanworth (Minneapolis: University of Minnesota Press, 1987), 81–97.

36. Judith Lorber, "Choice, Gift, or Patriarchal Bargain?" *Hypatia*, 4 (Fall 1989): 30.

37. Mary Anne Warren, "IVF and Women's Interests: An Analysis of Feminist Concerns, *Bioethics*, 2, 1 (1988): 40–41.

38. Raymond, "Reproductive Technologies," 133–42.

39. Ibid., 135.

40. Ibid., 137.

41. Deborah Poff, "Reproductive Technology and Social Policy in Canada," in Overall, *The Future of Human Reproduction*, 223.

42. Lorber, "Choice, Gift, or Patriarchal Bargain?" 24.

43. Vicki Van Wagner and Bob Lee, "Principles into Practice: An Activist Vision of Feminist Reproductive Health Care," in Overall, *The Future of Human Reproduction*, 238–58.

44. Nikki Colodny, "The Politics of Birth Control in a Reproductive Rights Context," in Overall, *The Future of Human Reproduction*, 43.

45. "Current Developments and Issues: A Summary," *Reproductive and Genetic Engineering*, 2, 3 (1989): 253, Wagner's emphasis.

46. Lorber, "Choice, Gift, or Patriarchal Bargain?" 23–26.

47. Annette Burfoot, "Exploitation Redefined: An Interview with an IVF Practitioner," *Resources for Feminist Research / Documentation sur la recherche féministe*, 18:2 (June 1989): 27.

Further Readings

Alberta Institute of Law Research and Reform. *Status of Children*. Report No. 20, 1976.

Bartels, D.M., et al., eds. *Beyond Baby M: Ethical Issues in New Reproductive Techniques*. Clifton, N.J.: Humana Press, 1990.

Bayles, Michael D. *Reproductive Ethics*. Englewood Cliffs, N.J.: Prentice Hall, 1984.

British Columbia Bar Association. *Report of the Special Task Force Committee on Reproductive Technology of the British Columbia Branch, The Canadian Bar Association*. Vancouver, June 1989.

British Columbia Royal Commission on Family and Children's Law. *Ninth Report of the Royal Commission on Family and Children's Law: Artificial Insemination.* Victoria, 1975.

Brodrib, S. *Women and Reproductive Technologies.* Ottawa: Status of Women Canada, May 1989.

Cahill, Lisa Sowle. "Moral Tradition, Ethical Language, and Reproductive Technologies." *J Med Philos* 14:5 (Oct. 1989): 497–522.

Congregation for the Doctrine of the Faith. Donum Vitae*: Instruction on Respect for Human Life in Its Origin and on the Dignity of Procreation.* Issued Feb. 22, 1987, Vatican.

Corea, G. *The Mother Machine: Reproductive Technologies from Artificial Insemination to Artificial Wombs.* New York: Harper and Row, 1986, p. 6.

Ethical Considerations of the New Reproductive Technologies. A Report of the Combined Ethics Committee of the Canadian Fertility and Andrology Society and the Society of Obstetricians and Gynecologists of Canada, 1990.

Gostin, L., ed. *Surrogate Motherhood: Politics and Privacy.* Bloomington: Indiana Univ. Press, 1990.

Gouvernement du Québec, Conseil du Statu de la Femme. *General Opinion of the Conseil du Statu de la Femme in Regard to New Reproductive Technologies.* Quebec City, 1989.

Health and Welfare Canada. *Report of the Advisory Committee on the Storage and Utilization of Human Sperm.* Ottawa: HWC, 1981.

Heller, Jan Christian. *Human Genome Research and the Challenge of Future Contingent Persons* Omaha: Creighton Univ. Press, 1996.

Holmes, H., B. Hoskins, and M. Gross. *The Custom-Made Child: Woman-Centered Perspectives.* Clifton, N.J.: Humana Press, 1981.

Knoppers, B.M. *Human Dignity and Genetic Heritage.* Study Paper for the Law Reform Commission of Canada. Ottawa: Law Reform Commission of Canada, 1991.

Lauritzen, Paul. "What Price Parenthood?" *Hastings Center Rep* 20:2 (Mar.–Apr. 1990): 38–46.

Law Reform Commission of Ontario. *Report on Artificial Human Reproduction and Related Matter.* Toronto: Ministry of the Attorney General, 1985.

Law Reform Commission of Ontario. "The Propriety of Artificial Conception Technologies." *Report on Artificial Human Reproduction*, vol. 2. Toronto: Ministry of the Attorney General, 1985, 140–149.

Law Reform Commission of Saskatchewan. *Tentative Proposals for a Human Artificial Insemination Act.* Regina, 1981.

Macklin, Ruth. "Artificial Means of Reproduction and Our Understanding of the Family." *Hastings Center Rep* 21:1 (1991): 5–11.

Okai T., Y. Kuwabara, Y. Imanishi, E. Muronosono, S. Kozuma, M. Mukubo, S. Shi, N. Unno, T. Maeda, N. Shinozuka, K. Nagaya, and M. Mizuno. "Development of Extrauterine Fetal Incubation System Using Extracorporeal Membrane Oxygenator: Recent Advances in Perinatology." *Excerpta Medica*, 1986: 131–138.

Ontario Law Reform Commission. *Report on Human Artificial Reproduction and Related Matters.* Toronto: Ministry of the Attorney General, 1985.

Rich, A. *Of Woman Born: Motherhood as Experiment and Institution.* New York: W.W. Norton and Co., 1976.

Somerville, M. "Weaving 'Birth' Technology into the Value and Policy 'Web' of Medicine, Ethics and Law: Should Policies on 'Conception' Be Considered?" *Nova Law Review* 13:2 (1989): 515–608.

South Australia. *Report of the Working Party on In Vitro Fertilization and Artificial Insemination by Donor*, 1984.

Suzuki, D., and P. Knudtson. *Genethics: The Clash Between the New Genetics and Human Values*. Cambridge, MA: Harvard Univ. Press, 1989.

U.K., Department of Health and Social Security. *Report of the Committee of Inquiry into Human Fertilization and Embryology*. Cmnd. 9314, 1984.

World Council of Churches, Working Group Sub-Unit on Church and Society. "Manipulating Life." *Church and Society* (Sept.–Oct. 1982).

Zimmerman, B. "Human Germ-line Therapy: The Case for Its Development and Use." *J Med Philos* 16 (1991): 593–612.

CHAPTER 17
THE USE OF THE NEW REPRODUCTIVE TECHNOLOGIES

Introduction

The selections in Chapter 16 dealt with the new reproductive technologies from a regulatory and policy perspective. However, regulations and policies are creatures of political process, whether that be in the secular or in the denominational setting, and considerations other than ethical ones play an important role in their development and implementation. For a truly ethical evaluation, therefore, it is important to consider them on their own terms. The selections in this chapter do just that. Given the breadth of the subject and the limitations of this chapter, it was impossible to include materials that deal with the whole problematic. However, an effort has been made to choose articles that illustrate the range of the current discussion while at the same time complementing the selections in the previous chapters — which may fruitfully be revisited in this connection.

Nancy Jecker asks us to consider whether it is ethical to use the new reproductive technologies for inherently non-reproductive purposes: namely, to produce a child who will provide cells that can be transplanted into an already existing child in order to save the latter's life. To paraphrase the title of her article, Is it ethical to produce a child to save a child? Among other things, therefore, her article deals with the very issue of objectification that is of major concern in *Donum vitae* in Chapter 16.

Jecker's article is based on an actual case that involves genetic prenatal screening, and it presents a whole host of ethical issues. However, the problematic she discusses increases in complexity as genetic engineering becomes a viable tool, for it means that it will become possible to produce a child according to required medical specifications. David Resnik deals with part of this problematic in the specific context of therapeutic versus enhancement-oriented genetic engineering. He suggests that it may be more difficult to draw the distinction between therapy and enhancement than is usually thought. He also argues that we should re-think the largely negative stance that most of us have towards germ-line genetic engineering — i.e., against genetic engineering that results in heritable traits as opposed to somatic-cell genetic therapy, which affects only the modified person.

Françoise Baylis discusses the issue of cloning. Reproductive cloning is outlawed by Bill C-13 (*Assisted Human Reproduction Act*) which was passed by the House of Commons in 2003,[1] by *Donum vitae* and by the CIHR Guidelines. However, cloning also occurs naturally: Identical twins and identical triplets, etc. are clones of each other. This raises the question of how something that occurs naturally can be ethically objectionable when it is done artificially. Baylis addresses this question. However, her main concern lies not here but with the whole tenor of the discussion about cloning as it is presently constructed. She believes that the debate is seriously miscast at the level of private relationships and reproductive choice, and that profound value questions about the potentially dramatic societal and species consequences are either inappropriately downplayed or exaggerated. In her mind, "only in recognizing the individual and species enhancement dimensions of cloning technology can we begin to recognize the broader issues and grapple with the threat/opportunity that cloning humans represents."

John Robertson's article focuses on the use of embryonic stem cells. That is to say, it is standard practice when engaging in IVF to retrieve and fertilize more ova — and to produce more blastocysts (embryos at an early stage of development) — than will be implanted. The reason for this is that it is uncertain how many fertilized ova will actually develop into blastocysts that can be implanted (the attrition rate exceeds 50%), and it is also uncertain how many blastocysts will be healthy enough to warrant implantation. Not unexpectedly, this approach sometimes results in "leftover" embryos. The question is, what to do with them? Scientifically and medically, they are very useful. They contain unspecialized pluripotent cells — so-called stem cells — that can develop into any kind of cell at all: liver cells, kidney cells, heart cells, etc. and even neurons. Therefore, the leftover embryos constitute a ready source of stem cells that could be harvested and transplanted into people who suffer from degenerative diseases like diabetes, heart disease or Parkinson's disease. Leftover embryos have been used for this purpose. Is this ethical? Is it more ethical than deliberately creating embryos for this purpose? What lends special bite to this problematic is that, strictly speaking, all of these embryos, no matter where they come from, are potential persons (thereby re-opening the abortion debate with a different twist). Robertson suggests that such use may not be as heinous as it is sometimes portrayed, and that it may even be appropriate to produce stem cells for purely therapeutic and research purposes.

Stem cells are the cellular basis of human life; with due alteration of detail, DNA constitutes the basis of human life at the molecular level. As the article by Robertson intimates, a whole range of concerns surrounds the modification of human DNA. However, there is another set of concerns that has nothing to do with its modification but instead centres on its commercial exploitation. The crux of the problem can be summed up in a single question: Is it ethical to treat the human genome and its constituents as marketable commodities?

To put this into perspective, let us consider an example. Certain forms of breast cancer are associated with a particular gene.[2] That gene, when isolated and incorporated into a pharmacological probe, can be used by oncologists to test for the risk of breast cancer. Like so many other diagnostic tools, this screening tool is not only diagnostically useful but also has tremendous commercial value. However, pharmacological products are very expensive to research and develop. There are no hard figures, but it is generally estimated that the cost of bringing a single new pharmaceutical to market ranges from $700,000 to $400,000,000. These costs have to be recovered by the companies that fund the research. Various countries — Canada included — have therefore allowed companies to patent human genes to allow them to recover their research costs and to encourage further development.[3-5] There are only two conditions the companies must meet: The patentors must be able to identify the proteins that the genes codes for, and they must be able to indicate a possible commercial use. The problem is that the genes themselves are the product of millions of years of evolution and as such are not the products of research and development. Moreover, more than 98% of the genes of all humans are the same. Ethically, does the fact that researchers have isolated the genes from the DNA in which they naturally occur give them an intellectual property right to the genes? Is this different from isolating an element like sodium from the compounds in which it naturally occurs? Does it mean that whoever owns the patent to a gene owns a part of all the people who share it? These are only some of the questions that are raised by the patenting of human genes. The article by Ruth Macklin provides a good introduction to what, ethically, is a very complex issue.

Notes

1. At the time of printing, Bill C-13 was before the Senate as Bill C-6. (For relevant excerpts, see pp. 423–426, *supra*.)

2. Implicated are, among others, BRCA1, BRCA2 and DBC2.

3. *Cf.* Council of Europe Directive on the Legal Protection of Biotechnological Inventions 98/44/EC, Article 3. The Directive came into force on 30 July 1998. The Netherlands and France have challenged the Directive. The U.S. has similar provisions in its patent law; Canada and most of the British Commonwealth have similar provisions.

4. Williamson, A.R. "Gene Patents: Are They Socially Acceptable Monopolies, Essential for Drug Discovery?" *Drug Discov Today* 6:21 (Nov. 1, 2001): 1092–1093.

5. Hoedemaekers, R., and Kennedy D.W. "Is There a Unique Moral Status of Human DNA That Prevents Patenting?" *Inst Ethics J* 11:4 (Dec. 2001): 359–86.

Conceiving a Child to Save a Child: Reproductive and Filial Ethics

Nancy S. Jecker

Introduction

Reproductive and filial ethics raise moral questions that touch our most intimate relationships with other persons. Often relationships within the family are infused with strong emotions that seem to defy rational argument. Many philosophers even doubt that ethical concepts, such as justice, apply at all in the context of filial relationships. Aristotle, for example, wrote that justice does not pertain to relationships between parents and offspring, because young children are an extension or part of their parents and "the just and the unjust always involve more than one person."[1] More recently, Ferdinand Schoeman has argued that "traditional moral boundaries, which give rigid shape to the self," do not apply in the context of intimate relationships, and that "talk about rights of others, respect for others, and even welfare of others is to a certain extent irrelevant."[2] Other philosophers direct little attention to filial ethics because they regard the family itself as legitimate. Plato reckoned that in a just state wives and children must be held in common by guardians in order to prevent "whatever tears [the city] apart into many communities instead of one."[3] In our own day, Rawls has characterized the family as violating a principle of fair equality of opportunity and considered the possibility that the family should be abolished![4]

One reason that contemporary moral philosophy may lend little assistance to persons wrestling with questions about filial ethics is that it tends to frame ethical questions against a backdrop of impersonal relationships. Kant, for example, concentrates on the moral law that holds for rational beings as such, not for rational beings as members of special groups and alliances, such as a family. Likewise, utilitarian ethics originally was developed to justify reforms in the British legal system and to craft a more humane system of punishment. Contemporary versions of utilitarianism focus on the effect actions have on the welfare of society at large and treat individual members as replaceable by other persons.

Contemporary ethical theory itself reflects the modern age. As Bernard Williams notes, inhabitants of the modern world achieve an immense amount through impersonal relations: "We do a great deal by relying on egoistic micromotivations, and it is a remarkable achievement of the modern world to have brought this about. Indeed, it is obvious beyond a certain level of social size and complexity that we must rely a lot on such motivations. ..."[5] Yet the presence of personal relationships in our lives is highly valued, even if seldom acknowledged. These relationships shape the very persons we become, and a life wholly void of personal relationships would

Nancy S. Jecker, "Conceiving a Child to Save a Child: Reproductive and Filial Ethics," *The Journal of Clinical Ethics* 1:2 (Summer 1990), 99–107. Copyright 1990 by *The Journal of Clinical Ethics*. All rights reserved. Reprinted from *The Journal of Clinical Ethics*.

hardly be worth living. We cannot hold personal relationships immune from ethical reflection then, nor can we afford to neglect thinking about our ethical responsibilities in personal relationships without paying a high price. Not considering personal relationships in ethical terms may make us less sensitive to close associates in situations where we find spontaneous support difficult to muster. It also may make it possible for the status quo to persist in personal relationships where it falls far short of ethical standards and ideals.

How should we begin, then, to view personal relationships in an ethical light? Although impartial theories may define, in broad brush, the contours of an ethics for personal relationships,[6] they cannot begin to complete a rich and finished picture. In this essay, I will examine some of the broad ethical guides that govern personal relationships generally, and filial relationships in particular. I focus this task by describing a specific case that raises ethical questions about reproduction and parenting.

The Case

In July 1989, a middle-aged couple from a Los Angeles suburb conceived a child to save the life of their teenage daughter who is dying of cancer. The couple, Abe and Mary Ayala, had learned two years prior that their daughter, Anissa, was suffering from leukemia and needed a bone marrow transplant to survive. Neither Anissa's parents nor her brother, Airon, have compatible bone marrow. A search for a non-related donor has been fruitless to date.

When the Ayalas first decided to conceive a child their chance of success was slim.[7] Abe, forty-four years old, had to undergo an operation to reverse a vasectomy performed sixteen years earlier. The chance of vasectomy reversal leading to pregnancy is 50 percent. Mary, at the

age of forty-two, had a 73 percent chance of becoming pregnant. Finally, the likelihood that any offspring Abe and Mary conceived would qualify as a bone marrow match for Anissa was 25 percent. Overall, the odds of Anissa's being cured of leukemia by her parents' effort to conceive a child to save her was 6.4 percent.

To date, many of these obstacles have been overcome. On April 3, 1990, Mary delivered a baby girl, Marissa, who is a suitable donor for her sister. While it was not possible to collect stem cells from Marissa's umbilical cord during delivery, doctors predict that once the baby grows enough bone marrow, surgery to obtain bone marrow from Marissa's hip will have a 70 to 80 percent chance of success. Family members apparently are delighted about their youngest member. "She's my baby sister," Anissa declares, "and we're going to love her for who she is not for what she can give me."[8] Mary adds, "Our baby is going to have more love than she can put up with."[9] Abe reflects that even if Anissa didn't survive, "we'd have another child in the house to help us with our sense of loss."[10]

Outside the family, the Ayalas' success is greeted with mixed emotions. Some argue that conceiving persons to benefit others insinuates the norms of production and commodification into the parent–child relationship. For example, George Annas asserts that "children aren't medicine" manufactured for other people.[11]Alternatively, it could be claimed that conceiving children to benefit others violates a principle that should guide ethical decision making regarding becoming a parent; namely, doing what will be best from the potential child's point of view.[12] It also could be contended that Marissa is likely to suffer psychological harm as a result of being conceived for the purpose of benefitting her sister. For example, she might be prone in the future to regard her worth as conditional on the benefits she can provide others. She might harbor resentment toward her parents for choosing to conceive her for this purpose, or toward her sister for reaping benefits from her conception. These feelings could present formidable obstacles to loving relationships within the family, and thereby handicap Marissa in the future. Family relationships profoundly shape our relationships with persons outside the family circle, and they influence the kind of person we strive to become. Finally, some have voiced the concern that conceiving a child for the purpose of saving another violates a principle of respect for persons, because it involves using a child as a means to another's end. "One of the fundamental precepts of ethics," Alexander Capron states, "is that each person is an end in himself or herself and is never to be used solely as a means to another person's ends without the agreement of the person being used."[13]

The Ethical Analysis

Depersonalizing Personal Relationships

Let us first consider whether conceiving children to benefit another family member is harmful to persons or to relationships within the family. One way harm might occur is that conceiving a child in this way imputes the norms of production into the parent–child relationship. It might be said, on the one hand, that producing Marissa in order to make bone marrow for her sister degrades Marissa, because it implies treating her body as a good to be manufactured and used. On the other hand, it could be argued that Mary's and Abe's procreative labor is itself degraded, because its primary function becomes making an object for use, rather than a child to love. If either of these objections is valid, then Marissa's conception may violate an important principle governing personal relationships: actions should not depersonalize

personal relationships, for doing so does violence to what these relationships are and to the intentions, desires, and hopes persons have in becoming involved in them.[14]

In response, it might be argued that prior to Marissa's conception, she did not stand in a personal relationship to her future parents; therefore, the decision to beget her does not depersonalize a personal relationship. After all, even if we may feel personally related to nonextant persons (for example, dead family members), the parties in personal relationships must be particular and nonsubstitutable individuals. For example, if I stand in a personal relationship to someone, then I must be the object of that person's attention. Prospective parents cannot possibly be personally involved with still-to-be-conceived offspring, since there is no particular future person that could be the object of this involvement. Even after Marissa's conception and birth it could be maintained that the parent–child relationship does not yet qualify as personal. To have a personal relationship with someone might be thought to imply "mutuality of meaning — either verbal or sign — because shared meanings are necessary for the mutual agreement on meaning that form the basis of the relationship."[15]

Initiating Personal Relationships

Yet perhaps the ethics that apply to personal relationships also govern relationships that are likely to be personal in the future. For example, initiating a personal relationship with ulterior objectives is ethically suspect, because this may harm a future personal relationship. One reason harm might occur is that the touchstone of having a personal relationship is that the motive for being in it and continuing it is that we value it for its own sake. For example, friends simply want to give and receive from one another because of the joy and value inherent in doing so.[16] In the case of the Ayalas, the relationship between Marissa and her sister, Anissa, could be harmed because Anissa comes to it in dire need. As John Hardwig states,

> If I see myself primarily as a being in need, I will be too focused on myself and my needs. I will then tend to depersonalize you as someone who can meet my needs. And I will also be generally unable to freely and joyously give. ... Characteristically and normatively, the appropriate motive for action in personal relationships is simply that we want to do these things.[17]

Likewise, the future intimacy between Marissa and her parents could be endangered because Mary and Abe established this relationship to aid their other child. In some respects, this would be analogous to a person learning that a man had shown romantic attention or initiated a sexual relationship in order to benefit someone else; for example, to benefit himself by making a former girlfriend jealous. In this case, the desire to initiate a personal relationship is born of some motive other than the desire to be in a personal relationship. Similarly, Marissa is conceived not because she is wanted, but because she can be useful. Hence, upon learning the reason for her conception, Marissa might feel betrayed.

Although these points initially may appear troublesome, upon reflection they are much less so. First, it is reasonable to suppose that intimacy and harmony already will have developed by the time Marissa is able to comprehend the circumstances of her conception. This intimate basis will make it more likely that harmony and good relationships can be restored if they are suspended or strained, because in once intimate associations the pain of disaffection and the desire for union offer strong motives for reconciliations.[18] Similarly, if the woman

betrayed by the man who displays affection finds out about his initial motives after many years of intimacy, there would be good reason to think that intimacy between the two would not wither. Of course, reparations may not restore harmony automatically, or entirely eliminate bad feelings. For example, these feelings can continue to operate at an unconscious level. But even if there can be no guarantee that strong family relations can be sustained, intimate associations always involve the risk of dissolution.

A second redeeming point is that, unlike other actions that can render personal relationships hurtful, the decision to conceive Marissa is not intended to hurt Marissa. For example, neither Abe, Mary, nor Anissa is motivated by spite or by a desire to harm Marissa. Quite the contrary, they say that they intend to love her. By contrast, someone who bestows romantic attention or sexual favors to make a former partner jealous does not intend to love the object of his favors (even if he later does).

In addition, it is far from clear that the act of conceiving Marissa for the purpose of benefitting Anissa could cause any tangible harm to Marissa. The argument here is that Marissa is better off having been conceived and living the life that she does, despite its added tensions, than she would be if she had never been conceived at all.[19] Presumably, Marissa will prefer to endure certain hardships so long as the hardships in question are necessary for her coming into existence.

Honesty in Personal Relationships

One way that her conception could impose a clear harm to Marissa is if she were not told about the facts surrounding it. Once an intimate relationship is formed, parties to it should establish honest and open relations. This is partly owing to the fact that the more time people spend together, the less likely it is that they can keep up a dishonest front.[20] Each can maintain an artificial posture for only so long. Another consideration about honesty that applies in the context of close relationships is that intimates have more reason to reveal important details of their lives because such revelations create and sustain their intimacy. By contrast, withholding important facts can bar intimacy or create the false appearance of intimacy where genuine intimacy is absent. False intimacy exists to varying degrees in personal relationships. It develops, for example, when we encourage distortions in another's view of us, or when we deny another's shortcomings. Shakespeare called these processes "love's best habit,"[21] and noted the costs associated with lovers' efforts to know each other. In the case of parent–child relationships, false intimacy would be created if, for example, Marissa's parents and sister concealed, altered, or denied the facts surrounding her conception. Yet, there is no reason to expect that this will occur. Marissa's family does not express shame about their decision or view it as something to hide. As one commentator puts it, "By all appearances the Ayalas are not an exploitive family. To them the ethical questions that swirl around them are airy abstractions, not the terrifying reality they daily confront."[22]

Privacy in Personal Relationships

In addition, the Ayalas' decision can be defended on the grounds that a sphere of privacy surrounds families and protects their decisions about whether and when to procreate. Family privacy might be elaborated in terms of a "family privacy right," which is a right to be free from surveillance and interference within the internal workings of the family.[23] This right implies that Mary and Abe should be left alone in making decisions about whether to conceive a child. It implies more generally that we should reject the position that the state is the proper

authority for making reproductive choices, a position which Plato states in stark terms: "If a man still of begetting years unites with a woman of child-bearing age without the sanction of the rulers ... we shall say that he brings into the city an unauthorized and unhallowed bastard ... born in darkness."[24]

Even if the state's interests did override a family's privacy right, it is unlikely that the state could bar couples from conceiving children where they are able to conceive on their own. Unlike conception that is carried out through new reproductive technologies and relies upon the assistance of others, reproductive acts between two consenting persons are far more difficult to control. Mary and Abe's sexual and procreative acts are as antithetical to regulation as are present efforts to prohibit consensual sodomy or homosexuality.

Respect for Individuals in Personal Relationships

Let us next turn to examine the question of whether conceiving a child to benefit another fails to accord proper respect to the child-to-be. One objection to Mary and Abe's decision was that respecting persons calls for treating persons as ends in themselves. According to this objection, by conceiving and bearing Marissa as a means to save their daughter's life, Mary and Abe treat Marissa as a means to their own end.

Yet this way of stating the objection glosses over important distinctions. First, parents have multiple reasons for conceiving, and it is not unethical if some of these involve using their child. For example, it is not unethical if a royal couple conceives to have an heir, or if a couple produces a second offspring to give their first a sibling, or if two people have a child to enrich their own lives. Second, reasons for reproducing reveal a lack of respect only if prospective parents do not also want and love their children. The point here is that there is nothing blatantly unethical about treating persons as means to our own ends. Using persons as means is unethical only when we regard persons as nothing but means. Respect for offspring requires recognizing, as Kant said, "that man, and in general every rational being, exists as an end-in-himself, not merely as a means for arbitrary use by this or that will," and that a person "must, in all his actions, whether they are directed to himself or to other rational beings, always be viewed at the same time as an end."[25]

Understood in this way, Abe and Mary's decision to conceive Marissa fails to show respect toward her only if their sole reason for conceiving is to use Marissa, for example, as a means to save their other daughter's life, or to keep the house from feeling empty if their other daughter dies. But their statements and actions indicate that they intend to love Marissa for who she is, quite apart from what she can give. Thus, the Ayalas' action is morally different from a situation where a couple intends to conceive a child to serve as a bone marrow donor and abort the child if it is not medically useful. It also is morally distinct from a situation where a woman becomes pregnant with the sole intention of providing fetal tissue to a parent with Parkinson's disease, and then terminates her pregnancy. In these cases the desire to create a child is disassociated from any intention to raise a child and value it for its own sake. Thus, in these instances prospective parents truly fail to respect the individual they call to life.

Now it might be argued that the injunction to treat rational beings always as ends does not even apply to Marissa, because she is not even minimally rational. Arguably, she will not be rational for some time to come. Her cerebral cortex did not form until late in the second trimester, and even well after birth she will not have developed her full rational powers. Kant states in *The*

Groundwork that "every rational being exists as an end-in-himself." This suggests that being rational is sufficient for being valuable as an end in oneself. He also states that "nothing but the idea of the law in itself, which ... is present only in rational beings ... can constitute that preeminent good which we call moral." This last passage suggests that being rational is necessary for possessing moral value within oneself. Are Abe and Mary absolved of the responsibility to treat Marissa as an end on the grounds that Marissa is not yet a person?

To answer this question, let us consider next what form respect should take in the context of personal relationships. One way of elaborating the requirement of respect in close relationships is that Marissa should be treated always as an end by persons who stand in a special relationship to her, regardless of whether she possesses the intrinsic moral qualities that confer strict moral status. Unlike animals of similar cognitive functioning, Marissa is Mary and Abe's daughter, and she is Anissa and Airon's sibling. Thus Mary, Abe, Anissa, and Airon are not entitled to treat Marissa as they would treat any being of similar cognitive functioning. Even if Marissa were never to develop rationality or consciousness, she merits respect by virtue of her position in a family.[26] Regardless of whether Marissa is a person in the Kantian sense, she is nonetheless a person in the social sense.[27]

Sacrifices in Personal Relationships

Should the above remarks quiet the concern that Marissa is not being fully or adequately respected, and that she deserves to be? One answer to this question is that treating persons as ends implies obtaining their consent before making them the subject of medical procedures.

Since Marissa obviously cannot give consent, perhaps it is disrespectful to harvest her marrow for transplant. Ordinarily, Mary and Abe would be vested with the ethical authority to make this decision,[28] but it could be argued that their obvious stake in the situation biases their ability to dispassionately weigh the pros and cons of the decision.

However, the ethical requirement of respect takes different shape when placed against a backdrop of personal relationships. Where an antecedent tie or bond exists between the person who makes some sacrifice and the person who benefits, the requirements of respect subtly shift. Relationships vary in the degree to which they are personal, and the closer and more personal a relationship is, the stronger the claims it can make ethically on our allegiance. This is not to say that persons can legitimately exploit those with whom they are most intimate. Rather, it establishes that family members are governed by stronger ethical responsibilities than strangers, and we expect them to serve each other's welfare to a greater extent.

The ethical quandary with which Mary and Abe are left is where to draw the line. How much can they ask of one daughter on behalf of another? The operation Marissa may undergo to extract marrow from her hipbone involves slight pain and minimal risks. Thus, it is considerably less than asking Marissa to give a kidney or other organ. It would have involved still less sacrifice if Marissa's marrow could have been taken from her umbilical cord at birth. In either case, I would argue that the demands placed upon Marissa do not exceed the ordinary sacrifices family members make and expect from one another. Marissa's sacrifice differs only in that it requires her to give a tangible product. Ordinarily, the benefits we bestow upon family members are more intangible, such as time and energy, or love and affection. What we give up is often less tangible as well; for example, other ways of using that time and attention.

It might be said, in response, that parents are required to do far more for offspring than offspring are required to do for siblings. After all, we choose whether to conceive, bear, and rear children, but children do not choose to be siblings. Yet, even so, we still owe far more to siblings than to strangers because of the presence of a close relationship. However, it might be argued that families are not always a locus of intimacy and closeness. Thus, if filial duties are founded on intimacy, then merely being someone's sibling does not show that one is required to make special sacrifices. In reply, it should be noted that families in fact are a common locus of intimacy, because we live in a family for an extended period during early formative years. The Ayala family's rallying around Anissa to save her life attests to the strength of their love. There is no reason to think that this love will not permeate Marissa's relationship with her sister.

Summary

I conclude that Mary and Abe's decision to conceive a child to save a child does not impose harm on persons or on relationships in the family. Nor does it evince a lack of respect for the child they have conceived. The ethical guidelines that support this conclusion can now be summarized. First, actions should not depersonalize or otherwise endanger personal relationships. Second, although ideally personal relationships are initiated and continued for their own sake, after a personal relationship has been established and sustained, the motives for establishing it recede in importance. Third, the requirement of honesty looms especially large in the context of personal relationships. Fourth, privacy protects personal relationships in the family from intrusion by the state. Fifth, even if those with whom we stand in personal relationships are not fully rational or self-conscious, we should treat them with respect. Finally, persons often are called upon to make greater sacrifices in personal relationships. These principles represent only the barest beginnings of an ethics for filial relationships. Nonetheless, they mark progress in the direction of developing a more complete account. We should not suppose that ethics in the family always will be spontaneous or "natural."[29] Over a century ago, Mill warned that nature and natural are "one of the most copious sources of false taste, false philosophy, false morality, and even bad law."[30] Especially in the wake of medical advances, such as recombinant DNA and new reproductive technologies, the complexity of filial ethics will only increase. The demographics of an aging society will add further complexity to filial contexts.[31] We can hardly afford to cling tenaciously to the idea that ethical conduct in the family will issue forth in a spontaneous fashion.

Notes

1. Aristotle, *Nicomachean Ethics,* trans. W.D. Rouse (Oxford: Clarendon Press, 1966), see especially 1138a19.

2. F. Schoeman, "Rights of Children, Rights of Parents and the Moral Basis of the Family," *Ethics* 91 (1980): 6–19.

3. Plato, *Republic,* trans. G.M.A. Grube (Indianapolis: Hackett Publishing Company, 1974), 123.

4. J. Rawls, *A Theory of Justice* (Cambridge: Harvard University Press, 1971), 511.

5. B. Williams, "Formal Structure and Social Reality," *Trust: Making and Breaking Cooperative Relations,* ed. D. Gambetta (Oxford: Basil Blackwell Press, 1989), 3–13.

6. N.S. Jecker, "Impartiality and Special Relationships," *Kindred Matters: Rethinking the Philosophy of the Family,* ed. D. Meyers, K. Knipnis, and N. Murphy (Ithaca, NY: Cornell University Press), [1993].

7. A. Toufexis, "Creating a Child to Save Another," *Time,* March 15, 1990, 56.

8. Ibid.

9. "(2) Having a Baby to Save Daughter," *New York Times,* February 17, 1990.

10. Toufexis, "Creating a Child to Save Another."

11. Quoted in Toufexis, "Creating a Child to Save Another."

12. Although this principle is stated in another context, it pertains in obvious ways to the case at hand. S. Callahan, "An Ethical Analysis of Responsible Parenthood," *Genetic Counseling: Facts, Values, and Norms,* ed. A.M. Capron (New York: Alan R. Liss, Inc., 1979), 217–38.

13. "(2) Having a Baby to Save Daughter."

14. J. Hardwig, "In Search of an Ethics of Personal Relationships," *Person to Person,* ed. G. Graham and H. LaFollette (Philadelphia: Temple University Press, 1989), 63–81.

15. S.J. Mills, "Conceptualizing Personal Relationships," *Generations* 10 (1986):6–9.

16. Ibid.

17. Ibid.

18. J. Deigh, "Morality and Personal Relations," *Person to Person*, ed. G. Graham and H. LaFollette (Philadelphia: Temple University Press, 1989), 106–23.

19. N.S. Jecker, "Reproductive Risk Taking and the Nonidentity Problem," *Social Theory and Practice* 13 (1987):219–35; D. Parfit, *Reasons and Persons* (Oxford: Clarendon Press, 1984), chapter 16.

20. G. Graham and H. LaFollette, "Honesty and Intimacy," *Person to Person*, ed. G. Graham and H. LaFollette (Philadelphia: Temple University Press, 1989), 167–81.

21. W. Shakespeare, Sonnet 138, in *Complete Works,* ed. W.J. Craig (London: Oxford University Press, 1980).

22. Toufexis, "Creating a Child to Save Another."

23. F. Schoeman, "Adolescent Confidentiality and Family Privacy," *Person to Person*, ed. G. Graham and H. LaFollette (Philadelphia: Temple University Press, 1989).

24. Plato, *Republic*, 122.

25. I. Kant, *Groundwork of the Metaphysic of Morals,* trans. H.J. Paton (New York: Harper and Row Publishers, 1964).

26. N.S. Jecker, "Anencephalic Infants and Special Relationships," *Theoretical Medicine*, 11 (1990):333–42.

27. N.S. Jecker, "The Moral Status of Patients Who Are Not Strict Persons," *The Journal of Clinical Ethics* 1 (1990):35–8.

28. N.S. Jecker, "The Role of Intimate Others in Medical Decision Making," *The Gerontologist* 30 (1990):65–71.

29. S.M. Okin, *Justice, Gender, and the Family* (New York: Basic Books, 1989); especially 33 ff.

30. J.S. Mill, "Nature," *Essential Works of John Stuart Mill,* ed. M. Lerner (New York: Bantam Books, 1961), 367–401.

31. N.S. Jecker, "Are Filial Duties Unfounded?" *American Philosophical Quarterly* 26 (1989):73–80.

The Moral Significance of the Therapy-Enhancement Distinction in Human Genetics

David B. Resnik

Introduction

The therapy-enhancement distinction occupies a central place in contemporary discussions of human genetics and has been the subject of much debate.[1–7] At a recent conference on gene therapy policy, scientists predicted that within a few years researchers will develop techniques that can be used to enhance human traits.[8] In thinking about the morality of genetic interventions, many writers have defended somatic gene therapy,[9,10] and some have defended germ-line gene ther-

Cambridge Quarterly of Healthcare Ethics (2000), 9, 365–377. Reprinted with the permission of Cambridge University Press.

apy,[11,12] but only a handful of writers defend genetic enhancement,[13] or even give it a fair hearing.[14–16] The mere mention of genetic enhancement makes many people cringe and brings to mind the Nazi eugenics programs, Aldous Huxley's *Brave New World,* "The X-Files," or the recent movie "Gattaca." Although many people believe that gene therapy has morally legitimate medical uses,[17,18] others regard genetic enhancement as morally problematic or decidedly evil.[19–21]

The purpose of this essay is to examine the moral significance of the therapy-enhancement distinction in human genetics. Is genetic enhancement inherently unethical? Is genetic therapy inherently ethical? I will argue that the distinction does not mark a firm boundary between moral and immoral genetic interventions, and that genetic enhancement is not inherently immoral. To evaluate the acceptability of any particular genetic intervention, one needs to examine the relevant facts in light of moral principles. Some types of genetic therapy are morally acceptable while some types of genetic enhancement are unacceptable. In defending this view, I will discuss and evaluate several different ways of attempting to draw a solid moral line between therapy and enhancement.[22]

Somatic versus Germline Interventions

Before discussing the therapy-enhancement distinction, it is important that we understand another distinction that should inform our discussions, viz. the distinction between somatic and germline interventions.[23,24] Somatic interventions attempt to modify somatic cells, while germline interventions attempt to modify germ cells. The gene therapy clinical trials that have been performed thus far have been on somatic cells. If we combine these two distinctions, we obtain four types of genetic interventions:

Somatic genetic therapy (SGT)

Germline genetic therapy (GLGT)

Somatic genetic enhancement (SGE)

Germline genetic enhancement (GLGE)

While I accept the distinction between somatic and germline interventions, it is important to note that even interventions designed to affect somatic cells can also affect germ cells: current SGT trials carry a slight risk of altering germ cells.[25] Even so, one might argue that this is a morally significant distinction because somatic interventions usually affect only the patient, while germline interventions are likely to affect future generations.[26] In any case, the therapy-enhancement distinction encompasses somatic as well as germline interventions, and my discussion of this distinction will include both somatic as well as germline interventions.

The Concepts of Health and Disease

Perhaps the most popular way of thinking about the moral significance of the therapy-enhancement distinction is to argue that the aim of genetic therapy is to treat human diseases while the aim of genetic enhancement is to perform other kinds of interventions, such as altering or "improving" the human body.[27–29] Since genetic therapy serves morally legitimate goals, genetic therapy is morally acceptable; but since genetic enhancement serves morally questionable or illicit goals, genetic enhancement is not morally acceptable.[30–33] I suspect that many people view the distinction and its moral significance in precisely these terms. W. French Anderson states a clear case for the moral significance of genetic enhancement:

> On medical and ethical grounds we should draw a line excluding

any form of genetic engineering. We should not step over the line that delineates treatment from enhancement.[34]

However, this way of thinking of medical genetics makes at least two questionable assumptions: (1) that we have a clear and uncontroversial account of health and disease, and (2) that the goal of treating diseases is morally legitimate, while other goals are not. To examine these assumptions, we need to take a quick look at discussions about the concepts of health and disease.

The bioethics literature contains a thoughtful debate about the definitions of health and disease and it is not my aim to survey that terrain here.[35,36] However, I will distinguish between two basic approaches to the definition of health, a value-neutral (or descriptive) approach and a value-laden (or normative) one.[37] According to the value-neutral approach, health and disease are descriptive concepts that have an empirical, factual basis in human biology. Boorse defended one of the most influential descriptive approaches to health and disease: a diseased organism lacks the functional abilities of a normal member of its species.[38] To keep his approach value-neutral, Boorse interprets "normal" in statistical terms, i.e., "normal" = "typical." Daniels expands on Boorse's account of disease by suggesting that natural selection can provide an account of species-typical functions: functional abilities are traits that exist in populations because they have contributed to the reproduction and survival of organisms that possessed them.[39] Thus a human with healthy lungs has specific respiratory capacities that are normal in our species, and these capacities have been "designed" by natural selection. A human who lacks these capacities, such as someone with cystic fibrosis or emphysema, has a disease.

According to the value-laden approach, our concepts of health and disease are based on social, moral, and cultural norms. A healthy person is someone who falls within these norms; a diseased person deviates from them. Someone who deviates from species-typical functions could be considered healthy in a society that views that deviation as healthy: although schizophrenia has a biological basis, in some cultures schizophrenics are viewed as "gifted" or "sacred," while in other cultures they are viewed as "mentally ill." Likewise, some cultures view homosexuality as a disease, while others do not.[40–42]

Many different writers have tried to work out variants on these two basic approaches to health and disease, and some have tried to develop compromise views,[43,44] but suffice it to say that the first assumption mentioned above — i.e., that we have a clear and uncontroversial account of health and disease — is questionable.

Even if we lack an uncontroversial account of disease, we could still ask whether either of the two basic approaches would condemn genetic enhancement unconditionally. Consider the descriptive approach first. If statements about disease merely describe deviations from species-typical traits, does it follow that we may perform genetic interventions to treat diseases but not to enhance otherwise healthy people? Since we regard the concept of disease as descriptive, we cannot answer this question without making some normative assumptions. Saying that someone has a disease is like saying that he or she has red hair, is five feet tall, or was born in New York City. These descriptions of that person carry no normative import. Hence the descriptive account of disease, by itself, does not provide us with a way of drawing a solid moral line between therapy and enhancement. For this approach to disease to draw moral boundaries between therapy and enhancement, it needs to be supplemented by a normatively rich account of the rightness of therapy and wrongness of enhancement.

Perhaps the normative approach fares better than the descriptive one. If we accept this view, it follows that therapy has some positive moral value, since therapy is an attempt to treat diseases, which are defined as traits or abilities that do not fall within social or cultural norms. If it is "bad" to have a disease, then we are morally justified in performing interventions that attempt to treat or prevent diseases, since these procedures impart "good" states of being. Thus this normative approach implies that therapy is morally right. But does it imply that enhancement is morally wrong? The answer to this question depends, in large part, on the scope of the concepts of health and disease. If we hold that the concept of health defines a set of traits and abilities that should be possessed by all members of society and that any deviations are diseases, then any intervention that results in a deviation from these norms would be viewed as immoral. Hence, enhancement would be inherently immoral. But this account of health and disease is way too broad; there must be some morally neutral traits and abilities. If there are no morally neutral traits and abilities, then any person that deviates from health norms is "sick." This view would leave very little room for individual variation, to say nothing of the freedom to choose to deviate from health norms. If we accept a narrower account of health and disease, then we will open up some room for morally acceptable deviations from health norms. But this interpretation implies that enhancement interventions could be morally acceptable, provided that they do not violate other moral norms, such as nonmaleficence, autonomy, utility, and so on. Enhancement would not be inherently wrong, in this view, but the rightness or wrongness of any enhancement procedure would depend on its various factual and normative aspects.

The upshot of this discussion is that neither of the two main approaches to health and disease provides us with solid

moral boundaries between genetic enhancement and genetic therapy. One might suggest that we examine alternative approaches, but I doubt that other, more refined theories of health and disease will provide us with a way of drawing sharp moral boundaries between genetic enhancement and genetic therapy. Perhaps we should look at other ways of endowing the distinction with moral significance.

The Goals of Medicine

A slightly different approach to these issues asserts that genetic therapy is on solid moral ground because it promotes the goals of medicine, while genetic enhancement promotes other, morally questionable goals. But what are the goals of medicine? This is not an easy question to answer, since medicine seems to serve a variety of purposes, such as the treatment of disease, the prevention of disease, the promotion of human health and well-being, and the relief of suffering. Many of the so-called goals of medicine, such as the prevention of disease and the promotion of human health, may also be promoted by procedures that we would classify as forms of enhancement.[45] For example, some writers have suggested that we might be able to perform genetic interventions that enhance the human immune system by making it better able to fight diseases, including cancer.[46] Most people would accept the idea that providing children with immunizations against the measles, mumps, and rubella promotes the goals of medicine. If we accept the notion that ordinary, nongenetic enhancement of the immune system promotes the goals of medicine, then shouldn't we also agree that genetic enhancements of the immune system serve the same goals? And what about other forms of healthcare, such as rhinoplasty, liposuction, orthodontics, breast augmentation, hair removal, and hair transplants? If these cosmetic procedures serve medical goals, then cosmetic uses of genetic technology, such as somatic gene therapy for baldness, and germline gene therapy for straight teeth, would also seem to serve medical goals. Finally, consider the procedures that are designed to relieve suffering, such as pain control and anesthesia. If we can develop drugs to promote these goals, then why not develop genetic procedures to meet similar objectives? It is not beyond the realm of possibility that we could use genetic therapy to induce the body to produce endorphins. Many forms of enhancement may serve medical goals. Once again, the therapy-enhancement [distinction] appears not to set any firm moral boundaries in genetic medicine.

One might attempt to avoid this problem by narrowly construing the goals of medicine: the goals of medicine are to treat and prevent diseases in human beings. Other uses of medical technology do not serve the goals of medicine. There are two problems with this response. First, it assumes that we agree on the goals of medicine and the definitions of health and disease. Second, even if we could agree that medicine's goals are to treat and prevent diseases and we can define "health" and "disease," why would it be immoral to use medical technology and science for nonmedical purposes? If a medical procedure, such as mastectomy, is developed for therapeutic purposes, what is wrong with using that procedure for "nonmedical" purposes, such as breast reduction surgery in men with overdeveloped breasts? Admittedly, there are many morally troubling nonmedical uses of medical science and technology, such as the use of steroids by athletes and the use of laxatives by anorexics, but these morally troubling uses of medicine are morally troubling because they violate various moral principles or values, such as fairness and nonmaleficence, not because they are nonmedical uses of medicine.

One might argue that those who use medical science and technology for nonmedical purposes violate medicine's professional norms, but this point only applies to those who consider themselves to be medical professionals. If a procedure violates medical norms, it is medically unethical, but this does not mean that the procedure is unethical outside of the context of medical care. For example, the American Medical Association holds that it is unethical for physicians to assist the state in executions, but this policy does not constitute an unconditional argument against capital punishment. To make the case against capital punishment, one must appeal to wider moral and political norms. Hence the goals of medicine also do not set a morally sharp dividing line between genetic therapy and enhancement.

Our Humanness

One might try to draw moral boundaries between genetic therapy and genetic enhancement by arguing that genetic enhancement is inherently immoral because it changes the human form. Genetic therapy only attempts to restore or safeguard our humanness, while enhancement changes those very features that make us human. Although GLGE and GLGT can more profoundly change human traits than SGE and SGT, both technologies can alter our humanness (or our humanity). To explore these issues in depth, we need to answer two questions: (1) What traits or abilities make us human? and (2) Why would it be wrong to change those traits or abilities? Philosophers have proposed answers to the first question ever since Aristotle defined man as "the rational animal." A thorough answer to the question of defining our humanness takes us way beyond the scope of this essay, but I will offer the reader a brief perspective.[47]

If we have learned anything from the abortion debate, we have learned that it is not at all easy to specify necessary and sufficient conditions for a thing to be human. Humanness is best understood as a cluster concept in that it can be equated with a list of characteristics but not with a set of necessary and sufficient conditions.[48] Some of these characteristics include:

a) physical traits and abilities, such as an opposable thumb, bipedalism, etc.

b) psychosocial traits and abilities, such as cognition, language, emotional responses, sociality, etc.

c) phylogenetic traits, such as membership in the biological species Homo sapiens.

The beings that we call "human" possess many of these traits and abilities, even though some humans have more of these traits and abilities than others. For example, a newborn and an adult have many of the same physical and phylogenetic traits and abilities, even though the adult has more psychosocial traits and abilities. For my purposes, I do not need to say which of these traits and abilities are more "central" to the concept of humanness, since I am not defending a definition that provides necessary or sufficient conditions.

The question I would like to explore in more depth concerns the wrongness of changing those traits that make us human. Would it be inherently wrong to alter the human form? This question presupposes the pragmatically prior question: Can we alter the human form? The answer to this question depends on two factors: (1) the definition of our humanness; and (2) our scientific and technological abilities. According to the definition I assume in this essay, it is possible to alter the human form, since the human form consists of a collection of physiological, psychosocial, and phylogenetic traits and abilities, which can be changed in principle.[49] Although we lacked the ability to

change the traits that constitute our humanness at one time, advances in science and technology have given us the ability to change human traits. Since we have good reasons to believe that we can change our humanness, we can now ask whether we should do so.

Most moral theories, with the notable exception of the natural law approach, imply that there is nothing inherently wrong with changing the human form. For the purposes of this essay, I will not examine all of these moral theories here but will only briefly mention two very different perspectives on morality that reach similar conclusions. According to utilitarianism, an action or policy that alters our humanness could be morally right or it could be morally wrong, depending on the consequences of that action or policy. If genetic enhancement produces a greater balance of good/bad consequences, then enhancement would be morally acceptable. For example, genetic interventions that enhance the human immune system might be morally acceptable, but interventions that result in harmful mutations would be unacceptable. Kantians would object to attempts to alter our humanness if those attempts violate human dignity and autonomy. Some, but not all, genetic interventions could threaten our dignity and autonomy. For example, using SGT to promote hair growth should pose no threat to human dignity and autonomy (if informed consent is not violated), but using GLGE to create a race of "slaves" or "freaks" would pose a dire threat to dignity and autonomy. The main point here is that most moral theories would hold that there is nothing inherently wrong with changing our humanness; the moral rightness or wrongness of such attempts depends on their relation to other moral concerns, such as utility, autonomy, natural rights, virtue, etc.[50]

However, the natural law approach to morality could be interpreted as implying that tampering with the human form is inherently wrong. This argument assumes that the human form has inherent worth and that any changes to that form defile or destroy its worth. The human form is morally sacred and should not be altered.[51] For example, one might hold that a great painting, such as the *Mona Lisa*, has inherent worth and it should therefore be left as it is; to change the *Mona Lisa* is to destroy it. Or perhaps one might argue that it would be wrong to change the formula for "Coke" or the plot of *Hamlet*. But what is inherently wrong with changing the human form?

One argument that changing the human form is inherently wrong is that natural selection has "designed" us to have specific traits, and that any attempt to change those traits would be a foolhardy and vain intervention in nature's wisdom. It has taken thousands of years of adaptation for the human species to evolve into its present form. How can we possibly improve on nature's perfection? We are more likely to make a major blunder or mistake with human genetic engineering than to make an important advance.[52] Human genetic engineering is likely to produce harmful mutations, gross abnormalities, Frankenstein monsters, etc.[53] There are two problems with this neo-Darwinian view. First, it is Panglossian and naïve: natural selection is not perfect — nature makes mistakes all the time. We possess many traits, such as the appendix, that serve no useful function. There are some traits that we could add, such as enhancements to the immune system, that could be very useful. Though we should not underestimate nature's wisdom and our ignorance, it is simply false that nature has made us perfect with no room for change or improvement.[54] Second, the argument overestimates human ignorance and carelessness. The history of medical technology allows us to see that while we have had many failures in altering the

human form, such as Nazi eugenics programs, we have also had some successes, such as artificial limbs and eyeglasses. Although we should exhibit extreme care, discretion, and circumspection in all genetic interventions, not all changes we make in the human form will result in natural disasters.

A second argument approaches the issue from a theological perspective. According to this view, God, not natural selection, has designed us to have specific traits. Hence any human attempt to change those traits would be a foolish (and arrogant) challenge to God's wisdom. Those who attempt to "play God" by changing human nature commit the mortal sin of hubris. One obvious difficulty with this argument is that it is not likely to convince nonbelievers, but let us set aside that problem and engage in some speculative theology. The question we need to ask in response to this argument is, Would God not want us to change human traits? Changes we can now make to human traits could promote human welfare and justice. Why would God allow us to have this power and not use it? Of course, God would not want us to use our power to increase human suffering or injustice, but why would He not want us to use this power for good purposes? Although several well-known theologians have taken a strong stance against human genetic engineering,[55] religious denominations are not united in their opposition to genetic engineering.[56] For example, the National Council of Churches adopted a resolution that the effort to use genetics to improve on nature is not inherently wrong, and the Council later stated that God has given men and women powers of cocreation, though these powers should be used with care.[57,58]

Regardless of whether one accepts the views of a particular church, it is not at all clear that a theologically based natural law theory provides us with good reasons for thinking that it is inherently wrong to change the human form. One could accept a theologically based approach to morality that leaves some room for human beings to alter the human form, provided that we exhibit wisdom, care, and restraint in changing our form.[59] Some changes (e.g., those that result in suffering or injustice) are morally wrong, but other changes (e.g., those that promote happiness or justice) are morally acceptable.

The Rights of the Unborn

Another way of arguing that at least some forms of genetic enhancement are inherently wrong is to claim that GLGE and GLGT violate the rights of unborn children.[60] These procedures are often said to violate the rights of unborn children because they:

a) are experimental procedures that violate the informed consent of unborn children;[61]

b) deny unborn children the right to have a germline that has not been genetically manipulated;[62]

    or

c) deny unborn children a right to an open future.[63]

All of these arguments make the morally controversial assumption that unborn children have rights. I will not challenge this assertion here.[64] Even if one assumes that unborn children have rights, it still does not follow that GLGE or GLGT violate those rights.

Let's consider (a) first. GLGT and GLGE do not violate the unborn child's right to informed consent because this right can be exercised by competent adults acting in the child's best interests. We allow proxy consent as a legitimate way of exercising informed consent for many procedures that can profoundly affect the welfare of children, such as fetal surgery and experimental surgery on newborns to repair congenital defects. If it makes sense to use proxy consent in

these kinds of experiments, then it should also make sense to use proxy consent for other types of experiments, such as GLGT or GLGE, provided that these experiments can be shown to be in the best interests of unborn children.[65]

[Point] (b) is a very esoteric position. What kind of right is the "right to have a genome that has not been genetically manipulated"? Most writers conceive of rights in terms of interests: rights function to protect the interests of individuals.[66] Interests are needs and benefits that most people require to have a fulfilling life, such as freedom, health, education, self-esteem, and so on. So do unborn children have an interest in being born with a genome that has not been manipulated? If such an interest exists, then it is highly unusual and certainly not universal. Children whose parents hold specific religious or philosophical doctrines that forbid germline manipulation may have an interest in being born with an unadulterated genome, but other children will not have this interest. For most children, being born with a genome that predisposes them to health and a wide range of opportunities is more important than being born with a genome that has not been manipulated.

This brings us to argument (c). A right to an "open future" is a right to make one's own choices and life plans on reaching adulthood.[67] Parents who excessively impose their own choices, values, and life plans on their children may violate this right. For example, parents who decide to have a son castrated in order to make sure that he becomes a good singer close off many choices and plans that he could have made as an adult, e.g., having children through natural means. The right to an open future is by no means an unusual or esoteric right, since almost all children have the interests that this right protects, e.g., freedom of choice, freedom of opportunity, etc. But even if we admit this much, does it follow that GLGT or GLGE constitute an inherent violation of this right? I don't think so. While some uses of genetic technology could be regarded as an overbearing imposition of parental values on children, other uses of GLGT and GLGE may augment a child's right to an open future. If parents use GLGE to enhance a child's immune system, then they could be increasing his opportunities to an open future by helping him fight diseases, which can limit opportunities. On the other hand, parents who attempt to produce an eight-foot-tall child in order to make her into a basketball player probably are violating her right to an open future by imposing their choices on her life.

However, there is not a sharp distinction between violating a child's right to an open future and being a responsible parent.[68] We readily accept the idea that parents should try to raise children who are healthy, intelligent, responsible, and happy, and we endorse various parental attempts to promote these values, such as private education, athletics, SAT preparation, and so on. Parents that act in the best interests of the children and have hope for their future are simply being good parents. But when does this healthy and responsible concern for a child's future interfere with the child's right to choose his own values and life plans? This is not an easy question to answer. In any case, this quandary supports my claim that GLGT and GLGE do not inherently violate a child's right to an open future. Some uses of these technologies might have this effect; others might not. The upshot of this section is that we have once again debunked several arguments that might be construed as proving that genetic enhancement is inherently wrong. It may be wrong under some circumstances, but not in others.

Eugenics

Some have attacked GLGT and GLGE on the grounds that they constitute a form of eugenics, an attempt to control the human gene pool.[69] Is eugenics inherently wrong? To understand this question, we can distinguish between positive and negative eugenics: positive eugenics attempts to increase the number of favorable or desirable genes in the human gene pool, while negative eugenics attempts to reduce the number of undesirable or harmful genes, e.g., genes that cause genetic diseases. We should also distinguish between state-sponsored and parental eugenics: under state-sponsored eugenics programs the government attempts to control the human gene pool; in parental eugenics parents exert control over the gene pool through their reproductive choices.[70]

Parental eugenics occurs every time people select mates or sperm or egg donors. Most people do not find this kind of eugenics to be as troubling as the state-sponsored eugenics programs envisioned by Aldous Huxley or implemented by Nazi Germany. Indeed, one might argue that this kind of eugenics is a morally acceptable exercise of parental rights.[71] Moreover, most parents do not make their reproductive choices with the sole aim of controlling the human gene pool; any effects these choices have on the gene pool are unintended consequences of parental actions. As long as we accept the idea that parents should be allowed to make some choices that affect the composition of the human gene pool, then parental eugenics is not inherently wrong.

But what about state-sponsored eugenics? One might argue that state-sponsored eugenics programs, such as involuntary sterilization of the mentally disabled or mandatory genetic screening, are morally wrong because they:

a)   constitute unjustifiable violations of individual liberty and privacy;

b)   are a form of genetic discrimination;

c)   can have adverse evolutionary consequences by reducing genetic diversity; and

d)   can lead us down a slippery slope toward increased racial and ethnic hatred, bias, and genocide.

Although these arguments do not prove that all forms of state-sponsored eugenics are morally wrong, they place a strong burden of proof on those who defend these programs. It is not my aim to explore state-sponsored eugenics in depth here.[72] However, even if we assume that state-sponsored eugenics is inherently wrong, this still only proves that some forms of GLGE or GLGT are inherently wrong. There is nothing inherently wrong with parental choices to use GLGE or GLGT to help children achieve health, freedom, and other values. Thus arguments that appeal to our concerns about eugenics do not prove that genetic enhancement is inherently wrong. Some forms of genetic enhancement, e.g., state-sponsored eugenics, are wrong, others are not.

Conclusion: The Significance of the Distinction

Two decades ago, James Rachels challenged the moral significance of the active–passive euthanasia distinction in a widely anthologized essay.[73] This paper has attempted to perform a similar debunking of the therapy-enhancement distinction in human genetics. It has considered and rejected a variety of different ways of arguing that the therapy-enhancement distinction in human genetics marks a solid, moral boundary. Genetic enhancement is not inherently immoral nor is genetic therapy inherently moral. Some forms of enhancement are immoral, others are not; likewise, some types of therapy are immoral, others are not. The implication of this view is that we should not use the therapy-enhancement distinction as our moral compass in human genetics. In evaluating the ethical aspects of any particular genetic intervention, we should ask not whether it is therapy or enhancement but whether the intervention poses significant risks, offers significant benefits, violates or promotes human dignity, is just or unjust, and so on.

Having said this much, I think some forms of enhancement can be morally justified, provided that they can be shown to be safe and effective. For example, using genetic technology to protect people against diseases could be justified on the grounds that it benefits patients. I think one can even justify the use of genetics for cosmetic purposes in terms of benefits to patients. We can also view some forms of genetic therapy as unacceptable (at present) because they pose unjustifiable risks to patients or future generations. For example, all forms of GLGT and some types of SGT, such as a procedure for fighting cancer at the genetic level, are too risky, given our current scientific and technical limitations. In any case, the moral assessment of these procedures depends on considerations of probable benefits and harms (as well as other moral qualities), not on their classification as "therapy" or "enhancement."

So what is the significance of the therapy-enhancement distinction? What role should it play in thinking about the ethics of human genetics? Can it guide public policy? The most I can say in favor of the distinction is that it defines moral zones without any sharp boundaries. The significance of the distinction may lie in its ability to address our fears and hopes: we hope that genetic therapy will help us treat diseases and improve human health, but we fear that genetic enhancement will lead us down a slippery slope toward a variety of undesirable consequences, such as discrimination, bias, eugenics, injustice, biomedical harms, and so on.[74] Genetic enhancement will probably always dwell in [the] shadow of the slippery slope argument, while genetic therapy will probably always bask in the glory of modern medicine. Our hopes and fears may or may not be warranted; only time will tell. In the meantime, even if the therapy-enhancement distinction does not draw any solid moral boundaries, we need to be aware of the distinction in public dialogues about genetics. In these dialogues, it may be useful to address the fears of enhancement and the hopes of therapy while attempting to grapple with the realities of the genetic revolution.

Notes

1. Juengst E. Can enhancement be distinguished from prevention in genetic medicine? *Journal of Medicine and Philosophy* 1997;22 125–42.

2. Holtug N. Altering humans — the case for and against human gene therapy. *Cambridge Quarterly of Healthcare Ethics* 1997;6 151–74.

3. Berger E, Gert B. Genetic disorders and the ethical status of germ-line gene therapy. *Journal of Medicine and Philosophy* 1991;16 667–83.

4. Anderson W. Human gene therapy: scientific and ethical considerations. *Journal of Medicine and Philosophy* 1985;10 275–91.

5. Anderson W. Human gene therapy — why draw a line?" *Journal of Medicine and Philosophy* 1989;14 81–93.

6. Anderson W. Genetics and human malleability. *Hastings Center Report* 1990;20(1) 21–4.

7. McGee G. *The Perfect Baby.* Lanham, Md.: Rowman and Littlefield, 1997.

8. Vogel G. Genetic enhancement from science fiction to ethics quandary. *Science* 1997;277 1733–4.

9. See note 4, Anderson 1985.

10. Fowler G, Juengst E, and Zimmerman B. Germ-line gene therapy and the clinical ethos of medical genetics. *Theoretical Medicine* 1989;19 151–7.

11. See note 3, Berger, Gert 1991.

12. Zimmerman B. Human germ-line gene therapy: The case for its development and use. *Journal of Medicine and Philosophy* 1991;16 593–612.

13. Glover J. *What Sort of People Should There Be?* New York: Penguin Books, 1984.

14. See note 7, McGee 1997.

15. Resnik D. Debunking the slippery slope argument against human germ line gene therapy. *Journal of Medicine and Philosophy* 1993;19 23–40.

16. Resnik D. Genetic engineering and social justice: a Rawlsian approach. *Social Theory and Practice* 1997;23(3) 427–48.

17. See note 3, Berger, Gert 1991.

18. See note 4, Anderson 1985.

19. See note 6, Anderson 1990.

20. Rifkin J. *Algeny,* New York: Viking Press, 1983.

21. Ramsey P. *Fabricated Man: The Ethics of Genetic Control.* New Haven: Yale University Press, 1970.

22. It is not my aim in this essay to argue that there is no distinction between therapy and enhancement. I am only attempting to question the moral significance of

the distinction. If it turns out that there is not a tenable distinction between therapy and enhancement, so much the worse for the moral significance of this distinction. For the purpose of this essay I will define "enhancement" as a medical intervention that has goals other than therapeutic ones. There may be many types of enhancement on this view. Some forms of enhancement, such as a circumcision, can have therapeutic aims as well, e.g., preventing urinary tract infections. Some forms of therapy, such as heart transplantation, could have enhancement effects, e.g., a person could acquire an above average heart. Some interventions, such as preventative medicine, could straddle the line between enhancement and therapy. For further discussion, see note 1, Juengst 1997.

23. See note 4, Anderson 1985.

24. Suzuki D, Knudtson P. *Genethics.* Cambridge, Mass.: Harvard University Press, 1989.

25. Resnik D, Langer P, Steinkraus H. *Human Germ-line Gene Therapy: Scientific, Ethical, and Political Issues.* Austin, Texas: RG Landes, 1999.

26. See note 24, Suzuki, Knudtson 1989.

27. See note 5, Anderson 1989.

28. See note 6, Anderson 1990.

29. Baird P. Altering human genes: social, ethical, and legal implications. *Perspectives in Biology and Medicine* 1994;37 566–75.

30. In the current debate in bioethics, several writers have attempted to use the concepts of health and disease to distinguish between genetic therapy and genetic enhancement.

31. See note 1, Juengst 1997.

32. See note 3, Berger, Gert 1991.

33. See note 5, Anderson 1989.

34. See note 6, Anderson 1990, 24.

35. Caplan A. The concepts of health, illness, and disease. In: Veatch R, ed. *Medical Ethics*, 2d ed. Sudbury, Mass.: Jones and Bartlett, 1997:57–74.

36. Khushf G. Expanding the horizon of reflection on health and disease. *Journal of Medicine and Philosophy* 1995;1–4.

37. Some writers distinguish between relativist and nonrelativist accounts; some others distinguish between biological and social accounts. But the basic insight is the same — the concepts of health and disease are normative or descriptive.

38. Boorse C. Health as a theoretical concept. *Philosophy of Science* 1977;44 542–73.

39. Daniels N. *Just Health Care.* Cambridge. Cambridge University Press, 1985.

40. Sigerist H. *Civilization and Disease.* Chicago: University of Chicago Press, 1943.

41. Pellegrino ED, Thomasma DC. *For the Patient's Good.* New York: Oxford University Press, 1988.

42. For an overview of the normative approach, see Caplan A. *Moral Matters.* New York: John Wiley and Sons, 1995.

43. Culver C, Gert B. *Philosophy in Medicine.* New York: Oxford University Press, 1982.

44. Lennox J. Health as an objective value. *Journal of Medicine and Philosophy* 1995;20 501–11.

45. See note 44, Lennox 1995.

46. Culver K. The current status of gene therapy research. *The Genetic Resource* 1993;7 5–10.

47. See note 25, Resnik, Langer, Steinkraus 1999.

48. English J. Abortion and the concept of a person. *Canadian Journal of Philosophy* 1975;5(2) 233.

49. It is possible to define "human" in such a way that it is logically impossible to change our humanness. If we stipulate that possession of single property is a necessary and sufficient condition for being human, then any changes we make in that property would result in people that are not human. For example, we can define "triangle" = "three-sided object." If we make an object that has four sides, it is not an altered triangle; it is not a triangle at all. For a definition of humanness that would seem to imply that it is difficult (though not impossible) to alter our humanness, see Anderson W. Genetic engineering and our humanness. *Human Gene Therapy* 1994;5 755–60.

50. See note 25, Resnik, Langer, Steinkrauss 1999.

51. For the purposes of this essay, I will not attribute this view to any particular author, since I think it deserves consideration on its own merit. For writers who come close to defending this view, see note 8, Vogel 1997, as well as Kass L. *Toward a More Natural Science.* New York: Free Press, 1985.

52. See note 20, Rifkin 1983.

53. These arguments do not address genetic enhancement per se, since they also apply to GLGT and they do not apply to SGT or SGE.

54. See note 25, Resnik, Langer, Steinkrauss 1999.

55. See note 21, Ramsey 1970.

56. Cole-Turner, R. Genes, religion, and society. The developing views of the churches. *Science and Engineering Ethics* 1997;3(3) 273–88.

57. National Council of Churches. *Human Life and the New Genetics.* New York: National Council of Churches of Christ in the U.S.A., 1980.

58. National Council of Churches. *Genetic Engineering: Social and Ethical Consequences.* New York: National Council of Churches of Christ in the U.S.A, 1983.

59. Peters T. *Playing God? Genetic Determinism and Human Freedom.* New York: Routledge, 1997.

60. For further discussion see Buchanan A, Brock D. *Deciding for Others.* Cambridge: Cambridge University Press, 1989.

61. Lappé M. Ethical issues in manipulating the human germ line. *Journal of Medicine and Philosophy* 1991;16 621–39.

62. Commission of the European Community, *Adopting a Specific Research and Technological Development Programme in the Field of Health.* Brussels: Commission of the European Community, 1989.

63. Davis D. Genetic dilemmas and the child's right to an open future. *Hastings Center Report* 1997;27(2) 7–15.

64. These arguments do not constitute an objection to SGT or SGE.

65. See note 25, Resnik, Langer, Steinkrauss 1999.

66. Feinberg J. *Social Philosophy*. Englewood Cliffs, N.J.: Prentice Hall, 1973.

67. Feinberg J. The child's right to an open future. In Aiken W and Lafollette H, eds. *Whose Child? Children's Rights, Parental Authority, and State Power.* Totowa, N.J.: Littlefield, Adam, 1980:124–53.

68. See note 7, McGee 1997.

69. For further discussion of eugenics, see Paul D. *Controlling Human Heredity, 1865 to the Present.* Atlantic Highlands, N.J.: Humanities Press International, 1995.

70. Kitcher P. *The Lives to Come.* New York: Simon and Schuster, 1997.

71. Robertson J. *Children of Choice.* Princeton, N.J.: Princeton University Press, 1994.

72. For further discussion, see Parens E. Taking behavioral genetics seriously. *Hastings Center Report* 1996;26(4) 13–8.

73. Rachels J. Active and passive euthanasia. *New England Journal of Medicine* 1975;292(2) 78–80.

74. See note 15, Resnik 1993.

Human Cloning: Three Mistakes and an Alternative

Françoise Baylis

I. Human Cloning: Three Mistakes and an Alternative[1]

Human cloning by somatic cell nuclear transfer is arguably the most exciting and at the same time foreboding technological-biological development of our times. Specifically, the prospect of cloning humans using nuclear transfer technology challenges our understanding of ourselves (i.e., what it is to be human), and our place in the world. When we reproduce by sexual intercourse we do not reproduce ourselves; what we reproduce or perpetuate is our own kind. Significantly, our kind is one that reproduces by recombining genes. In marked contrast, with nuclear substitution there is no recombination of the genes. We do not reproduce our kind, rather we reproduce, or more precisely, replicate ourselves.[2]...

... In late 1993, Jerry Hall and colleagues at George Washington University reported their success with cloning human polyploid embryos. The technique they developed involved blastomere separation at the two-cell to eight-cell stage, and transfer to an artificial zona pellucida for continued growth into separate but identical embryos (Hall et al., 1993). Seventeen chromosomally abnormal human embryos were divided, and 48 developing embryos were obtained. A few years later, in February 1997, Ian Wilmut and colleagues at the Roslin Institute announced the existence of Dolly, the cloned sheep (Wilmut, Schnieke, McWhir, Kind, & Campbell, 1997). The nucleus of a cell from a six-year-old sheep was removed, transferred to an unfertilized enucleated egg, and encouraged to develop. Two hundred and twenty-seven embryos were reconstructed; Dolly was the only success. ... Since then several other species have been cloned from adult somatic cells including mice, cows, the rhesus monkey and transgenic pigs (Kato et al., 1998; Onishi et al., 2000; PPL, 2000; Wakayama et al., 1998; Wells, Misica, & Territ, 1999; Wolf, Meng, Ouhibi, & Zelinski-Wooten, 1999). As regards the cloning of humans, in 1999 there was an unconfirmed report of human cloning from somatic cells by South Korean scientists (Watts & Morris, 1999). Then, in November 2001, Advanced Cell Technology (ACT) reported that it had cloned human embryos as a possible future source of stem cells for regenerative medicine (Cibelli et al., 2001).

... As the prospect of human cloning appeared to draw nearer ... committee reports, policy documents and legislation were issued specifically condemning human *reproductive*[3] cloning, where cloning technology is used to create whole beings. For example, in 1997, the Fiftieth World Health Assembly adopted the following resolution: "cloning for the replication of human individuals is ethically unacceptable and contrary to human dignity and integrity" (WHO, 1997). In the same year, the US National Bioethics Advisory Commission (NBAC) concluded that "it is morally unacceptable ... to attempt to create a child using somatic cell nuclear transfer cloning,"

(NBAC, 1997, p. 106) and President Clinton enacted the NBAC recommendation to extend the moratorium on the use of federal funding for such research for five years. Under President Bush, the US House of Representatives passed a bill in July 2001 that would make it a federal crime to clone humans either to produce children or to create embryos for research purposes (the US Senate has yet to vote on the bill). Meanwhile, in the UK, it is legal to clone human embryos for research purposes (Human Fertilisation, 2001), but the use of cloning for human reproduction is prohibited. And, closer to home, the Canadian government is poised to introduce legislation in 2002 that would prohibit the cloning of humans for either research or reproductive purposes (Health Canada, 2001).*

For some, these policy statements and legislative prohibitions are an important first step in precluding the further development of human cloning to replicate individuals. For others, these initiatives are at most useful temporizing maneuvers to preclude the trivial and misguided uses of cloning technology. Proponents of this latter view believe that the cloning of whole beings is inevitable. The underlying reasoning is as follows: (1) cloning humans represents an irresistible scientific and technological challenge which means that some research group(s) somewhere will develop the technology, and this effort will be defended on the grounds of freedom of scientific inquiry; (2) the commitment, in some jurisdictions, to free enterprise and personal choice, coupled with the burgeoning support for the compassionate use of cloning technology to assist certain infertile couples, means that the technology (once developed and shown to be rea-

---

* **Editor's note:** At the time of publication, the *Assisted Human Reproduction Act* had passed in the House of Commons as Bill C-13 and was before the Senate as Bill C-6. The Act as passed by the House can be accessed at **http://www.parl.gc.ca/37/2/parlbus/chambus/house/bills/ government/C-13/C-13_3/C-13_cover-E.html**; the Act before the Senate can be accessed at **http://www.parl.gc.ca/PDF/37/3/parlbus/chambus/house/bills/government/C-6_3.pdf**.

sonably safe and effective) will be "for sale"; and (3) once the technology is for sale, there will be eager customers.

The likely development and possible future use of cloning technology to create individuals raise important ethical questions about the common good and the integrity of the human species. These questions require timely and careful reflection. As Hans Jonas wrote more than twenty-five years ago:

> Since no less than the very nature and image of man [sic] are at issue, prudence becomes itself our first ethical duty, and hypothetical reasoning our first responsibility (Jonas, 1974, p. 141).

In this spirit, the reader's attention is drawn to some of the more pervasive and egregious mistakes with the current debate on the ethics of cloning humans using nuclear transfer technology.

II. A First Mistake

A first mistake with the public debate on the ethics of cloning humans is our apparent comfort with a discourse that lulls us into complacency about a technology that represents a fundamental challenge to our understanding of ourselves and the species to which we belong. Consider, for example, the following summary caricatures of potentially complex arguments against the cloning of humans as unnatural, as "playing God," as contrary to human dignity.

A. Cloning Humans Is Unnatural

According to some, cloning humans is "contrary to nature." While the splitting of human embryos does occur in nature, spaced twinning (using both embryo splitting and freezing), and somatic cell nuclear transfer do not. Further, while asexual reproduction does occur in

nature, it is unnatural for the species Homo Sapiens which practices sexual reproduction.

This argument against cloning humans presumes an understanding of nature as a primordial structure that is independent of, and authoritative with respect to, all other possible structures (for example, social structures). There are two common responses to this argument. One response posits a specific understanding of "human nature" that encompasses the desire for knowledge and the capacity for self-transformation. In this view, our nature includes mastering ourselves and choosing our own destiny (i.e., making plans for our own nature). Another response side-steps the debate about the scope and meaning of human nature and asks somewhat facetiously: "So what? So are all sorts of other interventions that we happily accept."

B. Cloning Humans Is "Playing God"

Warnings against "playing God" have been interpreted in multiple ways. What is common to these interpretations "is the idea that there is a natural order or structure, perhaps divinely ordained, and that proposals to exceed the limits which this natural order defines should be rejected out of hand — or at least considered very carefully" (Grey, 1998). In its religious applications, the phrase "playing God" alludes to God's omniscience and omnipotence and serves to identify acts or decisions outside the realm of legitimate human activity. Some of the religious interpretations of the phrase "playing God" are helpfully summarized in the NBAC report, *Cloning Human Beings*:

> Human beings should not probe the fundamental secrets or mysteries of life, which belong to God. Human beings lack the authority to make certain decisions about the beginning or ending of life. Such deci-

sions are reserved to divine sovereignty. Human beings are fallible and also tend to evaluate actions according to their narrow, partial, and frequently self-interested perspectives. Human beings do not have the knowledge, especially knowledge of outcomes of actions attributed to divine omniscience. Human beings do not have the power to control the outcomes of actions or processes that is a mark of divine omnipotence (NBAC, 1997, pp. 42–43).

In response, some argue that God expects us to use our reason, imagination, and freedom to improve our quality of life. In this view, human beings are created co-creators and human action is an expression of divine will (Hefner, 1998). An alternative response to the "playing God" argument against cloning is that, in a pluralistic society, discussions about the ethics of cloning humans should not be constrained by a particular conception of God as "the creator" (Silver, 1998, p. 172). More generally, others suggest that accusations of "playing God" sometimes operate as rhetorical devices that ultimately obfuscate rather than clarify discussion (Grey, 1998).

C. Cloning Humans Is Contrary to Human Dignity

This admonition against cloning humans rests, in part, on the Kantian view that persons should be treated as ends in themselves (Kahn, 1997). In this view, cloning humans is morally wrong because typically clones are created exclusively as a means for benefitting another. For example, clones may be created solely to satisfy an interest in having a biologically related child, to replace a dying or deceased loved one, or to serve as an organ or tissue donor.

In response, some insist that this argument against cloning is flawed inso-

far as it ignores the fact that typically there are multiple motives and reasons for procreating (whether by cloning or sexual relations), and that clones would never be created exclusively as a means to another's end. Others grant that some clones likely will be treated *as mere means*, but they argue that this problem is not unique to cloning since persons who conceive "in the usual way" sometimes also act instrumentally as, for example, when persons reproduce to save a failing marriage, to prove their virility, to continue their genetic line, or to have someone to care for them in their old age. Still others insist that it is a matter for debate whether human embryos fall within the scope of the Kantian categorical imperative (given their contested moral status) and, more generally, they argue that Kant's principle is sufficiently vague and open to selective interpretation as not to be very helpful (Harris, 1997).

These three arguments against cloning humans are "familiar" in that they rehearse old arguments against novel technologies. To be precise, versions of these arguments have been elaborated previously, for example, against the introduction of the contraceptive pill, the development of organ transplantation, and the use of life-extending technologies. The pattern that has emerged is one of initial condemnation, followed by ambivalence, questioning and limited use, followed in turn by a change in public perceptions, advocacy, and *finally* widespread acceptance. For those who are mindful of this pattern, there is a sense of *déjà vu* with the debate about cloning humans, and there is the expectation that both the debate and practice will evolve in a similar manner.

Another cluster of familiar arguments against cloning humans focus[es] on the possible/probable harmful consequences of the technology for society and for the individuals thus created. These arguments are worn because although the objections raised are unique to cloning technology, they do little more than reiterate concerns identified years ago when the prospect of cloning humans was pure science fiction. Consider, for example, the claim that cloning technology will be used purposely to create inferior beings to do boring and menial work (think, for example, of the "Deltas" of *Brave New World*). Or, consider the claim that cloning technology will be abused by power-hungry authoritative regimes to more effectively oppress others (think, for example, of *The Boys from Brazil*). As well, there is the claim that human cloning violates the clone's right to a unique genetic identity, and the clone's right to an open future — that is, a future with a reasonable range of opportunities (Brock, 1997).

Typically, responses to these sorts of arguments begin with a basic lesson on the science of cloning in an effort to correct mistaken views about the science and about genetic determinism. For example, it is explained that individuals cloned by nuclear transfer technology are not really identical to one another, though they may be very similar. This is because genes are not constant; they mutate. As well, there can be important differences in gene expression. Added to this is the fact that a fraction (0.05%) of the human genome comes from mitochondrial genes contributed by the egg so that with cloning by somatic cell nuclear transfer, the clonant and the clone cannot be genetically identical unless they have the same maternal lineage. At the same time, it is also explained that identity is shaped by environmental as well as genetic factors: "genes do not *determine* in tight detail how a creature turns out ... [they] merely propose possibilities. It is the environment that shapes the final outcome" (Wilmut, Campbell, & Tudge, 2000, pp. 302–303). For example, with cloning by somatic nuclear cell transfer, the clonant and the clone will have developed in different uterine environments. As well, they will be born years apart and thus be subject to different environmental choices and influences.

In addition to this introductory lesson, there are the usual responses to the specific concerns about societal harm. The most common of these express significant confidence in our ability to ensure that cloning technology will not be abused, but rather will be developed and practiced under controlled conditions (i.e., within appropriate professional, regulatory and legislative constraints). And as for the concerns about potential harm to individuals, it is noted that conventional identical twins are natural clones and they are not psychologically harmed by their lack of genetic uniqueness. This claim is morally relevant since genomic clones would be more different from each other than conventional identical twins. Further, it is argued that the concern about parents coercing their clones' development and subverting their independence by structuring the scope of their experiences and opportunities is not a unique feature of human cloning. This is also a risk for conventionally conceived children whose parents' hopes for their children quickly become expectations.

In my view, all of the arguments against cloning humans identified above and the typical rejoinders are not particularly interesting or challenging. Consistent with this view is Daniel Callahan's recent conclusion, based on his review of the cloning debate from the early 1970s to the present, that "[n]o arguments have been advanced this time that were not anticipated and discussed in the 1970s" (Callahan, 1998, p. 141). Interestingly, on this basis, Callahan credits bioethicists writing in the early 1970s — in particular, Paul Ramsey, Hans Jonas and Leon Kass — with remarkable prescience. But isn't this hubris on the part of bioethics? Shouldn't the fact that no new arguments have been introduced in the post-Dolly era be cause for concern, not congratulations? Others suggest that our imagination has stagnated even longer — that the issues currently addressed in the debate about cloning humans are no different from those that concerned Aldous Huxley in the 1930s when he originally published *Brave New World*, his fictional account of a cloned "utopia." How is it that greater knowledge of the science and a better understanding of the technological possibilities has not introduced new ethical questions or concerns, has not sparked the moral imagination? Are we to believe those who insist that "there are no new ethical issues in relation to the current hysteria over cloning" (Wolpert, 1999, p. 282)?

III. A Second Mistake

A second mistake with the current debate on the ethics of cloning humans — a mistake informed, in part, by a fear of eugenics — is that much of the discussion remains at the level of the personal, as though the *raison d'être* of the technology were to address individual needs and wants. This perspective is clearly evident in discussions about the motives for pursuing human cloning (Robertson, 1998).

It has been suggested, for example, that some couples may want to use cloning technology because it is the only way to have a child that is biologically related to each of the partners. This might include: infertile couples where both have no gametes (where the male partner could provide the somatic cell and the female partner could provide the enucleated oocyte); women undergoing *in vitro* fertilization (IVF) with too few oocytes who might benefit from embryo splitting; and lesbian couples (where one partner could provide the somatic cell and the other could provide the enucleated oocyte) (Baird, 1999). Others possibly interested in human cloning are couples at high risk of having a child with a serious genetic disease. Cloning could also be used to satisfy a wish to re-create a

deceased loved one; the usual example given is of parents who want to re-create a dying or deceased child. There may also be those who would use cloning technology to get a compatible organ or tissue donor for themselves or their offspring. Finally, there may be individuals who for reasons of "curiosity, vanity, the wish for personal power, or an undoubtedly misguided desire for immortality" (Wilmut et al., 2000, p. 306) want a genetic replica of themselves.

One consequence of the unrelenting focus on the personal is the perception of human cloning as a bi-generational issue. Human clones are described as "spaced twins," "later-born identical twins," "'delayed' genetic twins," and the "ultimate single-parent child." As well, the dominant image for human cloning is one of mass production with multiple images of the identical phenotype — "xeroxed human beings" and "carbon-copied humans" — not the traditional pedigree chart or family tree with missing or unusual linkages. Cloning is thus portrayed as horizontal multiplication, not as vertical, multigenerational replication.

With attention focused on the present and the next generation, priority is given to concerns about possible medical and psychological harms to future children and fundamental questions about what it means to be human are set aside. Notably, this dominant perspective is highly compatible with contemporary silence on the possible uses of human cloning to pursue public health or broader societal goals.

When the possibility of cloning humans was discussed in the 1960s, there was considerable speculation about the potential societal benefits of human cloning. One suggestion was to clone individuals with a high pain threshold or resistance to radiation (Haldane, 1963, pp. 353, 355). Another suggestion was to clone individuals skilled at certain jobs, for example, soldiers (Fletcher, 1971, p. 779). Today, the examples have changed and the focus is on cloning specific persons of extraordinary talent such as Beethoven or Einstein. As well, there is particular attention to the potential societal harms of human cloning resulting from the replication of persons with undesirable traits — the most common example being Hitler. In response to such fanciful claims, scientists have been successful in labeling most speculation about the eugenic applications of human cloning as "stupid talk" that obscures the real scientific issues (Butler & Wadman, 1997). To avoid the charge of "stupid talk" serious academics dutifully focus on the "more immediate and realistic possibilities" and abdicate their responsibility to engage in hypothetical reasoning.

IV. A Third Mistake

A third mistake with the current debate on the ethics of cloning humans is that it wrongly focuses much of the discussion on reproductive issues and reproductive freedom. Physicians and researchers, for example, justify human cloning as an aid for infertile couples and an aid in pre-implantation diagnosis. They also frequently note that cloning technology promotes procreative autonomy.

Among those who view cloning as a form of assisted conception are those who believe that the principle of reproductive freedom entrenches the right to reproduce by any means chosen. Dan Brock, for example, maintains that the right to reproductive freedom presumptively includes the right to select the means of reproduction that best serve one's interests and needs, including human cloning (Brock, 1997). Some even go so far as to argue that, in the United States at least, this is a constitutionally protected right. John Robertson, for example, maintains that "[t]he right of married and arguably even unmarried persons to procreate is a fundamental constitutional right that

cannot be restricted unless clearly necessary to protect compelling state interests" (Robertson, 1994, p. 13). In his view, cloning appears to fall within this fundamental freedom. At the other extreme are those who insist that human cloning is intrinsically wrong. George Annas, for example, counters that reproductive rights are not absolute and that cloning by somatic cell nuclear transfer is sufficiently different from other means of reproduction as not to be considered constitutionally protected (Annas, 1997). The Vatican insists that "human beings have a right to be 'born in a human way, and not in a laboratory'" (Butler & Wadman, 1997, p. 8).

Between these extremes are those who maintain that cloning humans should be prohibited for the time being because of potential medical and psychological harms to future clones (including harms arising from possible commodification). Only when human cloning is shown to be reasonably safe and effective might it become available to further reproductive goals, subject to appropriate constraints aimed at preventing possible abuses.[4] For example, a distinction might be drawn between frivolous reasons for cloning such as vanity, and "legitimate" socio-medical reasons for cloning such as allowing persons with otherwise untreatable infertility to have a biologically related child.

The cloning of humans, however, ought not to be construed narrowly as a reproductive technology. While it is certainly the case that cloning technology likely will be provided by those who currently work in, or are affiliated with, IVF clinics, it is a serious mistake to believe that cloning is just another means of assisted reproduction. As George Annas writes, cloning "represents a difference in kind, not in degree in the way that humans continue the species" (Annas, 1997, p. 80). With reproduction by means of sexual intercourse, each offspring (except for identical twins, triplets, or rarely even quadruplets) has a unique genetic make-up that is a combination of genes from his or her biological parents. Assisted reproductive technologies preserve this feature of human reproduction. In marked contrast, human cloning by somatic cell nuclear transfer not only separates reproduction from sexual relations, it also separates reproduction from recombination, as there is no reshuffling of the genes. Unlike current assisted reproductive technologies, therefore, this type of human cloning transgresses species norms. The ethics of transgressing species norms, though widely discussed in the literature on xenotransplantation, is not central to discussions about human cloning; instead, autonomy (procreative liberty), utility, and safety appear to be the predominant concerns.

Attempts to map the cloning debate onto the debate about reproductive freedom [are] not surprising since the domain of reproductive ethics is reasonably familiar territory. There is, for instance, much material in the bioethics literature on autonomy and reproductive choice on the one hand, and the sanctity of human life and the concept of family on the other. In comparison, there is little on transgenerational justice that spans more than one or two generations, and still less on the notion of species integrity that is not about the creation of transgenic animals — these issues merit careful consideration.

V. An Alternative

The way in which any discourse is framed informs (if not determines) the issues identified, the questions asked, the interpretations offered, and the range of responses advocated. The common view of cloning technology as a reproductive technology thus explains the current interest in rights (both reproductive rights and property rights), personal autonomy, informed consent, family privacy, safety, and potential harms to children. According to the NBAC, for example, "The unique and distinctive ethical issues raised by the use of somatic cell nuclear transfer to create children relate to, for example, serious safety concerns, individuality, family integrity, and treating children as objects" (NBAC, 1997, pp. 3–4). To be sure, these are important issues. There are, however, other equally important issues that are not identified, much less debated, with [in] the current analytical framework. To correct this, an alternative framework is recommended where human cloning is also viewed as an individual and a species enhancement technology — a mechanism for environmental and biological improvements on a scale never before possible.

Humans have always sought to enhance their own and their children's physical, intellectual, emotional, and moral capacities with a view to improving health, and increasing the prospects for happiness and "success." Common contemporary enhancements include: vaccines to enhance the immune response to specific diseases; good nutrition to enhance physical development; sound education to enhance intellectual, social and other abilities; music lessons to enhance manual dexterity and mathematical ability; dance lessons and gymnastics to enhance balance and posture; sports training (and/or steroids) to enhance athletic ability, build muscle mass and strength; and cosmetic surgery to enhance physical appearance. With adults the use of these enhancements is generally a matter of personal choice. With children, some of these enhancements are legally and morally required (e.g., vaccinations and basic education), others are optional (e.g., music lessons and cosmetic surgery). Elective enhancements are generally used at the discretion of parents, with or without consultation with the child, and based on their assessment of their child's abilities and interests. Significantly, parents may choose enhancements that will expand the range of opportunities for their child, or they may choose enhancements that will considerably narrow the range of opportunities because of a very limited focus on select talents that are not widely adaptable.

With the cloning of whole beings, parental efforts at enhancing children's capacities will intensify because of the available knowledge regarding the child's genetic structure. The cloning of humans thus will not simply be about having children but about having a unique opportunity to improve on a desired specimen (e.g., a clone of oneself or a loved one) by investing in enhanced genes and/or enhanced environments in order to increase/accentuate desired traits and/or to modify/eliminate negative traits. Consider the following scenario. A talented concert violinist chooses to clone herself using her egg (enucleated oocyte), her nucleus (somatic cell) and her uterus to achieve near perfect cloning. Like all parents, she wants her child to have a "better" life. This motivates her to embark on a unique enhancement project made possible by her decision to reproduce asexually. She does not want her daughter to suffer the disappointments she has known and is thus intent on enhancing her child's talent for creating (her understanding of) beautiful music. With germ-line gene transfer, the violinist hopes to improve her clone's dexterity, hearing, and memory. To be sure, attempts at genetically enhancing these traits will be difficult (if not ultimately impossible) because many genes affect these abilities and each of these genes may affect multiple body systems. Nonetheless, the violinist is willing to experiment. Also, persuaded that a little melancholy (sweet sorrow) will add a creative edge to her clone's music, she agrees to altering the genes responsible for the production of serotonin. When her child is a toddler, the environmental enhancement begins in earnest. The violinist teaches her clone special exercises to improve the genetically improved dexterity and memory. As well, there is the

drug regimen to alter the serotonin levels, the Stradivarius, and the Juilliard School music lessons that her own parents could not afford to give her until she reached her mid-teens. In these ways the violinist hopes that her child — a genetic replica of herself — will have a better future.

As illustrated above, with cloning by somatic cell nuclear transfer the parent (i.e., clonant) has intimate knowledge of the child's (i.e., clone's) future possibilities because of their shared genotype. This unique foreknowledge necessarily influences (possibly skews) the enhancements chosen, and this is not because of misguided views about genetic determinism. Our genes do not determine who we are, but they clearly do suggest certain possibilities and set certain boundaries. Foreknowledge of these possibilities and boundaries, which becomes possible with cloning technology, will influence the genetic, surgical, pharmaceutical and other medical enhancements that will be pursued in order to improve the clone's form. In turn, these biological enhancements may influence behaviour. For example, a physical change can alter/ improve an individual's psychological and social dispositions. As well, this unique foreknowledge will influence the choice of social, cultural, ecological, physical, and other environments to which the clone will be exposed in an effort to further improve performance. In this way, human cloning technology to produce a genetic replica of a person whose potential is known makes possible a unique and complex kind of biological and environmental enhancement.

To be sure, any cloning experiment ultimately may fail to achieve its objective. For example, the violinist's clone may become a disgruntled clerk at an airport car rental. Nonetheless, the point remains. Cloning (at least of those who have lived a reasonable life span) is not simply about reproduction. Rather, it is very much about "getting it right" (avoiding the errors of a previous generation), on the basis of unique advance knowledge about which genetic and environmental factors might benefit from enhancement.

If we now move the discussion from the means of enhancement to the goals of enhancement, an important difference emerges between the goals of *intentional individual enhancement* and the goals of *intentional species enhancement*. With the intentional biological and environmental enhancement of individual human beings, the goals are typically to promote health, happiness, and "success." In turn, these will be the *de facto* goals of inadvertent species enhancement — a phenomenon that will occur over time, as enhancements made at the individual level are passed on to subsequent generations (with or without further alternations), and as the environment of which these individuals are an integral part continues to evolve. In marked contrast, with *intentional species enhancement*, where changes are not merely the inadvertent cumulative long-term side-effect of idiosyncratic changes at the individual level, more communal goals can be pursued, such as the survival of the species, the elimination of misery and an improvement in the quality of life.

For example, in the not-too-distant future, if pollution and overpopulation were to cause our environment to deteriorate so significantly that our survival on the planet were threatened, the cloning of humans might be an important element of a survival strategy for the species. Individuals with certain biological traits conducive to survival in this emerging inhospitable environment could be cloned (and possibly genetically enhanced) while at the same time efforts were made to stabilize the deteriorating environment. In this way, it would be possible to enhance the species in a single generation and thereby increase the probability of survival.

From the perspective of some, however, a more immediate threat to our survival and the cause of considerable misery is "our limited capacity for altruism, and for the imaginative sympathy it depends on" (Glover, 1984, p. 181). Jonathan Glover

suggests, for example, that although war may appear to be the result of particular economic, social, and political arrangements, our failure to eliminate war suggests that psychological changes may be required in addition to political and social reforms. In this view, species enhancement using both genetic and environmental methods may be necessary to overcome certain emotional and imaginative limitations. This might involve direct genetic intervention to ensure that genes we value, such as those that contribute to our capacity for altruism and human sympathy, survive through cloning and are genetically and environmentally enhanced.

Finally, a less dramatic reason for pursuing biological species enhancement would be to improve our quality of life, perhaps by enhancing our intellectual capacities. We can, for example, imagine a time in the remote future when we will have exhausted our capacity to understand our world: "Just as calculus is too much for a dog's brain to grasp, so some parts of physics might turn out to be too difficult for us as we are" (Glover, 1984, p. 180). At that time, "[b]ecause our growing understanding of the world is so central a part of why it is good to be human," we may want to select from among us a number of good specimens for replication and genetic enhancement in order that we might transcend our intellectual limitations (Glover, 1984, p. 180). Before any such hypothetical need should arise, however, we can perhaps more easily imagine a world in which the increasing abilities of machines are fast outpacing those of humans. In response to this threat, humans might want to genetically enhance their cognitive skills by cloning good specimens to be genetically engineered in order to acquire new and increasingly sophisticated judgment, decision-making, and adaptation skills.

In addition to the obvious genetic planning that cloning technology makes possible for the species, it is important to stress the interesting possibilities for environmental species enhancement. The cloning of humans provides us with a unique opportunity to study the nature/nurture question on a grand scale. For the first time, it would be possible to hold constant one element of this dyad and, in so doing, to learn how best to cultivate/nurture desirable traits. Leaving aside, for the sake of argument, questions of research ethics, the same "gene bundles" could be exposed to different social, environmental and generational influences so that we might better understand human development and evolution. In an ideal world, this knowledge could then be used to improve our quality of life — to modify our political and economic systems, to alter our educational programs and to introduce social changes that would nurture the traits we value for ourselves and subsequent generations.

In closing, the benefit of regarding the cloning of humans as an enhancement technology is twofold. The first benefit is that this perspective will shed a new light on questions that are already the subject of intense debate. Among these questions: What are the moral costs of human cloning? What obligations do we have to subsequent generations who will be subject to an unprecedented measure of control from preceding generations? How are these obligations to be weighed against obligations to those who are living? What about issues of social justice? While many live in poverty and lack basic health care, can we responsibly devote energy and resources to the project of cloning humans? Is human cloning necessary? If so, necessary for what? Is human cloning progressive? If so, progressive towards what end? Is it efficient? If so, effecting what? Is it good for the species, for the individual clonant, for the individual clone, or is it good for its own sake? Answers to these questions will differ significantly depending upon the framework for analysis — whether one considers cloning to be a reproductive and/or an enhancement technology.

The second benefit of considering the cloning of humans as an enhancement technology is that this perspective will bring into sharp focus a range of novel questions that merit thoughtful reflection. For example: With the cloning of humans are we bound to embrace "volitional evolution" whereby we intentionally intervene in the shaping of human purpose? Would volitional evolution result in a domestication of the species? What is the value of diversity? What is the value of homogeneity? What social norms regarding race, gender, and appearance might (inadvertently or intentionally) be entrenched with cloning technology? While undeniably offensive in its eugenic implications, in the long term would homogenization of the species be a cure for such social and political ills as racism, sexism, classism, homophobia and so on, or would any initiative of this kind only serve to exacerbate existing prejudices?

As well, another cluster of questions might stem from an understanding of human cloning as the modern equivalent to reincarnation. This perspective might refashion our understanding of such concepts as "a life span" and "a life plan." For example, given the belief that reincarnation is a mechanism that allows individuals to improve upon themselves over time, in our modern production-oriented society would there develop an expectation that persons should avail themselves of cloning technology for the express purpose of improving upon the prior incarnation? What would be the end-point? Would it be culturally informed or socially stipulated? What would be the social, political, and moral responses to this new eugenics?

When the cloning of humans is considered solely as a reproductive technology, the questions listed above garner hardly any serious attention. Instead we concentrate on questions about possible harms to children and personal choice: "Is a clone any worse off than a 'normal' but unwanted child? Is Steve, who wants to clone himself, any more egotistical than Saul, who wants to conceive naturally, though his children will have a 25 percent chance of getting Tay-Sachs disease? And if cloning should be outlawed because it may undermine family values, should we outlaw divorce as well?" (Bilger, 1997, p. 19). In marked contrast, when the cloning of humans is considered an individual or species enhancement technology, broader societal and species-type questions outside the protected realm of personal and reproductive autonomy are "front and center."

Thus, it is salient to understand that the current debate on the ethics of cloning humans with its predominant focus on autonomy (individuals' rights, desires and choices) is profoundly unsatisfactory and lacking in imagination. This debate is sustained and remains sustainable, however, because it occurs in a social context sympathetic to the claim that "the principles of personal liberty and personal fortune are the primary determinants of what individuals are allowed and able to do" (Silver, 1997, p. 9). As a result, the debate about cloning humans stagnates at the level of the personal; it never really moves beyond the framework of private relationships and reproductive choice. Thus, profound value questions are set aside and potentially dramatic societal and species consequences arising from the use of cloning technology are inappropriately downplayed or exaggerated. Only in recognizing the individual and species enhancement dimensions of cloning technology can we begin to recognize the broader issues and grapple with the threat/opportunity that cloning humans represents. For all of us.

Notes

1. The research for this paper was supported by grants from the Social Sciences and Humanities Research Council of Canada and from Dalhousie University. This is a revised version of *Dr. John P. Maclean Memorial Lecture, Department of Medicine, University of Manitoba*, Winnipeg, Manitoba, April 1999, that was also presented at the Second Annual *International Bioethics Retreat*, Florence, Italy, October 1999.

2. I owe the distinction between "reproducing our kind" and "reproducing ourselves" to Ford Doolittle, Dalhousie University.

3. In the literature a distinction is drawn between *reproductive* cloning, where the aim is to reproduce whole beings, and *therapeutic* cloning, where the aim is to reproduce cell lines for the treatment of disease and disability.

4. The Report of the National Bioethics Advisory Commission would appear to fall in this general category. See National Bioethics Advisory Commission (1997). The Executive Summary (1997) of this report is reprinted in the *Hastings Center Report*, 27(3), 7–9.

References

Annas, G.J. (1997). Human cloning. *ABA Journal, 83,* 80–81.

Baird, P.A. (1999). Cloning of animals and humans: What should the policy response be? *Perspectives in Biology and Medicine, 42*(2), 179–194.

Bilger, B. (1997, September/October). Cell block. *The Sciences,* 17–19.

Bonnicksen, A.L. (1995). Ethical and policy issues in human embryos twinning. *Cambridge Quarterly of Healthcare Ethics, 4*(3), 268–284.

Brock, D. (1997). Cloning human beings: An assessment of the ethical issues pro and con. In: National Bioethics Advisory Commission. *Cloning human beings: Report and recommendations of the National Bioethics Advisory Commission, Volume II Commissioned Papers*. Rockville, Maryland.

Butler, D., & Wadman, M. (1997). Calls for cloning ban sell science short. *Nature*, 386, 8.

Callahan, D. (1998). Cloning: Then and now. *Cambridge Quarterly of Healthcare Ethics*, 7(2), 141–144.

Cibelli, J.B., Kiessling, A.A., Cunniff, K., Richards, C., Lanza, R.P., & West, M. (2001). Somatic cell nuclear transfer in humans: Pronuclear and early embryonic development. *E-biomed: The Journal of Regenerative Medicine*, 2, 25–31.

Fletcher, J. (1971). Ethical aspects of genetic controls. *New England Journal of Medicine*, 285, 776–783.

Glover, J. (1984). *What sort of people should there be?* Great Britain: Richard Clay (The Chaucer Press) Ltd.

Grey, W. (1998). Playing God. *Encyclopedia of applied ethics* (Vol. 3). USA: Academic Press.

Haldane, J.B.S. (1963). Biological possibilities for the human species in the next ten thousand years. In: G.E.D. Wolstenhome (Ed.), *Man and his future* (pp. 337–361). London: Churchill.

Hall, J.L., Engel, D., Gindoff, P.R., Motta, G.L., & Stillman, R.J. (1993). Experimental cloning of human polyploid embryos using an artificial zona pellucida. *The American Fertility Society, Co-jointly With the Canadian Fertility and Andrology Society. Program Supplement* [Abstract of the Scientific and Oral Poster Sessions, Abstract 0-001S1].

Harris, J. (1997). "Goodbye Dolly?" The ethics of human cloning. *Journal of Medical Ethics*, 23, 353–360.

Health Canada. (2001). *Draft Legislation on Assisted Human Reproduction.* **http://www. hc-sc.gc.ca/English/reproduction/legislation.pdf** (Editor's note: A revised version of this legislation was finally passed in 2003 as the *Assisted Human Reproduction Act* (Bill C-13). The Bill was passed by the Senate as Bill C-6 on March 11, 2004. It can be accessed at **http://www.parl.gc.ca/PDF/ 37/3/parlbus/chambus/house/bills/government/C-6_3.pdf**

Hefner, P. (1998). Cloning as quintessential human act. In: M. Ruse (Ed.), *Philosophy of biology* (pp. 352–256). Amherst, New York: Prometheus Books.

Human Fertilisation and Embryology (Research Purposes) Regulations. (2001). Statutory Instrument 2001 No. 188. **http://www.legislation.hmso.gov.uk/ si/si2001/20010188.htm**

Jonas, H. (1974). Biological engineering — a preview. In: H. Jonas (Ed.), *Philosophical essays: From ancient creed to technological man* (pp. 141–167). Englewood Cliffs, NJ: Prentice Hall.

Kahn, A. (1997). Clone mammals ... clone man. *Nature*, 386, 119.

Kato, Y., Tani, T., Sotomaru, Y., Kurokawa, K., Kato, J., Doguchi, H., Yasue, H., & Tsunoda, Y. (1998). Eight calves cloned from somatic cells of a single adult. *Science*, 282, 209–2098.

National Bioethics Advisory Commission (NBAC). (1997). *Cloning human beings: Report and recommendations of the National Bioethics Advisory Commission.* Rockville, MD: National Bioethics Advisory Commission.

Onishi, A., Iwamoto, M., Akita, T., Mikawa, S., Takeda, K., Awata, T., Hanada, H., & Perry, A.C.F. (2000). Pig cloning by microinjection of fetal fibroblast nuclei. *Science*, 289, 1188–1190.

PPL Therapeutics plc. (2000). *PPL produces world's first cloned pigs.* Press release March 5, **http://www.ppl-therapeutics.com**

Robertson, J. (1994). The question of human cloning. *Hastings Center Report*, 24(2), 6–14.

Robertson, J. (1998). Human cloning and the challenge of regulation. *New England Journal of Medicine*, 339(2), 119–122.

Silver, L.M. (1997). *Remaking Eden: Cloning and beyond in a brave new world*. New York: Avon Books.

Silver, L.M. (1998). Cloning, ethics, and religion. *Cambridge Quarterly of Healthcare Ethics*, 7(2), 168–172.

Wakayama, T., Perry, A.C., Zuccotti, M., Johnson, K.R., & Yanagimachi, R. (1998). Full-term development of mice from enucleated oocytes injected with cumulus cell nuclei. *Nature*, 394, 369–374.

Watts, J., & Morris, K. (1999). Human cloning trial met with outrage and scepticism. *The Lancet,* 353, 43.

Wells, D.N., Misica, P.M., & Territ, H.R. (1999). Production of cloned calves following nuclear transfer with cultured adult mural granulosa cells. *Biology of Reproduction*, 60, 996–1005.

Wilmut, I., Schnieke, A.E., McWhir, J., Kind, A.J., & Campbell, K.H.S. (1997). Viable offspring derived from fetal and adult mammalian cells. *Nature*, 385, 810–812.

Wilmut, I., Campbell, K., & Tudge, C. (2000). *The second creation: The age of biological control by the scientists that cloned Dolly*. London, England: Headline.

Wolf, D.P., Meng, L., Ouhibi, N., & Zelinski-Wooten, M. (1999). Nuclear transfer in the rhesus monkey: Practical and basic implications. *Biology of Reproduction*, 60, 199–204.

Wolpert, L. (1999). Is science dangerous? *Nature*, 398, 281–282.

World Health Organization. (1997, May 14). *Cloning in human reproduction*. Fiftieth World Health Assembly. WHA50.37 Supplementary agenda item. Geneva.

Ethics and Policy in Embryonic Stem Cell Research

John A. Robertson

Mammalian tissue and organs derive from pluripotent embryonic stem (ES) cells present at the blastocyst stage of embryo development. Embryonic stem cells were first isolated from the inner cell masses of mouse blastocysts in the early 1980s. In November 1998, a team of researchers at the University of Wisconsin and a team at Johns Hopkins University published reports of the first successful isolation and culturing of human ES cells (Thomson et al. 1998; Shamblott et al. 1998). Because ES cells are capable of self-renewal and differentiation into a wide variety of cell types, the ability to grow them in renewable tissue cultures could have broad applications in research and transplantation.

The research uses of human ES cells include *in vitro* studies of normal human embryogenesis, abnormal development, human gene discovery, and drug and ter-

Robertson, John A. "Ethics and Policy in Embryonic Stem Cell Research." *Kennedy Institute of Ethics Journal* 9:2 (1999), 109–136. © The John Hopkins University Press. Reprinted with permission of The Johns Hopkins University Press.

atogen testing. Potential clinical applications are as a renewable source of cells for tissue transplantation, cell replacement, and gene therapy. For example, if human ES cells could be directed to differentiate into particular tissues and immunologically altered to prevent rejection after engraftment, they could treat or cure thousands of patients who now suffer from diabetes, neurodegenerative disorders, heart disease, and other illnesses.

The growth of human ES cells in culture is a first but necessary step toward development of cell replacement or regeneration therapies. Future work will have to determine how to obtain human ES cells efficiently and reliably from the inner cell mass of human embryos or from primordial germ cells, grow them in culture, and then identify the growth factors that will direct them to differentiate into cells of particular types to produce the large enough number of pure cells that will be necessary for transplantation (Marshall 1998). Finally, clinical research using ES-derived cells will be needed to determine under what conditions they are therapeutic for the many conditions that they potentially could treat. Of major importance will be tailoring stem cells genetically to avoid attack by a patient's immune system.

The pace of stem cell research is likely to be affected by ethical and legal concerns beyond the issues of animal data, safety, informed consent, and IRB review that arise with any kind of clinical or human subjects research. The ability to regenerate vital tissues through ES cell technology could eventually transform our understanding of aging and personal identity, as well as place heavy burdens on medical care and social security systems from new ways to extend adult life. Some persons may have serious moral qualms about ES cell research for these reasons alone, and question whether public research support for cell regeneration technologies should be provided at all.

More immediately, ethical and legal issues arise with ES cell research because ES cells have to be derived from aborted fetuses or from the inner cell mass of human preimplantation embryos. Although the ethical and legal issues involved in the retrieval of cells from aborted fetuses and embryos differ in some respects, both sources of ES cells raise concerns about respect for human life at its earliest stages and the extent to which such life may be used or destroyed to provide cells or tissue for research or therapy.

Such questions are highly controversial. Unless ES cells could be obtained from spontaneously aborted fetuses or from preimplantation embryos without destroying them, which appears to be highly unlikely, questions of ES cell research and therapy are likely to rekindle bitter controversies over fetal tissue transplantation and embryo research. Research with more differentiated stem cells, such as mesenchymal stem cells, which already can be directed *in vitro* to become cartilage, bone, fat, tendon, or stroma, will raise fewer ethical and legal problems because those cells can be obtained from consenting persons (Vogel 1999). However, those cells will not meet the need for many kinds of tissue that can be derived only from pluripotent stem cells. A conflict between respect for the first stages of human life and the persons who will benefit from such research appears to be inevitable. ...

Are Human Embryonic Stem Cells Embryos?

Ethical questions arise about ES cell research because ES cells must first be derived from human aborted fetuses or preimplantation embryos. It should be clear, however, that ES cells are not themselves embryos because, although they are *pluripotent* in that they could develop into any cell or tissue of the body, they are not *totipotent*. They are not capable of forming a new individual, as a fertilized egg or single cell taken from a four cell embryo might if cultured *in vitro* and placed in a uterus. Culture of ES cells followed by placement in the uterus would not result in the implantation of an embryo and eventual birth of a child. ...

> Pluripotent stem cells are not organisms and do not have the capacity to develop into an organism that could perform all the life functions of a human being — in this sense they are not even precursors to human organisms. They are, rather, human cells that have the potential to evolve into different types of cells such as blood cells or insulin producing cells ... (Raab, 1999, pp. 2–3).

Two Kinds of Complicity

[There is a] ... belief that the derivation and use of ES cells cannot be morally or legally separated. If the initial derivation of ES cells from embryos or aborted fetuses is immoral, as many persons believe, then later research uses of those cells do not become morally acceptable merely because the research is separated from the derivation. Under this reasoning, the chain of complicity holds even if the actual ES cells used in research or therapy are the product of many later generations or passages of the original immorally derived ES cells.[1]

Such a view of complicity is a reasonable one up to a point. If the original immoral derivation of ES cells occurred with the intent to make later ES cell research possible, then it is reasonable to view the later researchers as complicit in the original derivation, on the causative theory that the derivation would not have occurred if the later use had not been contemplated. Complicity based on causation, however, would not exist if the

original immoral derivation of cells would have occurred regardless of the activities of any particular later researcher. Once the ES cells have been derived for particular kinds of research or for particular researchers, they exist and could be used by other researchers. Under a causative theory of complicity, making the ES cells available to later researchers would not make those researchers complicit in the immoral derivation of the ES cells if their research plans or actions had no effect on whether the original immoral derivation occurred.

The later researchers in this case would, of course, be profiting from or making use of that original immoral derivation and, in that sense, benefitting from another person's wrongdoing. However, a "no benefit from another's wrongdoing" theory of complicity seems much too broad to be a guide to moral or social practice. If taken seriously, it would mean that the taint of an original alleged immoral action, no matter how attenuated, could never be removed as long as it were still traceable to the original action.[2] Such a view would make us all morally complicit in any immoral action that at several removes still underlies or contributes to economic and social transactions from which we benefit. It would also bar the use of organs for transplant that resulted from a homicide or suicide, because the recipient would be benefitting from another's immoral action that occurred independently of the recipient's need for an organ transplant.

Ethics and Policy in Retrieval of ES Cells from Aborted Fetuses

Primordial germ cells retrieved from first trimester aborted fetuses provide one potential source of ES cells for research and therapy (Shamblott et al. 1998). It is unclear at this time whether fetal tissue or human preimplantation embryos will become the main source of ES cells. Current law, however, permits the use of federal funds to derive such cells from the tissue of aborted fetuses, though it prohibits the use of federal funds to isolate them from embryos.

Because primordial germ cells are removed from fetuses after their death, the derivation of ES cells from aborted fetuses does not cause their death as it does in the case of preimplantation embryos. Nor, with a million-plus electively induced abortions occurring annually in the United States, is there a strong basis for the claim that ES cell research using primordial germ cells would cause many women faced with an unwanted pregnancy to have abortions that would not otherwise have occurred simply because of the chance to donate fetal tissue for research (NBAC 1999, III-4).

Under a causative theory of complicity, neither derivation nor later use of ES cells from abortions that would otherwise have occurred would make one morally complicit in the abortion itself because there is no reasonable basis for thinking that donation of tissue for research after the decision to abort has been made would have caused or brought about the abortion. Thus persons who think that induced abortion is immoral could support the use of fetal tissue or ES cells derived from abortions as long as the derivation or later research or therapy had no reasonable prospect of bringing about abortion, just as they could support organ donation from homicide victims without approving of the homicide that made the organs available. To do so, however, such individuals would have to be convinced that research uses of fetal tissue from abortions otherwise occurring would not bring about future abortions or in some way make abortion appear to be a positive, praiseworthy act.

On the other hand, if persons who think that induced abortion is immoral hold the "no benefit from another's wrongdoing" view of complicity, they would object to the derivation of tissue from fetuses that would be aborted regardless of research plans, merely because one would be deriving benefit from what is viewed as an immoral act. It is unclear how many persons opposed to abortion hold the broader, "no benefit" theory of complicity. If they do hold such a view and are consistent, they should also object to transplanting or receiving organs from murder victims because that would constitute benefitting from another's wrongdoing. Similarly, they should object to any benefits that might in some traceable sense also be the result of another's wrongdoing. Because many common activities, practices, and social arrangements may be traceable to some past wrongdoing — e.g., wresting land from Native Americans — persons holding that view, if they are consistent, would have a difficult time living in the contemporary world. ...

Ethics and Policy in the Retrieval of ES Cells from Human Preimplantation Embryos

A major source of ES cells for research may turn out to be human preimplantation embryos rather than aborted fetuses (Thomson et al. 1998). As noted above, ES cells derived from embryos are not themselves embryos. However, the need at some point to isolate ES cells for research from live embryos raises ethical concerns of complicity in the destruction of those embryos. Because the embryo is alive at the time that ES cells are removed from the inner cell mass of the blastocyst, research that depends upon the isolation of ES cells from preimplantation embryos raises questions about the permissibility of destroying embryos for research. These questions arise under both the causative and the no-benefit theories of moral complicity, for in either case at least some embryos may be destroyed in order to facilitate or to carry out ES cell research.[3] If the embryos are donated by couples undergoing IVF, the embryos might otherwise have been discarded or kept indefinitely in storage. In some cases they may have been created specifically for the purpose of obtaining ES cells for research. In either case, however, the embryo, unlike the aborted fetus from whom ES cells are retrieved, is alive at the time that the ES cells are removed, even though it may be discarded or never transferred to a uterus if not used in research.

To assess the ethics and policy of ES cell research that is directly destructive of preimplantation embryos, we must revisit debates over embryo research and the status of embryos. Those debates have focused on two main issues: (1) may spare human embryos be destroyed in research when they are donated by couples undergoing IVF treatment for infertility? and (2) may human embryos be created for destructive research without ever having intended to transfer them to the uterus for implantation?

Use of Donated Spare Embryos in Research

Normative Concerns

The key ethical and policy debate in embryo research — whether such research should occur at all — has assumed that the embryos used in research would be spare embryos donated by couples undergoing IVF treatment for infertility. Only if such research is deemed acceptable does the second question — whether embryos may be created for research and then destroyed — arise.

The debate over whether embryo[s] may be destroyed in research when they are donated by couples undergoing IVF has turned on perceptions of the moral status of embryos and the extent to which

a rights-based or a deontologic/symbolic view of that status should determine the ethical acceptability of practices involving the first stages of human life. Biologically, there is agreement that the cells of preimplantation human embryos are not yet differentiated into organs or particular tissues. Nor are they clearly committed to individuation because spontaneous twinning can still occur until the time of implantation (Grobstein 1985). Indeed, the embryo's first cellular differentiation is between trophectoderm or placental tissue and the inner cell mass, which contains ES cells. Only after implantation does the embryonic disc and then the primitive streak, from which the brain, the nervous system, and other organs of the body grow, form.

Disagreement, however, attends the moral evaluation of these facts, with differences largely reflecting people's views about abortion. Many people who oppose abortion believe that the fertilized egg's potential to develop into a new human being automatically confers upon it full moral status as a person. They oppose all nontherapeutic embryo research regardless of its benefits, for they view any invasive procedure done to embryos, such as removing stem cells from the inner cell mass, as unjustifiably harming them. Individuals who hold this view are as offended by research with spare IVF embryos as they are with the creation of embryos solely for research. They would oppose any destructive derivation of ES cells from embryos and the research that causes it to occur.

Many other people, however, do not view the pre-viable fetus as an entity that has developed to the point that it has interests that justify overriding a pregnant woman's right to terminate pregnancy. Not surprisingly, persons holding this view about pre-viable fetuses view preimplantation embryos, which are much less developed than fetuses, as too rudimentary in structure or development to have moral status or interests in their own right. For them the attribution of moral status rationally depends upon at least the presence of a nervous system, if not also sentience, and not just its precursor cells. As a result, such individuals maintain that no moral duties are owed to embryos by virtue of their present status and that they are not harmed by research or destruction when no transfer to the uterus is planned. Under this view of embryo status, there is no moral objection to destroying spare, donated embryos to conduct ES cell research. Indeed, if not used in research, those embryos will be discarded or kept indefinitely in frozen storage.

Persons holding the latter view — that the embryo itself lacks interests or rights because of its extremely rudimentary development — do not, however, necessarily view embryos as identical to any other human tissue. Indeed, many such persons would say that embryos, though lacking rights or interests in themselves, deserve "special respect" because of the embryo's potential, if placed in a uterus, to become a fetus and eventually to be born. Even embryos that will not be placed in the uterus have some meaning in this regard for they operate as a symbol of human life or constitute an arena for expressing one's commitment to human life.

This distinction between intrinsic and symbolic valuation of the embryo is at the heart of debate over both abortion and embryo research (Robertson 1994; Dworkin 1993).[4] One can deny that something has intrinsic value as a moral subject, yet still value it or accord it meaning because of the associations or symbolism that it carries. This distinction has special relevance to the embryo research debate. Even persons who view the embryo as lacking rights or interests in itself are not comfortable with anything at all being done with embryos, for example, using them for toxicology testing of cosmetics or buying and selling them. Accordingly, they would accept the use of

spare embryos in research only when there is a good medical or scientific reason for doing so. In effect, the benefits of such research are deemed to outweigh whatever symbolic costs or losses arise from treating an entity that in other circumstances might be transferred to the uterus as if it lacked that potential.

Under this normative approach, embryo research has been deemed acceptable when necessary to pursue a legitimate scientific or medical end that cannot be pursued by other means, when there has been local or national review of the proposed research, and when the embryos have been donated for research with the informed consent of the providing couple. Additional safeguards, such as limiting the research purposes to which embryos might be put or requiring a national ethics advisory board review of such research, would further mark the symbolic importance of spare embryos when they are used in research. The need for additional procedural safeguards depends on the particular political circumstances of the national, state, and institutional context in which they arise. ES stem cell research with spare IVF embryos would clearly meet a high standard of need for conducting research with spare embryos. Its great potential to treat or prevent disease in many persons shows that destructive research with embryos that are unwanted for reproduction will be used for the beneficial purpose of preserving life. ...

Creation of Human Embryos for Research or Therapy

Although much ES cell research may occur with cells derived from embryos donated after IVF treatment for infertility, at some point in the future some types of stem cell research, such as efforts to develop or isolate tissue that is compatible with the immune system of prospective patients, may require the creation of embryos. For example, the ability to develop a large library of ES cell geno-types that encode different transplanta-tion antigens so that cell replacement therapies would be available for a large range of the population, likely would depend upon the creation of embryos expressly for that purpose. Or embryos might have to be created by nuclear transfer cloning from a prospective patient's own cells in order to obtain his-tocompatible ES cells for that patient. The ultimate permissibility of creating embryos solely for ES cell research may thus determine whether many important kinds of ES cell research occur.

The question of the acceptability of the creation of embryos for research has been a heated issue in the embryo research debate, but not between those who oppose and approve of research with spare embryos so much as within the group of those who find destructive research with spare embryos to be moral-ly acceptable. Of course, persons who oppose research with spare embryos on the ground that embryos themselves have intrinsic moral status also oppose the creation of embryos for research. However, persons who approve of research with spare embryos because of their view that embryos lack interests nevertheless disagree about whether embryos should be created for research purposes when there is never any intent to transfer those embryos to the uterus. Thus, a subset of persons exists who approve of research with spare embryos, but object to the creation of embryos sole-ly for research. Presumably these same persons would object to the creation of embryos solely to obtain ES cells for research or therapy. As a result, the eth-ical controversy over creating embryos specifically for research is likely to sur-face again if science progresses to the point that creation of embryos becomes necessary to obtain ES cells for certain types of research or therapy.

The opposition to creation of research embryos by persons who approve of re-search with spare IVF embryos cannot be justified on harm or rights-based grounds, for those persons also agree that embryos are too rudimentary in development to have interests or rights, and that they are not harmed by destructive research when donated by couples undergoing IVF. Such individuals oppose the creation of research embryos either because of conse-quentialist concerns about the effect of such practices on other persons or because of deontologic or symbolic/constitutive concerns about showing respect for human life. ...

> The moral problem with making embryos for research is that as a society we do no want to see *embryos treated as products or as mere objects*, for fear that we will *cheapen the value of parenting, risk commercializing procreation, and trivialize the act of procreation*. It is society's moral attitude toward pro-creation and the interests of those whose gametes are involved in making the embryos that provide the moral force behind the restric-tion or prohibition of the manufac-ture of embryos for nonprocreative uses. (Annas, Caplan, and Elias 1996, p. 1331)

Consequentialist Concerns in Creating Research Embryos

The consequentialist arguments against creating research embryos expressed in these excerpts assume that creation of embryos for well-justified research proj-ects will inevitably lead to bad conse-quences, yet they never show that those consequences are very likely to occur nor the mechanism by which they would come about. For example, Annas, Caplan, and Elias fear that creating embryos for responsible medical or scientific research will quickly lead to the production of human embryos for more trivial uses such as toxicology screening of drugs or cosmetics and the emergence of an industry that buys and sells human embryos. The HERP quotation cites persons who think that creating embryos will "cheapen or demean" respect for other research subjects. Annas, Caplan, and Elias also think that creating embryos for research will cheapen or demean procreation, thereby undermining respect for persons generally. It will also put at risk women who are induced to serve as donors of the eggs from which the embryos will be created.

It is highly unlikely, however, that such effects would occur if embryos retain the special symbolic respect that marks the HERP and NBAC approaches to research with spare embryos. Given the controversial and sensitive nature of creating embryos for research, it is likely, at least in federally-funded research institutions, that research embryos will be created only for compelling reasons, for example, when important research cannot be validly conducted with spare embryos. Creation of research embryos for meritorious research is thus unlikely to lead quickly to a wide use of created embryos for less compelling purposes, such as mass toxicology screening. Nor is a market that buys and sells embryos for research or procreative purposes likely to arise. Indeed, leading proponents of creating embryos for research agree that restrictions on the sale of embryos are desirable (NIH 1994).

It is similarly unlikely that the creation of embryos for research that could not easily be conducted in other ways will undermine respect for other research subjects. Apparently the theory for such an effect is that by creating human embryos to serve as instruments or means to obtain knowledge, researchers will be more likely to use other human subjects as mere means. This speculation rests on the counterintuitive premise that carefully limited laboratory research involving the creation of research embryos will affect the interactions that *different* clinical researchers have with human subjects

in other projects. The claim also ignores the well-entrenched system of IRB review and informed consent that protects the rights and welfare of research subjects. It is highly implausible that acceptable research projects involving created embryos would undermine or weaken this system or decrease respect for human life or persons generally.

The Annas-Caplan-Elias version of the consequentialist argument — namely, that the creation of research embryos will cheapen or demean human reproduction and parenting by commercializing procreation — assumes an unlikely scenario of embryos being created en masse for commercial purposes. Even if such a practice occurred, it still would not follow that all other acts of conception or procreation would be "demeaned," any more than the existence of prostitution (whether legal or illegal) demeans sexual intercourse between spouses or lovers (Radin 1996; Altman 1991). In any event, it is difficult to see how the creation of embryos for research when there is a good scientific or clinical need for the practice would "cheapen" or "demean" procreation and parenting generally, much less decrease societal respect for human life, nor do the authors specify how such an effect would come about.

A more substantial consequentialist concern is the effect that the practice of embryo creation might have on women who donate the eggs that are fertilized to create embryos for research (Gerrand 1993). Most of the oocytes that would be fertilized to provide embryos for research are likely to be donated by women who are donating eggs for reproductive purposes to an infertile couple or by women who are undergoing IVF but who produce more oocytes than they need for themselves. In some cases, however, researchers may have to recruit women to undergo ovarian hyperstimulation and egg retrieval in order to get eggs for research. The Annas-Caplan-Elias claim that such women would be undergoing significant risks "for no benefit" overlooks the personal benefits those women receive from choosing to serve as contributors to scientific research (a parallel to the altruistic component of oocyte donation for reproductive purposes) and the scientific benefits that the research aims to generate. In any event, all would agree that the rights and welfare of women asked to donate oocytes — whether for reproduction or research — should be carefully protected. They should be fully informed of the risks and benefits of such an act. If they are so informed and nevertheless wish to proceed, there is no justification for permitting egg donation for assisted reproduction but prohibiting it in the case of ES cell research. ES cell research needs are as compelling as the needs of infertile couples.

Deontologic and Symbolic/Constitutive Concerns in Creating Research Embryos

Much of the opposition to the creation of research embryos from persons who reject the notion that embryos have intrinsic moral status rests on deontological or symbolic/constitutive grounds.[5] ... [O]pponents of creating embryos for research have argued that it is inherently wrong to create an embryo with no intent to transfer it to a uterus because such a practice treats the created embryo as a mere means or instrument to others' ends, thereby expressing "inherent disrespect" for human life. They distinguish the IVF practice of fertilizing more oocytes than can safely be placed in the uterus on the ground that the embryos were created for the purpose of procreation and that *ex ante* fertilization each potential embryo had an equal chance with the others to be transferred to the uterus (NIH 1994; Annas, Caplan, and Elias 1996).

Persons holding the view that the creation of research embryos is wrong try to draw support from the Kantian deontologic tradition that it is wrong to treat human beings as mere means or instruments to the ends of others. This deontologic claim, however, assumes that the preimplantation embryo is already a human being or human subject with interests that are harmed by treatment as a mere means. Yet the persons asserting this ground also agree that spare IVF embryos are too rudimentarily developed to be harmed, and thus may ethically be donated for use in research. Therefore, they cannot object to the creation of research embryos on the ground that doing so would violate ethical norms against using persons as mere means. As they concede, embryos created for research are not persons who can be used to their detriment. If they disagree with this conclusion, then they should object to research with spare embryos as well, for they too become means to serve the needs of others once the decision to use them in research is made (Gerrand 1993).

A more useful way to view nonconsequentialist claims against the creation of embryos for research is as symbolic/constitutive assertions of a person or community's attitudes toward the importance of human life (Robertson 1995). Because preimplantation embryos are the first stage of a new human life, they ordinarily are created for the purpose of bringing such a life into the world. Accordingly, they function as a powerful symbol of human life and provide the occasion for demonstrating or expressing commitment to human life generally, for example, by condemning creation of embryos for research as being "inherently disrespectful" of human life. In taking such a stance, persons define or constitute themselves as highly protective of human life.

This articulation of the issue tracks very closely the earlier discussion about intrinsic versus symbolic concerns in research with spare embryos and points to a similar resolution. Although embryos do not themselves have rights, they are an occasion for expressing or symbolizing one's views about the importance or value of human life, thereby constituting one's moral or national character in the process. People differ, however, over the degree and the intensity of the symbolic associations that attach to non-rights-bearing entities such as embryos. The importance of signifying or constituting a highly protective attitude toward human life by objecting to certain kinds of embryo research is thus more determined by personal or public policy preferences than it is by the obligations of moral duty.

Individuals might thus accept that the embryo has symbolic/constitutive importance, but find that in particular circumstances other actions connected with the protection of human life also have importance.[6] As we have seen, one could reasonably find that the research and clinical benefits from research with spare IVF embryos outweighs the symbolic detriment that might accrue from using discarded spare embryos as a means of producing knowledge. A similar judgment could be made about the creation of embryos for research. If one concluded that the benefits of the research made possible by the creation of embryos outweighed the symbolic or expressive detriments that some persons perceive to flow from such a practice, then one would find the practice to be ethically acceptable. A good example would be research that creates embryos through nuclear transfer cloning to obtain recipient-compatible tissue or cells for transplant.

In making such judgments, one inevitably compares the symbolic or constitutive costs of a particular research practice with its benefits — e.g., does creating research embryos when necessary to conduct important research so diminish respect for human life that those research benefits should be foregone in order to demonstrate respect for human life in this way? Given the highly person-

al nature of symbolic/constitutive claims, there is no definitive answer to this question. The answer will depend on the nature and purpose of the research, the availability of alternatives, a person's values and commitments, and public perceptions of a practice.

The ethical acceptability of creating embryos for ES cell research will thus turn on the symbolic/constitutive meanings associated with such a practice in light of the benefits that such research will provide. The conclusion will depend on individual perceptions of the importance of the ES cell research project and the harm to respect for human life that creation of embryos for ES cell research is perceived to cause. Some persons would argue that creation of research embryos raises symbolic or expressive harm beyond that which exists with research with spare embryos and which cannot be justified by the uncertain benefits that the research in question might bring. Other persons, however, might reasonably conclude that the additional symbolic harm of creating embryos for ES cell research that could not otherwise validly occur is minimal. To mark the greater symbolic importance of such research, they might limit it to the most important kinds of research and require additional review procedures. ...

Public Research Policy at the Beginning of Life

With advances now rapidly occurring in the understanding and manipulation of human ES cells, current federal policy against funding any destructive embryo research needs to be reassessed to avoid discouraging or preventing such research. ... A ban ... on federal funding of either the derivation or the use of ES cells creates a barrier to further progress in ES technology. For example, permitting federally funded research with ES cells derived in the private sector still leaves researchers facing intellectual property and other barriers to obtaining privately-derived ES cells. Those barriers could deter some researchers from undertaking ES cell research and thus slow the pace of progress in the field.

Only the group of persons who view fertilized eggs, early embryos, and fetuses as themselves persons or subjects with intrinsic rights strongly object to the use of aborted fetuses or spare embryos for ES cell research.[7] Their view of the intrinsic moral status of embryos — that spare or created embryos are persons that cannot be destroyed in research — is not required by our legal and constitutional traditions and should not drive federal research policy. Indeed, the basis in this position for imputing intrinsic value to the embryo is more the reflection of religious or spiritual perspectives than it is of a persuasive philosophical or normative position about when protected human life begins. It has been rejected by most advisory commissions that have studied the matter.

Precisely because people differ so deeply over personal spiritual and value commitments, one group should not erect its own view of the matter into public policy. Indeed, doing so exacts a high cost

from those who would benefit from such research. Their health needs are held hostage to a set of religious positions held by a minority that has inordinate sway in the legislative process. Prohibition of federal funding for ES cell research is also a major barrier to further research and development in this field. In addition, it leaves private sector researchers without a clear set of ethical or regulatory guidelines for the ES cell research, which they do, and will continue to, conduct.

A more fruitful approach to research issues at the beginning of life is to recognize that for most persons the ethical or normative questions that arise are less about the duties intrinsically owed to embryos or fetuses than they are about symbolizing or expressing the high respect that most persons have for human life generally. This respect is shown, not by banning all research with embryos or aborted fetuses, but by allowing such research only when good reasons exist for engaging in it and an institutional, or even national, review process to assess those reasons has been implemented. ...

The author thanks Andrea Bonnicksen for helpful comments on an earlier draft.

Notes

1. Many persons, of course, do not think that the original derivation of ES cells either from aborted fetuses or the abortions that make such donation possible or from live embryos is immoral, and they thus do not see the problem of moral complicity that those who object to ES cell removal do.

2. For example, the United States Supreme Court's equal protection jurisprudence has rejected a "benefit from" view of past racial and gender discrimination in assessing race or gender-neutral public policies that have a disproportionate or disparate racial or gender impact. See *Massachusetts v. Feeny* (442 U.S. 256 (1979)), in which past discrimination against women by the military does not render state preferences for veterans for civil service jobs discriminatory under the fourteenth amendment.

3. Persons who hold a causative theory of complicity and who believe that embryo destruction is immoral should object to ES cell research only when it can reasonably be shown that embryos would not have been destroyed if the ES cell research

had not been planned or contemplated. However, those same persons need not object to ES cell research that cannot reasonably be shown to have brought about the destruction of the embryos.

4. Ronald Dworkin makes a similar distinction in his discussion of abortion in *Life's Dominion* with his use of the labels "derivative" and "detached" to correspond to the notions of "intrinsic" or "rights-based" and "symbolic," "expressive," or "constitutive" protection used here. John Fletcher (1999), in an important background paper prepared for NBAC, has skillfully shown how Dworkin's distinction helps cross the gap to those who highly value early embryos and fetuses. His overall analysis is similar to the analysis contained in this article.

5. In Dworkin's terminology, such concerns are "detached" from the interests of actual persons and not "derivative" of their status as rights-holders.

6. Such a cost-benefit judgment explains the acceptability in IVF therapy of fertilizing more oocytes than can be safely transferred to the uterus, with the excess then discarded or never transferred. Although this practice causes embryos to be created and then destroyed in order to achieve pregnancy and childbirth, it serves a legitimate, valued need that negates the disrespect for human life that symbolically might occur if embryos were created and then destroyed for trivial purposes.

7. If such individuals hold a causative view of complicity, they should accept derivation of primordial germ cells from aborted fetuses when the derivation is clearly separated from the decision to abort, as now exists in federal law. They should also accept ES cell research with cells destructively derived from embryos as long as the research was not a cause of the derivation.

References

Altman, Scott. 1991. (Com)modifying Experience. *Southern California Law Review* 65: 293–340.

Andrews, Lori. 1994. State Regulation of Embryo Research. In *Papers Commissioned for the Human Embryo Research Panel*, vol. II, pp. 297–407. Bethesda, MD: National Institutes of Health.

Annas, George; Caplan, Art; and Elias, Sherman. 1996. The Politics of Human-Embryo Research-Avoiding Ethical Gridlock. *New England Journal of Medicine* 334: 1329–32.

Clinton, William Jefferson. 1994. Statement by the President on NIH Recommendation Regarding Human Embryo Research. *U.S. Newswire* (2 December).

Davis, Mathew. 1999a. Administration Supports Publically Funded Stem Cell Research, But Not to the Point of Seeking Changes in the Embryo Research Ban. *Washington Fax* (19 July): 1–3.

———. 1999b. Presidential Bioethics Advisors May Come Down on the Side of Federal Funding of Research on Stem Cells Derived from Embryos. *Washington Fax* (4 March): 1–2.

DHEW. U.S. Department of Health, Education, & Welfare, Ethics Advisory Board. 1979. *HEW Support of Research Involving Human In Vitro Fertilization and Embryo Transfer*. 44 *Federal Register*: 35,033.

Dworkin, Ronald. 1993. *Life's Dominion: An Argument About Abortion, Euthanasia, and Individual Freedom*. New York: Alfred Knopf.

Fletcher, John. 1999. Deliberately Incrementally on Human Pluripotential Stem Cell Research. National Bioethics Advisory Commission Background Papers on Embryonic Stem Cell Research.

Gerrand, Nicole. 1993. Creating Embryos for Research. *Journal of Applied Philosophy* 10: 175–87.

Grobstein, Clifford. 1985. The Early Development of Human Embryos. *Journal of Medicine and Philosophy* 10: 213–20.

Marshall, Eliot. 1997. Varmus Grilled Over Breach of Embryo Research Ban. *Science* 276: 1963.

———. 1998. A Versatile Cell Line Raises Scientific Hopes, Legal Questions. *Science* 282: 1014–15.

———. 1999. Britain Urged to Expand Embryo Studies. *Science* 282: 2167–68.

Nagy, Andras; Rosant, Janet; Nagy, R.; et al. 1993. Derivation of Completely Cell Culture-Derived Mice from Early-Passage Embryonic Stem Cells. *Proceedings of the National Academy of Sciences — USA* 90: 8424–28.

NBAC. National Bioethics Advisory Commission. 1999. *The Ethical Use of Human Stem Cells in Research*. Draft Report (9 July). Rockville, MD: NBAC.

NIH. National Institutes of Health. 1989. *Report of the Panel on Fetal Tissue Transplantation Research*. Bethesda, MD: NIH.

———. 1994. *Report of the Human Embryo Research Panel*. Bethesda, MD: NIH.

Raab, Harriet. 1999. Memorandum to Harold Varmus, M.D., Director, NIH, Federal Funding for Research Involving Human Pluripotent Stem Cells, 15 January.

Radin, Margaret Jane. 1996. *Contested Commodities*. Cambridge: Harvard University Press.

Robertson, John A. 1986. Embryo Research, *Western Ontario Law Review* 24: 15–37.

———. 1993. Abortion to Obtain Fetal Tissue for Transplant. *Suffolk University Law Review* 27: 1362–69.

———. 1994. *Children of Choice: Freedom and the New Reproductive Technologies*. Princeton: Princeton University Press.

———. 1995. Symbolic Issues in Embryo Research. *Hastings Center Report* 25 (1): 37–38.

———. 1999. Two Models of Human Cloning. *Hofstra Law Review* 27: 609–39.

Shamblott, Michael J.; Axelman, Joyce; Wang, Shunping; et al. 1998. Derivation of Pluripotent Stem Cells from Cultured Human Primordial Germ Cell. *Proceedings of the National Academy of Sciences — USA* 95: 13726–31.

Thomson, James A.; Itskovitz-Eldor, Joseph; Shapiro, Sander; et al. 1998. Embryonic Stem Cell Lines Derived from Human Blastocysts. *Science* 282: 1145–47.

United Kingdom. 1984. *Report of the Committee of Inquiry into Human Fertilisation and Embryology*. Department of Health & Social Security.

———. 1989. *Review of the Guidance on the Research Use of Fetuses and Fetal Material*. London: HMSO, Cm 762.

———. 1990. Human Fertilisation and Embryology Act of 1990.

Vogel, Gretchen. 1999. Harnessing the Power of Stem Cells. *Science* 283: 1432.

Wade, Nicholas. 1998. Ethics Panel Is Guarded About Hybrid of Cow Cells. *New York Times* (21 November): A7.

———. 1999. Ruling in Favor of Stem Cell Research Draws Fire of Seventy Lawmakers. *New York Times* (17 February): A12.

The Ethics of Gene Patenting

Ruth Macklin

Is it ethical to patent human genes and gene sequences? Like many questions about what is ethically permissible or impermissible, this query has layers of complexity. These include fundamental questions about what should and should not be patentable from an ethical perspective, as well as what is or is not patentable under existing patent laws. A second layer of legal questions asks whether existing patent laws are adequate to address the somewhat unique ethical concerns raised by patenting human genes. A related inquiry looks into differences in these laws in different countries. Even if current patent laws can be interpreted to allow gene patenting (Looney, 1994, pp. 231–272, Resnik, 1997, pp. 43–61) we can always pose an ethical challenge to an existing law. ...

An ethical analysis begins by asking: Are human genes somehow unique, and should they therefore be treated differently from other things for which the biotechnology industry has obtained patents? Do genes and gene sequences occupy a zone of personal privacy that would be violated by assigning patent rights to others? (Looney, 1994, p. 239). Are genes and gene sequences parts of our common heritage, so that information about them belongs in the public domain? Theologians have weighed in on the side of clear opposition to gene patenting, contending that all aspects of life are gifts of God and neither individuals nor companies should be granted "property rights" to such items. Also opposed are groups in the United States such as the Council for Responsible Genetics (CRG), a nongovernmental organization of scientists, public health advocates, trade unionists, environmentalists, feminists, disability activists, and other concerned citizens. CRG opposes gene patenting for several related reasons, which can be grouped under the heading "rejection of the commercialization of life" (Teitel, 1996, pp. 1–3).

How can we sort out the multiple and complex issues surrounding the debates over gene patenting? In this, as in many ethical and policy debates, reasons and arguments comprise a mix of consequentialist and nonconsequentialist elements. Sometimes these elements are pitted directly against one another, as illustrated by one debate about the likely consequences of gene patenting. One side contends that granting patent rights to an individual or organization results in limiting the application of knowledge from scientific work; the opposing position maintains that pursuit of patents leads to an increase in the general knowledge base and in the creation of useful products (Looney, Resnik).

At other times, a principled opposition to gene patenting holds fast despite consequentialist arguments promising great benefits that will accrue from allowing patents (Resnik, 1997). An example is the view that it is simply wrong to patent life — whatever financial gains or scientific advances may result — since patenting human ele-

"The Ethics of Gene Patenting" by Ruth Macklin. *Genetic Information*, eds. Thompson and Chadwick (Plenum Publishing, New York, 1999), pp. 129–137. Reprinted by permission of Kluwer Academic Publishers.

ments of any sort involves a commodification or commercialization that should be rejected. Still another debate pits one conception of justice against another. Before turning to these opposing views, let me address the "threshold" question: What can and cannot be patented?

1. What Is Patentable?

The argument over whether genes and gene sequences should be considered patentable from a legal standpoint persists. The legal line distinguishes between a *discovery* of something that exists in nature, which is not patentable, and a true *invention*, which requires that human beings contribute something of significance (Looney, 1994, Resnik, 1997). One prevalent opinion holds that there is a legal basis for patenting invented nonnaturally occurring genes and DNA sequences, parts or combinations of chromosomes, as well as the uncontroversial processes for manufacturing, analyzing, sequencing, or recombining human genes. What is not patentable are naturally occurring human genes or their combinations (Resnik, 1997). To show that human genes and sequences meet the threshold test, it is necessary to demonstrate significant human intervention. Courts ... have already ruled that human innovation in the biotechnology realm enables living things to be patented. Nevertheless, a dispute remains at the conceptual level over whether gene sequences are a discovery or an invention (Looney, 1994).

...

If the present legal uncertainty relies on a resolution of the conceptual controversy over whether genes and gene sequences should be considered discoveries or inventions, a conceptual decision must be taken. As in any conceptual dispute, the answer cannot be reached by "discovering" the right answer, but only

by providing persuasive arguments for adopting one interpretation rather than the other.

This brings us directly to the ethical basis for the dispute over patenting genes and gene sequences. Items that are patented are considered "intellectual property," and a patent grants to the holder certain rights over that property (Resnik, 1997). Opponents of gene patents contend that genes are not a subject matter for which individual property rights should be granted because they are part of our common human heritage. Therefore, they should not belong to individuals or to corporations but rather should remain in the public domain. Defenders of patenting genes ... argue that ownership of artificial human genes or artificial combinations of genes are no different, in principle, from many other items relating to human beings for which patents have been granted. But even if ... patent law could properly allow for the patenting of genes and gene sequences, the deeper ethical question remains: should gene patenting be permitted?

2. Nonconsequentialist Arguments

2.1. The Theological Position

In 1995 a group of 186 religious leaders from all major faiths called for a moratorium on patents of human and animal life based on the premise that genes are creations of God and not human inventions. Theologians contended that patents on animal as well as human genes are a violation of the sanctity of life. Although this religious viewpoint may appeal to people who readily accept the theistic first premise, it is unlikely to be compelling in the secular realm of science. Moreover, if the patentability of genes and gene sequences requires a showing of human invention or innovation, then it is not the genes themselves, as found in nature, that are patentable but rather the processes invented by humans to identify and sequence them. The theological argument can get off the ground only if the conclusion is reached that genes and gene sequences are "discoveries" rather than "inventions." But in that case, they would not be patentable even under the broad provisions of ... patent law. To the extent that the religious position rests on theological distinctions, it raises issues separate from the philosophical inquiry. I shall not discuss the religious objection further.

Not all nonconsequentialist arguments begin with a religious premise, however. Others start with a premise of human dignity or a conception of our humanness that is thought to be undermined by patenting. The following two nonconsequentialist arguments rely not on theological underpinnings but rather on these secular notions.

2.2. Human Gene Patents and Human Dignity

The first nontheological argument is described by a philosopher, David Resnik, as taking a Kantian perspective. The argument contends that gene patenting is wrong because it treats persons as things that can be bought and sold, traded, or modified. In three simple steps, the argument proceeds as follows: 1) the practice of patenting human genes treats persons as property; 2) it is morally wrong to treat persons as property; 3) the practice of patenting human genes is morally wrong (Resnik, 1997, p. 54).

Resnik contends that gene patenting does not treat persons as property if it allows only for ownership of inventions for analyzing, sequencing, manipulating, or manufacturing human genes. This is analogous to patents for making other kinds of artificial human body parts, such as hair, bones, or hearts, and so the Kantian perspective does not preclude

patenting of genes or gene sequences. However, the Kantian perspective would not allow for patents on genetically engineered humans to extend to the whole human animal, as patents have already done for genetically engineered mice. Resnik concludes that a prohibition should exist against patents on processes for making entire human beings, but that ownership of a process for making or manipulating a part of a human body need not constitute ownership of a person (Resnik, 1997, pp. 54–55). This conclusion is seconded by Caplan and Merz, who write: "... while strong theological reservations exist, it is hard to equate assigning a patent to a DNA strip with ownership of a human body. Selling bodies into slavery is exploitative, because our personal identity is so intimately tied to our bodies. It is not so obviously a violation of the human spirit to assign rights to exclusive use and development over a segment of chromosome 13 to a government agency or a biotechnology concern" (Caplan and Merz, 1996).

2.3. Patenting Human Genes and Our Humanness

The next nonconsequentialist argument, like the preceding one, appeals to the dignity of human beings. It relies on a conception of humanness as somehow morally "sacred." Patenting human genes is thus dehumanizing because it alters our view of humans from beings with dignity and respect into objects that can be bought, sold, or modified. Resnik rejects this view first, by noting that there is no good reason to think that the practice of patenting human genes will be any more "dehumanizing" than our present and past uses of the human body (p. 56). Second, Resnik observes that there is a variety of different subjective conceptions of what constitutes our "humanness," and no one conception can serve as a basis for a public policy banning gene patenting (Resnik, 1997, p. 57).

2.4. The "Common Property" Argument

Still another nonconsequentialist argument is the view that human genes should be treated as common property, not belonging to a single individual or corporation (Resnik, 1997, p. 57). This view, Resnik argues, rests on a mistaken understanding of gene patents. This takes us back to the threshold question, "what is patentable?" since patenting does not allow ownership of naturally occurring genes, only inventions relating to genes and gene sequences. Since ownership of the processes of copying, sequencing, modifying, and analyzing human genes does not constitute ownership of our naturally occurring, common genes, this argument is flawed.

But there is a different sort of "common property" argument, one that does not rely on a determination of what is patentable. This position begins by noting that in the U.S., at least, the resources for mapping and sequencing the human genome have come largely from the publicly funded National Institutes of Health. According to one commentary: "If government funds have been used to map and sequence the human genome, why should the fruits of that effort be turned over to a single owner? Permitting patents of simple segments of the genome, rather than for products and inventions, would seem to be contrary to the public interest" (Caplan and Merz, 1996).

2.5. The Commodification Argument

A supporter of the Council for Responsible Genetics puts forward a paradigm of the commodification position opposed to gene patenting. There is some overlap with the two arguments pertaining to human dignity and conceptions of our humanness, but the commodification view centers more on the aspect of commercialization. Martin Teitel refers to

those seeking to patent genetic information as "the new commodifiers": "Just as the new those seeking to patent commodifiers abruptly lay claim to the cultural heritage of generations of traditional societies, they also assert their ownership of the fantastically intricate genetic code that represents the current end point of millions of years of biological evolution. It is difficult to imagine a greater presumption" (Teitel, 1996, p. 2). This position does not mount an argument but relies on a value conception that rejects the idea that everything may be subjected to the forces of the marketplace. The position is summed up in statements like this:

> As we recognize the nature and scope of the new commodification, we need to begin investigation, analysis, education and action. In spite of the power and reach of the huge corporations, universities and governments promoting the commercialization of life, we are in truth faced only with the actions of ordinary greedy people who can and should be stopped (Teitel, 1996, p. 3).

Since patents serve a primarily economic function (Looney, 1994, p. 233), it becomes necessary to decide whether progress in the science of human genetics and its applications should be governed solely by economic considerations.

2.6. Competing Conceptions of Justice

A final nonconsequentialist argument appeals to one conception of justice. A view of gene patenting derived from the concept of distributive justice argues that the proper distribution of benefits and burdens in society (in this case, the world) requires that no group be deprived of the benefits of genomic research. Since less developed countries lack the resources of wealthier countries, it would be unjust for the benefits of genomic research to be located only in those richer nations that sponsor the research and obtain the patents (Looney, 1994). However, distributive justice is only one of several different conceptions of justice. A competing conception relies on a marketplace conception of justice as fairness. This view grants to researchers and financial investors a fair return on their efforts and expenditures. Since they have spent time and money on the genetic research yielding information about the human genome, they are entitled to the just reward of patent protection. Both of these opposing views rely on a conception of justice, but whereas the former claims that justice in distribution is the relevant conception, the latter maintains that providing just deserts should be the ruling view (Looney, 1994, pp. 240–42).

3. Consequentialist Arguments

At least four separate arguments on both sides of the issue appeal to the consequences of gene patenting. They revolve around the question: Does gene patenting result in limiting or increasing knowledge and its applications? These four arguments are as follows.

3.1. Delays in Disseminating Information

One view holds that researchers awaiting a patent they have applied for are likely to withhold information until the patent is granted, therefore delaying dissemination of important information (Looney, 1994, p. 244). An opposing view contends that patents provide protection and thus permit disclosure of scientific knowledge before an actual product is ready for the market. The consequence of not being allowed to patent would lead to the more detrimental consequence of maintaining secrecy in research.

A leading U.S. geneticist, David Botstein, who shares in a number of

genetic technology patents, argues that not only do patents protect a scientist's self-interest, but they also promote the dissemination of research findings. Botstein agrees with those who say that one of the primary purposes of patents is to reduce the economic motivation for excessive trade secrecy, which has a negative effect on progress (Hoke, 1995, p. 1). Jonathan King, a molecular biologist, proposes a directly opposite view:

> Contrary to the claims of the biotech industry, gene patents retard progress in the biomedical arena, introduce secrecy where openness is essential, and slow the publication and sharing of important results. This follows from the fact that once a result is reported publicly, it cannot be patented. Thus researchers drawn into the web of the patent process do not report their results, even informally, until they have passed through the expensive patent application and granting process (King, 1996, p. 11).

3.2. Development of New Drugs

An analogous pair of opposing consequences are envisaged with respect to development of new drugs. One position argues that "the next generation of modern medicines will never get out of research labs if efforts to halt the patenting of genes are successful" (Feldbaum, 1996, p. 10). This view is supported with evidence taken from other areas of biomedical technology, where patents have been granted for blood clotting agents for hemophiliacs, products for breaking up blood clots, a vaccine for Hepatitis B, along with numerous other drugs and diagnostic products (Feldbaum, 1996). The opposing position contends that the extraordinary advances in biomedical knowledge and technology in the past 40 years have been largely a result of public funding of biomedical research (King, 1996).

3.3. Promoting versus Stifling International Collaboration

Still another pair of opposing consequences appears in the discussion of international collaboration. In the absence of international agreements that would prohibit gene patenting, countries simultaneously doing research may feel compelled to seek to obtain patents in order to avoid losing a competitive advantage. ... In contrast is the view that patenting promotes, rather than stifles, international research. This latter view relies on the notion that an inability to patent leads to fewer inventions, since sponsors will not invest in research that does not promise a good return that would be guaranteed by having exclusive commercial rights.

3.4. Assigning Different Weights to Different Consequences

A different sort of opposition arises out of assigning higher or lower values to the different potential consequences of gene patenting. One position contends that patent protection promotes efficiency, reducing duplicative research and wasteful funding that would otherwise occur when independent efforts simultaneously go forward. On this view of consequences, more knowledge and its applications can be obtained more quickly by allowing patenting. In contrast is the consequence that some genetic research unlikely to be profitable will fall by the wayside, therefore resulting in loss of benefits to classes of persons afflicted by rare disorders.

3.5. Restrictions on What Is Patentable Related to the Consequences

Even among those who would allow patenting of some genetic information, concerns about stifling research lead to calls for restrictions. For example, in a letter to the Commissioner of Patents and Trademarks in the U.S. Patent and Trademark Office, the President of the Council of the National Academy of Sciences (NAS), Bruce Alberts, wrote: "I write to encourage you to make every effort to insure that any future patents granted for DNA sequences do not unfairly impede research and innovation in biotechnology" (Alberts, 1997). The specific concern Alberts identified was that EST (expressed sequence tags) patents will become impediments to research, slowing progress in biomedical research. On behalf of the Council of the NAS, Alberts suggested that "DNA sequences per se should not be patentable unless the patent clearly discloses specific 'real world' utilities for the particular DNA sequences in question that can be implemented without substantial further developmental research."

...

4. Conclusion

... The central ethical question about patenting human genes turns on the consequences: whether patenting results in more benefits than harms. An answer to the conceptual question — whether the methods to identify genes and gene sequences constitute an invention or a discovery — is partly legal and partly philosophical. It requires further discussion and debate. But even assuming that the threshold question yields the answer that genes are, indeed, patentable, only an examination of the likely consequences, for all who stand to be affected, will be persuasive for making public policy.

From a global perspective, as well as within nations, it is important to determine whether patenting of genes and gene sequences is in the public interest. Who stands to gain, and who stands to lose by the patenting of genetic material? Is national or regional regulation warranted? Should a high priority be placed on international harmonization of patent laws? A major impediment to determining what are the likely consequences of gene patenting is the lack of clear evidence that would support one side or the other. A multidisciplinary, systematic study should be conducted; it could begin by examining the effect of patents granted in other areas of biotechnology. Also needed are the views and experiences of biomedical researchers who do not have ties to the increasing number of biotechnology companies that are among the most aggressive pursuers of patents on genes and gene sequences. Although a systematic inquiry is needed in order to provide relevant evidence that could shed light on the controversy, the more gene patents that are aggressively pursued in the United States and the more time that elapses, the harder it will become to turn back the clock in the event that the predicted negative consequences of gene patenting begin to emerge.

On the nonconsequentialist side, my own view is that commodification of human material for any purpose is unsavory, and ought to be avoided whenever possible. Yet "unsavoriness" may not be a category of moral disvalue strong enough to warrant prohibition. If commodification of genetic material does not involve a violation of a moral principle or the rights of any person or group, then a stronger basis for a ban on gene patents would have to be found. Although it seems correct to say that commodification does not violate any ethical principle, it can nevertheless be viewed as an unsavory feature of modern society, at least in those countries where almost everything is subject to market forces. This involves a judgment about what kind of society we value: one in which almost everything can be subjected to commercial exchanges or one in which some things should be treated as social goods for the common benefit of all. Although my own values strongly favor the latter view, it is hard to find a principled moral argument that would exempt genes and gene sequences from the commercial forces that govern other aspects of modern biomedical technology.

References[*]

Albert, B. (1997), letter to Bruce A. Lehman, Commissioner of Patents and Trademarks (published June 19 on the World Wide Web).

Caplan, A.L. and Merz, Jon. (1996), "Patenting Gene Sequences." *BMJ* Editorial, Vol. 312, 13 **http://bmj.bmjjournals.com/archive/7036e.htm**

Feldbaum, C. (1996). "Gene Patents Deemed Essential to Next Generation of Cures," *Gene Watch,* Vol. 10.

GAEIB. (1993), Opinions Submitted by *The Group of Advisers on the Ethical Implications of Biotechnology* to the European Commission, Brussels: No. 3 Opinion on Ethical Questions Arising from the Commission Proposal for a Council Directive on Legal Protection for Biotechnological Inventions, 30 September.

GAEIB. (1996), "Opinion of the Group of Advisers on the Ethical Implications of Biotechnology of the European Commission," Brussels: No. 8 Ethical Aspects of Patenting Inventions Involving Elements of Human Origin, 25 September.

Hoke, F. (1995). *The Scientist*, Vol. 9. April 17.

King, J. (1996), "Gene Patents Retard the Protection of Human Health," *GeneWatch*. Vol. 10.

---

[*] URL was revised in April 2004 from the original source for inclusion in this book.

Looney, B. (1994). "Should Genes Be Patented? The Gene Patenting Controversy: Legal, Ethical, and Policy Foundations of an International Agreement," *Law and Policy in International Business*, Vol. 26.

Resnik. D.B., (1997), "The Morality of Human Gene Patents." *Kennedy Institute of Ethics Journal*, Vol. 7.

Teitel, M. (1996), "The Commercialization of Life," *GeneWatch*. Vol. 10.

Further Readings

American College of Medical Genetics, Policy on Patenting Human Genes, **http://www.faseb.org/genetics/acmg/pol-34.htm**

Barton, J.H. "Research-tool Patents: Issues for Health in the Developing World." *Bull World Health Organ* 80:2 (2002): 121–5.

Baylis F. "Human Embryonic Stem Cell Lines: The Ethics of Derivation." *J Obstet Gynaecol Can* 24:2 (Feb. 2002): 159–163.

Boyle, R.J., and J. Savulescu. "Ethics of Using Preimplantation Genetic Diagnosis to Select a Stem Cell Donor for an Existing Person." *BMJ* 323:7323 (Nov. 24, 2001): 1240–1243.

Cahill, L.S. "Genetics, Commodification, and Social Justice in the Globalization Era." *Kennedy Inst Ethics J* 11:3 (Sept. 2001): 221–238.

Chadwick, D., et al., eds. *Human Genetic Information: Science, Law, Ethics*. New York: Wiley, 1990.

Clark, J.T.R. "Screening for Carriers of Tay-Sachs Disease: Two Approaches." *CMAJ* 119 (1978): 450.

Davis, D.S. "Stem Cells, Cloning, and Abortion: Making Careful Distinctions." *Am J Bioeth* 2:1 (Winter 2002): 47–49.

Directive No 98/44/EC: *Official Journal of the European Communities*, 1998, L213/13.

Herdegen, M. "Patenting Human Genes and Other Parts of the Human Body under EC Biotechnology Directive." *Bio-Science Law Review* 13 (Dec. 2001).

Hoedemaekers, R., and W. Dekkers. "Is There a Unique Moral Status of Human DNA That Prevents Patenting?" *Kennedy Inst Ethics J* 11:4 (Dec. 2001): 359–86.

Kluge, E.-H.W. "Patenting Human Genes: When Economic Interests Trump Logic and Ethics." *Health Care Anal* 11:2 (June 2003): 119–130.

Knoppers, B.M. *Human Dignity and Genetic Heritage*. Study Paper for the Law Reform Commission of Canada. Ottawa: Law Reform Commission of Canada, 1991.

McLaren, A. "Ethical and Social Considerations of Stem Cell Research." *Nature* 414:6859 (Nov. 1, 2001): 129–31.

Meyer, J.R. "Human Embryonic Stem Cells and Respect for Life." *J of Med Ethics* 26:3 (2000): 166–170.

Nelkin, D., and L. Tancredi. *Dangerous Diagnostics: The Social Power of Biological Information*. New York: Basic Books, 1989.

Outka, G. "The Ethics of Human Stem Cell Research." *Kennedy Inst Ethics J* 12:2 (June 2002): 175–213.

Overall, C. *Ethics and Human Reproduction: A Feminist Analysis*. Boston: Allen and Unwin, 1987.

Resnik, D.B. "The Commercialization of Human Stem Cells: Ethical and Policy Issues." *Health Care Anal* 10:2 (2002): 127–154.

Robertson, J.A., J. P. Kahn, and J.E. Wagner. "Conception to Obtain Hematopoietic Stem Cells." *Hastings Cent Rep* 32:3 (May–June 2002): 34–40.

Useful Web Sites

http://www.merck.com/overview/98ar/p17.htm   Merck is a major biotechnology and pharmaceutical company. Their web site provides some insight into the research direction in which international biotechnology companies are moving in the field of genetics. The reason the Merck web site is singled out is that Merck, together with the Wellcome Trust, is working to identify and place human genes into the public domain so that they cannot be patented.

http://europa.eu.int/eur-lex/en/search/search_lif.html   This URL leads to the European Union's legal database. It is useful in tracking legal developments that affect European biotechnology in general and gene technology in particular.

http://www.who.int/bulletin/en/   This is the URL for the *WHO Bulletin*. It contains links to various declarations, statements and other developments that occur under the auspices of the WHO. The web site can be queried in various languages.

http://www.lawtext.com/default.asp?calltype=BIOSCIENCE&content=home   This is the URL for the *Bioscience Law Review*. It is a useful research tool for the biosciences, but unfortunately most of it can be accessed free of charge only if your university subscribes to the retrieval service.

http://www.gene.ucl.ac.uk/hugo/ethics.html   This is the URL of the HUGO. It offers access to reports, statements, conference details and various developments dealing with the human genome.

REFERENCES

PART I: HEALTH CARE AND ETHICS

Chapter 1: Ethical Theory

Eike-Henner W. Kluge: Brief discussion of ethical approaches and theories.

Chapter 2: Health as an Ethical Issue

1. Preamble: Constitution of the World Health Organization, reproduced by permission of WHO from *Basic Documents: Thirty-Ninth Edition* (Geneva: World Health Organization, 1992), 1–2.
2. Daniel Callahan, "The WHO Definition of Health," *Hastings Center Report* 1:3 (1973).
3. W. Miller Brown, "On Defining 'Disease,'" *The Journal of Medicine and Philosophy*, 10:4 (1985), 311–328.

Chapter 3: The Right to Health Care

1. Canada Health Act, Government of Canada.
2. *Building on Values: The Future of Health Care in Canada*, Final Report of the Royal Commission on the Future of Health Services, pp. xx–xxi and xxiv–xxxiv, © 2002. Reproduced with the permission of the Minister of Public Works and Government Services, 2003, and Courtesy of the Privy Council Office.
3. Benjamin Freedman and Françoise Baylis, "Purpose and Function in Government-Funded Health Coverage," *Journal of Health Politics, Policy and Law* 12:1 (Spring 1987), 97–112.

Chapter 4: Allocation of Resources

(a) Macro-allocation
1. Robert M. Nelson and Theresa Drought, "Justice and the Moral Acceptability of Rationing Medical Care: The Oregon Experiment," *Journal of Medicine and Philosophy*, vol. 17, no. 1 (1992), pp. 97–117.
2. Alan Williams, "Rationing Health Care by Age," *British Medical Journal* 314 (Mar. 15, 1997) 820.

(b) Micro-allocation
3. Alvin H. Moss and Mark Siegler, "Should Alcoholics Compete Equally for Liver Transplantation?" *Journal of the American Medical Association* (1991) 265; 1295–1298.
4. Martin F. McKneally, Bernard M. Dickens, Eric M. Meslin, Peter A. Singer, "Bioethics for clinicians: 13. Resource allocation," *Canadian Medical Association Journal*, 157:2 (1997), 163–167.

5. Robert D. Truog, Allan S. Brett, and Joel Frader, "The Problem with Futility," *New England Journal of Medicine*, 326:23 (June 4, 1992), 1560–1564.

PART II: THE PATIENT AND THE HEALTH CARE PROFESSIONAL

Chapter 5: The Health Care Professional–Patient Relationship

1. James F. Childress and Mark Siegler, "Metaphors and Models of Doctor–Patient Relationships: Their Implications for Autonomy," *Theoretical Medicine and Bioethics* 5 (1984), 17–30.

2. Janet L. Storch, "Moral Relationships Between Nurse and Client: The Influence of Metaphors." This article was written in January 1998 especially for the second edition of *Readings in Biomedical Ethics: A Canadian Focus*.

PART III: CONSENT TO HEALTH CARE

Chapter 6: Informed Consent and the Competent Patient

1. *Reibl v. Hughes,* 16 O.R. (2d) 306, 78 D.L.R. (3d) 35, reversed 21 O.R. (2d) 14, 6 C.C.L.T., 227, 89 D.L.R. (3d) 112; reversed [1980] 2 S.C.R. 880, 14 C.C.C.T.I., 114 D.L.R. (3d) 1, 33 N.R., 17.

2. Benjamin Freedman, "A Moral Theory of Informed Consent," *Hastings Center Report* 5:4 (August 1975); 32–39.

3. Insoo Hyun, "Waiver of Informed Consent, Cultural Sensitivity, and the Problem of Unjust Families and Traditions," *Hastings Center Report* 32:5 (2002).

Chapter 7: Consent and the Incompetent Patient

1. *Re S.D.* (1983) 3 W.W.R. 618 (B.C.S.C.). Reproduced with the permission of Thomson Canada Ltd.

2. Eike-Henner W. Kluge, "After "Eve": Whither Proxy Decision Making?" *Canadian Medical Association Journal*, 137 (October 15, 1987), 715–720.

3. Christine Harrison, Nuala P. Kenny, Mona Sidarous, Mary Rowell, "Involving Children in Medical Decisions," *Canadian Medical Association Journal*, 15 Mar 1997; 156:6, 825–828.

Chapter 8: Advance Directives

1. *Malette v. Shulman* (1990) 72 O.R. (2d) 417 (C.A.) pp. 17–42.

2. Peter Singer et al., "Advance Directives: Are They an Advance?" *Canadian Medical Association Journal*, 15 Jan 1992; 146:2, 127–134.

Chapter 9: Information and Medical Treatment

1. *McInerney v. MacDonald* 93 D.L.R. (4th) 415.
2. Howard Brody, "The Lie That Heals: The Ethics of Giving Placebos," *Annals of Internal Medicine* 97:1 (1982), 112–118.

PART IV: RESEARCH INVOLVING HUMAN SUBJECTS

Chapter 10: Research and Experimentation Involving Competent Persons

1. *Tri-Council Policy Statement: Ethical Conduct for Research Involving Humans,* 1998, Interagency Advisory Panel on Research and Ethics. Reproduced with permission of the Minister of Public Works and Government Services Canada, 2003.
2. *Halushka v. University of Saskatchewan et al.* 436 Dominion Law Reports 53 (2d).
3. Charles Weijer, "Placebo Trials and Tribulations," *Canadian Medical Association Journal*, March 2002; 166:5, 603–604.
4. Steven Lewis, Patricia Baird, Robert G. Evans, William A. Ghali, Charles J. Wright, Elaine Gibson, Françoise Baylis, "Dancing with the Porcupine: Rules for Governing the University–Industry Relationship," *Canadian Medical Association Journal*, 18 September 2001; 165:6, 783–785.

Chapter 11: Research and Experimentation Involving Persons with Diminished Competence

1. D. J. Manning, "Presumed Consent in Emergency Neonatal Research," *Journal of Medical Ethics* 2000; 26: 249–253.
2. B. Mahendra, "Some Ethical Issues in Dementia Research," *Journal of Medical Ethics* 1984; 10: 29–31.

PART V: DECISIONS ABOUT LIFE AND DEATH

Chapter 12: Personhood

1. *Re A. (in utero),* (U.F.C.) 75 O.R. (2d) 82 [1990] O.J. No. 1347 Action No. C/766/90.
2. *R. v. Kitching and Adams* (1976) 6 W.W.R. 697 (Manitoba Court of Appeal). Reproduced with the permission of Thomson Canada Ltd.
3. Roland Puccetti, "Does Anyone Survive Neocortical Death?" in Richard M. Zaner, ed., *Death: Beyond Whole-Brain Criteria* (Dordrecht: Kluwer Academic Publishers, 1988), 75–90.
4. Gareth Jones, "The Problematic Symmetry Between Brain Birth and Brain Death," *Journal of Medical Ethics* 1998; 24: 237–242.

Chapter 13: Abortion

1. *R. v. Morgentaler* [1988] 1 S.C.R. 30, 63 O.R.(2d)281, 26 O.A.C. 1, 44 D.L.R.(4th) 385, 82 N.R. 1, 3 C.C.C.(3d)449, 62 C.R.(3d)1, 31 C.R.R.

2. L. W. Sumner, "Toward a Credible View of Abortion," *Canadian Journal of Philosophy* 4 (September 1974), 163–181.

3. Susan Sherwin, "Abortion Through a Feminist Ethics Lens," *Dialogue* XXX (1991), 327–342.

Chapter 14: Assisted Suicide, Euthanasia and Cessation of Treatment

1. *Rodriguez v. British Columbia (Attorney General)* [1993] 3 S.C.R. 519.

2. James Rachels, "Active and Passive Euthanasia," *New England Journal of Medicine*, 292:2, (January 9, 1975), 78–80.

3. Richard Doerflinger, "Assisted Suicide: Pro-Choice or Anti-Life?" *Hastings Center Report* 19:1 (January/February 1989) suppl. 16–19.

4. Timothy E. Quill, Rebecca Dresser and Dan W. Brock, "The Rule of Double Effect: A Critique of Its Role in End-of-Life Decision Making," *New England Journal of Medicine*, 337:4, 1768–1771.

5. Canadian Medical Association, "Joint Statement on Resuscitative Interventions," *Canadian Medical Association Journal*, 1 Dec 1995; 153:11, 1652A–C.

PART VI: REPRODUCTIVE ETHICS

Chapter 15: The Right to Have Children

1. "Responsible Family Planning," excerpt from the *White Paper on Family Planning*, People's Republic of China.

2. Canadian Medical Association, "The Right to Have Children," reprinted from Canadian Medical Association 1991, 40–52, by permission of the publisher.

3. *Eve v. Mrs. E.* [1987], 3 D.L.R. (4th) S.C.C., [1987] 2 S.C.R. 388 (S.C.C.).

4. Eike-Henner W. Kluge, "Sterilisation of the Mentally Severely Handicapped: A Violation of the Right to Have Children?" *Ethical Problems in Reproductive Medicine* 1989; 1:1, 12–15.

5. L. M. Purdy, "Genetic Diseases: Can Having Children Be Immoral?" in *Genetics Now: Ethical Issues in Genetic Research*, J. J. Buckley, Jr., ed. (Washington, D.C.: University Press of America, 1978), 25–39.

Chapter 16: The New Reproductive Technologies

1. *Bill C-13: An Act Respecting Assisted Human Reproduction*, Government of Canada.

2. Human Pluripotent Stem Cell Research Guidelines for CIHR-Funded Research, clauses 3.0, 4, 5, 7-8. http://www.cihr-irsc.gc.ca/e/publications/1487.shtml, Canadian Institutes of Health Research, updated: 2003/04/09.

3. *Respect for Human Life (Donum Vitae), Instruction on Respect for Human Life in Its Origin and on the Dignity of Procreation Replies to Certain Questions of the Day,* Congregation for the Doctrine of the Faith. February 22, 1987, Vatican.

4. Christine Overall, "Access to In Vitro Fertilization: Costs, Care and Consent," *Dialogue* XXX (1991), 383–397.

Chapter 17: The Use of the New Reproductive Technologies

1. Nancy S. Jecker, "Conceiving a Child to Save a Child: Reproductive and Filial Ethics," *The Journal of Clinical Ethics* 1:2 (Summer 1990), 99–107.

2. David B. Resnik, "The Moral Significance of the Therapy Enhancement Distinction in Human Genetics," *Cambridge Quarterly of Healthcare Ethics* (2000) 9, 365–377.

3. Françoise Baylis, "Human Cloning: Three Mistakes and an Alternative," *The Journal of Medicine and Philosophy* 27:3 (2002), 319–337.

4. John A. Robertson, "Ethics and Policy in Embryonic Stem Cell Research," *Kennedy Institute of Ethics Journal* 9:2 (1999), 109–136.

5. Ruth Macklin, "The Ethics of Gene Patenting," in *Genetic Information,* Thompson and Chadwick, eds. (Plenum Publishing, New York, 1999), 129–137.